Michael D. Johnson

Human Biology
Concepts and Current Issues

Custom Edition for Valencia College
BSC 1020

Taken From:
Human Biology: Concepts and Current Issues, Seventh Edition
by Michael D. Johnson

Cover Art: Courtesy of Photodisc/Getty Images.

Taken from:

Human Biology: Concepts and Current Issues, Seventh Edition
by Michael D. Johnson
Copyright © 2014, 2012, 2010 by Pearson Education, Inc.
Upper Saddle River, New Jersey 07458

Pearson Learning Solutions, 501 Boylston Street, Suite 900, Boston, MA 02116
A Pearson Education Company
www.pearsoned.com

Printed in the United States of America

6 7 8 9 10 V0UD 19 18 17 16 15

000200010271786510

CW

ISBN 10: 1-269-38990-4
ISBN 13: 978-1-269-38990-7

About the Author

Dr. Michael D. Johnson spent most of his youth in the fields and forests of rural Washington, observing nature. He earned his B.S. degree in zoology from Washington State University and then moved east to earn a Ph.D. in physiology from the University of Michigan. After completing a Postdoctoral Research Fellowship at Harvard Medical School he joined the faculty of West Virginia University, where he remained for most of his career.

In 2001 Dr. Johnson moved to the Middle East, where he served first as the founding dean of Oman Medical College in the Sultanate of Oman, and then as associate dean for premedical education at Weill Cornell Medical College in Qatar. In both positions he directed the premedical education of students from more than 25 countries. He returned to the United States in 2011 to focus on his writing.

Dr. Johnson received several teaching awards during his career, including the West Virginia University Foundation Outstanding Teacher award and the Distinguished Teacher Award of the School of Medicine. He is a member of the American Physiological Society, the Human Anatomy and Physiology Society, the National Association of Biology Teachers, and the American Association for the Advancement of Science.

Whether teaching undergraduates or medical students, Dr. Johnson has always had a keen interest in instilling in students an appreciation of science. He seeks to show students how the advancement of scientific knowledge sometimes raises unforeseen ethical, political, economic, and social issues for all of us to discuss and solve. Through this book, he encourages students to become scientifically literate so that they will feel comfortable making responsible choices as consumers of science.

You can contact Dr. Johnson at mdj5412@gmail.com with comments or questions about this book.

Contents

9

The Immune System and Mechanisms of Defense   188

11

The Nervous System: Integration and Control   244

Current Issue
Head Trauma in Young Athletes   244

12

Sensory Mechanisms   276

Current Issue
DWD: Driving While Distracted   276

13   The Endocrine System   300

Current Issue
Endocrine Disruptors in the Environment   300

19   Genetics and Inheritance   444

Current Issue
The Promises and Perils of Genetic Testing   444

Preface

In 1997 scientists copied (cloned) an adult animal for the first time. In 2003 the entire sequence of a complete set of human DNA (the human genome) was first published. A legal battle that began in 2010 over whether human genes (notably two genes responsible for an increased risk of breast cancer) can be patented was still unresolved by 2012.

Those of us who find scientific discoveries and news stories such as these fascinating—and yes, even exciting!—have an obligation to help our students understand science and the impact science has on their lives. Science is too much fun and far too important to be left to scientists.

New to This Edition

Changes to this edition are designed to encourage students who do not have a strong background in science to become actively engaged in the course. Improved pedagogy helps students focus their learning, directs their attention to key concepts and current issues in biology today, and encourages thoughtful analysis and critical thinking.

- **Addition of BlogInFocus.** To rouse students' interest in the science they encounter in their everyday lives, we've incorporated references to the author's blog within each chapter, along with a handy way to connect directly to these blog entries through MasteringBiology. Each chapter includes two to four such references. It is hoped that these references to the author's website will encourage students to explore other topics that interest them.
- **BlogInFocus Questions.** At the end of each chapter are one to two questions that relate directly or indirectly to specific blog topics on the author's blog. These are meant to be thought-provoking questions that require analysis and critical thinking. Students are referred to the blog entry, which can be found on MasteringBiology, for help with the question if they wish. Answers to the questions can be found in the Study Area of MasteringBiology.
- **MasteringBiology.** Because human biology courses are rapidly moving online or being taught as an online/on-campus hybrid and to intertwine media more closely with the book, we have more fully integrated the text with MasteringBiology. Activities, quizzes, tutorials, and animations are all now in one place, and instructors can assess student learning by means of online assignments that are automatically graded. Interactive Physiology for Human Biology is now a fully online component, and more BlogInFocus questions have been added as assignable items. Coaching activities have also been expanded to help students understand difficult concepts.

- **Refreshed Visual Content.** To revitalize the visual content, almost 50 new photos replace images from the previous edition, and 10 figures are new. Almost 60 other figures have been improved from the previous edition.
- **Updated Features, Graphs, Tables, and Text.** Key features of this text are currency and accuracy. Time-dependent data has been updated with the latest information available. The popular Health and Wellness feature has been expanded to cover eight more topics.

The Focus Is on the Student

This book is written for students who do not yet have a strong background in science so that they, too, might share in the joy and wonder of science. Every effort is made to make the book accurate and up to date while keeping it inviting, accessible, and easy to read. The look and feel of the text is intentionally like that of a news magazine, peppered with short features likely to be of interest to the student and with a strong visual appeal.

Each chapter begins with a Current Issue that highlights a recent controversy or ethical/social/political issue related to human biology. The main narrative of each chapter begins with Key Concepts that summarize the most important points within the chapter. Quick Check questions throughout the narrative or linked to select figures allow the students to check their understanding as they go along. Finally, each chapter ends with 15 multiple-choice questions so that students can check their progress.

Students are naturally curious about how their own bodies work and about human diseases. We capitalize on this curiosity with Health & Wellness boxes that highlight timely health topics. In addition, organ system chapters generally conclude with a section covering the more common human diseases and disorders.

A new feature of this edition is BlogInFocus, brief references to a blog website written by Dr. Johnson in support of this text, http://www.humanbiologyblog.blogspot.com. Two to four BlogInFocus entries per chapter highlight recent discoveries or news items relevant to the subject of each chapter. We hope that BlogInFocus entries and the author's blog will encourage curious students to dig a little deeper into topics that interest them.

Unifying Themes Tie the Subjects Together

Several unifying themes in biology hold the chapters together. Homeostasis, the state of dynamic equilibrium in which the internal environment of an organism is maintained fairly constant, is one of those recurrent themes. The concept of homeostasis ties in with another recurrent theme: structure and function are related. Structure/function relationships are the very core of the study of anatomy and physiology, and both of these fields in turn rely on the most unifying concept in all of biology: evolution. Only in the context of evolution can anatomy and physiology be fully understood; without the concept of evolution, very little in biology makes sense.

A predominant theme of this book is that each of us has choices to make—choices that will affect ourselves, other humans, and the entire planet. Should all children be vaccinated against childhood diseases? Should we spend time and money preparing for a pandemic that may never occur? Will we be willing and able to slow the rate of global warming? Is it important that we save other species from extinction, and if so, how should we go about it? Students are encouraged to formulate their own views on these and other topics so that they will feel comfortable with the choices they make.

The Organization Fits the Course

This book was designed to accommodate the fairly standard format for college courses in human biology. There are chapters that introduce science and chemistry; chapters that cover basic human biology from cells through the human organ systems; and finally chapters on evolution, ecosystems and populations, and human impacts on the environment.

With such broad coverage, however, there is never enough time to teach all that is interesting, exciting, and relevant about human biology in one semester. Fortunately, because each chapter was written to stand on its own, this book allows for a certain degree of flexibility. Instructors wishing to emphasize the basics of human anatomy and physiology or focus on the medical aspects of human biology could omit or de-emphasize the last two chapters. Instructors should also feel free to present the organ system chapters in a different order if they feel more comfortable doing so. Within chapters, sections on diseases and disorders could be omitted or considered optional. Those interested in a more cellular or molecular approach might want to give greater emphasis to Chapters 3–4 and 17–21 and move more quickly through the organ systems chapters. Those more interested in the broader picture of where humans came from and how humans fit into the world order may want to allow sufficient time for the last three chapters, even if it means that they must move quickly or selectively through the organ system chapters. All of these approaches are equally valid.

However much you cover, dig in and enjoy your course!

Michael D. Johnson

Chapter-specific Changes

Chapter 1 Human Biology, Science, and Society

- New Quick Check
- BlogInFocus topics:
  - Vaccines and autism
  - Bacterial resistance to antibiotics
  - Drug package lists of side effects

Chapter 2 The Chemistry of Living Things

- Two new Quick Checks
- New Health & Wellness feature, "Radon: A Known Cancer Risk"
- BlogInFocus topics:
  - Should you add dietary supplements to your diet?
  - Energy drinks containing caffeine and alcohol

Chapter 3 Structure and Function of Cells

- New Quick Check
- New Health & Wellness feature, "Can Antioxidants Slow the Rate of Cellular Aging?"
- BlogInFocus topics:
  - Politics of human stem cell use
  - Stem cell therapy for a human disease

Chapter 4 From Cells to Organ Systems

- Updated *Current Issue* "Reshaping Your Body"
- BlogInFocus topics:
  - FDA's position on Lipodissolve
  - Is it okay to get skin sutures wet?

Chapter 5 The Skeletal System

- New Quick Check
- New text discussion and figure on the hyoid bone
- New figure comparing the pelvis bones of males and females
- BlogInFocus topics:
  - Gaucher disease
  - Using stem cells to treat joint injuries
  - Should "pre-osteoporosis" be treated?

Chapter 6 The Muscular System

- BlogInFocus topics:
  - Drug abuse and drug testing in sports
  - An innovative way to reduce muscle cramps?

Chapter 7 Blood

- New text discussion of "Blood Substitutes"
- New Quick Check
- Added renal failure to the list of causes of anemia
- BlogInFocus topics:
  - Use of platelet-rich plasma to treat connective tissue injuries
  - Cleansing blood with magnets

Chapter 8 Heart and Blood Vessels

- New Quick Check
- New text discussion on "Replacing a Failing Heart"
- New photos added of artificial hearts
- BlogInFocus topics:
  - Replacing damaged heart cells
  - Recommended maximum heart rate for women during exercise
  - New technique for replacing heart valves
  - Creating a beating heart in the laboratory

Chapter 9 The Immune System and Mechanisms of Defense

- New Quick Check
- New Health & Wellness feature, "The Case for Breast Milk"
- Substantially revised and updated information on HIV/AIDS
- BlogInFocus topics:
  - Prion-like activity in neurodegenerative disorders
  - Using bacteria to fight bacteria
  - Pills to prevent HIV infection?

Chapter 10 The Respiratory System: Exchange of Gases

- New text discussion on the topic of "Mesothelioma"
- BlogInFocus topics:
  - Bans on outdoor smoking
  - Using breath analysis to diagnose disease
  - Why is asthma on the rise?

Chapter 11 The Nervous System: Integration and Control

- New Quick Check
- New *Current Issue* "Head Trauma in Young Athletes"

- Expanded text discussion of Alzheimer's disease
- **BlogInFocus** topics:
  - Why do the eyes move rapidly during sleep?
  - Using a cancer drug to treat spinal cord injuries

Chapter 12 Sensory Mechanisms

- Substantially revised the *Current Issue* "DWD: Driving While Distracted"
- **BlogInFocus** topics:
  - Is texting while driving legal where you live?
  - Tasting bitter foods
  - Myopia (nearsightedness)

Chapter 13 The Endocrine System

- New *Current Issue* "Endocrine Disruptors in the Environment"
- New Health & Wellness, "Dealing with Diabetes"
- **BlogInFocus** topics:
  - Endocrine disruptor Bisphenol A (BPA)
  - Glucose monitoring devices—how accurate are they?

Chapter 14 The Digestive System and Nutrition

- New Health & Wellness, "Do You Know Someone With an Eating Disorder?"
- Updated text on the USDA's dietary guidelines and educational website, ChooseMyPlate.gov
- New text section on reading and understanding food labels
- **BlogInFocus** topics:
  - Taking a stand against self-harm blogs
  - Bans on trans-fats
  - Simeons Therapy diet

Chapter 15 The Urinary System

- Two new Quick Checks
- New Health & Wellness, "Is It Safe to Donate a Kidney?"
- New text section, "Urinary Incontinence"
- **BlogInFocus** topics:
  - Should kidney donors be paid?
  - Gender bias in kidney transplants
  - Using urine to diagnose disease

Chapter 16 Reproductive Systems

- Revised *Current Issue*, "Would You Like a Boy or a Girl?"
- New Health & Wellness, "Have You Had Your Gardasil?
- **BlogInFocus** topics:
  - Accuracy of fetal gender tests
  - Morning-after pill

- Antibiotic-resistant gonorrhea
- Human Papilloma Virus (HPV) vaccine

Chapter 17 Cell Reproduction and Differentiation

- New Quick Check
- Revised *Current Issue*, "Should We Clone Humans?"
- **BlogInFocus** topics:
  - Birth dating human cells
  - Are your fat cells ever replaced?

Chapter 18 Cancer: Uncontrolled Cell Division and Differentiation

- New Quick Check
- New text discussions on leukemia, skin cancer, and uterine cancer
- Added two photos illustrating tumor visualization by sonography (ultrasound) and Positron Emission Tomography (PET)
- Rearranged the top 10 cancers by deadliness, rather than incidence
- **BlogInFocus** topics:
  - Cell phones and cancer
  - Does aspirin reduce cancer risk?
  - New treatment for chronic lymphocytic leukemia

Chapter 19 Genetics and Inheritance

- New Quick Check
- **BlogInFocus** topics:
  - Genetic screening tests in newborns
  - Genetic disorders that are protective against disease
  - New test for Down syndrome in the fetus

Chapter 20 DNA Technology and Genetic Engineering

- New Health & Wellness, "DNA-Based Vaccines Against Viruses"
- **BlogInFocus** topics:
  - Patenting human genes
  - Genetic engineering to improve crop yields
  - Transgenic chickens to thwart bird flu

Chapter 21 Development and Aging

- **BlogInFocus** topics:
  - Gender determination in sports
  - Cashing in on telomere tests for aging
  - Risks of female hormone replacement therapy

Chapter 22 Evolution and the Origins of Life

- **BlogInFocus** topics:
  - Using DNA analysis to redefine evolutionary relationships
  - Is *Australopithecus sediba* a close human relative?
  - Origin of Australian aborigines

Chapter 23 Ecosystems and Populations

- New text discussion (and photo) of invasive species
- **BlogInFocus** topics:
  - Why swine flu killed primarily healthy young adults
  - Effect of a rising global atmospheric CO_2 concentration on plants
  - Dwindling global phosphorus supplies

Chapter 24 Human Impacts, Biodiversity, and Environmental Issues

- **BlogInFocus** topics:
  - CO_2 absorption by forests
  - Creating biodiesel fuel from just sunlight, water, and CO_2
  - Technologies for storing solar and wind energy

Acknowledgments

The Seventh Edition of *Human Biology: Concepts and Current Issues* is once again the product of the continued hard work and dedication of the people at Pearson Education, led by Editor-in-Chief Beth Wilbur, Executive Director of Development Deborah Gale, and Senior Acquisitions Editor Star Mackenzie. Star directs a team that functions as smoothly and professionally as any in the business.

On a day-to-day basis, I depended on Project Editor Kim Wimpsett. I am convinced that Kim worked seven days a week, judging by the rapidity with which she responded to my e-mails. I am blessed to have had her support. A special thanks also goes to Assistant Editor Frances Sink, who read and provided suggestions for improvements for every chapter.

Changes to the art and photos in the Seventh Edition are the result of the hard work of artists at Imagineering and photo coordinator Donna Kalal. Once again, photo researcher Kristin Piljay found the new photos you see in this edition.

Accuracy and clarity have been checked and rechecked by the hundreds of insightful faculty members around the country over the past ten years. Reviewers specific to this edition are listed below.

Thanks go to the outstanding support team at Pearson Education, BenjaminCummings. It includes Senior Media Producer Jonathan Ballard, Supplements Editor Susan Berge, Production Project Manager Camille Herrera, Copyeditor Nicole Schlutt, and Proofreader Christine Sabooni.

Once again, the textbook is supported by a wonderful set of ancillary materials. Thanks go to Robert Sullivan of Marist College, who wrote the Instructor Guide, to Suzanne Long of Monroe Community College, who developed the PowerPoint Lecture Slides and revised the Test Bank, to James Murphy, also of Monroe Community College, who checked it for accuracy, and to Bert Atsma of Union County College, whose Laboratory Manual continues to complement the best human biology courses. In addition, Robert Sullivan also revised the Web Publishing System (WPS) Multiple Choice Quizzes, Judy Stewart supplied the MasteringBiology Reading Quizzes, and Erwin Bautista of UC Davis was responsible for the Instructor Quiz Shows. Nancy O'Keefe of Purdue University Calumet supplied the Web Tutorials, Web Links, Biology in the News Essay, Weighing the Issues, and Crosswords.

Last but not least, I'd like to thank my wife, Pamela, for her wholehearted support and understanding over the years.

Reviewers

Andrea Abbas,
Washtenaw Community College

Wade Bell,
Virginia Military Institute

Samantha Butler,
University of Southern California

Anne Casper,
Eastern Michigan University

Chris Chabot,
Plymouth State University

Jennifer Ellie,
Wichita State University

Tom Kennedy,
College of New Mexico

Gary Lange,
Saginaw Valley State University

Suzanne Long,
Monroe Community College

Nancy O'Keefe,
Purdue University Calumet

Samiksha Raut,
Dalton State College

Lisa Runco,
New York Institute of Technology

Sean Senechal,
CSU Monterey Bay

Derek Sims,
Hopkinsville Community College

Corinne Ulbright,
Indiana University–Purdue University, Indianapolis

Peggy Wright,
Columbia College

Human Biology, Science, and Society

Crew of the space shuttle Atlantis, November 20, 2007.

Mandatory Childhood Vaccinations

On January 1, 2009, New Jersey became the first state to require flu shots for children who attend licensed day care and preschool programs. New Jersey now requires immunization (vaccinations) for 13 vaccine-preventable communicable diseases, more than any other state. New Jersey is not alone, however, in requiring vaccinations—all 50 states currently have some kind of school immunization requirement. (All 50 states also permit exemptions under certain conditions.)

Childhood Vaccinations Save Lives

The states' rationale is clear: Childhood vaccines introduced since the 1950s have all but wiped out many communicable diseases in the United States, including measles, mumps, whooping cough (pertussis), polio, and diphtheria. In the 1940s and '50s, before vaccines against these diseases were available, the five diseases combined caused an estimated 900,000 cases of disease and 7,700 deaths per year. By 2004 there were only 27 deaths from all five diseases combined—a 99.6% reduction. The number of cases of measles dropped from

more than 500,000 per year before the measles vaccine was available to only 62 cases per year in recent years.

Recently, however, public health officials have noticed an uptick in the number of cases of measles and whooping cough, two diseases that are highly sensitive to vaccination rates. In the first 10 months of 2010 there were more than triple the usual number of cases annually in the United States, according to the Centers for Disease Control and Prevention. Most of the measles victims had not been vaccinated, even though they were eligible for the vaccine (children under 12 months of age are not yet eligible).

Parents Resist Mandatory Vaccination

The rise in measles and whooping cough coincides with more than a doubling of exemptions from school immunization programs granted for "philosophical or personal beliefs" between 1991 and 2004. Why are parents increasingly refusing to have their children vaccinated when the evidence is so overwhelming that vaccinations prevent communicable diseases? Their reasons tend to fall into two categories: 1) a belief that the vaccines (or something in them) may be contributing to what they view as an epidemic of childhood chronic diseases, including autism, and 2) a dislike of government intervention into personal decisions.

Compared to parents who vaccinate their children, parents who choose not to vaccinate their children tend to believe that the risk of their child getting the disease is low and that the disease itself is not very severe. The latter view is understandable, because most parents today have not lived through a major outbreak of any communicable disease. Today's parents were born after the scourge of polio, for example. Polio killed nearly 10% of its victims and crippled countless others for life before the polio vaccine became available in 1955.

Public health officials are watching these developments with concern. Not all people in a community can be vaccinated, and so the prevention of widespread outbreaks of vaccine-preventable diseases in communities depends in part on "herd immunity." The concept is that when most people in a community (or herd) have been vaccinated, the disease has a much harder time spreading from individual to individual. In other words, high vaccination rates benefit the community overall (especially young children), in addition to protecting the individual who has been vaccinated. Says Dr. Anne Schuchat, director of the National Center for Immunization and Respiratory Diseases, "The vaccine against measles is highly effective in preventing infections, and high immunization levels in the community are effective at preventing or drastically reducing the size of outbreaks."[1]

A Link Between Vaccinations and Autism?

Parents who oppose mandatory vaccinations for safety reasons often point to cases of children who developed autism shortly after receiving a vaccine. Their celebrity spokesperson is actress and former *Playboy* model Jenny McCarthy, whose son is autistic. Ms. McCarthy is on the board of Generation Rescue, a nonprofit organization that claims to be able to treat autism effectively with a special diet.

Actress Jenny McCarthy has appeared on the *Oprah Winfrey Show* opposing mandatory vaccinations.

Medical professionals and research scientists continue to point out that the available scientific evidence does not support the argument that vaccination can cause childhood diseases, including autism. But for many parents, scientific studies are not as convincing as an appearance by Ms. McCarthy on the *Oprah Winfrey Show* with an emotional story about ill children.

Some parents oppose mandatory childhood vaccinations because they are philosophically opposed to government intervention into what they see as a personal choice. Says Barbara Loe Fisher, a mother and the cofounder of the National Vaccine Information Center, representing parents against forced vaccinations, "... If the State can tag, track down and force citizens against their will to be injected with biologicals of unknown toxicity today, there will be no limit on which individual freedoms the State can take away in the name of the greater good tomorrow."[2]

Parents in favor of vaccines are mounting lobbying campaigns as well. Their celebrity advocate is actress Amanda Peet, now a spokesperson for Every Child By Two, a vaccine-advocacy group founded by former first lady Rosalynn Carter. Ms. Peet once called anti-vaccine parents "parasites" for relying on other children's immunity to protect their own. She later apologized for the word, and suggested that parents should get their advice from doctors, not celebrities like herself (and presumably Ms. McCarthy).

It would be a shame if vaccines became such a hot-button issue that preventable diseases such as polio returned. We need to find a way to address parents' concerns about vaccine safety and about the role of government in our lives, while at the same time protecting the public from preventable, communicable diseases. How we choose to do that is up to all of us.

QUESTIONS TO CONSIDER

1 What should medical professionals, politicians, or even just concerned citizens do, if anything, to help parents understand the risks and benefits of vaccines?

2 Will you vaccinate your children? Why or why not? What would you like to know in order to make an informed decision?

[1] www.cdc.gov/media/pressrel/2008/r080821.htm
[2] www.vaccineawakening.blogspot.com

THE FACTS...

- Childhood vaccination programs have been effective in all but eliminating certain communicable diseases.
- All 50 states have childhood vaccination (immunization) programs as a requirement for school attendance—all states also allow for certain exemptions.
- Exemptions from vaccination (and communicable diseases) are on the rise. Many parents object to mandatory vaccination programs out of concern that the vaccines may cause autism or certain other chronic childhood diseases.
- The available scientific evidence does not support the argument that vaccinations can cause childhood diseases, including autism.

>> **Living things have certain characteristics** that make them different from nonliving things. Living things harness energy and use energy to create unique chemical compounds, grow, and ultimately reproduce.

>> **Humans are just one of several million different life-forms** on Earth. Our closest relatives are the other primates (including monkeys and apes). Features that *taken together* define humans as unique are bipedalism, opposable thumbs, a large brain, and a capacity for complex language.

>> **Science is a process for studying the natural world.** It is based on observable, quantifiable data obtained by repeatedly questioning, observing, and drawing conclusions.

>> **Science helps us understand what *is*, not what *should* be.** It does not provide us with "right" answers or give meaning to our lives.

>> **We make choices** about how to use scientific knowledge every day whether we are consciously aware of it or not. We owe it to ourselves to make informed choices.

Y**ou were born into exciting times,** when scientific discoveries are happening more rapidly than at any other time in human history. Like the Industrial Revolution of the nineteenth century and the discovery of DNA in the twentieth, today's scientific innovations will change the human condition forever.

In your lifetime people may be able to select or modify their children's features before they are born. People may even be able to have clones (copies) made of themselves. At the very least, certain diseases that threaten us now will become curable. Perhaps your grandchildren will not even know what AIDS is because the disease will have disappeared.

What you are witnessing is the power of science. **Science** is the study of the *natural world*, which includes all matter and all energy. Because all living organisms are also made of matter and energy, they are part of the natural world (Figure 1.1). Biology is one of many branches of science. More specifically, **biology** (from the Greek words *bios*, meaning "life," and *logos*, meaning "word or thought") is the study of living organisms and life's processes. It is the study of life. Other branches of science are chemistry, physics, geology, astronomy, and related fields such as medicine.

This text is specifically about *human* biology. We will explore what it means to be alive. We will see how the molecules that make up our bodies are created from molecules in the air and in our food and drink. We will learn how our cells grow and divide, and how we evolved from single-celled

organisms that arose from nonliving chemical elements nearly 3.5 billion years ago. We will explore how our bodies function, why we get diseases, and how we manage to survive them. We will look at how we develop into adults, reproduce, and influence the destinies of other organisms on Earth.

With the power of science comes an awesome responsibility. All of us, individually and collectively, must choose how to use the knowledge that science gives us. Will human cloning be acceptable? Can we prevent global warming? Should your insurance company be able to reject you for coverage because genetic testing shows that you may develop cancer 40 years from now? Should you be required to vaccinate your children against certain infectious childhood diseases? (See the Current Issue feature, *Mandatory Childhood Vaccinations*.)

BlogInFocus MB

What happened to the doctor who first suggested that vaccinations might cause autism? To find out, visit MJ's blog in the Study Area in MasteringBiology and look under "Vaccines and Autism."

We all have to make responsible decisions concerning not only our own health and well-being but also the long-term well-being of our species. This book considers many aspects of human interaction with the natural world. We'll contemplate human functioning within the environment and the impact of humans on the environment. Along the way we'll confront a variety of social and personal issues and discuss the choices we might make about them. Because biology is the study of life, we begin by defining life itself.

⏎ **Recap** Science is the study of the natural world, which consists of all matter and energy. Biology is the study of living organisms. ▪

1.1 The characteristics of life

What is life? On the one hand, this question seems easy and on the other hand so abstract that it is more like a riddle. We all think we can recognize life even if we can't define it easily. Children learn early to distinguish between living and nonliving things. Remember that childhood game "animal, vegetable, or mineral"? In it, children distinguish what is alive (animals and plants) from what is not (minerals).

Most biologists accept the following criteria as signs of life:

▪ *Living things have a different molecular composition than nonliving things.* Everything in the natural world, both living and nonliving, is composed of the same set of approximately 100 different chemical *elements*. However, only a few elements are present in any abundance in living organisms. In addition, living organisms can combine elements in unique ways, creating certain *molecules* (combinations of elements) that nonliving things cannot create. These molecules of life (proteins,

Photo taken from the Hubble Space Telescope showing a tiny portion of the universe. Studies by astronomers have shown that all matter on Earth originated inside stars or with the Big Bang.

Studying unusual species such as this deep sea glass squid allows biologists to understand the processes by which a species successfully survives. Many different environments exist in the world, but the same physical and chemical laws govern them all.

The natural world comprises all matter and energy. An erupting volcano spewing liquid rock and heat is the result of energy that still remains from the creation of Earth nearly 4.6 billion years ago.

Jane Goodall has dedicated her life to studying the needs and behaviors of chimpanzees. The DNA of humans and chimps is almost the same, yet important physical and behavioral differences are obvious. Evolution examines how these differences arose.

Figure 1.1 Studies of the natural world.

carbohydrates, lipids, and nucleic acids) are found in all living organisms and often persist in the remains of dead organisms. Variations in these molecules in different life-forms account for the diversity of life.

- *Living things require energy and raw materials.* The creation of the molecules of life doesn't happen by accident, at least under present conditions on Earth. The transformation of molecules from one form to another requires energy. The term **metabolism** refers to the physical and chemical processes involved in transforming energy and molecules so that life can be maintained. All living things take in raw materials and energy from the environment and metabolize them into the molecules and energy that they need to survive. Plants use the energy of sunlight and chemicals obtained from soil, water, and air. Animals and all other forms of life ultimately obtain their energy and raw materials from water, air, plants, or other animals.

- *Living things are composed of cells.* A **cell** is the smallest unit that exhibits all the characteristics of life (**Figure 1.2.**). All cells originate only from existing cells. Living things always have at least one cell, and some organisms (called *unicellular* organisms) are *only* one cell. *Multicellular* organisms are composed of many cells or many different types of cells.
- *Living things maintain homeostasis.* All living organisms must maintain an internal environment compatible with life, and the range of chemical and physical conditions compatible with life is very narrow. The maintenance of a relatively constant internal environment is called **homeostasis**. Living things have developed remarkable ways of regulating their internal environment despite sometimes dramatic changes in the external environment. Single cells and unicellular organisms are surrounded by a membrane that allows the cell (or organism) to maintain internal homeostasis by providing a selective barrier to the entry and exit of various substances.

a) Several *Staphylococcus aureus*, one of several types of bacteria that causes food poisoning (SEM × 50,000).

b) Some of the many cells that line the inner surface of the human stomach (SEM × 500).

Figure 1.2 Cells are the smallest units of life. Some organisms consist of just one cell (unicellular), whereas others contain many cells (multicellular).

In multicellular organisms the tissues, organs, and organ systems work together to maintain homeostasis of the fluid that surrounds all cells. We discuss the importance of homeostasis further in Chapter 4.

- *Living things respond to their external environment.* Stay out in the cold too long and you are likely to respond by moving to a warm room. Plants respond to their environment by turning their leaves toward light or by growing roots toward sources of nutrients and water. Even bacteria respond to their environment by moving toward nutrients (and away from noxious stimuli) and by increasing their growth rate.

- *Living things grow and reproduce.* Living organisms have the capacity to grow and ultimately produce more living organisms like themselves (Figure 1.3). The ability to grow and reproduce is determined by the genetic material in cells, called deoxyribonucleic acid (DNA). Some nonliving things can get larger, of course; examples are glaciers and volcanic mountains. However, they cannot create copies of themselves.

- *Populations of living things evolve.* The various forms of life may change over many generations in a process known as evolution. Evolution explains why there are so many different forms of life on Earth today.

✅ **Quick Check** *Why do living things require energy? Where does that energy ultimately come from?* ▪

Although all these characteristics are necessary to describe life fully, not all of them apply to every living thing all the time. Individual organisms do not evolve, nor do they necessarily reproduce or always respond to their surroundings. However, populations of similar organisms have the *capacity* to perform these functions.

Mycobacterium dividing

Milkweed going to seed

Bison and calf

Figure 1.3 Living things grow and reproduce.

🔄 **Recap** All living things are composed of cells. Living things require energy and raw materials, maintain homeostasis, respond to their external environments, grow and reproduce, and evolve over many generations. ▪

1.2 How humans fit into the natural world

Living things are grouped according to their characteristics

To find order in the diversity of life, biologists have long sought ways to categorize living things. Although methods of classification have changed over time and several schemes can be found in the literature, the most common classification system today is one that defines all organisms by a hierarchical system of categories from largest to smallest, based on common features. The categories of the classification system (from largest to smallest) are **domain**, **kingdom**, **phylum**, **order**, **class**, **family**, **genus**, and **species**.

The classification system begins with three domains (**Figure 1.4**). Figure 1.4 also shows how the three domains are thought to have evolved from the first primitive life-forms. Organisms in the domains Bacteria and Archaea are all single-celled bacteria without nuclei. (Cells without nuclei are called *prokaryotes*; organisms whose cells have nuclei are called *eukaryotes*.) Most of the bacteria with which you may be familiar belong to the domain Bacteria. The bacteria in domain Eukarya tend to live in unique environments under extreme conditions, such as in deep-sea thermal vents.

All organisms whose cells have nuclei belong to the domain Eukarya. This domain is further divided into four kingdoms: Protista (protozoans and algae), Animalia (animals), Fungi (fungi), and Plantae (plants).

The kingdom **Protista** comprises unicellular and relatively simple multicellular eukaryotes such as protozoa, algae, and slime molds. The remaining three kingdoms (Animalia, Plantae, and Fungi) all consist of multicellular organisms. The criteria

for classifying animals, plants, and fungi are based largely on the organism's life cycle, structure, and mode of nutrition. Plants, for example, contain a green pigment called *chlorophyll* that allows them to capture the energy of sunlight, which they convert for their own use in a process called **photosynthesis**. Animals get the energy they need by eating plants or other animals, which requires structures specialized to digest and absorb food. Most animals can move about to obtain food. Fungi (yeasts, molds, and mushrooms) are *decomposers*, meaning that they obtain their energy from decaying material.

Humans belong to the domain Eukarya, kingdom Animalia. Based on their features in common with other animals, humans are further classified into the phylum Chordata (animals with neural cords), class Mammalia (chordates with mammary glands for nursing their young), order Primates (humans, lemurs, monkeys and apes), family Hominidae (ancient and modern humans), and finally, genus and species (*Homo sapiens*).

A species is one or more populations of organisms with similar physical and functional characteristics that interbreed and produce fertile offspring under natural conditions. All living humans currently living on Earth belong to the genus and species *Homo sapiens*. We share common features that make us different from any other species on Earth, and we can interbreed.

No one knows how many species of living organisms exist on Earth. Estimates range from about 3 million to 30 million, but only about 2 million species have been identified so far.

✅ **Quick Check** *While studying a drop of pond water under a microscope, you notice two tiny single-celled organisms, one with a nucleus and one without. What can you say about what domain and kingdom each is in? Which one is more closely related to humans? Explain.* ◼

Figure 1.4 Domains and kingdoms. Classification of living organisms is based on common features. All organisms in domains Bacteria and Archaea are single-celled bacteria without nuclei (prokaryotes). Organisms in the domain Eukarya have nuclei; that is, they are eukaryotes. The domain Eukarya is subdivided into four kingdoms.

The defining features of humans

Humans are not the largest animal, nor the fastest or strongest. Our eyesight and hearing are not the best. We cannot fly, we swim poorly, and we don't dig holes in the ground very well with our hands. Nevertheless we possess several features that, taken together, define how we are different from other organisms and explain how we have managed to survive for so long:

- *Bipedalism.* Humans are the only mammals that prefer to stand upright and walk on two legs. Bipedalism (from the Latin *bi-*, meaning "two," and *pes*, meaning "foot") frees our hands and forearms for carrying items ranging from weapons to infants. Birds walk upright, too, of course, but they do not have the advantage of being able to carry things with their forelimbs.
- *Opposable thumbs.* Humans and several other primates have thumbs that can be moved into position to oppose the tips of the fingers. However, only humans have the well-developed muscles that enable us to exert a certain type of precise control over the thumb and fingers. For instance, we tend to pick up and manipulate small objects between the tip of the thumb and the tip of either the index or second finger (Figure 1.5). In contrast, chimpanzees more naturally grasp objects between the thumb and the side of the index finger. Threading a needle or suturing a wound would be difficult for a chimpanzee.

- *Large brain.* Humans have a large brain mass relative to body size. The evolution of a large brain seems to have coincided with the advent of stone tools, leading some scientists to suggest that a large brain was required for the complex motions associated with tool use. Other scientists believe that a large brain was necessary for language, and that language developed as social interactions among humans became more important.
- *Capacity for complex language.* Many animals vocalize (produce sounds) to warn, threaten, or identify other members of their species, and a few (such as dolphins) have developed fairly complex forms of communication. However, humans have developed both complex vocal language and a system of signs, symbols, and gestures for communicating concepts and emotions. Throughout the world, every group of human beings has developed a complex spoken language. Humans have also placed their languages into written form, permitting communication over great distances and spans of time (Figure 1.6).

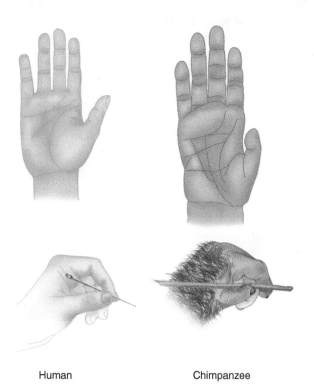

Human　　　　　Chimpanzee

Figure 1.5 How humans and chimpanzees hold small objects. Although the hands of humans and chimpanzees seem similar, only humans tend to hold objects between the tip of a thumb and the tips of the fingers.

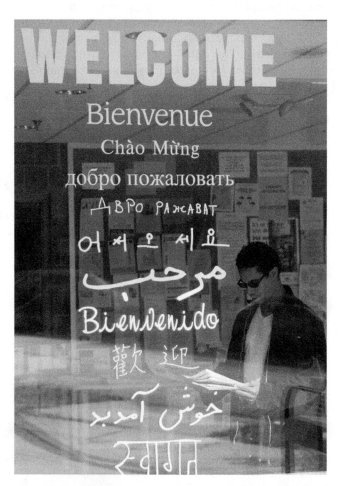

Figure 1.6 Language. This welcome sign is in English, French, Vietnamese, Russian, Ukrainian, Korean, Arabic, Spanish, Chinese, Farsi, and Hindi.

It should be stressed that none of these features necessarily make us any better than any other species, only different.

✅ **Quick Check** *Suppose you are a scientist who has just uncovered a complete fossil skeleton of a human-like primate. Which areas of the skeleton could you study to determine whether the fossil is closely related to humans? Explain your reasoning.* ▪

Human biology can be studied on any level of biological organization

Figure 1.7 shows how humans fit into the grand scheme of things in the natural world. The figure also shows how humans—or any living thing, for that matter—can be studied on any level of biological organization, from the level of the atom to the level of the biosphere. This text examines human biology on progressively larger scales.

Figure 1.7 Levels of organization in human biology.

Our study of human biology begins with the smallest units of life. Like rocks, water, and air, humans are composed of small units of natural elements called *atoms* and *molecules*. We'll start by introducing the basic chemistry of living things and then we'll look at how the atoms and molecules of living things are arranged into the smallest of living units, called *cells*. Next we'll learn how groups of similar cells become *tissues*, how groups of tissues that carry out a specific function constitute an *organ*, and how organs work together in an *organ system* to carry out a more general function. Then we'll take a look at the structures and functions of specific human organs and organ systems. For example, we'll learn why—and how—more blood flows through the lungs than through any other organ and what happens to your dinner as it makes its way through your digestive system. Next we'll consider humans as complete *organisms*, including how cells reproduce, how we inherit traits from our parents, and

how we develop, age, and die. Finally, we'll discuss how life began, how *communities* of living organisms evolved, and how humans fit into and alter the *ecosystems* in which we live and the entire *biosphere* of the natural world.

Table 1.1 lists some current issues, controversies, and "hot topics" that relate to human biology. Many of these issues and controversies also concern fields outside the sphere of science, such as economics, law, politics, and ethics. What you learn in this course will help you make informed decisions about these and future issues that will come up in your lifetime.

Your ability to make good judgments in the future and to feel comfortable with your decisions will depend on your critical thinking skills. We turn now to a discussion of what science is, how we can use the methodology of science to improve our critical thinking skills, and how science influences our lives.

Table 1.1 Examples of issues and controversies associated with the levels of human biology

Level of organization	Definition	Issues and controversies
Atom and molecule	**Atom:** Smallest unit of an element of matter **Molecule:** More than one atom in a stable association	Disposing of radioactive wastes Role of unstable molecules (free radicals) in cancer and aging
Cell	Smallest unit of life	Cloning adult animals, plants, and humans from a single cell
Tissue	An association of cells with the same general structure and function	Using human fetal tissues in research
Organ	An association of several tissue types that carry out a specific function	Increasing the supply of human organs for transplantation Transplanting animal organs into humans
Organ system	Two or more organs that work together to carry out a general function, such as digestion or movement	Enhancing human performance with drugs or by genetic engineering
Organism	An individual living being composed of several organs or organ systems	Testing for heritable diseases for which there are no cures Abortion Deciding who should pay for human behavior-related illnesses such as those caused by smoking
Population	A group of individuals of the same species living in the same area	Rationing medical care Determining who gets the scarce human organs available for transplantation
Community	Several populations of different species who inhabit the same area and interact with each other	Impact of humans on the well-being and survival of other species Genetic engineering of plants and animals for human purposes Using animals in medical research and cosmetics testing
Ecosystem	All of the organisms in a given area plus all of the nonliving matter and energy	Environmental pollution Destruction of ecosystems due to overuse by humans
Biosphere	All ecosystems combined. The portion of Earth occupied by living organisms, plus those organisms.	Global warming Destruction of the ozone layer

Recap Classification systems place living things into groups. The most inclusive group is a domain, and the smallest is a species. Humans belong to the kingdom Animalia within the domain Eukarya. Our genus and species is *Homo sapiens*. Humans walk on two legs (are bipedal) and can grasp small objects between the tips of the thumb and first finger. Humans also have large brains relative to body mass, and the capacity for complex spoken and written languages. Biology can be studied at any level, from atom to biosphere.

1.3 Science is both a body of knowledge and a process

We have already said that science is the study of the natural world. More explicitly, science is two things: *knowledge* (organized, reliable information) about the natural world and the *process* we use to get that knowledge. *Scientific knowledge* refers to information about the natural world. The process of science, or the way scientific knowledge is acquired, is generally called the **scientific method**, although

in practice this term encompasses a variety of methods. Throughout this book you will be presented with scientific knowledge, but it's worth remembering that this information was obtained slowly over time by the scientific method.

Scientific knowledge enables us to describe and predict the natural world. Scientific knowledge is also empirical, which means that it relies on observation and experimentation. Through the scientific method, scientists strive to accumulate information that is as free as possible of bias, embellishment, or interpretation.

The scientific method is a process for testing ideas

Although there is more than one way to gather information about the natural world, the scientific method is a systematic process for developing and testing predictions (**Figure 1.8**). You probably already use the scientific method, or at least elements of it, in your own everyday problem solving. Sometimes we go through the steps without thinking about them consciously, but we follow them nevertheless.

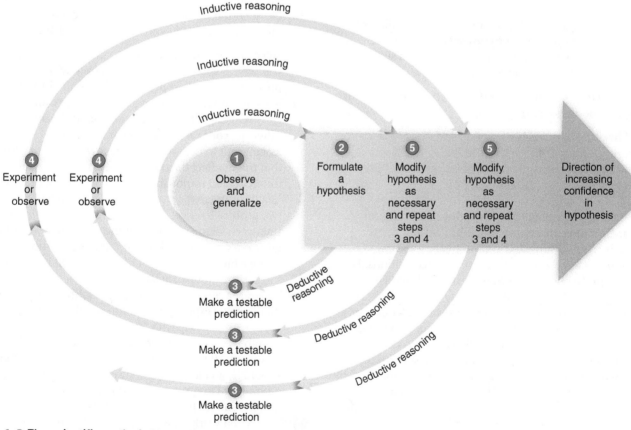

Figure 1.8 The scientific method. Observations and generalizations lead to the formulation of a hypothesis. From the hypothesis, specific predictions are made that can be tested by experimentation or observation. The results either support the hypothesis or require that it be modified to fit the new facts. The cycle is repeated. Ultimately the scientific method moves in the direction of increased confidence in the modified hypothesis.

✓ *Explain in your own words the difference between inductive and deductive reasoning, and explain why the scientific method needs both.*

Step 1: Observe and generalize When we observe the world around us and make generalizations from what we learn, we are employing *inductive reasoning* (extrapolating from the specific to the general case).

Usually we don't even think about it and don't bother to put our observations and generalizations into any kind of formal language, but we do it just the same. For example, you are probably convinced that it will *always* be colder in winter than in summer (a generalization) because you have observed that every winter in the past was colder than the preceding summer (specific observation). The difference between common experience and good science is that science uses generalization to make a prediction that can be tested. Taking an example from biological research, let's start with two observations and a generalization:

> *Observation 1:* Rats given a particular drug (call it Drug X) have lower blood pressures than rats not fed the drug.
>
> *Observation 2:* Independently, researchers in Canada showed that Drug X lowers blood pressures in dogs and cats.
>
> *Generalization:* Drug X lowers blood pressure in all mammals.

Step 2: Formulate a hypothesis Observations and generalizations are used to develop a *hypothesis*. A **hypothesis** is a tentative statement about the natural world. Importantly, it is a statement that can lead to testable deductions.

> *Hypothesis:* Drug X would be a safe and effective treatment for high blood pressure in humans.

☑ **Quick Check** *Consider the following statement: "Giant apes called Sasquatches are living in the forests of the Pacific Northwest, but they avoid people and leave no evidence of their existence." Does this statement qualify as a scientific hypothesis?* ▪

Step 3: Make a testable prediction Hypotheses that cannot be tested are idle speculation, so much hot air. But many hypotheses are so sweeping and comprehensive that ways must be found to test them under a variety of conditions. For example, you probably would not be convinced that Drug X is safe and effective for all people under all conditions until you had at least tested it in quite a few people under many different conditions. To have confidence in your hypothesis, you must make testable predictions (also called *working hypotheses*) based on the hypothesis and then test them one at a time. Predictions employ *deductive reasoning* (applying the general case to the specific). Often they are put in the form of an "if...then" statement, in which the "if" part of the statement is the hypothesis. For example:

> *Prediction: If* Drug X is a safe and effective treatment for high blood pressure in humans, *then* 10 mg/day of Drug X will lower blood pressure in people with high blood pressure within one month.

Notice that the prediction is very specific. In this example the prediction specifies the dose of drug, the medical condition of the persons on whom it will be tested, the expected effect of the drug if the prediction is correct, and a specified time period for the test. Its specificity makes it testable—yes or no, true or false.

☑ **Quick Check** *Suppose you are designing a research study to test the hypothesis that regular exercise helps people sleep better. Develop a specific, testable prediction from this hypothesis.* ▪

Step 4: Experiment or observe The truth or falsehood of your prediction is determined by observation or by experimentation. An **experiment** is a carefully planned and executed manipulation of the natural world to test your prediction. The experiment that you conduct (or the observations you make) will depend on the specific nature of the prediction.

When testing a prediction, scientists try to design experiments that can be conducted under strictly controlled conditions. Experiments conducted under specific, controlled conditions are called *controlled experiments* because they have the distinct advantage of accounting for all possible **variables** (factors that might vary during the course of the experiment) except for the one variable of interest, called the *controlled variable*. In this case the controlled variable is blood pressure. Therefore, in the example of Drug X, you could follow these steps in your controlled experiment (Figure 1.9):

- Select a large group of human subjects. In this case you would specifically choose people with high blood pressure rather than people with normal blood pressure.
- *Randomly* divide the larger pool of subjects into two groups. Designate one the **experimental group** and the other the **control group**. The importance of random assignment to the two groups is that all other factors that might affect the outcome (such as age or gender differences in responsiveness to the drug, or other previous health problems) are automatically equalized between the two groups. In effect, the control group accounts for all unknown factors. If you treat the experimental and control groups identically at this point, the probability is that the average blood pressures of the groups will be equal, as long as the groups are large enough.
- Treat subjects in the two groups *exactly* the same except that only the experimental group gets the drug. Treat the experimental group with 10 mg/day of Drug X for one month and the control group with a **placebo**, or "false treatment." If you deliver Drug X in a pill, the placebo should be an identical-looking pill with no drug in it. If you administer Drug X as an injection in a saline solution, the placebo should be an injection of the same volume of saline.

When working with human subjects, scientists must take the power of suggestion into account. It is important that no subjects in either group know which group has received the drug. If members of the experimental group find out that they are getting a drug to lower their blood pressure, this knowledge may accidentally influence the outcome of the experiment. To eliminate the power of suggestion as a variable,

Select a large number of appropriate subjects.

Randomly divide the subjects into two groups.

Group 1   Group 2

Treat the groups equally in all ways but one.

Experimental group: receives treatment

Control group: receives placebo

Observe or make measurements.

Are blood pressures lower in the experimental group?

Compare results.

Yes   **No**

Hypothesis received support.

Modify hypothesis to fit the new findings.

Figure 1.9 The steps in a controlled experiment. In this example the experimental variable is blood pressure. Because of the way the experiment is designed, the only difference between the two groups is the presence or absence of the experimental treatment itself.

✔ *Suppose that instead of randomly assigning subjects to the two groups, subjects with high blood pressure are more likely to be put in the experimental group. Would this be a better or a worse experiment, or would it make no difference? Explain.*

researchers conduct experiments "blind," meaning that the subjects don't know whether they are getting the placebo or the drug. Sometimes experiments are done "double-blind," so that even the person administering the drugs and placebos does not know which is which until the experiment is over.

■ Measure blood pressures in both groups at the end of one month and compare them using the appropriate statistical (mathematical) tests. If the experimental group's blood pressures are statistically lower, then your prediction is verified and your hypothesis receives support.

✔ **Quick Check** *A researcher tries to test the hypothesis that "exercise helps people sleep better" with the following study: He asks 50 regular joggers and 50 non-joggers how well they sleep at night. What are some problems with this experiment?* ■

Step 5: Modify the hypothesis as necessary and repeat steps 3 and 4 If your prediction turns out to be false, you will have to modify your hypothesis to fit the new findings and repeat steps 3 and 4. For example, perhaps the drug would lower blood pressure if you increased the dose or gave it for a longer period of time.

Even if your prediction turns out to be true, you're still not done. This is because you've tested only one small part of the hypothesis (its effectiveness under one specific set of conditions), not all the infinite possibilities. How do we know the drug is safe, and how safe is "safe," anyway? Does it cause a dangerous drop in blood pressure in people with normal blood pressures? Does it cause birth defects if taken by pregnant women? Does long-term use lead to kidney failure? Does the drug's effectiveness diminish over time? Specific predictions may have to be stated and tested for each of these questions before the drug is allowed on the market.

Only after many scientists have tried repeatedly (and failed) to disprove a hypothesis do they begin to have more confidence in it. A hypothesis cannot be proved true; it can only be supported or disproved. As this example shows, the scientific method is a process of elimination that may be limited by our approach and even by our preconceived notions about what to test. We move toward the best explanation for the moment, with the understanding that it may change in the future.

Making the findings known

New information is not of much use if hardly anybody knows about it. For that reason, scientists need to let others know of their findings. Often they publish the details in scientific journals to announce their findings to the world. Articles in *peer-reviewed* journals are subjected to the scrutiny of several experts (the scientists' peers) who must approve the article before it can be published. Peer-reviewed journals often contain the most accurate scientific information.

An unspoken assumption in any conclusion is that the results are valid only for the conditions under which the experiment was done. This is why scientific articles go into such detail about exactly how the experiment was performed. Complete documentation allows other scientists to repeat the experiments themselves or to develop and test their own predictions based on the findings of others.

Try to apply the scientific method to a hypothesis dealing with some aspect of evolution or to a global problem such as cancer or AIDS, and you begin to appreciate how scientists

The Growing Threat of Antibiotic-Resistant Bacteria

When antibiotics—drugs that kill bacteria—became available in the 1940s, they were hailed as a breakthrough. Indeed, many people owe their lives to them. But there is a downside: Indiscriminate use of antibiotics leads to antibiotic resistance in some strains of bacteria. For example, in recent years a new strain of the *Staphylococcus aureus* bacterium has appeared that is resistant to all penicillin-type antibiotics. This frightening superbug, called MRSA (methicillin-resistant *Staphylococcus aureus*) can cause serious skin infections and even penetrate bones and lungs, killing approximately 20% of those with severe infections. Over 25% of all *Staphylococcus aureus* ear/nose/throat infections in children are now MRSA.

The rise of MRSA actually makes biological sense. Whenever an antibiotic kills most but not all of a population of bacteria, the surviving bacteria are the ones that are naturally most resistant to the antibiotic. With the total population of bacteria now decreased, these antibiotic-resistant survivors multiply. So the more we use antibiotics, the more we encourage the rise of resistant strains of bacteria.

Because antibiotics have been so effective in the past, we have grown to rely on them, and we tend to use them indiscriminately. Over 50 million pounds of antibiotics are produced each year in the United States, about half of which are fed to livestock or sprayed on fruit trees. Researchers estimate that fully one-third

Skin lesions caused by MRSA.

of all antibiotic prescriptions given to nonhospitalized patients in the United States are not needed. Many hand creams, soaps, and laundry detergents are advertised as containing antibiotics as well.

The key to preserving the effectiveness of antibiotics is to use them only when necessary. Things we can do:

- Don't ask your doctor for antibiotics for a viral illness such as a cold or flu. Antibiotics kill bacteria but have no effect on viruses.
- Take antibiotics only when needed and as prescribed. Complete the full course of treatment.
- Reduce your use of antibacterial hand creams, soaps, and laundry detergents.
- Support farmers' efforts to reduce their use of antibiotics in cattle feed and on fruit trees.
- Support research efforts to find new antibiotics.

Used properly and judiciously, antibiotics will remain in our antibacterial arsenal for many years. ■

---

can spend a lifetime of discovery in science (and enjoy every minute!). At times the process seems like three steps forward and two steps back. You can bet that at least some of what you learn in this book will not be considered accurate 10 years from now. Nevertheless, even through our mistakes we make important new observations, some of which may lead to rapid advances in science and technology. Just in the last 100 years we've developed antibiotics, sent people to the moon, and put computers on millions of desks.

Many people associate science with certainty, whereas in reality scientists are constantly dealing with uncertainty. That is why we find scientists who don't agree or who change their minds. Building and testing hypotheses is slow, messy work, requiring that scientists constantly question and verify each other.

A well-tested hypothesis becomes a theory

Many people think that a *theory* is a form of idle speculation or a guess. Scientists use the word quite differently. To scientists, a **theory** is a broad hypothesis that has been extensively tested and supported over time and that explains a broad range of scientific facts with a high degree of reliability.

A theory is the highest status that any hypothesis can achieve. Even theories, however, may be modified over time as new and better information emerges. Only a few hypotheses have been elevated to the status of theories in biology. Among them are the theory of evolution and the cell theory of life.

↺ **Recap** The scientific method is a systematic process of observation, hypothesis building, and hypothesis testing. A theory is a broad hypothesis that has withstood numerous tests. ■

1.4 Sources of scientific information vary in style and quality

We are constantly bombarded by scientific information, some of it accurate and some not. What can you believe when the facts seem to change so quickly? All of us need to know how to find good information and evaluate it critically.

Different sources of scientific information may have very different goals, so look for those that can best inform you at your own level of understanding and interest.

Some scientific knowledge is highly technical. As a result, scientists have a tendency to speak on a technical level and primarily to each other. As we've already mentioned, scientists often communicate by means of articles in specialized peer-reviewed journals such as *Nature* and *Science*. Articles in peer-reviewed journals are concise, accurate, and documented so thoroughly that another scientist ought to be able to duplicate the work after reading the article. Generally they refer extensively to previous literature on the subject. Articles in peer-reviewed journals make for laborious reading, and they are usually as dry as toast. But bear in mind that their purpose is primarily to inform other experts.

Other helpful print sources are science magazines and nonfiction books meant for the well-educated public. The goal is to inform the interested reader who may have only a limited background in science. The authors are usually science writers or experts who translate the finer scientific points into language that we can all understand. The information is generally accurate and readable, although the reader may not understand some of the details. Generally these articles and books tell readers who want to delve more deeply into the subject where to find more information.

General interest news magazines and daily newspapers also report on selected hot topics in science. Their goal is to get the information out as quickly as possible to a wide audience. Coverage is timely but less in-depth than in science magazines, and may not include the details you need to check the validity of the statements. A decided plus is that magazines and newspapers often discuss social, political, economic, legal, or ethical ramifications of the scientific findings, something generally lacking in the previous sources. Although the scientific information is usually accurate, the reporter may not understand the subject fully and may not provide adequate context. The best articles point readers to the original sources. Television (for instance, the Discovery Channel, *Nova*) also presents science-related topics to the public.

BlogInFocus MB

What sexually transmitted disease bacteria is now showing signs of antibiotic resistance? Where are antibiotic-resistant bacteria showing up in drinking water? For the latest information on bacterial resistance to antibiotics, visit MJ's blog in the Study Area in MasteringBiology and look under "Antibiotic Resistance."

Since the 1980s, scientists and researchers have used the Internet to communicate and share ideas. The recent expansion of the World Wide Web has made the Internet accessible to the general public, opening exciting new sources of scientific information. Nearly all universities now have Web pages; the site addresses end in ".edu"

(for "educational") rather than ".com" (for "commercial"). A number of scientific and professional organizations have created Web sites that offer helpful information for both scientists and consumers. Examples of organizations with Web sites include the National Institutes of Health, the American Cancer Society, and the American Heart Association. The Web addresses of government agencies and nonprofit organizations generally end in ".gov" and ".org," respectively.

Be aware that the Internet can also be a source of misinformation. At present the Internet is less closely regulated than print and broadcast media, so it can be difficult to tell the difference between objective reports and advertisements. In addition, participants in online chat rooms and special-interest groups may promote their own opinions as proven truths. It pays to be skeptical.

Recap The best sources of scientific information translate difficult or complex information accurately into understandable terms and have enough references that you can check the information if you wish. ∎

1.5 Learning to be a critical thinker

Many scientists are motivated by strong curiosity or a sense of wonder and awe about how the natural world works. Exploring the frontiers of knowledge requires a great deal of creativity and imagination. Like many people, however, scientists may leap to conclusions or resist new ideas. A few may be driven by self-interest. To combat these natural human tendencies, good scientists try to use certain tools of critical thinking. You too can learn to use these tools, regardless of whether you choose a career in science. The following sections describe some of the simple tools that anyone can use to improve their critical thinking skills.

Become a skeptic

Good scientists combine creativity and imagination with **skepticism**, a questioning attitude. If you've ever bought something based on claims about how well it works and then been disappointed, you know the value of skepticism. Question everything and dig a little deeper before believing something you read and hear. Here are some questions you might ask yourself:

- Who says that a particular statement is true?
- What evidence is presented?
- Are the persons speaking on a subject qualified by training or skill to speak authoritatively about it?
- Are they being paid, and if so, how might that affect what they have to say?
- Where is the evidence to back up a claim?

Skepticism is particularly important for claims that are new, startling, and not yet verified by other scientists.

Listen carefully to the debate between scientists in the public arena. A new scientific claim may take several years to be checked out adequately.

Appreciate the value of statistics

Statistics is the mathematics of organizing and interpreting numerical information, or **data**. Scientists use statistics to determine how much confidence they should place in information. Most scientists would be willing to accept experimental results with confidence if (according to statistical tests) they would get the same outcome 19 of every 20 times they repeat the experiment, or 95% of the time. When you see numerical averages followed by a smaller "+/–" number, the smaller number represents an expression of confidence in the certainty of the results, called the "standard error." In graphs, the standard errors are represented as small lines that extend above and below the average number.

Statistics are important in many disciplines. During elections, we may hear pollsters report, for example, that "52% of the respondents said that they will vote for the president. The poll has a margin for error of +/– 3%." This tells you the pollsters are relatively certain that the actual percentage who will vote for the president is somewhere between 49 and 55%, still too close to call.

Learn how to read graphs

Just like a picture, a graph is worth a thousand words. Graphs display data obtained from observations and experimental results in a way that is economical and easy to grasp. Graphs can also be used to clarify the meaning of experimental results.

Most graphs are plotted on two lines, or axes (singular: axis). The horizontal axis at the bottom is called the *abscissa* (from math you may know this as the *x*-axis), and the vertical axis is called the *ordinate* (*y*-axis). By convention the *independent*

variable, such as time, distance, age, or another category that defines groups, is generally plotted on the abscissa. The *dependent variable*, so called because its variation may depend on the independent variable, is plotted on the ordinate.

Graphs can take a variety of forms, from plots of individual data points to lines or bars of average values (Figure 1.10). When reading a graph, first check the scales and the legends on the abscissa and the ordinate to determine what the graph is about. Be careful to look for a "split axis," in which the scale changes. An example is shown in Figure 1.11. A split axis is sometimes a convenient way of representing data that cover a wide range on one axis, but it can also be used to deliberately mislead people unfamiliar with reading graphs.

Distinguish anecdotes from scientific evidence

Anecdotal evidence takes the form of a testimonial or short unverified report. Although an anecdote may be true as stated, it in no way implies scientific or statistical certainty. It cannot be generalized to the larger population because it is not based on empirical evidence. Advertising agencies sometimes use anecdotes to influence you. The actor on television who looks sincerely into the camera and says "Drug X worked for me" may be telling the truth—the drug may work for him. But this does not prove the drug will work for everyone, or even for 10% of the population.

Nonscientists (and even scientists) often say things like "My grandmother swears by this remedy." Again, the statement may be true, but it is not scientific evidence. Listen carefully to how the evidence for a statement is presented.

✅ **Quick Check** *One brand of cold medication has a personal testimonial on its Web site from a famous actor. Another brand of cold medication has testimonials from 10 people who are not actors. Does it make any difference in deciding which medication is better? Why or why not?* ■

a) **A scatter plot showing enrollment at each individual college.** Each data point is known as an observation.

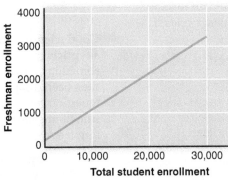

b) **A line graph representing the best straight line fit of the data in a).**

c) **A bar graph in which university enrollments are lumped together in three class sizes and the freshman enrollments are then averaged.** Standard error bars indicate that the data have been analyzed statistically.

Figure 1.10 Types of graphs. Each of these graphs reports the relationship between freshman enrollment and total student enrollment at approximately 1,500 U.S. colleges and universities.

✅ *In the bar graph, why are the standard error bars in the third bar much higher than in the first bar? Put another way, what do standard error bars actually tell us? (Look back at the first graph for a hint.)*

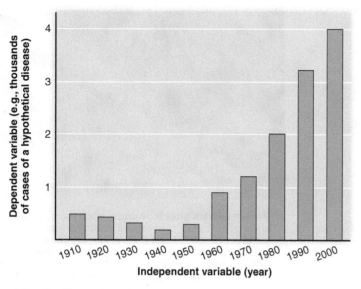

a) Graph with regular axis.

b) Graph with split axis.

Figure 1.11 How a split axis affects a graph. The graph in b) is redrawn from the data in a) by splitting the abscissa and omitting the data for the years 1920–1950. The effect is a consolidated graph that fits in less space, but it might mislead you into thinking that the number of cases of the disease has been rising steadily since 1910, instead of only since 1960.

Separate facts from conclusions

A *fact* is a verifiable piece of information, whereas a *conclusion* is a judgment based on the facts. The news media often mix facts with conclusions without indicating which is which. Almost every evening on the business news we hear statements like "The Dow Jones Industrial Average declined 50 points today on renewed concern over the consumer price index." The first half of the sentence (about the decline) is a verifiable fact. The second half is conjecture on the part of the reporter.

Or consider the following: "The average global temperature was 0.1 °C higher this year than last year. The rise in temperature proves that global warming is occurring." Again, fact is followed by conclusion. The conclusion may not be warranted if temperature fluctuations up and down of 0.3 °C are normal from year to year.

Understand the difference between correlation and causation

A close pattern or relationship (a correlation) between two variables does not necessarily mean that one causes the other. The catch-phrase is *"correlation does not imply causation."* A good example of a correlation without causation is the close correlation between ice cream sales and drownings—when ice cream sales are up in the summer months, so are drownings. Does that mean that eating ice cream causes people to drown? Hardly. Ice cream sales and drownings also correlate with (and are most likely caused by) a third factor not mentioned in the original correlation—warmer temperatures during the summer.

If the above example seems too obvious, try this one: In 1999 a study at a major university found that children who slept with a light on were more likely to develop nearsightedness (myopia) later in life. But does this mean that sleeping with a light on *causes* nearsightedness? In fact, a follow-up study in 2000 found no direct causal relationship between sleeping with a light on and the development of nearsightedness. The follow-up study showed that children who develop nearsightedness are more likely to have parents who are nearsighted, suggesting (but not proving) a genetic cause. It also showed that parents who are nearsighted are just more likely to leave the light on!

In the above example, the original scientific observation was stated correctly (lights-on *correlates* with nearsightedness). But anyone who became convinced that sleeping with a light on *causes* nearsightedness would have been wrong. Be skeptical of causal statements that are based only on a good correlation, for the true cause may not be obvious at first. (See MJ's Human Biology Blog, Correlation Versus Causation.)

BlogInFocus MB

Why do some drug package inserts list so *many* drug side effects? Should you be worried when you read them, or should you just ignore them? To learn more, visit MJ's blog in the Study Area in MasteringBiology and look under "Drug Side Effects."

Of course, a close correlation is likely whenever a true causal relationship does exist. So although a correlation does not necessarily prove causation, it can be a strong hint that you *may* have found the true cause, or at least that the true cause is nearby and may even be linked to both of the variables you're observing.

Recap Healthy skepticism, a basic understanding of statistics, and an ability to read graphs are important tools for critical thinking. Know anecdotal evidence when you see it, and appreciate the differences between fact and conclusion and between correlation and causation. ◾

1.6 The role of science in society

How do we place science in its proper perspective in our society? Why do we bother spending billions of dollars on scientific research when there are people starving in the streets? These are vital questions for all of us, so let's look at why we study the natural world in the first place.

Science improves technology and the human physical condition

Science gives us information about the natural world upon which we can base our societal decisions. Throughout history some of the greatest benefits of science have been derived from the *application* of science, called **technology**, for the betterment of humankind (**Figure 1.12**). Time and time again, scientific knowledge has led to technological advances that have increased the productivity and hence prosperity of both industries and nations. Science has given us larger crop yields, more consistent weather predictions, better construction materials, better health care, and more efficient and cleaner sources of power, to name just a few benefits. It has made global transportation and communication possible.

Many people are concerned that overuse of our technological capabilities may lead to problems in the future. Science can help here, too, by helping us identify problems early on. We can see the early warning role of science in the "Health & Wellness" discussion of bacterial resistance to antibiotics. Only by understanding a problem can we learn how to solve it. Science helps us correct our mistakes.

Science has limits

Scientific knowledge is limited to physical explanations for observable events in the natural world. It cannot prove or disprove the existence, or importance to us, of things that fall outside the realm of the natural world, such as faith or spiritual experiences. Many scientists have a strong faith or belief that cannot be tested by science, because faith does not depend on logical proof or material evidence. They believe that the search for meaning and the search for knowledge are complementary, not contradictory.

In addition, science alone cannot provide us with the "right" answers to political, economic, social, legal, or ethical dilemmas. Humans have minds, a moral sense, and a sense of history and the future. How we use scientific

a) Modern farmers grow food crops much more efficiently than in the past, thanks to advances in such diverse fields as genetics, chemistry, and even the aerospace industry. Global positioning satellites and computers allow farmers to administer fertilizers precisely where needed, thereby eliminating waste, reducing environmental degradation, and improving yields.

b) This scientist is collecting insects from a tree-top in a tropical rainforest. Studies such as this improve our understanding of the interrelationships of organisms in an ecosystem and have yielded rare natural chemical compounds that may prove useful in human and animal medicine.

Sep 22 2004

c) A satellite map documenting depletion of the ozone layer over Antarctica in 2004. The area of greatest depletion appears dark blue. Studies such as this one allow scientists to document when and where ozone depletion occurs so that they can better understand its causes and cures.

Figure 1.12 Benefits of science. These photos show typical scenes of scientists and the application of science (technology) for the betterment of the human condition.

knowledge is up to all of us, not just scientists. For example, given the current state of knowledge about how cells grow and divide, scientists may eventually be able to clone an adult human being. Whether or not we should permit cloning, and under what circumstances, are important topics of public debate. It's not for scientists to decide alone.

This does not mean scientists are without moral obligation. As experts in their fields, they are in a unique position to advise us about the application of scientific knowledge, even if the choices ultimately rest with all of us.

A practical limitation of science is that some information, including data that may be useful in improving human health, cannot be obtained by observation or experimentation. Our society places a very high value on human life, and therefore we don't experiment on humans unless the experiment is likely to be of direct benefit to the subject (the use of experimental cancer drugs falls into this category). This is why it is hard to investigate the danger of street drugs like cocaine or anabolic steroids. No good scientist would ever deliberately give healthy humans a drug that might cause injury or death, even if the resulting information could save lives in the future. Our society currently does permit experiments on animals as substitutes for human subjects, however, provided that federal guidelines are strictly followed (**Figure 1.13**).

The importance of making informed choices

You live in a science-oriented society. Throughout this book we present a common theme: Every day you make decisions about how you and society choose to use the knowledge that science gives us. Whether or not you are conscious of it, whether or not you deliberately take action, you make these choices daily.

Should Olympic athletes be allowed to use bodybuilding drugs? Do you think the use of pesticides is justified in order to feed more people? How do you feel about the cloning of human beings? Are you willing to eat a proper diet to stay

Figure 1.13 Animals in research. In this society we allow the use of animals for research in certain circumstances. This researcher is using a noninvasive technique for measuring blood flow in the skin as part of a study of vascular diseases.

healthy—and by the way, what *is* a proper diet? Who should pay for health care for the poor?

Our knowledge has advanced rapidly. By the end of this book you will know more about genetics and evolution than did the scientists who originally developed the theories about them. With knowledge comes the responsibility for making choices. From global warming to genetic engineering to personal health, each of us must deal with issues that concern our well-being and the future of the biological world in which we live. We owe it to ourselves, as individuals and as a society, to acquire the knowledge and skill we need to make intelligent decisions. Your choices can make a difference.

Recap Science and technology have improved the human condition. Science cannot, however, resolve moral dilemmas. Scientists can advise us on issues of science, but we as a society must decide how to put this scientific knowledge to use. ■

Chapter Summary

The characteristics of life *p. 4*

- All living things acquire both matter and energy from their environment, transforming them for their own purposes.
- The basic unit of life is a single cell.
- Living things maintain homeostasis, respond to their external environments, and reproduce.

How humans fit into the natural world *p. 7*

- The biological world can be organized into kingdoms. A common scheme classifies life into five kingdoms: Monera, Protista, Fungi, Plantae, and Animalia.

- Features that define humans are bipedalism, well-developed opposable thumbs, a large brain, and the capacity for complex language.
- Humans are part of communities of different organisms living together in various ecosystems.

Science is both a body of knowledge and a process *p. 11*

- Scientific knowledge allows us to describe and make predictions about the natural world.
- The *scientific method* is a way of thinking, a way of testing statements about the natural world (*hypotheses*) by trying to prove them false.
- A *theory* is a hypothesis that has been extensively tested and that explains a broad range of scientific facts with a high degree of reliability.

Sources of scientific information vary in style and quality *p. 14*

- Articles in peer-reviewed scientific journals are generally written for other scientists. They may be difficult to read but are very accurate.
- Journals, books, and television shows on popular science present scientific knowledge efficiently to the general public.
- Web sites vary widely in the quality and accuracy of the information they present.

Learning to be a critical thinker *p. 15*

- Skepticism is a questioning attitude ("prove it to me"). Critical thinking requires skepticism.
- Knowing how to read graphs and understand basic statistics can help you evaluate numerical data.
- Being able to recognize an anecdote, tell fact from conclusion, and distinguish between correlation and causation can help you evaluate the truth of a claim.

The role of science in society *p. 18*

- The application of science is called technology.
- Science is limited to physical explanations of observable events.
- How to use science is up to us.

Terms You Should Know

biology, *4*
cell, *5*
control group, *12*
data, *16*
experiment, *12*
experimental group, *12*
homeostasis, *5*
hypothesis, *12*

metabolism, *5*
photosynthesis, *7*
placebo, *12*
science, *4*
scientific method, *11*
theory, *14*
variables, *12*

Concept Review

Answers can be found in the Study Area in MasteringBiology.

1. Living things have a different molecular composition from non-living things. What makes this possible?
2. Explain the meaning of the term *homeostasis*.
3. Name four features that together contribute to our uniqueness and define us as human.
4. Describe the difference between a hypothesis and a prediction (or working hypothesis).
5. Discuss the role of scientists in helping us solve economic, social, and ethical dilemmas.

Test Yourself

Answers can be found in Appendix A.

1. To which of the following domains of life do humans belong?
   a. prokarya
   b. eukarya
   c. animalia
   d. mammalia

2. To which of the following domains do unicellular organisms which lack nuclei belong?
   a. Eukarya
   b. Archaea
   c. Bacteria
   d. both Archaea and Bacteria

3. New scientific knowledge is gained through a multistep process known as
   a. the scientific method
   b. hypothesis development
   c. variable testing
   d. observation testing

4. An experiment designed and conducted under strictly managed conditions is a:
   a. replicated experiment
   b. controlled experiment
   c. "blind" experiment
   d. peer-reviewed experiment

5. A broad hypothesis that has been supported by repeated experimentation is known as:
   a. a proven hypothesis
   b. a supported hypothesis
   c. a theory
   d. a dogma

6. Which of the following is used when developing a hypothesis?
   a. observations
   b. inductive reasoning
   c. controlled experiments
   d. both observations and inductive reasoning

7. The smallest unit of life that demonstrates all the properties of life is:
   a. an organism
   b. an organ system
   c. a molecule
   d. a cell

8. Consider all of the organisms (human as well as nonhuman) that occupy your college campus. From a biological standpoint, this would be:
   a. a community
   b. an ecosystem
   c. a biome
   d. a population

9. Which of the following lists the steps of the scientific method in order?
   a. observation—prediction—experimentation—hypothesis development
   b. hypothesis development—observation—experimentation—prediction
   c. prediction—hypothesis development—experimentation—observation
   d. observation—hypothesis development—prediction—experimentation

10. In graphs, which of the following is usually plotted on the abscissa (*x* axis)?
   a. controlled variable
   b. independent variable
   c. dependant variable
   d. placebo

11. An acceptable scientific hypothesis:
    a. can be tested
    b. can be proven true
    c. can be proven false
    d. both (a) and (c)

12. Drug A is being tested for its effectiveness in shortening the duration and severity of influenza in humans. In designing an experiment to test Drug A, which of the following would be an important consideration?
    a. Participants can choose whether to be in the experimental or control group.
    b. The experimental group will contain only males and the control group will contain only females.
    c. The experimental group should contain 1,000 subjects, but the control group should include 100 subjects.
    d. The experimental group will receive Drug A and the control group will receive a placebo.

13. Jenna has been telling her friends about how successful she was at losing 10 pounds by using a dietary supplement she purchased at a health food store. This is an example of:
    a. a proven hypothesis
    b. anecdotal evidence
    c. a controlled experiment
    d. a scientific theory

14. The maintenance of a relatively stable internal environment is:
    a. metabolism
    b. evolution
    c. constancy
    d. homeostasis

15. All of the following are features that collectively distinguish humans from other animals except:
    a. bipedalism
    b. large brain
    c. ability to evolve as a species
    d. capacity for complex language

Apply What You Know

Answers can be found in the Study Area in MasteringBiology.

1. A magician has a coin that he says (hypothesizes) has heads on both sides, but he's unwilling to show you both sides. To convince you, he flips it three times and gets heads each time. Do you believe that the coin has two heads? What if he gets heads 10 times in a row? 100 times? What would it take (by coin flip) to prove that the coin does *not* have two heads? With this example, explain the difference between having relative confidence in the truth of a hypothesis, proving it to be true, and proving it to be false.

2. Your roommate is writing a paper on the subject of cocaine and birth defects in humans and wonders why there don't seem to be published reports of controlled experiments in humans on the subject; all the studies are on rats! Describe to her how such a controlled experiment would have to be designed and conducted, and convince her that it would never be permitted by any responsible regulatory agency.

3. You have a friend who truly believes in the existence of ghosts and says he has scientific evidence; he and his two roommates have all seen them. Explain to your friend what it means to have scientific evidence. Think about what data are, how they

are gathered, and why personal experiences do not meet the criteria to be considered scientific evidence.

4. An episode of an old TV show was about doctors living in a tropical environment where the heat is unusually oppressive. An orderly comes to seek relief from the heat, and one doctor gives a supply of sugar pills to the orderly and tells him they are an experimental drug designed to keep humans cool in hot weather. The gullible orderly takes them, and while others are sweating, he claims to suffer no effects from the heat to the point of not even sweating. He later finds out the drug is fake, and immediately complains of being overheated.

   This is a fictitious demonstration of the "placebo effect." Explain how the placebo effect can be avoided when testing new drugs.

5. You are trying to convince your friend who smokes cigarettes that he should quit. You explain to him that smoking and the incidence of lung cancer are strongly correlated. Your friend says that that does not prove smoking causes lung cancer. Is your friend correct? If so, explain why he is correct. What would you say to him?

6. On the radio, you hear an interview with a climatologist discussing global warming. The interviewer asks the scientist what proof she has that humans are to blame for global warming and the resulting rise in sea levels. The scientist responds that while we cannot prove humans are to blame for global warming, there is much evidence that human activities are responsible for the rising temperatures. The interviewer says, "Aha, so you have no proof that humans are to blame, and this is all nothing more than a theory, and isn't a theory nothing more than an opinion?" What differentiates a scientific theory from an opinion?

7. Explain why religious explanations cannot disprove a scientific theory, and conversely, why science cannot prove or disprove a religious belief.

BlogInFocus

Answers can be found in the Study Area in MasteringBiology.

1. Political decisions are sometimes influenced more by public opinion than by scientifically supported evidence. What, if anything, should be done about it? (For an example of a political decision that overrode science, visit MJ's blog in the Study Area in MasteringBiology and look under "The Politics of Ozone Emissions.")

2. Should new vaccines be tested in children (as is currently done in adults) before they are allowed on the market? Why or why not? (For a current controversy involving the anthrax vaccine, visit MJ's blog in the Study Area in MasteringBiology and look under "Vaccine Testing in Children.")

MasteringBiology®

Go to MasteringBiology for practice quizzes, activities, eText, videos, current events, and more.

The Chemistry of Living Things

Crystals of lactose, a carbohydrate. Human milk contains 6% lactose.

Functional Foods and Dietary Supplements—Safe and Effective?

Red Bull energy drink to boost our energy; glucosamine and chondroitin for our aching joints; extracts of *Ginkgo biloba* to improve our memories: We seem to have an appetite for functional foods and dietary supplements that promise to improve our health or make us feel better. But do they work?

Functional foods, also sometimes called "nutraceuticals," are food or drink products that are said to have benefits beyond basic nutrition. Some are natural products; others are fortified foods or completely artificially created products. Red Bull is a functional food because of the manufacturer's claim that it "boosts energy levels."

Dietary supplements are products that are not normally part of the diet, but that you choose to take to improve your health or well-being. They include your daily multivitamin, as well as any supplemental minerals, amino acids, hormones, body-building products, and plant extracts (herbal remedies) you take by choice.

Traditional herbal remedies are by far the oldest of the dietary supplements. In some cultures they have been in use for hundreds or even thousands of years, long before we thought to call them dietary supplements. Some of the ingredients in herbal remedies may indeed have specific health benefits. However they

have never been tested scientifically to *prove* that they are safe and effective. To understand why, you need to understand how new pharmaceutical drugs are tested and approved, and why the same approval process would never work for functional foods and dietary supplements.

Regulatory Issues

The U.S. Food and Drug Administration (FDA) is responsible for overseeing the safety and efficacy of pharmaceutical drugs (drugs created specifically for the treatment or prevention of disease). By law, a pharmaceutical company must prove beyond a reasonable doubt that a

Do you know what is in this can?

new drug is safe and effective in humans before it can be sold to the public. On average it takes 12 to 15 years and costs about $800 million to bring one new drug to market. Companies can afford it only because they can patent the drug, giving them exclusive ownership and marketing rights for a certain number of years. Although patients sometimes complain about the high cost of prescription medications, pharmaceutical companies respond that the price reflects their steep development costs.

Because the ingredients in functional foods and dietary supplements occur in nature, they cannot be patented. Anyone can purify and package them. But without the assurance of patent protection, manufacturers and producers cannot afford to spend what it would cost to test their safety and effectiveness. Recognizing this, in 1994 the dietary supplement manufacturers asked for (and were granted) an exemption from the FDA drug approval process. Under the Dietary Supplements Health and Education Act of 1994, dietary supplements and functional foods can be produced and sold until they are *proven unsafe*. And why would any manufacturer

choose to spend time and money to prove its own product unsafe? The FDA does not even need to be notified of "adverse events"; the agency must rely on voluntary information supplied by consumers and health professionals. As a result, the FDA reported only about 500 adverse events per year associated with dietary supplements over a five-year period. In contrast, the American Association of Poison Control Centers received nearly 7,000 reports involving dietary supplements in one year alone.

Producers and distributors of functional foods and dietary supplements also have considerable latitude in advertising their products; the only restriction is that they are not allowed to claim that their products prevent or treat specific medical conditions or diseases. For example, producers of cranberry juice products are free to say that cranberry juice "helps maintain urinary tract health" (a rather vague health claim), but they cannot claim that cranberry juice "prevents the recurrence of urinary tract infections" because that would represent a specific medical claim. Nevertheless, many consumers do use cranberry juice to treat urinary tract infections or to prevent their recurrence, simply because they believe that it works. And indeed it may; it is just that it has never been scientifically tested to the standards of a pharmaceutical drug.

With all that latitude in producing and marketing their products, it is not surprising that the functional foods and dietary supplements industries and the advertising industry that supports them have grown rapidly. U.S. sales of dietary supplements now top $18 billion a year.

Questions of Safety and Efficacy

Proponents of functional foods and dietary supplements argue that because many of these products have been in use for a long time, any adverse effects should have shown up by now. Critics argue that many of the ingredients can now be synthesized

How will you determine if the supplement you are taking is safe and effective?

chemically, and thus used at much higher concentrations and in different combinations than ever occur in nature. Slam Energy drink, for example, contains over 100 mg of caffeine in only two ounces of liquid. Health officials worry that too much caffeine in a user unaccustomed to it could raise heart rate and blood pressure to potentially dangerous levels.

Other concerns include inaccurate product labeling and improper manufacturing processes. Manufacturers are not required to report quality control information to the FDA, so there is no assurance that the product actually contains what the manufacturer says it does. For example, independent tests found that products labeled as containing the same dosage of ginseng actually varied by a factor of 10 (some contained none at all). And California investigators found that nearly one-third of all imported Asian herbal remedies they tested contained lead, arsenic, mercury, or drugs not mentioned on the label.

Consumers want to be assured that the dietary supplements and natural and fortified food products they use are safe. They would like to know that the health claims about these products are true. How to achieve that goal and still ensure that the products remain available is an ongoing issue. In the meantime, it is up to you to know what is in the products you choose to put in your body.

QUESTIONS TO CONSIDER

1 Who do you think should be responsible for ensuring that dietary supplements and functional foods are safe? Would you be willing to accept more regulation if it meant fewer products would be available? Explain your position.

2 What dietary supplements or functional foods do you use? Do you know what is in them and do you understand why you are using them?

THE FACTS...

- Functional foods and dietary supplements are popular with consumers. Americans consume more than $18 billion worth of dietary supplements every year.

- Functional foods and dietary supplements don't pass through the same rigorous approval procedure that is required of all new pharmaceutical drugs.

- Some products may not be effective; others may not be safe. However, increased regulation to ensure efficacy and safety would mean fewer products would be available.

>> **The natural world consists of matter and energy.** The smallest functional unit of matter is an atom.

>> **Chemical bonds link atoms together to form molecules.** These bonds form naturally because the molecules are more stable than the atoms that comprise them. One of the most important naturally occurring stable molecules is water.

>> **Water is the universal biological solvent.** Water comprises most of the fluid within cells and also surrounds all cells in multicellular organisms. Most of life's chemical reactions take place in it.

>> **Living things harness energy and use it to make complex molecules not otherwise found in nature.** The four classes of "organic" molecules made by living organisms are proteins, carbohydrates, lipids, and nucleic acids.

>> **Carbon is the common building block of all four classes of organic molecules** because of the many ways it can form chemical bonds with other atoms.

The natural world consists of matter and energy.
Chemistry is the study of matter and the energy that causes matter to combine, break apart, and recombine into all the substances, both living and nonliving, that exist in the natural world. Every substance is made from the same basic units of matter and the same types of energy (Figure 2.1). Everything in the natural world, including us, is governed by the laws of chemistry.

BlogInFocus 🔵

Should you add supplements to your diet? For more on the safety and efficacy of functional foods and dietary supplements, visit MJ's blog in the Study Area in MasteringBiology and look under "Supplements."

Yet there is something very special about the chemistry of living things. Living organisms have the ability to grow and reproduce, unlike inanimate objects. Living things have evolved to take advantage of the rules of chemistry that govern the natural world. Living organisms create special combinations of matter not generally found in nonliving things. They also have developed the ability to store energy so that they may later turn it to their own purposes.

In this chapter we consider how the laws of chemistry serve life. We begin with an introduction to basic chemistry.

2.1 All matter consists of elements

Matter is anything that has mass and occupies space. All matter is composed of elements. An **element** is a fundamental (pure) form of matter that cannot be broken down to a simpler form. Aluminum and iron are elements, and so are oxygen and hydrogen. Just over 100 known elements account for all matter on Earth. The *periodic table of elements* arranges all known elements into groups according to their similar properties (Figure 2.2).

a) A magnified view (× 15,000) of a portion of a skeletal muscle cell.

b) A magnified view (× 30) of a crystal of aspirin.

Figure 2.1 All matter is made of atoms. The three most common atoms in both muscle and aspirin are carbon, hydrogen, and oxygen.

Figure 2.2 The periodic table shows all known elements in order of increasing atomic number.
For example, nitrogen (N) has 7 protons, so its atomic number is 7. The table also organizes
elements into groups based on the number of electrons in their outer shells (elements in group 1
have one electron, those in group 3 have three electrons, and so on). Scientists are interested in
the number of electrons in the outer shell because these particles affect how an atom interacts with
other elements.

Atoms are the smallest functional units of an element

Elements are made up of particles called *atoms*. An **atom** is the smallest unit of any element that still retains the physical and chemical properties of that element. Although we now know that atoms can be split apart under unusual circumstances (such as a nuclear reaction), atoms are the smallest units of matter that can take part in chemical reactions. So, for all practical purposes, atoms are the smallest functional units of matter.

The central core of an atom is called the *nucleus*. The nucleus is made of positively charged particles called **protons** and a nearly equal number of neutral particles called **neutrons**, all tightly bound together. An exception is the smallest atom, hydrogen, whose nucleus consists of only a single proton. Smaller negatively charged particles called **electrons** orbit the nucleus. Because electrons are constantly moving, their precise position at any one time is unknown. You may think of electrons as occupying one or more spherical clouds of negative charge around the nucleus called *shells*. Each shell can accommodate only a

certain number of electrons. The first shell, the one closest to the nucleus, can hold two electrons, the second can accommodate up to eight, and the third shell (if there is one) also accommodates eight. Each type of atom has a unique number of electrons. Under most circumstances the number of electrons equals the number of protons, and, as a result, the entire atom is electrically neutral (**Figure 2.3**).

Protons and neutrons have about the same mass, and both have much more mass than electrons. (*Mass* is measured chemically and is not dependent on gravity. For the purpose of this text, however, mass and *weight* are about the same.) The protons and neutrons in the atom's nucleus account for over 99.9% of the atom's mass.

In the periodic table and in chemical equations, atoms are designated by one- or two-letter symbols taken from English or Latin. For example, oxygen is designated by the letter O, nitrogen by N, sodium by Na (from the Latin word for sodium, *natrium*), and potassium by K (Latin *kalium*). A subscript numeral following the symbol indicates the numbers of atoms of that element.

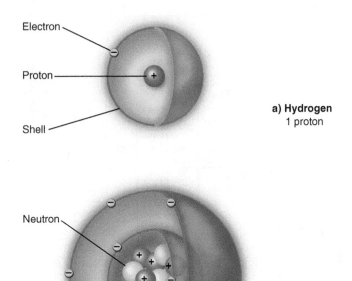

Electron
Proton
Shell

a) Hydrogen
1 proton

Neutron
Nucleus

b) Oxygen
8 protons
8 neutrons
8 electrons
in 2 shells

c) Sodium
11 protons
11 neutrons
11 electrons
in 3 shells

Figure 2.3 The structure of atoms. Atoms consist of a nucleus, comprising positively charged protons and neutral neutrons, surrounded by spherical shells of negatively charged electrons.

For example, the chemical formula O_2 represents two atoms of oxygen linked together, the most stable form of elemental oxygen.

In addition to a symbol, atoms have an *atomic number* representing the characteristic number of protons in the nucleus and an *atomic mass* (or mass number), which is generally fairly close to the total number of neutrons and protons.

☑ **Quick Check** *Nitrogen's atomic number is 7. Just from the atomic number, can you determine how many protons, neutrons, and electrons a nitrogen atom has, and how many electrons are in its first and second electron shells? (Assume the atom is electrically neutral.)* ▪

Isotopes have a different number of neutrons

Although all the atoms of a particular element have the same number of protons, the number of neutrons can vary slightly. Atoms with either more or fewer neutrons than the usual number for that element are called **isotopes**. Isotopes of an element have the same atomic number as the more common atoms but a different atomic mass. For example, elemental carbon typically consists of atoms with six protons and six neutrons, for an atomic mass of 12. The isotope of carbon known as carbon-14 has an atomic mass of 14 because it has two extra neutrons.

Isotopes are always identified by a superscript mass number preceding the symbol. For instance, the carbon-14 isotope is designated ^{14}C. The superscript mass number of the more common elemental form of carbon is generally omitted because it is understood to be 12.

Many isotopes are unstable. Such isotopes are called *radioisotopes* because they tend to give off energy (in the form of radiation) and particles until they reach a more stable state. The radiation emitted by radioisotopes can be dangerous to living organisms because the energy can damage tissues.

Certain radioisotopes have a number of important scientific and medical uses. Because the rate of decay to more stable energy states is known for each radioisotope, scientists can determine when rocks and fossils were formed by measuring the amount of radioisotope still present. The carbon-14 isotope is commonly used for this purpose. In medicine, radioisotopes are used to "tag" molecules so that radiation sensors can track their location in the body. For example, physicians use radioisotopes to locate areas of damaged tissue in a patient's heart after a heart attack. Radioisotopes are also used to target and kill certain kinds of cancer. Certain radioisotopes that emit energy for long periods of time are used as a power supply in heart pacemakers.

↻ **Recap** Atoms are made up of protons, neutrons, and electrons. Radioisotopes are unstable atoms with an unusual number of neutrons that give off energy and particles as they decay to a more stable state. ▪

Answers to ☑ **questions can be found in Appendix A.**

Health & Wellness

Radon: A Known Cancer Risk

In the lower-right corner of the periodic table of the elements is radon, an odorless, colorless gas designated by the symbol Rn (see Figure 2.2). We don't talk much about radon in biology because it is not an important molecule in biological systems. That's because radon is inert; unlike carbon and nitrogen, for example, it does not combine readily with other elements to create the kinds of complex molecules required by living systems. Radon exists in nature primarily as just elemental radon gas. Most of it is trapped in the soil beneath rock layers.

However, radon gas is highly diffusible. Although it cannot diffuse through solid rock, it can pass right through semisolid objects such as cardboard, wood, and sheet rock (wallboard), even cement blocks typically used in home construction. As a result, in areas of the world with a high concentration of radon in the soil and where houses typically have basements, radon readily diffuses out of the soil and into the air in the basement. People who spend a lot of time in their basements may be exposed to potentially dangerous levels of radon gas in the air they breathe.

Why is radon considered dangerous? A key property of radon is that it is a radioisotope, meaning it gives off radiation energy as it decays to other elements of lower energy. In terms of human health, radiation exposure from radon is a known risk for lung cancer. Radon is the number one cause of lung cancer in nonsmokers, and the second leading cause of lung cancer overall.

EPA Map of Radon Zones

Key: ■ Zone 1   ■ Zone 2   □ Zone 3

How much radon you may be exposed to depends on a number of factors, including where you live, whether or not you have a basement, how much time you spend in the basement, and how often the air in your basement exchanges with outside air. The EPA publishes maps of the average levels of radon found in basements in different regions of the country. Levels typically found in Zone 1 are considered dangerous to human health. The EPA and the U.S. Surgeon General recommend that you test your basement for radon even if you live in Zones 2 and 3.

Fortunately, you can determine the level of radiation exposure from radon in your basement with a simple $25 test kit available from most megastores. If you do find high levels of radon, it may be advisable to take steps to increase the rate of air exchange in the basement in order to flush out as much radon as possible. ■

2.2 Atoms combine to form molecules

A **molecule** consists of a stable association between two or more atoms. For example, a molecule of water is two atoms of hydrogen plus one atom of oxygen (written H_2O). A molecule of ordinary table salt (written NaCl) is one atom of sodium (Na) plus one atom of chlorine (Cl). A molecule of hydrogen gas (written H_2) is two atoms of hydrogen. To understand *why* atoms join together to form molecules, we need to know more about energy.

Energy fuels life's activities

Energy is the capacity to do "work," the capacity to cause some change in matter. Joining atoms is one type of work, and breaking up molecules is another—and both require energy. Stored energy that is not actually performing any work at the moment is called **potential energy** because it has the *potential* to make things happen. Energy that is actually *doing* work—that is, energy in motion—is called **kinetic energy** (Figure 2.4).

You can visualize the difference between potential energy and kinetic energy in the water held behind a dam: there is tremendous potential energy in the water held in reserve. When the water is released, potential energy is converted into kinetic energy: rushing water that can be put to work turning turbines. Similarly, the spark of a match converts the potential energy in firewood to kinetic energy in the form of heat and light.

Potential energy is stored in the bonds that hold atoms together in all matter, both living and nonliving. Living organisms take advantage of this general principle of chemistry by using certain molecules to store energy for their own use. When the chemical bonds of these energy-storage molecules are broken, potential energy becomes kinetic energy. We rely on this energy to do biological work, such as breathing, moving, digesting food, and many other tasks.

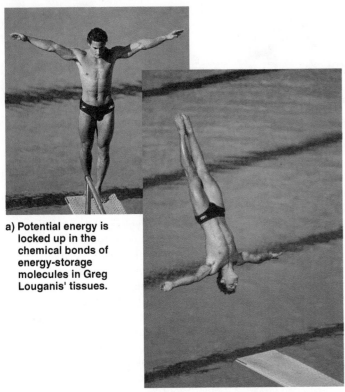

a) **Potential energy is locked up in the chemical bonds of energy-storage molecules in Greg Louganis' tissues.**

b) **Kinetic energy is energy in motion.**

Figure 2.4 Energy.

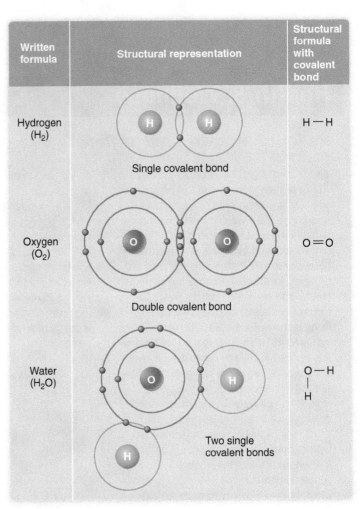

Figure 2.5 Covalent bonds. Sharing pairs of electrons is a way for atoms to fill their outermost shell.

✅ *Draw the structural formula of CH4. Hint: Carbon has 2 electrons in its inner shell and 4 in its second shell.*

Recall that electrons carry a negative charge, whereas protons within the nucleus have a positive charge. Electrons are attracted to the positively charged nucleus and repelled by each other. As a result of these opposing attractive and repulsive forces, each electron occupies a specific shell around the nucleus. Each shell corresponds to a specific level of electron potential energy, and each shell farther out represents a higher potential energy level than the preceding one closer to the nucleus. When an electron moves to a shell closer to the nucleus, it loses energy. To move to a shell that is farther from the nucleus, the electron must absorb energy.

Chemical bonds link atoms to form molecules

A key concept in chemistry is that atoms are most stable when their outermost electron shell is completely filled with the maximum number of electrons that it can accommodate. An atom whose outermost electron shell is not normally completely filled tends to interact with one or more other atoms in a way that fills its outermost shell. Such interactions generally cause the atoms to be bound to each other by attractive forces called **chemical bonds**. The three principal types of chemical bonds are called covalent, ionic, and hydrogen bonds.

Covalent bonds involve sharing electrons. One way that an atom can fill its outermost shell is by sharing a pair of electrons with another atom. An electron-sharing bond between atoms is called a **covalent bond** (Figure 2.5). Covalent bonds between

atoms are among the strongest chemical bonds in nature, so strong that they rarely break apart. In structural formulas, a covalent bond is depicted as a line drawn between two atoms. For example, the structural formula for hydrogen is H—H.

Hydrogen gas offers an example of how a covalent (electron-sharing) bond fills the outermost shells of two atoms. Each of the two hydrogen atoms has just one electron in the first shell, which could accommodate two electrons. When joined together by a covalent bond (forming H_2 a gas), each atom has, in effect, a "full" first shell of two electrons. As a result, H_2 gas is more stable than the same two hydrogen atoms by themselves. The sharing of one pair of electrons, as in H_2 is called a *single* bond.

Oxygen gas is another example of covalent bonding. An oxygen atom has eight electrons: two of these fill the first electron shell, and the remaining six occupy the second electron shell (which can accommodate eight). Two oxygen atoms may join to form a molecule of oxygen gas by sharing two pairs of electrons, thus completing the outer shells of both atoms. When two pairs of electrons are shared, the bond is called a *double bond*. In structural formulas, double bonds are indicated by two parallel lines. For example, the structural formula for oxygen is O=O.

A molecule of water forms from one oxygen and two hydrogen atoms because this combination completely fills the outermost shells of both hydrogen and oxygen. The prevalence of water on Earth follows from the simple rule that matter is most stable when it contains the least potential energy. Both hydrogen and oxygen are more stable when bonded together (as H_2O) than as independent atoms.

✓ **Quick Check** *Can you determine the number of bonds between atoms in a single molecule of carbon dioxide, CO_2? Hint: Oxygen has eight electrons and carbon has six electrons.* ▪

Ionic bonds occur between oppositely charged ions. A second way that atoms can fill their outer shell of electrons is to give up electrons completely (if they have only one or two electrons in their outermost shell) or to take electrons from other atoms (if they need one or two to fill their outermost shell). Such a loss or gain of electrons gives the atom a net charge, because now there are fewer (or more) electrons than protons in the nucleus. The net charge is positive (+) for each electron lost and negative (−) for each electron gained.

An electrically charged atom or molecule is called an **ion**. Examples of ions are sodium (Na^+), chloride (Cl^-), calcium (Ca^{2+}), and hydrogen phosphate (HPO_4^-) Notice that ions can have a shortage or surplus of more than one electron. (Ca^{2+} has lost two electrons.)

Ever heard the expression "opposites attract"? It should come as no surprise that oppositely charged ions are attracted to each other. When two oppositely charged ions come together, an **ionic bond** is formed (Figure 2.6). In aqueous (watery) solutions, ionic bonds are much weaker than covalent bonds, and so ionic bonds tend to break rather easily. In the human body, for example, almost all of the sodium is in the form of Na^+ and most of the chlorine is in its ionized form, called *chloride* (Cl^-) Very little exists as NaCl.

Ions in aqueous solutions are sometimes called *electrolytes* because solutions of water containing ions are good conductors of electricity. As you will see, cells can control the movement of certain ions, creating electrical forces essential to the functioning of nerves, muscles, and other living tissues.

Weak hydrogen bonds form between polar molecules. A third type of attraction occurs between molecules that do not have a net charge. Glance back at the water molecule in Figure 2.5 and note that the two hydrogen atoms are found not at opposite ends of the water molecule, but fairly close together. Although the oxygen and the two hydrogen atoms share electrons, the sharing is unequal. The shared electrons in a water molecule actually spend slightly more of their time near the oxygen atom than near the hydrogen atoms because the oxygen atom attracts electrons more strongly than do the hydrogen atoms. The uneven sharing gives the oxygen region of a water molecule a partial negative charge and the two hydrogen regions a partial positive charge, even though the water molecule as a whole is electrically neutral.

Molecules such as water that are electrically neutral overall but still have partially charged regions, or *poles*, are called **polar** molecules. According to the principle that opposites attract, polar molecules arrange themselves so that the partial negative pole of one molecule is oriented toward (attracted by) the partial positive pole of another molecule. The weak attractive force between oppositely charged regions of polar molecules that contain covalently bonded hydrogen is called a **hydrogen bond**.

Hydrogen bonds are important in biological molecules. They're what give proteins their three-dimensional shape, and they keep the two strands of the DNA molecule together. The structures of both proteins and DNA are described later in this chapter.

Table 2.1 summarizes covalent, ionic, and hydrogen bonds.

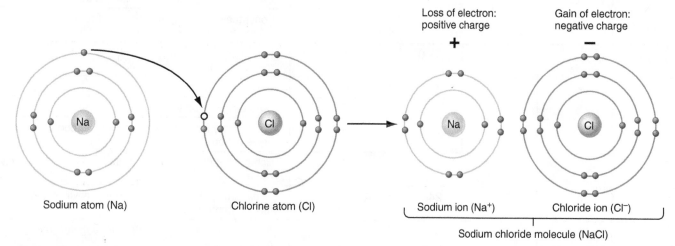

Loss of electron: positive charge +

Gain of electron: negative charge −

Sodium atom (Na)   Chlorine atom (Cl)   Sodium ion (Na^+)   Chloride ion (Cl^-)

Sodium chloride molecule (NaCl)

Figure 2.6 Ionic bonds. Electrically charged ions form when atoms give up or gain electrons. The oppositely charged ions are attracted to each other, forming an ionic bond.

Table 2.1 Summary of the three types of chemical bonds

Type	Strength	Description	Examples
Covalent bond	Strong	A bond in which the sharing of electrons between atoms results in each atom having a maximally filled outermost shell of electrons	The bonds between hydrogen and oxygen in a molecule of water
Ionic bond	Moderate	The bond between two oppositely charged ions (atoms or molecules that were formed by the permanent transfer of one or more electrons)	The bond between Na^+ and Cl^- in salt
Hydrogen bond	Weak	The bond between oppositely charged regions of molecules that contain covalently bonded hydrogen atoms	The bonds between molecules of water

Living organisms contain only certain elements

Although there are nearly 100 different elements in nature, living organisms are constructed from a limited number of them. In fact, about 99% of your body weight consists of just six elements: oxygen, carbon, hydrogen, nitrogen, calcium, and phosphorus (Table 2.2). However, the less common elements are still important, and life on Earth as we know it would not be possible without them.

Even the largest atoms are small compared to the structures in living organisms. To appreciate the vast size differences between the atoms, cells, and organs in your body, imagine that a sodium atom is the size of a penny. On this scale, one of your red blood cells would be half a mile in diameter, and your heart would be larger than the entire Earth!

Next, let's look at some of the most important matter of living systems: water, hydrogen ions, and a host of molecules that contain a backbone of carbon atoms.

Recap Electrons farthest from the nucleus have more potential energy than electrons close to the nucleus. Strong covalent bonds form between atoms when they share pairs of electrons, ionic bonds form between oppositely charged ions, and weak hydrogen bonds occur between oppositely charged regions of polar molecules. ▪

Table 2.2 The most common and important elements in living organisms*

Element	Atomic symbol	Atomic number	Atomic mass	% of Human weight	Functions in life
Oxygen	O	8	16.0	65	Part of water and most organic molecules; also molecular oxygen
Carbon	C	6	12.0	18	The backbone of all organic molecules
Hydrogen	H	1	1.0	10	Part of all organic molecules and of water
Nitrogen	N	7	14.0	3	Component of proteins and nucleic acids
Calcium	Ca	20	40.1	2	Constituent of bone; also essential for the action of nerves and muscles
Phosphorus	P	15	31.0	1	Part of cell membranes and of energy storage molecules; also a constituent of bone
Potassium	K	19	39.1	0.3	Important in nerve action
Sulfur	S	16	32.1	0.2	Structural component of most proteins
Sodium	Na	11	23.0	0.1	The primary ion in body fluids; also important for nerve action
Chlorine	Cl	17	35.5	0.1	Component of digestive acid; also a major ion in body fluids
Magnesium	Mg	12	24.3	Trace	Important for the action of certain enzymes and for muscle contraction
Iron	Fe	26	55.8	Trace	A constituent of hemoglobin, the oxygen-carrying molecule

*The elements are listed in descending order of their contribution to total body weight. Atomic number represents the number of protons in the nucleus. Atomic mass is roughly equivalent to the total number of protons and neutrons because electrons have very little mass. Note that 99% of your body weight is accounted for by just six elements.

2.3 Life depends on water

No molecule is more essential to life than water. Indeed, it accounts for 60% of your body weight. The following properties of water are especially important to living organisms:

- Water is an excellent solvent.
- Water is a liquid at body temperature.
- Water can absorb and hold heat energy.
- Evaporation of water uses up heat energy.
- Water participates in essential chemical reactions.

Water is the biological solvent

A **solvent** is a liquid in which other substances dissolve, and a **solute** is any dissolved substance. Water is the ideal solvent in living organisms specifically because it is a polar liquid at body temperature. As the solvent of life, water is the substance in which the many chemical reactions of living organisms take place. Let's look at a simple example of a solute dissolving in water to better understand how the polar nature of water facilitates the reaction.

Consider a common and important solid, crystals of sodium chloride (NaCl), or table salt. Crystals of table salt consist of a regular, repeating pattern of sodium and chloride ions held together by ionic bonds (**Figure 2.7**). When salt is placed in water, individual ions of [Na^+] and [Cl^-] at the surface of the crystal are pulled away from the crystal and are immediately surrounded by the polar water molecules. The water molecules form such a tight cluster around each ion that they are prevented from reassociating back into the crystalline form. In other words, water keeps the ions dissolved. Note that the water molecules are oriented around ions according to the principle that opposite charges attract.

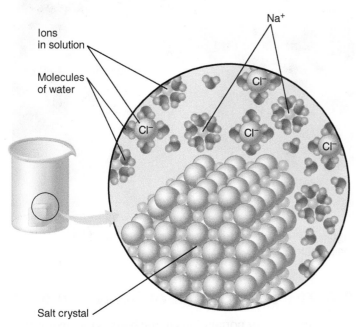

Ions in solution

Molecules of water

Na^+

Cl^-

Cl^-

Cl^-

Cl^-

Salt crystal

Figure 2.7 How water keeps ions in solution. The slightly negative ends of polar water molecules are attracted to positive ions, whereas the slightly positive ends of water molecules are attracted to negative ions. The water molecules pull the ions away from the crystal and prevent them from reassociating with each other.

Polar molecules that are attracted to water and interact with it easily are called **hydrophilic** molecules (Greek, meaning "water-loving"). Nonpolar, neutral molecules such as cooking oils do not interact easily with water and generally will not dissolve in it. They are said to be **hydrophobic** (Greek, meaning "water-fearing"). When water and oil are mixed, the water molecules tend to form hydrogen bonds with each other, excluding the oil from regions occupied by water. Over time the oil is forced together into larger and larger drops until it is separated from the water completely.

✅ **Quick Check** *A red dye is placed in a container that contains an equal amount of cooking oil and water. After the mixture is shaken you notice that the water is red but the oil is not. From what you know about the properties of oil and water, what can you say about the dye: is it comprised of neutral, polar, or charged molecules? Explain your reasoning.* ▪

Water is a liquid at body temperature

Water is a liquid at temperatures between zero and 100 degrees. That is because within this temperature range there is just enough heat energy in water to temporarily break some of the weak hydrogen bonds between water molecules. New hydrogen bonds will soon re-form with other nearby water molecules, but the pattern of bonding between adjacent water molecules is seemingly random. Adjacent water molecules are constantly moving about as these bonds break and re-form; that is why water is a liquid (**Figure 2.8a**). However, when the temperature falls below zero degrees centigrade there is no longer enough heat energy to break the hydrogen bonds between water molecules. Below zero degrees centigrade the water molecules orient themselves into a stable, unchanging, rigid lattice structure (ice; **Figure 2.8b**). At the other end of the temperature scale (above 100 degrees centigrade) all hydrogen bonds between adjacent water molecules are broken completely, and water molecules escape into the atmosphere as a gas (water vapor).

Because water is a liquid at body temperature, it is an excellent medium for transporting solutes from one place to another in our bodies. Indeed, transport is the primary function of the blood (which is about 90% water) in our cardiovascular system. Under pressure generated by the heart, blood transports oxygen and nutrients to all living cells and cellular wastes (including carbon dioxide) away from the cells.

Water is the main constituent of all of the fluid-filled spaces within our bodies. It fills our cells (the intracellular space); it occupies the spaces between cells (the intercellular space); it even fills the fluid-filled spaces not occupied by living cells, such as the urine in our bladders, the watery solutions in our digestive system, and the fluid in our eyes. Of course these fluids contain many important dissolved solutes and solids as well. Overall, though, approximately 60% of our body weight is water.

Water helps regulate body temperature

An important property of water is that it can absorb and hold a large amount of heat energy with only a modest increase in temperature. In fact, it absorbs heat better than

Water   Ice

Figure 2.8 Hydrogen bonds in water and ice. In water, weak hydrogen bonds continually form, break, and re-form between adjacent water molecules. Ice is a solid because a repeating pattern of hydrogen bonds forms between adjacent water molecules.

most other liquids. Water thus may prevent large increases in body temperature when excess heat is produced. Water also holds heat well when there is a danger of too much heat loss (for instance, when you go outdoors wearing shorts on a cool day). The ability of water to absorb and hold heat helps prevent rapid changes in body temperature when changes occur in metabolism or in the environment.

Our bodies generate heat during metabolism. We usually generate more heat than we need to maintain a constant body temperature of 98.6° Fahrenheit (37° Celsius), so being able to lose heat is important to our survival. One way we can lose heat quickly is by evaporation of water (**Figure 2.9**). It takes a great deal of energy to break all of the hydrogen bonds between adjacent water molecules. That energy comes from excess heat generated by the body and transported to the skin by the blood. Evaporation of sweat is just one of several mechanisms involved in the overall maintenance of a constant body temperature (see Chapter 4).

You can demonstrate the cooling power of evaporation for yourself. The next time you perspire heavily, notice that your exposed skin may actually feel cool to the touch.

Water participates in chemical reactions

Water is involved in many of the chemical reactions within living organisms. Examples are the synthesis and breakdown of carbohydrates, lipids, and proteins, all of which are essential to life. The equivalent of a water molecule is either used up or created anew whenever these molecules are synthesized or later deconstructed, as you will see later in this chapter.

 Recap Most biological molecules dissolve readily in water because water is a polar molecule. The liquid nature of water facilitates the transport of biological molecules. Water absorbs and holds heat and can lower body temperature through evaporation. It also participates in essential chemical reactions. ▪

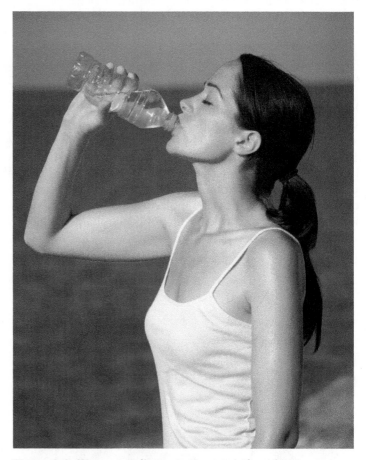

Figure 2.9 Water contributes to the regulation of body temperature.

2.4 The importance of hydrogen ions

One of the most important ions in the body is the hydrogen ion (a single proton without an electron). In this section we will see how hydrogen ions are created and why it is so important to maintain an appropriate concentration of them.

Acids donate hydrogen ions, bases accept them

Although the covalent bonds between hydrogen and oxygen in water are strong and thus rarely broken, it can happen. When it does, the electron from one hydrogen atom is transferred to the oxygen atom completely, and the water molecule breaks into two ions—a *hydrogen ion* (H^+) and a *hydroxide ion* (OH^-)

In pure water, only a very few molecules of water are dissociated (broken apart) into H^+ and OH^- at any one time. However, there are other sources of hydrogen ions in aqueous solutions. An **acid** is any molecule that can donate (give up) an H^+ ion. When added to pure water, acids produce an *acidic* solution, one with a higher H^+ concentration than pure water. (By definition, an aqueous solution with the same concentration of H^+ as that of pure water is a *neutral* solution.) Common acidic solutions are vinegar, carbonated beverages, black coffee, and orange juice. Conversely, a **base** is any molecule that can accept (combine with) an H^+ ion. When added to pure water, bases produce a basic or *alkaline* solution, one with a lower H^+ concentration than that of pure water. Common alkaline solutions include baking soda in water, detergents, and drain cleaner.

BlogInFocus (MB)

Do you drink energy drinks or alcoholic drinks containing caffeine? To learn more about such drinks and about the latest developments in their regulation, visit MJ's blog in the Study Area in MasteringBiology and look under "Caffeine."

Because acids and bases have opposite effects on the H^+ concentration of solutions, they are said to neutralize each other. You have probably heard that a spoonful of baking soda in water is a time-honored way to counteract an "acid stomach." Now you know that this home remedy is based on sound chemical principles.

The pH scale expresses hydrogen ion concentration

Scientists use the pH scale to indicate the acidity or alkalinity of a solution. The **pH scale** is a measure of the hydrogen ion concentration of a solution. The scale ranges from 0 to 14, with pure water having a pH of 7.0, the neutral point. A pH of 7 corresponds to a hydrogen ion concentration of 10^{-7} moles/liter (a *mole* is a term used by chemists to indicate a certain number of atoms, ions, or molecules). An *acidic* solution has a pH of *less* than 7, whereas a *basic* solution has a pH of *greater* than 7. Each whole number change in pH represents a 10-fold change in the hydrogen ion concentration in the opposite direction. For example, an acidic solution with a pH of 5 has an H^+ concentration of 10^{-5} moles/liter (100 times greater than pure water), whereas an alkaline solution with a pH of 9 has an H^+ concentration of 10^{-9} moles/liter (1/100 that of water). Figure 2.10 shows the pH scale and indicates the pH values of some common substances and body fluids.

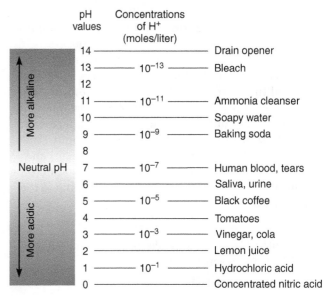

Figure 2.10 The pH scale. The pH scale is an indication of the H^+ concentration of a solution.

The pH of blood is 7.4, just slightly more alkaline than neutral water. The hydrogen ion concentration of blood plasma is low relative to the concentration of other ions. (The hydrogen ion concentration of blood plasma is less than one-*millionth* that of sodium ions, for example.) It is important to maintain homeostasis of this low concentration of hydrogen ions in the body because hydrogen ions are small, mobile, positively charged, and highly reactive. Hydrogen ions tend to displace other positive ions in molecules, and when they do they alter molecular structures and change the ability of the molecule to function properly.

Changes in the pH of body fluids can affect how molecules are transported across the cell membrane and how rapidly certain chemical reactions occur. They may even alter the shapes of proteins that are structural elements of the cell. In other words, a change in the hydrogen ion concentration can be dangerous because it threatens homeostasis.

✓ **Quick Check** *A chemist has a solution that has a pH of 3. She adds a chemical to it, and shortly afterwards the solution has a pH of 5. What was the concentration of hydrogen ions before adding the chemical, what was it afterwards, and did she add an acid or a base? Explain.* ●

Buffers minimize changes in pH

A **buffer** is any substance that tends to minimize the changes in pH that might otherwise occur when an acid or base is added to a solution. Buffers are essential to our ability to maintain homeostasis of pH in body fluids.

In biological solutions such as blood or urine, buffers are present as *pairs* of related molecules that have opposite effects. One of the pair is the acid form of the molecule (capable of donating an H^+ ion), and the other is the base form (capable of accepting an H^+ ion). When an acid is added and the number of H⁺ ions increases, the base form of the buffer pair accepts some of the H⁺ ions, minimizing the fall in pH that might otherwise occur. Conversely, when a base is added that might take up too many H⁺ ions, the acid form of the buffer pair releases additional H⁺ ions and thus minimizes the rise in pH. Buffer pairs are like absorbent sponges that can pick up excess water and then can be wrung out to release water when necessary.

One of the most important buffer pairs in body fluids such as blood is bicarbonate (HCO_3^- the base form) and carbonic acid (H_2CO_3 the acid form). When blood becomes too acidic, bicarbonate accepts excess H⁺ according to the following reaction:

$$HCO_3^- + H^+ \rightarrow H_2CO_3$$

When blood becomes too alkaline, carbonic acid donates H⁺ by the reverse reaction:

$$HCO_3^- + H^+ \leftarrow H_2CO_3$$

In a biological solution such as blood, bicarbonate and carbonic acid take up and release H⁺ all the time. Ultimately a chemical *equilibrium* is reached in which the rates of the two chemical reactions are the same, as represented by the following combined equation:

$$HCO_3^- + H^+ \leftrightarrow H_2CO_3$$

When excess acid is produced, the combined equation shifts to the right as the bicarbonate combines with H⁺. The reverse is true for alkalinity.

The body has many other buffers as well. The more buffers that are present in a body fluid, the more stable the pH.

Recap Acids can donate hydrogen ions to a solution, whereas bases can accept hydrogen ions from a solution. The pH scale indicates the hydrogen ion concentration of a solution. The normal pH of blood is 7.4. Buffers help maintain a stable pH in body fluids. ●

2.5 The organic molecules of living organisms

Organic molecules are molecules that contain carbon and other elements held together by covalent bonds. The name "organic" came about at a time when scientists believed that all organic molecules were created only by living organisms and all "inorganic" molecules came from nonliving matter. Today we know that organic molecules can be synthesized in the laboratory under the right conditions and that they probably existed on Earth before there was life.

Carbon is the common building block of organic molecules

Carbon (**Figure 2.11**) is relatively rare in the natural world, representing less than 0.03% of Earth's crust. However, living organisms actively accumulate it. Carbon accounts for about 18% of body weight in humans.

a) **Diamonds are formed only under conditions of extreme temperature and pressure.** The structure of diamond resembles the steel framework of a large building; each atom is covalently bonded to four neighboring carbon atoms. This explains the hardness of diamonds.

b) **Graphite is produced as a result of decay of older carbon-based substances.** Its structure consists of layers of hexagonal rings of carbon atoms. Graphite is fairly soft (hence its use in pencils) because these layers of carbon atoms can slide past one another.

Figure 2.11 Carbon. Graphite and diamond are both elemental forms of carbon.

Carbon is the common building block of all organic molecules because of the many ways it can form strong covalent bonds with other atoms. Carbon has six electrons; two in the first shell and four in the second. Because carbon is most stable when its second shell is filled with eight electrons, *its natural tendency is to form four covalent bonds with other molecules.* This makes carbon an ideal structural component, one that can branch in a multitude of directions.

Using the chemist's convention that a line between the chemical symbols of atoms represents a pair of shared electrons in a covalent bond, **Figure 2.12** shows some of the many structural possibilities for carbon. Carbon can form covalent bonds with hydrogen, nitrogen, oxygen, or another carbon. It can form double covalent bonds with oxygen or another carbon. It can even form five- or six-membered carbon rings, with or without double bonds between carbons.

In addition to their complexity, there is almost no limit to the size of organic molecules derived from carbon. Some, called *macromolecules* (from the Greek *makros*, meaning "long"), consist of thousands or even millions of smaller molecules.

Macromolecules are synthesized and broken down within the cell

Macromolecules are built (synthesized) within the cell itself. In a process called **dehydration synthesis** (also called the condensation reaction), smaller molecules called *subunits* are joined by covalent bonds, like pearls on a string. The name of the process accurately describes what is happening: Each time a subunit is added, the equivalent of a water molecule

is removed ("dehydration") (**Figure 2.13**). The subunits needed to synthesize macromolecules come from the foods you eat and from the biochemical reactions in your body that break down other large molecules into smaller ones.

The synthesis of macromolecules from smaller molecules requires energy. That is one reason we need energy to survive and grow. It is no accident that children seem to eat enormous amounts of food. Growing children require energy to make the macromolecules necessary to create new cell membranes, muscle fibers, and other body tissues.

Some macromolecules are synthesized specifically for the purpose of storing energy within our cells. The ability to store energy internally allows organisms to survive even when food is not plentiful. Other macromolecules serve as structural components of cells or of extracellular (outside the cell) structures such as bone. Still others direct the many activities of the cell or serve as signaling molecules between cells.

a) In carbon dioxide, a carbon atom forms two covalent bonds with each oxygen atom.

b) Lipid molecules (a portion of one is shown here) contain long chains of carbon atoms covalently bound to hydrogen.

c) Carbon is the backbone of amino acids, the building blocks of protein. This amino acid is phenylalanine.

Figure 2.12 **Examples of the structural diversity of carbon.**

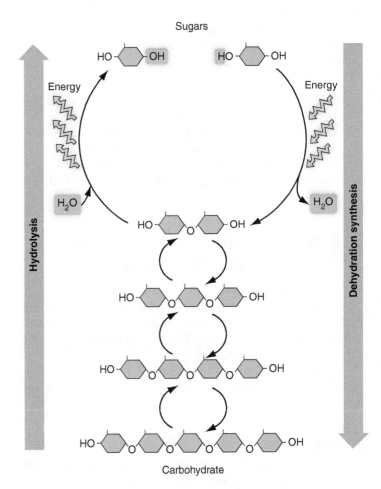

Figure 2.13 **Dehydration synthesis and hydrolysis.** The synthesis of larger molecules by dehydration synthesis requires energy, whereas the breakdown of molecules into smaller units by hydrolysis liberates stored energy. In this example the smallest units are simple sugars and the macromolecule is a carbohydrate.

Organic macromolecules are broken down by a process called **hydrolysis**. During hydrolysis the equivalent of a water molecule is added each time a covalent bond between single subunits in the chain is broken. Notice that hydrolysis is essentially the reverse of dehydration synthesis, and thus it should not surprise you that the breakdown of macromolecules releases energy. The energy was stored as potential energy in the covalent bonds between atoms. The body obtains much of its energy through hydrolysis of energy-storage molecules. Hydrolysis is also used to break down molecules of food during digestion, to recycle materials for reuse, and to get rid of substances that are no longer needed by the body.

Living organisms synthesize four classes of organic molecules, known as *carbohydrates, lipids, proteins,* and *nucleic acids.* The many different molecules within each class are constructed of the same handful of chemical elements. However, there is essentially no limit to the number of different molecules that could be created. No one knows for sure how many different organic molecules there are in humans. On a chemical level, the tremendous diversity among the many species of organisms on Earth is due to differences in their organic molecules, especially their proteins and nucleic acids.

🔄 **Recap** Carbon is a key element of organic molecules because of the multiple ways it can form strong covalent bonds with other molecules. Synthesizing organic molecules requires energy; breaking them down liberates energy. The four classes of organic molecules are carbohydrates, lipids, proteins, and nucleic acids. ▪

2.6 Carbohydrates: Used for energy and structural support

A clue to the basic structure of carbohydrates is found in their name. Carbohydrates have a backbone of carbon atoms with hydrogen and oxygen attached in the same proportion as they appear in water (2-to-1); hence the carbon is "hydrated," or combined with water.

Most living organisms use carbohydrates for energy, and plants use at least one carbohydrate (cellulose) as structural support.

Monosaccharides are simple sugars

The simplest kind of carbohydrate is called a **monosaccharide** (meaning "one sugar"). Monosaccharides have relatively simple structures consisting of carbon, hydrogen, and oxygen in a 1-2-1 ratio. The most common monosaccharides contain five or six carbon atoms arranged in either a five- or six-membered ring (Figure 2.14).

a) The five-carbon monosaccharides ribose and deoxyribose.

Sucrose (a disaccharide)

b) Two 6-carbon monosaccharides (glucose and fructose) are joined together by dehydration synthesis, forming sucrose.

Figure 2.14 Monosaccharides. By convention, in a ringed structure the symbol C for carbon is often omitted because its presence is inferred by the union of two bond lines at an angle.

Ribose, deoxyribose, glucose, and *fructose* are four of the most important monosaccharides in humans. Ribose and deoxyribose (Figure 2.14a) are both five-carbon monosaccharides that are components of nucleotide molecules, discussed below. The only difference between the two is that deoxyribose has one less oxygen atom than ribose. Glucose, a six-carbon monosaccharide, is an important source of energy for cells. When more energy is available than can be used right away, glucose molecules can be linked together by dehydration synthesis to form larger carbohydrate molecules (Figure 2.14b).

Oligosaccharides: More than one monosaccharide linked together

Oligosaccharides are short strings of monosaccharides (*oligo* means "a few") linked together by dehydration synthesis. One common oligosaccharide is table sugar, or sucrose. Sucrose is also called a *disaccharide* because it consists of just two monosaccharides (glucose + fructose). Another is lactose (glucose + galactose), the most common disaccharide in human milk and an important source of energy for infants.

Some oligosaccharides are covalently bonded to certain cell-membrane proteins (called *glycoproteins*). Glycoproteins participate in linking adjacent cells together and in cell-cell recognition and communication.

> ☑ **Quick Check** *When simple monosaccharides are linked together into larger oligosaccharides by the process of dehydration synthesis, what other molecule is created?* ▪

Polysaccharides store energy

Complex carbohydrates called **polysaccharides** (*poly* means "many") form when thousands of monosaccharides are joined together into straight or branched chains by dehydration synthesis. Polysaccharides are a convenient way for cells to stockpile extra energy by locking it in the bonds of the polysaccharide molecule.

The most important polysaccharides in living organisms consist of long chains of glucose monosaccharides. In animals the storage polysaccharide is **glycogen** (Figure 2.15), whereas in plants it is **starch**. The flour we obtain by grinding plant grains is high in starch, which we then utilize for our own energy needs by breaking it down to glucose. Any glucose not consumed for energy in the short term can be used to create glycogen or lipids and stored within our cells for later use.

Cellulose is a slightly different form of glucose polysaccharide. Plants use it for structural support rather than for energy storage. The nature of the chemical bonds in cellulose is such that most animals, including humans, cannot break cellulose down to glucose units (which is why we cannot digest wood). But there is plenty of energy locked in the chemical bonds of cellulose, as demonstrated by the heat generated by a wood fire.

Undigested cellulose in the food we eat contributes to the fiber or "roughage" in our diet. A certain amount of fiber is thought to be beneficial because it increases the movement of wastes through the digestive tract. The more rapid excretion of wastes decreases the time of exposure to any carcinogens (cancer-causing agents) that may be in the waste material.

> ↩ **Recap** Carbohydrates contain carbon, hydrogen, and oxygen in a 1-2-1 ratio. Simple sugars such as glucose provide immediate energy for cells. Complex carbohydrates, called polysaccharides, store energy (in animals and plants) and provide structural support (in plants). ▪

a) Glycogen is formed by dehydration synthesis from glucose subunits.

b) A representation of the highly branched nature of glycogen.

c) A portion of an animal cell showing granules of stored glycogen (blue). The large pink structures are mitochondria.

Figure 2.15 **Glycogen is the storage carbohydrate in animals.**

☑ *Name two common polysaccharides made by plants. Are they also made of glucose? Can we digest both of them, and why or why not?*

2.7 Lipids: Insoluble in water

For biology, the most important physical characteristic of the class of organic molecules called **lipids** is that they are relatively insoluble, meaning they do not dissolve in water. The most important subclasses of lipids in your body are *triglycerides*, *phospholipids*, and *steroids*.

Triglycerides are energy-storage molecules

Triglycerides, also called neutral fats or just fats, are synthesized from a molecule of glycerol and three fatty acids (**Figure 2.16a**). **Fatty acids** are chains of hydrocarbons (usually about 16 to 18 carbons long) that end in a group of atoms known as a carboxyl group (COOH). Fats vary in the length of their fatty acid tails and the ratio of hydrogen atoms to carbon atoms in the tails.

Saturated fats have a full complement of two hydrogen atoms for each carbon in their tails (**Figure 2.16b**). In saturated fats, the tails are fairly straight, allowing them to pack closely together. As a result, saturated fats are generally solid at room temperature. Animal fats, such as butter and bacon grease, are saturated fats. A diet rich in saturated fats is thought to contribute to the development of cardiovascular disease.

Unsaturated fats, also called *oils*, have fewer than two hydrogen atoms on one or more of the carbon atoms in the tails (**Figure 2.16c**). As a result, double bonds form between adjacent carbons, putting kinks in the tails and preventing the fats from associating closely together. Consequently, unsaturated fats (oils) are generally liquid at room temperature.

Triglycerides are stored in adipose (fat) tissue and are an important source of stored energy in our bodies. Most of the energy is located in the bonds between carbon and hydrogen in the fatty acid tails.

✓ **Quick Check** *Cocoa butter is solid at room temperature; canola oil is liquid at room temperature. Which lipid has more double bonds between the carbon atoms (and fewer than two hydrogen atoms per carbon atom) in its fatty acid tails? Explain.* ■

Phospholipids are the primary component of cell membranes

Phospholipids are a modified form of lipid. They are the primary structural component of cell membranes.

Like fats, phospholipids have a molecule of glycerol as the backbone, but they have only two fatty acid tails. Replacing the third fatty acid is a negatively charged phosphate group (PO_4^-) and another group that varies depending on the phospholipid but is generally positively charged (**Figure 2.17**). The presence of charged groups on one end gives the phospholipid a special property: One end of the molecule is polar and thus soluble (dissolves) in water, whereas the other end (represented by the two fatty acid tails) is neutral and therefore relatively insoluble in water.

Steroids are composed of four rings

Steroids do not look at all like the lipids described previously but are classified as lipids because they are relatively insoluble in water. Steroids consist of a backbone of three 6-membered carbon rings and one 5-membered carbon ring to which any number of different groups may be attached.

One steroid you may be familiar with is **cholesterol** (**Figure 2.18a**). High levels of cholesterol in the blood are associated with cardiovascular disease. However, we all need a certain amount of cholesterol. It is a normal and essential structural component of animal cell membranes and is also

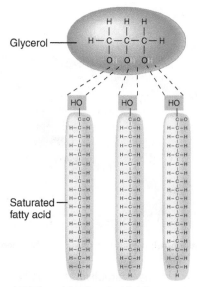

a) Triglycerides (neutral fats) are synthesized from glycerol and three fatty acids by dehydration synthesis.

b) Triglycerides with saturated fatty acids have straight tails, allowing them to pack closely together.

c) Triglycerides with unsaturated fatty acids have kinked tails, preventing them from packing closely together.

Figure 2.16 Triglycerides.

a) Cholesterol:
A normal component of the cell membrane.

b) Estrogen (estradiol):
Female sex hormone synthesized from cholesterol.

c) Testosterone:
Male sex hormone synthesized from cholesterol.

Figure 2.18 Steroids. Steroids consist of a backbone of three 6-membered carbon rings and one 5-membered ring.

↩ **Recap** Lipids (triglycerides, phospholipids, and steroids) are all relatively insoluble in water. Triglycerides are an important source of stored energy. Phospholipids, an important component of cell membranes, have a polar (water-soluble) head and two fatty acid (water-insoluble) tails. Steroids, such as cholesterol, have a four-ring structure. ▪

2.8 Proteins: Complex structures constructed of amino acids

Proteins are macromolecules constructed from long strings of single units called **amino acids**. All human proteins are constructed from only 20 different amino acids (Figure 2.19). Each amino acid has an *amino group* (NH_3) on one end, a carboxyl group on the other, a C—H group in the middle, and an additional group (designated "R") that represents everything else. Some of the R groups are completely neutral, others are neutral but polar, and a few carry a net charge (either positive or negative). Differences in the charge and structure of the amino acids affect the shape and functions of the proteins constructed from them. Our bodies can synthesize (make) 11 of the amino acids if necessary. However, we generally get enough of most of them, including the 9 we cannot synthesize, in the food we eat.

Like complex carbohydrates and fats, proteins are formed by dehydration synthesis (Figure 2.20). A single string of 3 to 100 amino acids is called a **polypeptide**. A polypeptide is generally referred to as a **protein** when it is longer than 100 amino acids and has a complex structure and a function. Some proteins consist of several polypeptides linked together.

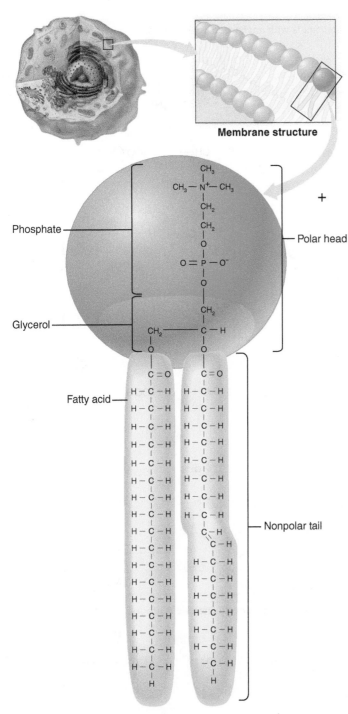

Membrane structure

Phosphate

Polar head

Glycerol

Fatty acid

Nonpolar tail

Figure 2.17 Phospholipids. Phospholipids are the primary constituent of animal cell membranes.

☑ *Why is the head of each phospholipid molecule oriented toward the outer surface of each side of the membrane (toward water), instead of toward the middle of the membrane interior? In other words, what prevents a phospholipid molecule from orienting the wrong way?*

the source of several important hormones, including the sex hormones estrogen and testosterone (Figure 2.18b and 2.18c). Our bodies manufacture cholesterol even though we generally get more than we need from our diet.

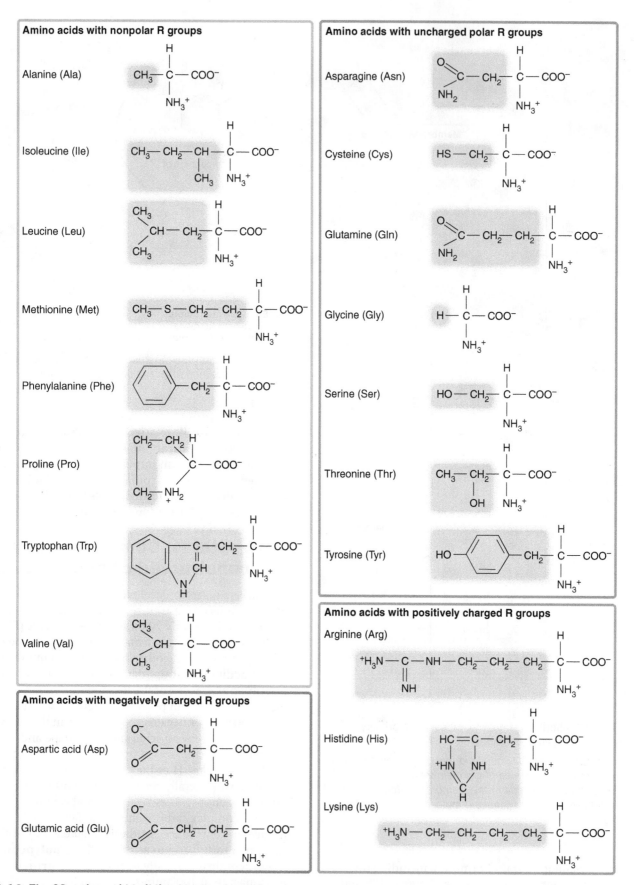

Figure 2.19 The 20 amino acid building blocks of proteins. The portions of amino acids that make them different from each other, called R groups, are colored. The three-letter codes in parentheses designate the amino acids in written formulas.

Figure 2.20 The synthesis of proteins. Proteins are created from amino acids by dehydration synthesis.

Protein function depends on structure

The function of every protein depends critically on its structure. We can define protein structure on at least three levels and sometimes four levels (**Figure 2.21**):

- *Primary structure.* The primary structure of a protein is represented by its amino acid sequence. In writing, each amino acid is indicated by a three-letter code (review Figure 2.19).
- *Secondary structure.* The secondary structure describes how the chain of amino acids is oriented in space. A common secondary structure of proteins is an *alpha (α) helix.* An *(α)* helix is a right-hand spiral that is stabilized by hydrogen bonds between amino acids at regular intervals. Another common secondary structure also stabilized by hydrogen bonds is a flat ribbon called a *beta (β) sheet.* A *β* sheet is formed when hydrogen bonds join two primary sequences of amino acids side by side. In addition to forming these two structures, proteins can coil into an almost infinite variety of shapes depending on which amino acids make up the sequence.
- *Tertiary structure.* Tertiary structure, the third level, refers to how the protein twists and folds to form a three-dimensional shape. The protein's three-dimensional structure depends in part on its sequence of amino acids, because the locations of the polar and charged groups within the chain determine the locations of hydrogen bonds that hold the whole sequence together. In addition, occasionally a covalent bond called a *disulfide* (S—S) bond forms between the sulfur molecules of two cysteine amino acids (see Figure 2.19). Finally, proteins tend to fold in such a way that neutral amino acids are more likely to end up in the interior, whereas charged and polar amino acids are more likely to face the outside (aqueous environment). Proteins acquire their characteristic tertiary structure by a folding process that occurs either during synthesis or shortly thereafter.
- *Quaternary structure.* The quaternary (fourth) structure of some proteins refers to how many polypeptide chains make up the protein (if there is more than one) and how they associate with each other.

The human body has thousands of different proteins, each serving a different function. Some proteins are primarily for structural support. Others are involved in muscle contraction. Others form part of the cell membrane, where they help transmit information and materials into and out of cells. Still others, called *enzymes*, regulate the rates of biochemical reactions within cells (see next section).

Because the links that determine the secondary and tertiary structures of protein are relatively weak hydrogen bonds, they may be broken by nearby charged molecules. This means that *the shape of proteins can change* in the presence of charged or polar molecules. The ability to change shape is essential to the functions of certain proteins.

Protein structure can also be damaged, sometimes permanently, by high temperatures or changes in pH. **Denaturation** refers to permanent disruption of protein structure, leading to a loss of biological function. An egg becomes hard when it is exposed to high temperatures because the soluble proteins in the egg become denatured and clump together as a solid mass.

Most proteins are water soluble, meaning that they dissolve in water; however, there are exceptions. Many of the proteins that are part of our cell membranes either are insoluble in water or have water-insoluble regions. Water-insolubility allows them to associate with the water-insoluble regions of the phospholipids that comprise most of the cell membrane's structure.

✔ **Quick Check** *You've isolated an unknown macromolecule, and you are trying to identify it. So far, all you know is that it consists mostly of carbon and hydrogen, it doesn't contain any nitrogen at all, and it is insoluble in water. Is it most likely to be a protein, a carbohydrate, or a lipid? Explain.* ▪

Enzymes facilitate biochemical reactions

An **enzyme** is a protein that functions as a biological catalyst. A **catalyst** is a substance that speeds up the rate of a chemical reaction without being altered or consumed by the reaction. Enzymes help biochemical reactions to occur, but they do not change the final result of the reaction. That is, they can only speed reactions that would have happened

Figure 2.21 The structure of proteins. In the diagrams of secondary structure the R groups have been omitted so that the basic backbone can be seen more easily.

anyway, although much more slowly. A chemical reaction that could take hours by itself might reach the same point in minutes or seconds in the presence of an enzyme.

Without help from thousands of enzymes, most biochemical reactions in our cells would occur too slowly to sustain life. Each enzyme facilitates a particular chemical reaction or group of reactions. Some enzymes break molecules apart; others join molecules together. In general, the enzyme takes one or more *reactants* (also called *substrates*) and turns them into one or more *products.* Enzymes serve as catalysts because, as proteins, they can change shape. The ability to change shape allows them to bind to other molecules and orient them so that they may interact. Figure 2.22 illustrates how a typical enzyme works.

Just how important are enzymes? As one example, the reason we can digest glycogen and starch is that we possess specific enzymes that break the chemical bonds between the glucose monosaccharides in these molecules. In contrast, we cannot digest cellulose because we lack the right enzyme to break it apart. Termites can utilize cellulose only because their digestive systems harbor bacteria that have a cellulose-digesting enzyme.

The changeable shape of an enzyme shows why homeostasis within our cells is so important. Protein shape is in part determined by the chemical and physical environment inside a cell, including temperature, pH, and the concentrations of certain ions. Any deviation from homeostasis can affect the shapes and biological activities of dozens of different enzymes and thus alter the course of biochemical reactions within the cell.

Recap Proteins consist of strings of amino acids. The function of a protein relates to its shape, which is determined by its amino acid sequence and the twisting and folding of its chain of amino acids. Enzymes are proteins that facilitate biochemical reactions in the body. Without enzymes, many biochemical reactions would occur too slowly to sustain life. ∎

2.9 Nucleic acids store genetic information

Another important class of organic molecules is the *nucleic acids*, **DNA (deoxyribonucleic acid)** and **RNA (ribonucleic acid)**. You have probably heard of such subjects as cloning, genetic engineering, and DNA "fingerprinting." These subjects relate to the nucleic acids: DNA and RNA.

DNA, the genetic material in living things, directs everything the cell does. It is both the organizational plan and the set of instructions for carrying the plan out. Because it directs and controls all of life's processes including growth, development, and reproduction, DNA is key to life itself. RNA, a closely related macromolecule, is responsible for carrying out the instructions of DNA, and in some cases, of regulating the activity of DNA itself. In some viruses RNA (rather than DNA) serves as the genetic material.

To fully appreciate the importance of DNA and RNA, consider that

- DNA contains the instructions for producing RNA.
- RNA contains the instructions for producing proteins.
- Proteins direct most of life's processes.

Both DNA and RNA are composed of smaller molecular subunits called **nucleotides**. Nucleotides consist of (1) a five-carbon sugar, (2) a single- or double-ringed structure containing nitrogen called a *base*, and (3) one or more phosphate groups. Eight different nucleotides exist: four in DNA and four in RNA.

Figure 2.23 shows the structures of the four nucleotides that make up DNA. Each nucleotide is composed of a five-carbon sugar molecule called *deoxyribose* (like the five-carbon sugar ribose but missing one oxygen atom), a phosphate group, and one of four different nitrogen-containing base molecules (*adenine, thymine, cytosine,* or *guanine*). In a single strand of DNA, these nucleotides are linked together by covalent bonds between the phosphate and sugar groups. The complete molecule of DNA is actually composed of two intertwined strands of nucleotides that are held together by weak hydrogen bonds (Figure 2.24). The sequence of one strand determines the sequence of the other (they are complementary strands), because adenine can form hydrogen bonds only with thymine (A with T) and cytosine can form bonds only with guanine (C with G).

The "code" for making a specific protein resides in the specific sequence of base pairs in one of the two strands of the DNA molecule. Notice that the entire genetic code is based entirely on the sequence of only four different molecular units (the four nucleotides). You will learn more about DNA and the genetic code when we discuss cell reproduction and inheritance.

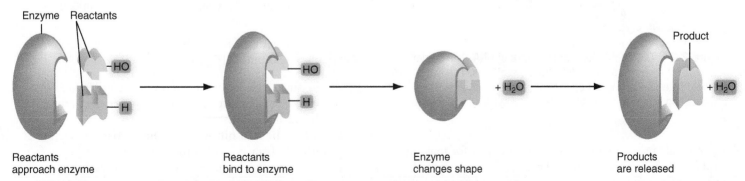

Enzyme   Reactants

Reactants approach enzyme

Reactants bind to enzyme

Enzyme changes shape

Products are released

Figure 2.22 Enzymes facilitate chemical reactions. This particular enzyme facilitates a dehydration synthesis reaction in which two reactants join to create one larger product plus a molecule of water. Note that the enzyme is not used up during the reaction.

Figure 2.23 The four nucleotides that compose DNA. The phosphate and sugar groups are identical in all four nucleotides.

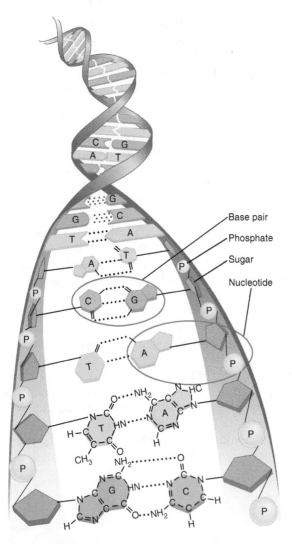

Figure 2.24 The double helical structure of DNA. The single strands of DNA are formed by dehydration synthesis. The two strands are held together by two hydrogen bonds between adenine and thymine and three hydrogen bonds between cytosine and guanine.

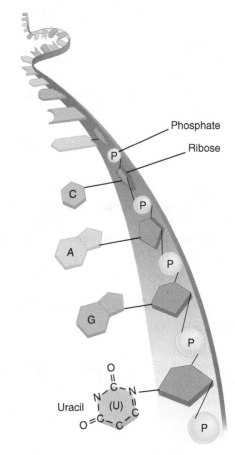

Figure 2.25 The structure of RNA. RNA is a single strand of nucleotides in which the base uracil substitutes for thymine. The sugar is ribose in RNA (as opposed to deoxyribose in DNA).

smaller fragments of RNA. RNA is structurally like DNA, with a few exceptions (**Figure 2.25**):

- The sugar unit in all four of the nucleotides in RNA is *ribose* rather than deoxyribose (hence the name ribonucleic acid).
- One of the four nitrogen-containing base molecules is different (uracil is substituted for thymine).
- RNA is a single-stranded molecule, representing a complementary copy of a portion of only *one* strand of DNA.

A single molecule of DNA carries the code for making a lot of different proteins. It is like an entire bookshelf of information, too big to be read all at once. To carry out their function, portions of the DNA molecule are transcribed into

- RNA is shorter, representing only the segment of DNA that codes for one or more proteins.

    In Chapter 17 we discuss how RNA is used to make proteins, as well as RNA's possible role in regulating the activity of DNA.

↩ **Recap** DNA and RNA are constructed of long strings of nucleotides. Double-stranded DNA represents the genetic code for life, and RNA, which is single-stranded, is responsible for carrying out those instructions. ▪

2.10 ATP carries energy

One additional related nucleotide with an important function is **ATP (adenosine triphosphate)**. ATP is identical to the adenine-containing nucleotide in RNA except that it has two additional phosphate groups. ATP consists of an adenine base, the five-carbon sugar ribose (together they are called *adenosine*), and three phosphate groups (*triphosphate*) (Figure 2.26). ATP is a universal energy source for cells because the bonds between the phosphate groups contain a great deal of potential energy. Any time a cell needs energy for virtually any function, it can break the bond between the last two phosphate groups of ATP and release energy according to the following equation:

$$ATP \rightarrow ADP + P_i + energy$$

The breakdown of ATP produces **ADP (adenosine diphosphate)** plus an inorganic phosphate group (P_i) which is not attached to an organic molecule, plus energy that is now available to do work. The reaction is reversible, meaning that ATP is replenished by using another source of energy to reattach P_i to ADP. The energy to replenish ATP may come from stored energy in the food we eat, or from the breakdown of energy storage molecules such as glycogen or fat. You will learn more about ATP as an energy source when we discuss energy utilization by muscles (Chapter 6).

↩ **Recap** ATP is a nearly universal source of quick energy for cells. The energy is stored in the chemical bonds between phosphate groups. ▪

a) **The structure of ATP.**

b) **The breakdown and synthesis of ATP.** The breakdown (hydrolysis) of ATP yields energy for the cell. The reaction is reversible, meaning that ATP may be resynthesized using energy from other sources.

Figure 2.26 Adenosine triphosphate (ATP).

Chapter Summary

All matter consists of elements *p. 24*

- Atoms, the smallest functional unit of any element, contain a nucleus and a cloud of electrons.
- The protons and neutrons in an atom's nucleus account for most of its mass.
- Radioisotopes are unstable isotopes; an isotope has more or fewer neutrons than the usual number for that atom.

Atoms combine to form molecules *p. 27*

- Energy exists as either kinetic energy or potential energy.
- Three types of chemical bonds account for the structures of molecules: covalent, ionic, and hydrogen bonds. Covalent bonds are the strongest; hydrogen bonds are the weakest.

- Over 99% of your body weight consists of just six elements: oxygen, carbon, hydrogen, nitrogen, calcium, and phosphorus.

Life depends on water *p. 31*

- The polar nature of the water molecule accounts for its physical properties and for its unusually good qualities as a solvent for most other molecules and ions.
- Water is important in human temperature regulation.

The importance of hydrogen ions *p. 32*

- Molecules that can donate a hydrogen ion (H^+) are called acids. Molecules that can accept H^+ are called bases.
- The hydrogen ion concentration of a solution is expressed as pH.
- Buffers are pairs of molecules that tend to minimize changes in pH when an acid or base is added to a solution.

The organic molecules of living organisms *p. 34*

- The backbone of all organic molecules is carbon.
- Organic molecules are formed by a process called dehydration synthesis (requiring energy) and broken down by a process called hydrolysis (releasing energy).

Carbohydrates: Used for energy and structural support *p. 36*

- Monosaccharides, or simple sugars, are a source of quick energy for cells.
- Complex carbohydrates (polysaccharides) are formed by linking simple sugars (monosaccharides) together by dehydration synthesis.
- Carbohydrates are primarily energy-storage molecules. Plants use them for structural support as well.
- In animals the storage molecule is glycogen; in plants it is starch.

Lipids: Insoluble in water *p. 38*

- Lipids include fats and oils, phospholipids, and steroids. Lipids are insoluble in water.
- Fats store energy. Phospholipids and cholesterol are important structural components of the cell membrane. The sex hormones are steroids synthesized from cholesterol.

Proteins: Complex structures constructed of amino acids *p. 39*

- Proteins have unique three-dimensional structures that depend on their primary structure (their amino acid sequences). Living organisms construct a tremendous number of different proteins using just 20 different amino acids.
- The human body contains thousands of proteins, each with a different function.
- Enzymes are proteins that facilitate the rates of chemical reactions.

Nucleic acids store genetic information *p. 43*

- DNA is composed of two long strands of nucleotides inter-twined into a double helix. DNA is constructed from just four different DNA nucleotides.
- RNA is a shorter single strand of RNA nucleotides, representing the code for one or more proteins.

ATP carries energy *p. 45*

- The nucleotide ATP is an energy source for cells. The energy is stored in the bonds between phosphate groups.

Terms You Should Know

acid, *33*	ion, *29*
atom, *25*	ionic bond, *29*
ATP (adenosine triphosphate), *45*	lipid, *38*
base, *33*	molecule, *27*
buffer, *33*	neutron, *25*
catalyst, *41*	pH scale, *33*
covalent bond, *28*	protein, *39*
DNA (deoxyribonucleic acid), *43*	proton, *25*
electron, *25*	RNA (ribonucleic acid), *43*
enzyme, *41*	solvent, *31*
hydrogen bond, *29*	solute, *31*

Concept Review

Answers can be found in the Study Area in MasteringBiology.

1. Describe the electrical charges and relative masses of protons, neutrons, and electrons.
2. Explain why two atoms of hydrogen tend to combine into a molecule of hydrogen gas (H_2)
3. Explain why polar and charged molecules tend to be soluble in water.
4. How is a covalent bond different from an ionic bond?
5. Compare and contrast potential energy and kinetic energy.
6. Distinguish between *saturated* and *unsaturated* fats.
7. Describe the process known as *dehydration synthesis*.
8. Explain why proteins come in an almost unlimited variety of shapes.
9. Discuss the importance of enzymes in living organisms.
10. Describe the role of ATP in energy transfer within a cell.

Test Yourself

Answers can be found in Appendix A.

1. If a molecule of starch is repeatedly hydrolyzed, which of the following would be the final product?
   a. glucose
   b. fructose
   c. ribose
   d. sucrose
   e. deoxyribose
2. Which of these molecules would be described as hydrophobic?
   a. glucose
   b. sodium chloride
   c. cholesterol
   d. DNA
   e. RNA
3. _____ bonds form between the oxygen and hydrogen within water molecules, whereas _____ bonds form between different water molecules.
   a. hydrogen...... covalent
   b. covalent....... hydrogen
   c. ionic.......hydrogen
   d. hydrogen.......ionic
   e. covalent.......ionic
4. ^{13}C and ^{14}C are _____ of carbon.
   a. isotopes
   b. ions
   c. compounds
   d. molecules
   e. isomers
5. Which of the following substances has the lowest hydrogen ion concentration?
   a. water (pH 7)
   b. bleach (pH 13)
   c. baking soda (pH 9)
   d. vinegar (pH 3)
   e. black coffee (pH 5)

6. When sugar is dissolved in water, sugar is the _____ and water is the .
   a. acid.........base
   b. base.........acid
   c. solvent......solute
   d. solute........solvent
   e. inorganic molecule.......organic molecule

7. A monosaccharide is to a polysaccharide as an amino acid is to a _____.
   a. nucleic acid
   b. carbohydrate
   c. protein
   d. nucleotide
   e. triglyceride

8. Which of these bonds is the easiest to disrupt, simply by raising the temperature?
   a. hydrogen bonds
   b. ionic bonds
   c. polar covalent bonds
   d. nonpolar covalent bonds
   e. peptide bonds

9. The primary structure of a protein is maintained by _____ bonds.
   a. hydrophilic
   b. hydrophobic
   c. hydrogen
   d. covalent
   e. ionic

10. DNA ultimately contains the instructions for the assembly of:
    a. proteins
    b. polysaccharides
    c. triglycerides
    d. nucleotides
    e. steroids

11. If one strand of DNA has the sequence A-A-C-T-G-T-G, what will be the nucleotide sequence of the complementary strand?
    a. A-A-C-T-G-T-G
    b. U-U-G-A-C-A-C
    c. T-T-G-U-C-U-C
    d. G-G-C-A-G-A-G
    e. T-T-G-A-C-A-C

12. Which of the following is true regarding the synthesis of a triglyceride?
    a. Three water molecules would be removed.
    b. The triglyceride would be hydrophilic.
    c. It would require three amino acids.
    d. It would require three monosaccharides.
    e. Hydrolysis reactions would be involved.

13. Which of the following is true regarding enzymes?
    a. The synthesis of an enzyme involves hydrolysis reactions.
    b. Enzymes provide energy for biochemical reactions.
    c. One enzyme can catalyze many different types of reactions.
    d. The instructions for the synthesis of an enzyme are found in DNA.
    e. Each enzyme molecule can be used only once.

14. Synthesis of proteins requires the input of energy, which can be provided by:
    a. enzymes
    b. synthesis of ATP from ADP and P_i
    c. hydrolysis of ATP to form ADP and P_i
    d. amino acids
    e. isotopes

15. The element phosphorus (P) has an atomic number of 15 and a mass number of 31. Which of the following represents the numbers of subatomic particles in phosphorus?
    a. 15 protons, 15 electrons, 31 neutrons
    b. 15 protons, 16 electrons, 15 neutrons
    c. 31 protons, 31 electrons, 15 neutrons
    d. 15 protons, 15 electrons, 16 neutrons
    e. 16 protons, 16 electrons, 15 neutrons

Apply What You Know

Answers can be found in the Study Area in MasteringBiology.

1. Athletes are sometimes advised to eat large amounts of complex carbohydrates (such as whole-wheat pasta) for a day or two before a competitive event. Explain the reasoning behind this.

2. Physicians become concerned about the potential for irreversible brain damage when body temperatures approach 105°F Which of the four classes of macromolecules do you think is most likely affected by high temperatures? Explain.

3. Many people use cholesterol-lowering drugs to reduce their high cholesterol, because they know that a high cholesterol level is a risk factor for heart disease. Would it be advisable to take a little extra dose of these drugs to try to lower your cholesterol to below normal levels, just to be on the safe side?

4. In Miami when it is 90 degrees outside and very humid, the heat feels stifling. Yet most people report feeling fine in Arizona, where the humidity is generally low, even when it is 100 degrees. Why does the humidity have such an effect on our perception of comfort in terms of temperature?

5. Coca-Cola is a very acidic drink; its pH is around 3. Blood has a pH of about 7. Yet when you drink a Coke the pH of the blood does not change measurably. Why is that?

6. Although normal physiological processes produce small amounts of free radicals, it is possible that your behavior, lifestyle, or environment might contribute to an increased production of free radicals. What behavioral or environmental risks do you think you have that might promote the formation of free radicals?

BlogInFocus

Answers can be found in the Study Area in MasteringBiology.

1. Hormones are sometimes added to food products. Explain why this is this permissible. (Hint: Visit MJ's blog in the Study Area in MasteringBiology and look under "Melatonin in Brownies.")

2. Marketers of dietary supplements sometimes engage in deceptive sales practices. Based on what you have learned in this chapter, what do you think would be considered deceptive or illegal and what is allowed? (For more on this subject, visit MJ's blog in the Study Area in MasteringBiology and look under "Deceptive Sales Practices.")

MasteringBiology®

Go to MasteringBiology for practice quizzes, activities, eText, videos, current events, and more.

Structure and Function of Cells

Fluorescent light micrograph of fibroblast cells from connective tissue.

The Use of Human Stem Cells

What do boxing champion Muhammad Ali and actor Michael J. Fox have in common? They both suffer from Parkinson's disease, a debilitating neurological disorder. The key to curing Parkinson's disease and many other diseases and health problems including Alzheimer's disease, leukemia, diabetes, and spinal cord injuries may be **stem cells**.

A stem cell is a cell from which other types of more specialized cells originate (or stem). The ultimate stem cell is the fertilized egg, because *all* of the specialized cells of the body originate from it. The first eight cells of a human embryo are also stem cells, because they have not yet begun to differentiate (become different from each other). But shortly after the eight-cell stage the cells begin to specialize. Some become muscle; others become skin; still others become nerve cells in the brain.

Stem cells have several properties that make them desirable for research and for the treatment of certain diseases. They are easier to work with in the laboratory than adult cells because they don't adhere tightly to each other, and they grow better in culture (in controlled conditions, such as in a laboratory). They generally don't provoke a "tissue

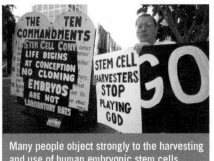

Many people object strongly to the harvesting and use of human embryonic stem cells.

rejection" immune response in the patient because they are undifferentiated and thus not recognized as foreign cells. They are also easier to administer to a patient—usually they can be injected and allowed to migrate to their target site rather than having to be surgically transplanted. And most important, they still have the capacity to become the type of specialized cell the patient needs, under the direction of the patient's own cell division/differentiation control mechanisms.

Traditionally most human embryonic stem cells have come from very early-stage embryos. Currently, the only available embryos of this age are those created "in excess of clinical need" by in vitro fertilization at private fertility clinics. Only a few researchers have access to such embryos. However, cells used to treat specific diseases don't need to be completely undifferentiated. If nerve cells are needed, a good source of young cells is the very first embryonic neural tissue in the human fetus. Already, over 100 people with Parkinson's disease have received fetal nerve cell transplants worldwide, and some have shown measurable improvements in brain function. Nonliving human fetuses are widely available as a consequence of the more than one million legal abortions performed in the United States each year.

Controversy and Compromise

Not surprisingly, the use of human embryonic cells from fertilized eggs and undifferentiated fetal cells from legally aborted fetuses is highly controversial. On the one hand, patient advocacy groups recognize the potential benefits of human embryonic and fetal cells and promote efforts to harvest and use them. On the other, some human rights groups object strongly to harvesting or using human embryonic stem cells or fetal cells under any circumstances, calling such research the destruction of precious human life. Both sides believe strongly in their position and both sides are active politically, and as a result politicians have been forced to take a stand.

According to guidelines developed under the Bush administration in 2001,

Muhammad Ali and Michael J. Fox, both sufferers of Parkinson's disease, support stem cell research.

federal funds could only be used to study stem cell lines derived from embryos before 2001. (A stem cell "line" is a group of identical cells grown from a single stem cell.) In effect, the 2001 federal guidelines prohibited the National Institutes of Health, which funds most biomedical research, from financing any stem cell research that might require the *future* death of a human embryo, but allows research on cells harvested from embryos in the past. However, the guidelines stopped short of prohibiting human stem cell research altogether; privately funded human embryonic stem cell research is still permitted under certain conditions.

The guidelines developed under President Bush were a political compromise at best. They allow selected federally funded research projects to go forward with the few stem cell lines that already existed at the time the law was passed (2001), while respecting concerns about the sanctity of human life. The guidelines were opposed by stem cell researchers, who contended that the limited number of cell lines available were not enough for the United States to stay in the forefront of this important research area. Some stem cell researchers moved to Britain, which had developed a facility for storing thousands of cell lines, or to other places in the world where stem cell research was not only allowed, but encouraged.

The election of President Obama changed the political environment yet again. Shortly after taking office in 2009, President Obama signed an executive order lifting the restrictions on stem cell research laid down by President Bush. Federally funded researchers are now free to use the hundreds of stem cell lines in existence today, as well as new stem cell lines created by private funding in the future. But there is still a prohibition in place, called the Dickey-Wicker Amendment of 1996, which prohibits federal funding for research "in which human embryos are created, destroyed, discarded, or knowingly subjected to risk of injury or death." Although federally funded researchers will be able to use stem cell lines created by private funds (because the researchers themselves did not destroy any embryos), they will still be prohibited from creating their own new cell lines from human embryos. Obviously, the controversy over stem cells is not over.

What Is the Solution?

Both sides in this controversy actually do have something they can agree on; they both hope that someday we will not need to use stem cells from embryos or fetuses at all. The key may be the development of methods to create undifferentiated stem cells from fully differentiated adult cells—in essence, reversing the entire process of cellular differentiation and specialization. Several groups of scientists already claim to have done it successfully. But some scientists caution that new techniques for creating stem cell lines may not necessarily translate quickly into cures for specific diseases. It would be a shame if a well-meaning public, convinced that human embryonic stem cells are no longer necessary, came to accept laws that severely restrict human embryonic stem cell research in this country. Although the day may yet come when human embryonic stem cells truly aren't necessary, that day has not yet arrived. Just ask Michael J. Fox or Mohammed Ali.

QUESTIONS TO CONSIDER

1 What is your opinion on this controversy? What basic beliefs do you hold that cause you to feel as you do?

2 Suppose that you and your spouse held frozen embryos at a private fertility clinic and that you knew you would never need them. Would you donate them for stem cell research? Why or why not?

THE FACTS...

- Stem cells obtained from human embryos and fetuses have the potential to treat or cure diseases.
- Research using cells obtained from human embryos or fetuses is controversial.
- In the United States, stem cell research has been affected by changes in the political environment.
- In the distant future, human embryos and fetuses may no longer be needed as a source of stem cells.

>> **A single cell is the smallest unit of life.** All living things are comprised of one or more cells (plus cell products), and all cells come only from preexisting cells.

>> **Human cells are surrounded by a plasma membrane.** The plasma membrane serves to contain the cellular structures within the cell and to regulate the kinds and quantities of molecules that can enter and exit the cell.

>> **The nucleus of a human cell contains the cell's DNA.** The genetic code of DNA specifies the amino acid sequences of the proteins produced by the cell.

>> **Mitochondria, which are cell structures, produce usable energy in the form of adenosine triphosphate (ATP).** Most of the energy for making ATP comes from the complete breakdown of glucose, a mitochondrial process that requires oxygen and results in the production of carbon dioxide, a waste product.

>> **Other cell structures use ATP to carry out cellular functions,** including manufacturing and exporting biological molecules; providing for cell support, movement, growth, and division; defending against foreign cells and toxic chemicals; and getting rid of cellular waste.

Scientists first observed living cells under a microscope in 1674. Since then, countless observations and experiments have confirmed the **cell doctrine**, which consists of three basic principles:

1. All living things are composed of cells and cell products.
2. A single cell is the smallest unit that exhibits all the characteristics of life.
3. All cells come only from preexisting cells.

If we examine any part of the human body under a microscope, we find living cells and/or cell products. "Cell products" include materials composed of dead cells (such as the outer layer of your skin) and substances resulting from cellular activity (such as the hard crystalline elements of bone). There are no living units smaller than cells. All of our cells—all 100 trillion of them—are derived from earlier cells, going all the way back to our first cell, the fertilized egg. Even that original cell came from preexisting cells: the sperm and egg from our parents.

3.1 Cells are classified according to their internal organization

All cells are surrounded by an outer membrane called the **plasma membrane**. The plasma membrane encloses the material inside the cell, which is mostly water but also contains ions, enzymes, and other structures the cell requires to maintain life. All living cells are classified as either eukaryotes or prokaryotes, depending on their internal organization.

Eukaryotes have a nucleus, cytoplasm, and organelles

Human cells, like those of most species, are **eukaryotes** (*eu-* means "true" and *karyote* means "nucleus"). Nearly every eukaryotic cell has three basic structural components (Figure 3.1a):

1. A plasma membrane. The plasma membrane forms the outer covering of the cell.
2. A nucleus. *Nucleus* is a general term for "core." In the last chapter, we saw that chemists define a nucleus as the core of an atom. In biology, the nucleus is a membrane-bound compartment that houses the cell's genetic material and functions as its "information center." Most eukaryotic cells have one nucleus; however, there are a few exceptions, to be discussed in later chapters.
3. Cytoplasm ("cell material"). The cytoplasm includes everything inside the cell except the nucleus. It is composed of a soft, gel-like fluid called the *cytosol* ("cell solution"). The cytosol contains a variety of microscopic structures called **organelles** ("little organs") that carry out specialized functions, such as digesting nutrients or packaging cellular products.

Prokaryotes lack a nucleus and organelles

Prokaryotes (*pro-* means "before" and *karyote* means "nucleus") are the bacteria (kingdom Monera; Figure 3.1b). Prokaryotes have a plasma membrane that is surrounded by a rigid cell wall. Their genetic material is concentrated in a particular region, but it is not specifically enclosed within a membrane-bound nucleus. Prokaryotes also lack most of the organelles found in eukaryotes. Nevertheless they are living organisms that fit the definition of a cell according to the cell doctrine.

In the rest of this chapter and throughout the book, we concentrate on the structure and function of eukaryotic cells. However, we discuss bacteria again in terms of how they can make us ill (Chapter 9) and in the context of evolution (Chapter 22).

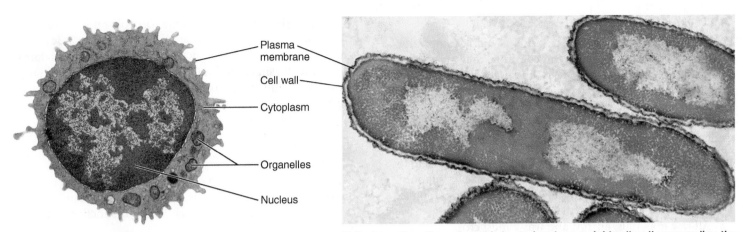

a) **A eukaryotic animal cell has a large nucleus and numerous small organelles.** The cytoplasm is enclosed by a flexible plasma membrane.

b) **Prokaryotic cells such as this bacterium have a rigid cell wall surrounding the plasma membrane.** The genetic material is not surrounded by a membrane, and there are no organelles in the cell. The elongated bacterium in the center of the photo is about to divide in two, as its genetic material is concentrated at both ends of the cell.

Figure 3.1 Eukaryotes versus prokaryotes.

3.2 Cell structure reflects cell function

Eukaryotic cells are remarkably alike in their structural features regardless of which organism they come from. This is because all cells carry out certain activities to maintain life, and there is a strong link between structure and function.

All cells must gather raw materials, excrete wastes, make macromolecules (the molecules of life), and grow and reproduce. These are not easy tasks. The specific activities carried out by a living cell (and the structures required to perform them) would rival those of any large city or even a country! There is an outer structure that defines its border; an infrastructure for support; an information center; manufacturing facilities; refining, packaging, and shipping centers; transportation systems for supplying raw materials and energy; stockpiles of energy; and mechanisms for recycling or removing toxic waste. Cells even possess sophisticated defense mechanisms to combat invaders.

Most of the structural differences between cells reflect differences in function (Figure 3.2). Muscle cells contain numerous mitochondria that produce the energy for muscle contraction. Many nerve cells are long and thin; the longest nerve cells carry impulses all the way from your toes to your spinal cord. The cells that line the kidney tubules are cube shaped and tightly bound together, reflecting their role in the transport of water and other molecules. Essentially every cell has a specialized function of some sort or it would be of little use to the organism.

Cells that serve the same function are often remarkably similar between species. For example, a human nerve cell has more in common (structurally and functionally) with a nerve cell in a cockroach than it does with a human liver cell. Furthermore, cells in a mouse are not that much different in size from those in an elephant; an elephant just has more of them.

a) **A portion of several muscle cells of the heart** ($\times$ 1,500).

b) **Nerve cells of the central nervous system** ($\times$ 830).

c) **Cells lining a tubule of a kidney** ($\times$ 250).

Figure 3.2 Human cells vary in shape.

Cells remain small to stay efficient

Despite their structural differences and incredible complexity, all cells have at least one feature in common: they are small in one or more dimensions. Given the variety of life-forms on Earth, why are there are so few giant cells? (An exception is the egg of some species.)

The answer shows that nature obeys certain simple and understandable principles:

- The total metabolic activities of a cell are proportional to its volume of cytoplasm, which is in effect its size. To support its activities, every cell needs raw materials in proportion to its size. Every cell also needs a way to get rid of its wastes.
- All raw materials, energy, and waste must cross the plasma membrane to enter or leave the cell.
- As objects get larger, their volume increases more than their surface area. For both spheres and cubes, for example, an eightfold increase in volume is accompanied by only a fourfold increase in surface area.

The larger a cell gets, then, the more likely that its growth and metabolism will be limited by its ability to supply itself across the plasma membrane (Figure 3.3). Put another way, the smaller a cell is, the more effectively it can obtain raw materials and get rid of wastes.

a) One large cell. b) Eight small cells. c) Cell with microvilli on one surface.

Figure 3.3 **Cell size and plasma membrane shape affect surface area and volume.** The volume is the same in these three groups of cells, but the ratio of volume to surface area is different in a), b), and c). Compared to the cell in a), the eight small cells in b) have twice the surface area. c) The surface area of any cell can be increased by the presence of microvilli.

Some cells have numerous microscopic projections of the plasma membrane called *microvilli* (see Figure 3.3c). Microvilli are an effective way to increase surface area relative to volume. Plasma membranes with microvilli are especially common in cells that transport substances into and out of the body, such as the cells that line the digestive tract and the tubules of the kidneys.

Visualizing cells with microscopes

Because they can't be seen effectively with the naked eye, the only way to visualize cells is with the use of one or more types of microscopes. Each has its distinctive features and uses.

The light microscope (LM). If you've ever used a microscope at all, this is undoubtedly the type you used. Small enough to sit on a laboratory bench, the light microscope uses visible light and a series of glass lenses to magnify a small sample up to about 1,000-fold. Focus can be difficult to maintain if objects are at different depths in the sample. Light does not transmit well through very dense or thick samples, and many cells cannot be seen well without staining beforehand. Nevertheless, light microscopes have been in use for over 300 years. They're still the microscope of choice when the magnifications required are relatively low, and they're still the only microscopes that can be used on living samples (Figure 3.4a).

The transmission electron microscope (TM). A transmission electron microscope, as the name implies, bombards a thin object with electrons, some of which are transmitted through the sample to create a visual image. Electrons behave like light waves, but because the wavelengths of electrons are shorter than visible light, magnifications of up to 100,000-fold, or 100 times greater than a light microscope, are possible. The images are two-dimensional (flat) because the sample must be very thin, but one can see structural details not possible with the light microscope (Figure 3.4b).

a) The light microscope (LM). b) The transmission electron microscope (TEM). c) The scanning electron microscope (SEM).

Figure 3.4 **Visualizing cells with microscopes.** Photographs taken by the various methods of microscopy are called photomicrographs. All three of the photomicrographs shown here are of *Escherichia coli*, a normally harmless bacterium found in the digestive tract.

The scanning electron microscope (SEM). The scanning electron microscope produces what appears to be a three-dimensional image of the surface of an object. The object to be visualized is coated with a thin coat of metal so that electrons cannot penetrate, and then scanned with a narrow beam of electrons. As the beam passes over the object, secondary electrons are given off which can be recorded to produce a visual image of the object's surface (Figure 3.4c). Like the transmission electron microscope, the scanning electron microscope produces magnifications of about 100,000-fold.

BlogInFocus (MB)

To follow the continuing legal battle over the use of human stem cells in research, visit MJ's blog in the Study Area in MasteringBiology and look under "Stem Cell Research."

Scanning electron microscopes and transmission electron microscopes are large and very expensive, so you won't see one in a student laboratory. The computer images they produce are only black and white, so they are usually colorized after the image is obtained. You may see the designation "false-color SEM" (or TEM) to indicate that they have been colorized, but nowadays it is generally just assumed that they have been.

↻ **Recap** **Common features of nearly all eukaryotic cells are a plasma membrane, a nucleus, organelles, and the cytoplasm. Cells exchange materials with their environment across their plasma membrane. Cells are small because this makes them more efficient at obtaining nutrients and expelling wastes. ▪**

3.3 A plasma membrane surrounds the cell

Consider a house. Its walls and roof are composed of special materials that prevent rain and wind from entering. They also form a barrier that allows the temperature inside the house to stay warmer or cooler than the temperature outside. At the same time, the house interacts with its environment. Windows allow light in; doors open and close to allow entry and exit. Water and power lines permit the regulated entry of water and energy, and sewer lines remove wastes. The house exchanges information with the outside world through mail slots, telephone lines, and computer cables.

The exterior structure of a living cell is its plasma membrane. Like the roof and walls of a house, the plasma membrane must permit the movement of some substances into and out of the cell yet restrict the movement of others. It must also allow the transfer of information across the membrane.

The plasma membrane is a lipid bilayer

The plasma membrane is constructed of two layers of phospholipids, called a *lipid bilayer,* plus some cholesterol and various proteins (Figure 3.5). Each of the three components contributes to the membrane's overall structural and functional properties:

▪ *Phospholipids.* Recall that phospholipids are a particular type of lipid with a polar head and neutral nonpolar tails. In the plasma membrane the two layers of phospholipids are arranged so that the

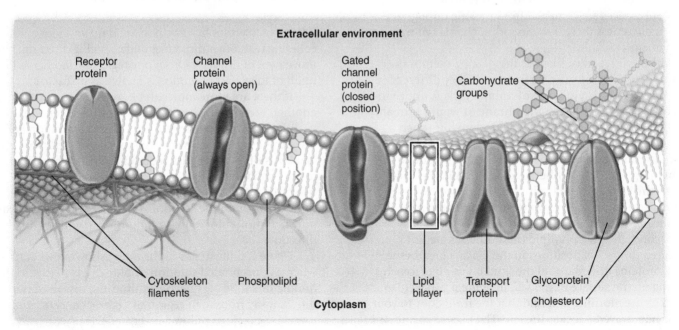

Figure 3.5 The plasma membrane. The plasma membrane is a phospholipid bilayer containing cholesterol and proteins. Cholesterol provides mechanical strength. The proteins transfer information, permit the passage of certain molecules, and provide structural support for the cytoskeleton.

nonpolar tails meet in the center of the membrane. One layer of polar (water-soluble) heads faces the watery solution on the outside of the cell, and the other layer of polar heads faces the watery solution of the cell's cytoplasm.

- *Cholesterol.* Cholesterol increases the mechanical strength of the membrane by preventing it from becoming either too rigid or too flexible. It also prevents the phospholipids from moving around too much and helps to anchor the proteins within the membrane.

- *Proteins.* Various proteins are embedded in the phospholipid bilayer of the plasma membrane. Like the doors, windows, and wires of a house, they provide the means for transporting molecules and information across the plasma membrane. A few membrane proteins anchor the cell's internal scaffold-like support network. Some proteins span the entire membrane; others protrude from only one surface. Plasma membrane proteins generally have one region that is electrically neutral and another that is electrically charged (either + or −). The charged regions tend to extend out of the membrane and thus are in contact with water, whereas the neutral portions are often embedded within the phospholipid bilayer.

The phospholipid bilayer of the plasma membrane is only about 3.5 nanometers thick (a nanometer, abbreviated nm, is a billionth of a meter), too small to be seen in detail even with microscopes. To appreciate relative sizes, imagine (as we did in Chapter 2) that a single sodium ion is the size of a penny. At this scale the phospholipid bilayer of a typical cell would be about 13 inches thick. It is no wonder that many substances are restricted from passing through the membrane unless there is some sort of channel or transport mechanism available.

Although we have likened the plasma membrane to the exterior of a house, there are two key differences. First, the plasma membrane of animal cells is not rigid. If you could touch a plasma membrane, it would probably feel like a wet sponge, giving way under your touch and springing back when you remove your hand. Most cells do maintain a certain shape, but it is mainly due to a supporting network of fibers inside the cell, the fluid within the cell, and the limitations imposed by contact with surrounding cells, not the stiffness of the plasma membrane itself.

Second, the phospholipids and proteins are not anchored to specific positions in the plasma membrane. Many proteins drift about in the lipid bilayer like icebergs floating on the surface of the sea. Imagine if you were to get up in the morning and find that the front door to your house had moved 3 feet to the left! The plasma membrane of animal cells is often described as a "fluid mosaic" to indicate that it is not a rigid structure and that the pattern of proteins within it constantly changes.

↩ **Recap** The plasma membrane is comprised of phospholipids, cholesterol, and proteins. The proteins transfer information and transport molecules across the membrane and provide structural support. ▪

3.4 Molecules cross the plasma membrane in several ways

The plasma membrane creates a barrier between the cell's external environment and the processes of life going on within. Life was impossible until these functions could be enclosed and concentrated in one place, keeping what was needed for growth and reproduction inside and limiting the entry of other materials. Molecules (and ions) cross the plasma membrane in three major ways: (1) passive transport (diffusion and osmosis), (2) active transport, and (3) endocytosis or exocytosis.

BlogInFocus (MB)

The first clinical trial of a therapy based on human stem cells is now under way. To read about it, visit MJ's blog in the Study Area in MasteringBiology and look under "Stem Cell Therapy Trial."

Passive transport: Principles of diffusion and osmosis

Passive transport is "passive" because it transports a molecule without requiring the cell to expend any energy. Passive transport relies on the mechanism of diffusion.

Diffusion Molecules in a gas or a liquid move about randomly, colliding with other molecules and changing direction. The movement of molecules from one region to another as the result of this random motion is known as **diffusion**.

If there are more molecules in one region than in another, then strictly by chance more molecules will tend to diffuse away from the area of high concentration and toward the region of low concentration. In other words, the *net* diffusion of molecules requires that there be a difference in concentration, called a *concentration gradient*, between two points. Once the concentration of molecules is the same throughout the solution, a state of equilibrium exists in which molecules diffuse randomly but equally in all directions.

Figure 3.6 illustrates diffusion by showing what happens when a concentrated solution of blue dye is placed in the middle of a tube of water. Over time, the dissolved molecules diffuse away from their region of highest concentration and toward the regions of low concentration.

Water also diffuses from the region of its highest concentration toward the region of its lowest concentration. However, the concentration of water (the liquid, or solvent)

cm inches

Figure 3.6 **Diffusion.** At time zero a concentrated solution of a blue dye was placed in the middle of a tube of water. To prevent the movement of water by bulk flow, a stabilizing agent had been added previously to the water. Over time the random motion of molecules in solution has caused some molecules of dye to move from the region of highest dye concentration to the region of low dye concentration. Although not visible, water has diffused in the opposite direction, from the region of highest water concentration (pure water) toward the region of lower water concentration (the region occupied by dye). Note that diffusion is effective only over short distances; it has taken 24 hours for the dye to move only 1 cm in any direction.

in a solution is *opposite* to that of the molecules other than water (the solutes). The higher the concentration of solutes, the lower the concentration of water. Pure water is the solution with the highest possible concentration of water. Net diffusion of water is always toward the solution with the higher concentration of solutes and away from the solution with a higher concentration of water.

Osmosis Not all substances diffuse readily into and out of living cells. The plasma membrane is **selectively permeable**, meaning that it allows some substances to cross by diffusion but not others. It is highly permeable to water but not to all ions or molecules. The net diffusion of water across a selectively permeable membrane is called **osmosis**.

Figure 3.7 demonstrates the process of osmosis. In Figure 3.7a, a selectively permeable membrane—in this case permeable only to water—separates pure water from a solution of glucose in water. Although the glucose cannot diffuse, the water diffuses toward its region of lower concentration, from right to left. As osmosis occurs, the volume in the left chamber rises, creating a fluid pressure that begins to oppose the continued osmosis of water (Figure 3.7b). Eventually the movement of water from left to right (because of differences in fluid pressure) equals the movement from right to left (by osmosis), and there is no further net change in the volume of water on each side of the membrane.

◀------- **Diffusion of water (osmosis)**
——▶ **Pressure-induced water movement**

Figure 3.7 **Generation of osmotic pressure by osmosis.** Starting in a), there is a net movement of water from right to left until the diffusion of water (osmosis) is opposed by movement of water due to osmotic pressure c).

☑ *In the third figure, what would happen if you now add glucose to the right side—adding exactly the same total number of glucose molecules as are in the left side? Explain your answer.*

The fluid pressure required to exactly oppose osmosis is called *osmotic pressure.* In Figure 3.7c osmotic pressure is represented by the extra weight of the higher column of water on the left than on the right.

Passive transport moves with the concentration gradient

Most substances cross cell membranes by passive transport. Passive transport always proceeds "downhill" with respect to the concentration gradient, meaning that it relies on diffusion in some way. Three forms of passive transport across the cell membrane are (1) diffusion through the lipid bilayer, (2) diffusion through channels, and (3) facilitated transport (Figure 3.8).

Diffusion through the lipid bilayer The lipid bilayer structure of the plasma membrane allows the free passage of some molecules while restricting others. For instance, small uncharged nonpolar molecules can diffuse right through the lipid bilayer as if it did not exist. Such molecules simply dissolve in the lipid bilayer, passing through it like a ghost through a wall. Polar or electrically charged molecules, in contrast, cannot cross the lipid bilayer because they are not soluble in lipids.

Two important lipid-soluble molecules are oxygen (O_2), which diffuses into cells and is used up in the process of metabolism, and carbon dioxide (CO_2), a waste product of metabolism, which diffuses out of cells and is removed from the body by the lungs. Another substance that crosses the lipid bilayer by diffusion is

urea, a neutral waste product removed from the body by the kidneys.

Quick Check *Do you think sodium (Na^+) or chloride (Cl^-) ions can diffuse directly through the lipid bilayer? How about water molecules? Explain.*

Diffusion through channels Water and many ions diffuse through channels in the plasma membrane. The channels are constructed of proteins that span the entire lipid bilayer. The sizes and shapes of these protein channels, as well as the electrical charges on the various amino acid groups that line the channel, determine which molecules can pass through.

Some channels are open all the time (typical of water channels). The diffusion of any molecule through the membrane is largely determined by the number of channels through which the molecule can fit. Other channels are "gated," meaning that they can open and close under certain conditions. Gated channels are particularly important in regulating the transport of ions (sodium, potassium, and calcium) in cells that are electrically excitable, such as nerve cells (Chapter 11). Look at Figure 3.5, which represents a number of the proteins instrumental in transport.

Facilitated transport In **facilitated transport**, also called *facilitated diffusion*, the molecule does not pass through a

Answers to ✓ questions can be found in Appendix A.

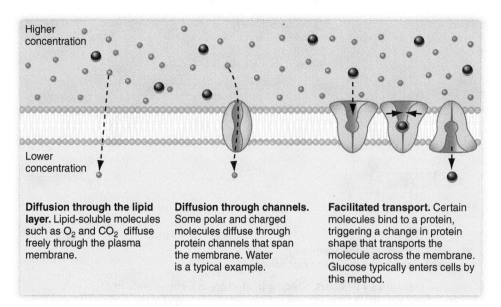

Diffusion through the lipid layer. Lipid-soluble molecules such as O_2 and CO_2 diffuse freely through the plasma membrane.

Diffusion through channels. Some polar and charged molecules diffuse through protein channels that span the membrane. Water is a typical example.

Facilitated transport. Certain molecules bind to a protein, triggering a change in protein shape that transports the molecule across the membrane. Glucose typically enters cells by this method.

Figure 3.8 The three forms of passive transport. All involve transport down a concentration gradient without the expenditure of additional energy.

channel at all. Instead it attaches to a membrane protein, triggering a change in the protein's shape or orientation that transfers the molecule to the other side of the membrane and releases it there. Once the molecule is released, the protein returns to its original form. A protein that carries a molecule across the plasma membrane in this manner, rather than opening a channel through it, is called a **transport protein** (carrier protein).

Facilitated transport is highly selective for particular substances. The direction of movement is always from a region of higher concentration to one of lower concentration, and thus it does not require the cell to expend energy. The normal process of diffusion is simply being "facilitated" by the transport protein. Glucose and other simple sugars enter most cells by this method.

Active transport requires energy

All methods of passive transport allow substances to move only down their concentration gradients, in the direction they would normally diffuse if there were no barrier. However, **active transport** can move substances through the plasma membrane *against* their concentration gradient. Active transport allows a cell to accumulate essential molecules even when their concentration outside the cell is relatively low, and to get

rid of molecules that it does not need. Active transport requires the expenditure of energy.

Like facilitated transport, active transport is accomplished by proteins that span the plasma membrane. The difference is that active transport proteins must have some source of energy to transport certain molecules. Some active transport proteins use the high-energy molecule ATP (adenosine triphosphate) for this purpose (**Figure 3.9a**). They break ATP down to ADP (adenosine diphosphate) and a phosphate group (P_i) and use the released energy to transport one or more molecules across the plasma membrane against their concentration gradient. Imagine that the active transport protein is a conveyor belt moving objects uphill, powered by a gasoline engine. In this analogy, ATP is the gasoline and ADP the exhaust (with one difference: the ADP "exhaust" in the cell can be recycled to ATP).

Proteins that actively transport molecules across the plasma membrane are sometimes called "pumps." Some pumps can transport several different molecules at once and even in both directions at the same time. One of the most important plasma membrane pumps is the **sodium-potassium pump**, which uses energy derived from breaking down ATP to transport sodium out of the cell and potassium into the cell.

Not all active transport pumps use ATP as the energy source. Some derive energy from the "downhill" facilitated

a) **In active transport using ATP, energy derived from the breakdown of ATP is used to change the shape of the carrier protein.**

b) **Some carrier proteins use energy derived from the downhill transport of one molecule to transport another molecule uphill.** In this example, the energy to transport the square molecules comes from the facilitated transport of the spearhead molecules.

Figure 3.9 Active transport. A cell can employ active transport to move a molecule against a concentration gradient. Because this is an "uphill" effort, energy is required.

transport of one molecule and use it to transport another molecule "uphill," against its concentration gradient (Figure 3.9b). This type of transport is analogous to an old-fashioned mill that grinds grain into flour by using energy derived from the downhill movement of water.

☑**Quick Check** *You've discovered a membrane protein that seems to be necessary for cells to transport fructose from higher to lower concentration. Predict whether this membrane protein requires ATP to function, and name the type of transport that it is most likely doing. Explain your reasoning.* ◼

Endocytosis and exocytosis move materials in bulk

Most ions and small molecules move across the cell membrane by one or more of the passive and active transport mechanisms just described. However, some molecules are too big to be transported by these methods. To move large molecules or transport several kinds of molecules in bulk, some cells resort to endocytosis and/or exocytosis. These two processes are based on the same principle but have different directions of movement. **Endocytosis** moves materials into the cell, and **exocytosis** moves materials out of the cell.

Figure 3.10 shows the processes of endocytosis and exocytosis. In endocytosis, molecules dissolved in the extracellular fluid are surrounded by a pocket formed by an infolding of the plasma membrane. Eventually the pocket

pinches off, forming a membrane-bound **vesicle** within the cell. To facilitate the selection of the right molecules for endocytosis, some vesicles have receptors on their surface that bind only to certain specific molecules. Insulin and certain enzymes enter cells by this method. Other vesicles are nonselective, engulfing whatever is in the extracellular fluid, such as nutrients and water. Vesicles of this type are often found in cells lining the digestive tract. Some white blood cells engulf and destroy whole bacteria by endocytosis (Chapter 9).

In exocytosis, a vesicle already present within the cell fuses with the plasma membrane and releases its contents into the fluid surrounding the cell. This is how certain cells release toxic waste products, get rid of indigestible material, or secrete their special products.

Information can be transferred across the plasma membrane

Receptor proteins that span the plasma membrane can receive and transmit information across the membrane. The information received by receptor proteins generally causes something to happen within the cell even though no molecules cross the membrane.

Figure 3.11 illustrates how a receptor protein works. A molecule approaches the membrane and binds to a specific *receptor site* in a lock-and-key fashion. This binding triggers a series of biochemical events that ultimately cause changes within the cell. Receptor proteins

— Extracellular environment
— Plasma membrane
— Cytoplasm
— Vesicle

a) Endocytosis. In endocytosis, material is surrounded by the cell membrane and brought into the cell.

b) Exocytosis. In exocytosis, a membranous vesicle fuses with the plasma membrane, expelling its contents outside the cell.

c) Photomicrograph showing various stages of endocytosis.

Figure 3.10 **Endocytosis and exocytosis.**

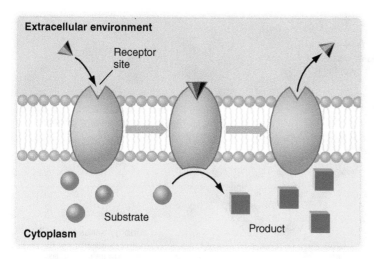

Extracellular environment

Receptor site

Substrate

Product

Cytoplasm

Figure 3.11 Receptor protein action. A specific molecule approaches a receptor site on a receptor protein and binds to it. The binding of the molecule to the receptor protein causes a series of chemical reactions within the cell. In this example, a particular cellular product (the squares) is produced from substrate molecules (the circles).

are highly specific for a particular molecule or a group of similar molecules. For example, the receptor protein for the hormone insulin responds only to insulin and not to any other hormone. Furthermore, different cells have different sets of receptor proteins, which explains why some cells and tissues respond to a particular hormone and others do not.

We discuss receptor proteins and hormones in more detail in when we review the endocrine system. For now, remember that certain molecules can influence what happens inside a cell merely by coming in contact with the cell's outer surface.

The sodium-potassium pump helps maintain cell volume

Probably the most critical task facing a cell is maintaining its volume. Why? Recall that the plasma membrane is soft and flexible. It cannot withstand much stretching or high fluid pressures. Furthermore, cells tend to accumulate certain materials depending on what is available in their *extracellular* environment (the area outside the cell, beyond the plasma membrane). Cells already contain a nucleus and organelles. In addition, they produce or stockpile molecules, including amino acids, sugars, lipids, ions, and many others. These molecules are necessary for the cell to function normally, but they represent a lot of solute particles within the cell.

Because water can diffuse across the plasma membrane rather easily, you might expect that water would diffuse

into the cell, toward the high cytoplasmic solute concentration. This inward diffusion would increase cell volume, eventually causing the cell to swell and even rupture.

The only way to avoid this is for the cell to keep the solute concentration in its cytoplasm identical to the solute concentration of the extracellular fluid. Then there is no net driving force for the diffusion of water. What the cell actually does is get rid of ions it *doesn't* need in large quantities (primarily sodium) in exchange for those it must stockpile. This is the primary function of a specialized protein embedded in the cell membrane called the sodium-potassium pump.

Figure 3.12a shows how the sodium-potassium pump works. The pump has three binding sites for sodium that are accessible from inside the cell. The binding of three cytoplasmic sodium ions triggers the breakdown of an ATP molecule to ADP and an inorganic phosphate. The energy released by ATP causes the pump to change shape, expelling the sodium ions and exposing two binding sites for potassium that are accessible only from outside the cell. The binding of potassium triggers another change of shape, and the potassium ions are transported into the cell.

One effect of this three sodium/two potassium exchange is to lower slightly the number of ions within the cell. More importantly, the plasma membrane is much more permeable to potassium than to sodium because it contains many potassium channels but very few sodium channels. Effectively, the cell keeps the number of sodium ions in the cytoplasm low by pumping them out again just as soon as a few leak in. The inward active transport of potassium does not increase the intracellular potassium concentration very much because they can leak back out so easily.

As **Figure 3.12b** shows, the sodium-potassium pump effectively controls cell volume. To reduce its volume, the cell increases the activity of the sodium-potassium pumps, getting rid of more sodium than usual. Water also exits to maintain osmotic equilibrium. To expand its volume, the cell lowers the activity of the pumps and retains water along with the extra sodium. Because potassium can diffuse so quickly no matter how much is pumped, the rate of potassium transport by the pumps is not relevant to the control of cell volume.

A single red blood cell may have over a hundred sodium-potassium pumps in its plasma membrane. In addition, the pump is essential to the ability of nerve cells to generate an electric current. We discuss the sodium-potassium pump in more detail when we review the nervous system (Chapter 11).

Quick Check *If a cell's sodium-potassium pumps are poisoned so that they stop working, will the cell tend to swell, shrink, or stay the same? Explain.* ▪

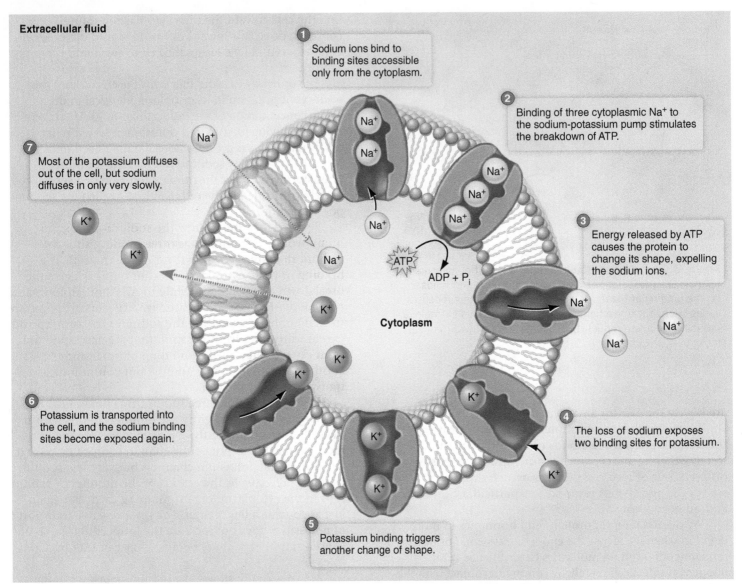

Extracellular fluid

1. Sodium ions bind to binding sites accessible only from the cytoplasm.

2. Binding of three cytoplasmic Na$^+$ to the sodium-potassium pump stimulates the breakdown of ATP.

3. Energy released by ATP causes the protein to change its shape, expelling the sodium ions.

4. The loss of sodium exposes two binding sites for potassium.

5. Potassium binding triggers another change of shape.

6. Potassium is transported into the cell, and the sodium binding sites become exposed again.

7. Most of the potassium diffuses out of the cell, but sodium diffuses in only very slowly.

Cytoplasm

ATP

ADP + P$_i$

a) The cell membrane contains Na$^+$-K$^+$ pumps, and also channels that permit the rapid outward diffusion of K$^+$ but only a slow inward diffusion of Na$^+$.

Key:

Active transport of Na$^+$

Sodium-potassium pump

Diffusion of K$^+$

Diffusion of Na$^+$

Diffusion of H$_2$O

In the steady-state, the rate of outward sodium transport equals the rate of inward diffusion.

When the rate of outward sodium transport exceeds inward diffusion, water diffuses out and the cell shrinks.

When the rate of outward sodium transport is less than the rate of inward diffusion, water diffuses in and the cell swells.

b) The rate of transport by the Na$^+$-K$^+$ pumps determines cell volume.

Figure 3.12 **Control of cell volume by the sodium-potassium pump (Na$^+$-K$^+$ pump)**

Isotonic extracellular fluid also maintains cell volume

Tonicity refers to the relative concentrations of solutes in two fluids (*tonic* means "strength" or "tone"). Because water can diffuse across the cell membrane so easily, the ability of a human cell to control its volume also depends on the tonicity of the extracellular fluid (Figure 3.13).

Extracellular fluid that is **isotonic** (Greek *isos*, meaning "equal") has the same solute concentration as the *intracellular* fluid. Cells maintain a normal volume in isotonic extracellular solutions because the concentration of water is the same inside and out. In humans, isotonic extracellular fluid is equivalent to about 9 grams of salt dissolved in a liter of solution. Regulatory mechanisms in the body ensure that the extracellular fluid solute concentration remains relatively constant at that level.

When cells are placed in a **hypertonic** solution, one with a concentration of solutes *higher* than the intracellular fluid, water diffuses out of the cells, and the cells shrink. Eventually this impairs normal function and the cells die.

Conversely, when cells are placed in a **hypotonic** solution with a *lower* concentration of solutes than intracellular fluid, water enters the cells and causes them to swell. Pure water is the most hypotonic solution possible. Most human cells quickly swell, burst, and die when placed in pure water.

↩ **Recap** **Molecules may move across the plasma membrane by diffusion, by passive or active transport, or by endocytosis/exocytosis. Sodium-potassium exchange pumps in the cell membrane are essential for the regulation of cell volume. In addition, homeostatic regulatory processes keep the tonicity of the extracellular fluid relatively constant.** ▪

3.5 Internal structures carry out specific functions

So far we have discussed the plasma membrane that surrounds the cell. Now we move inside the cell, where we find a number of different membrane-bound and non-membrane-bound structures. The membrane-bound structures are called *organelles*, because they are like tiny organs in that they have a specific function to perform. Figure 3.14 presents a cutaway view of an animal cell with its nucleus and organelles.

The nucleus controls the cell

The most conspicuous organelle of a living eukaryote is its *nucleus* (Figure 3.15). As the information center of a cell, the nucleus contains most of the cell's genetic material in the form of long molecules of DNA. (As you will learn, mitochondria have their own DNA.) Ultimately, DNA controls nearly all the activities of a cell. Details of how DNA controls cellular function are discussed when we review cell reproduction and genetic inheritance (Chapters 17 and 19).

The outer surface of the nucleus consists of a double-layered membrane, called the *nuclear membrane*, that keeps the DNA within the nucleus. The nuclear membrane is bridged by *nuclear pores* that are too small for DNA to pass through but that permit the passage of certain small proteins and RNA molecules.

Within the nucleus is a dense region called the **nucleolus**, where the components of ribosomes (RNA and ribosomal proteins) are synthesized. The components pass through the nuclear pores, to be assembled into ribosomes in the cytoplasm.

Ribosomes are responsible for protein synthesis

Ribosomes are small structures composed of RNA and certain proteins that are either floating freely in the cytosol or are attached to the endoplasmic reticulum, the cell organelle that synthesizes most biological molecules. Ribosomes are responsible for making specific proteins. They assemble amino acids into proteins by connecting the

Isotonic	Hypertonic	Hypotonic
9 grams of salt in 1 liter of solution	18 grams of salt in 1 liter of solution	Pure water

a) Water movement into and out of human red blood cells placed in isotonic, hypertonic, and hypotonic solutions. The amount of water movement is indicated by the sizes of the arrows.

b) Scanning of electron micrographs of red blood cells placed in similar solutions.

Figure 3.13 The effect of extracellular fluid tonicity on cell volume.

☑ *Suppose a woman runs a marathon on a hot summer day and becomes extremely dehydrated. Would you expect that her extracellular fluid would be isotonic, hypotonic, or hypertonic? Predict what might happen to her red blood cells.*

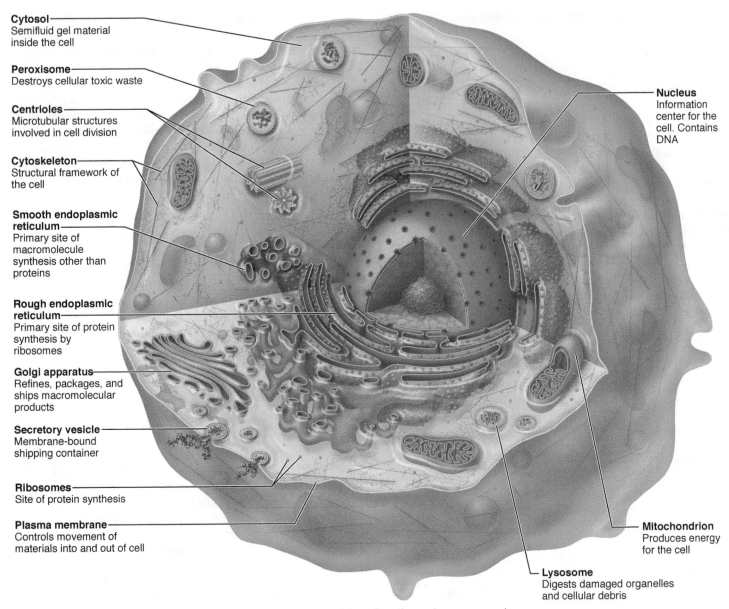

Cytosol
Semifluid gel material inside the cell

Peroxisome
Destroys cellular toxic waste

Centrioles
Microtubular structures involved in cell division

Cytoskeleton
Structural framework of the cell

Smooth endoplasmic reticulum
Primary site of macromolecule synthesis other than proteins

Rough endoplasmic reticulum
Primary site of protein synthesis by ribosomes

Golgi apparatus
Refines, packages, and ships macromolecular products

Secretory vesicle
Membrane-bound shipping container

Ribosomes
Site of protein synthesis

Plasma membrane
Controls movement of materials into and out of cell

Nucleus
Information center for the cell. Contains DNA

Mitochondrion
Produces energy for the cell

Lysosome
Digests damaged organelles and cellular debris

Figure 3.14 A typical animal cell. Not shown in this cell are cilia, a flagellum, glycogen granules, or fat deposits, as only certain cells have these features.

Nucleolus

Nuclear membrane

A transmission electron micrograph (× 6,000) of the nucleus of an animal cell

Nuclear pores

Nuclear membrane

Figure 3.15 The nucleus. The nucleus contains the cell's genetic material. The nucleolus produces the protein and RNA components of ribosomes. These components exit the nucleus through nuclear pores.

appropriate amino acids in the correct sequence according to an RNA template. We describe this process in more detail in when we review how cells reproduce (Chapter 17).

Ribosomes that are attached to the endoplasmic reticulum release their proteins into the folds of the endoplasmic reticulum. Many of these proteins are packaged in membrane-bound vesicles, transported to the cell membrane, and secreted. Free-floating ribosomes generally produce proteins for immediate use by the cell, such as enzymes that serve as catalysts for chemical reactions within the cytoplasmic fluid.

The endoplasmic reticulum is the manufacturing center

The **endoplasmic reticulum (ER)**, in conjunction with its attached ribosomes, synthesizes most of the chemical compounds made by the cell. If a cell were an industrial city, then the ER would be the city's steel mills, sawmills, and chemical plants. Like the output of a steel mill, the materials manufactured by the ER are often not in their final form. They are refined and packaged by the Golgi apparatus, discussed later.

Figure 3.16 shows the structure of the ER and its role in the manufacture of proteins and other materials. The ER is an extensively folded, membranous system surrounding a fluid-filled space. A portion of the ER connects to the nuclear membrane. Some regions of the ER's outer surface are dotted with ribosomes, giving those regions, called *rough ER*, a granular appearance. Regions without ribosomes are called *smooth ER*.

The rough ER is involved in the synthesis of proteins, as you may guess from the presence of ribosomes. Most of the proteins synthesized by the attached ribosomes are released into the

fluid-filled space of the ER. Eventually they enter the smooth ER, where they are packaged for transfer to the Golgi apparatus.

The smooth ER synthesizes macromolecules other than protein. Most notable among these are the lipids, including some hormones. Numerous enzymes embedded in the inner surface of the ER membrane facilitate the chemical reactions necessary for macromolecule synthesis.

The smooth ER is also responsible for packaging the proteins and lipids for delivery to the Golgi apparatus. Newly synthesized proteins and lipids collect in the outermost layers of smooth ER. There, small portions of the fluid-filled space are surrounded by ER membrane and pinched off, forming vesicles that contain fluid, proteins, and lipids. The vesicles migrate to the Golgi apparatus, fuse with the Golgi apparatus membrane, and release their contents into the Golgi apparatus for further processing.

☑ Quick Check *The cells of the pancreas make large quantities of proteins that are constantly secreted outside the cell. Would you expect a pancreatic cell to have a relatively large or small number of ribosomes, and would you expect it to have a lot of smooth or rough ER (compared to a cell that does not secrete proteins)?* ▪

The Golgi apparatus refines, packages, and ships

The **Golgi apparatus** is the cell's refining, packaging, and shipping center. To continue our analogy of the cell as an industrial city, here is where steel bars are shaped into nails and screws, raw lumber assembled into doors and window frames, and grain turned into bread.

Figure 3.17 diagrams the structure of the Golgi apparatus and the processes that occur there. In cross section

Vesicle

Smooth ER

Nucleus

Rough ER

Figure 3.16 The endoplasmic reticulum (ER). The rough ER is studded with ribosomes, where proteins are made. The smooth ER packages the proteins and other products of the ER and prepares them for shipment to the Golgi apparatus in vesicles.

Figure 3.17 The Golgi apparatus. The Golgi apparatus receives substances from the ER, refines them into final products, and packages them into vesicles for their final destinations.

the Golgi apparatus appears as a series of interconnected fluid-filled spaces surrounded by membrane, much like a stack of plates. Like the ER, it contains enzymes that further refine the products of the ER into final form.

The contents of the Golgi apparatus move outward by a slow but continuous process. At the outermost layer of the Golgi apparatus, the products are finally ready to be packaged into vesicles and shipped to their final destinations.

Vesicles: Membrane-bound storage and shipping containers

Vesicles are membrane-bound spheres that enclose something within the cell. There are several types of vesicles, each with a different origin and purpose.

Vesicles that ship and store cellular products These vesicles enclose and transport the products of the ER and Golgi apparatus. Each vesicle contains only one product out of the thousands of substances made by the Golgi apparatus.

The contents of each vesicle depend on certain proteins in the vesicle membrane that act as "shipping labels." They determine which product is put into the vesicle and where the vesicle is sent. If a vesicle's products are not immediately needed it remains in the cell cytoplasm, like a box stored in a warehouse awaiting shipment.

Secretory vesicles Secretory vesicles contain products destined for export from the cell. They migrate to the plasma membrane and release their contents outside the cell by exocytosis. Because most secretory products are made in the Golgi apparatus, secretory vesicles generally derive from Golgi apparatus membrane.

Endocytotic vesicles These structures enclose bacteria and raw materials from the extracellular environment. They bring them into the cell by endocytosis.

Peroxisomes and lysosomes These vesicles contain enzymes so powerful that they must be kept within the vesicle to avoid damaging the rest of the cell. Both are produced by the Golgi apparatus. **Figure 3.18** shows their functions.

The enzymes in **peroxisomes** destroy various toxic wastes produced in the cell, including hydrogen peroxide (H_2O_2). They also destroy compounds that have entered the cell from outside, such as alcohol. The detoxification process occurs entirely within the peroxisome.

Lysosomes (from the Greek *lysis*, meaning "dissolution," and *soma*, meaning "body") contain powerful digestive enzymes. Lysosomes fuse with endocytotic vesicles within the cell, digesting bacteria and other large objects. Lysosomes also perform certain housekeeping tasks, such as dissolving and removing damaged mitochondria and other cellular debris. When their digestive task is complete they become "residual bodies," analogous to small bags of compacted waste. Residual bodies can be stored in the cell, but usually their contents are eliminated from the cell by exocytosis.

Mitochondria provide energy

Nearly all of a cell's functions require energy. Energy is available in the chemical bonds of the food we eat, but cells cannot use it directly. Most energy in ingested nutrients must be converted to a more usable form before it can power the chemical and physical activities of living cells.

Mitochondria are the organelles responsible for providing most of this usable energy; they are often called the cells' "power plants." Not surprisingly, their number within different cells varies widely according to the energy requirements of the cells. A cell with a high rate of energy consumption, such as a muscle cell, may contain over 1,000 mitochondria.

Figure 3.19 shows a photograph of a single mitochondrion and diagrams its structure and function. A smooth outer membrane, similar to the plasma membrane, covers the entire surface. Within the outer membrane is an inner membrane

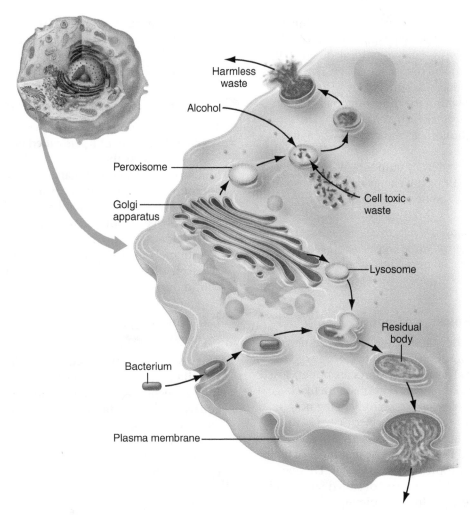

Harmless
waste

Alcohol

Peroxisome

Golgi
apparatus

Cell toxic
waste

Lysosome

Residual
body

Bacterium

Plasma membrane

Figure 3.18 Lysosomes and peroxisomes. Lysosomes formed by the Golgi apparatus fuse with endocytotic vesicles containing a bacterium. Following digestion of the bacterium the residual waste is excreted by exocytosis. Peroxisomes take up toxic wastes (including alcohol) and degrade them to harmless waste, which is also excreted.

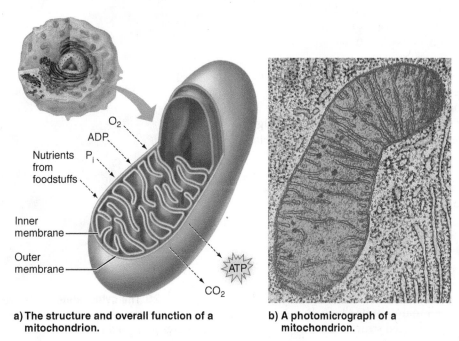

O_2

ADP

Nutrients
from
foodstuffs

P_i

Inner
membrane

Outer
membrane

ATP

CO_2

a) **The structure and overall function of a mitochondrion.**

b) **A photomicrograph of a mitochondrion.**

Figure 3.19 Mitochondria.

with numerous folds that increase its surface area. The inner membrane and the fluid in its folds contain hundreds of protein enzymes, which serve as catalysts to break down chemical bonds in our food and release the energy. This process consumes oxygen and produces carbon dioxide.

The energy liberated within the mitochondria is used to create high-energy molecules such as ATP. ATP is then exported from the mitochondria to the cytosol, where it is available as a quick source of energy for the cell. Like electric power, ATP is useful for a variety of purposes. We have already seen one of its uses—providing the energy used to transport sodium and potassium across the plasma membrane.

✅**Quick Check** *While studying a human cell under a microscope, you spot a small, round organelle that seems to have a single membrane. Is it more likely to be a nucleus, ribosome, vesicle, or mitochondrion? What might it contain?* ▪

Fat and glycogen: Sources of energy

The mitochondria generally manufacture ATP as it is needed. To avoid the possibility of running out of fuel, some cells store energy in raw form. These energy stores are not enclosed in any membrane-bound container. They are more like large piles of coal on the ground, awaiting delivery to the power plants (mitochondria) for conversion to electricity (ATP).

Some cells store raw energy as lipids (fat). Our so-called fat cells are so specialized for this purpose that most of their volume consists of large droplets of stored lipids. Dieting and exercise tend to reduce the amount of stored fat—that is, they make the fat cells leaner. However, dieting and exercise do not reduce their number. The cells are available to store fat again, which is why it is so hard to keep lost weight off.

Other cells store energy as glycogen granules (review Figure 2.15). Muscle cells rely on glycogen granules rather than on fat deposits because the energy stored in the chemical bonds of glycogen can be used to produce ATP more quickly than the energy derived from fat.

↩ **Recap The nucleus contains most of the cell's genetic material. Ribosomes are responsible for protein assembly. The endoplasmic reticulum manufactures most other cellular products in rough form. The Golgi apparatus refines cellular products and packages them into membrane-bound vesicles. Some vesicles store, ship, and secrete cellular products; others digest and remove toxic waste and cellular debris. Mitochondria manufacture ATP for the cell.** ▪

3.6 Cells have structures for support and movement

The soft plasma membrane is supported by an internal scaffolding that helps the cell maintain its shape. In addition, some cells have specialized structures to help

them move around, and all cells contain structures that are involved in moving cellular components during cell division. Structural elements for support and movement include the cytoskeleton, cilia and flagella, and centrioles.

The cytoskeleton supports the cell

The **cytoskeleton** (Figure 3.20) consists of a loosely structured network of fibers called *microtubules* and *microfilaments*. As their names imply, microtubules are tiny hollow tubes, and microfilaments are thin solid fibers. Both are composed of protein. They attach to each other and to proteins in the plasma membrane, called *glycoproteins*, which typically have carbohydrate group components.

The cytoskeleton forms a framework for the soft plasma membrane, much as tent poles support a nylon tent. The cytoskeleton also supports and anchors the other structures within the cell.

Cilia and flagella are specialized for movement

A few cells have hairlike **cilia** (singular: cilium) or longer **flagella** (singular: flagellum) that extend from the surface. Cilia are generally only 2 to 10 microns long (1 micron equals one-millionth of a meter). In cells that have them, cilia are numerous. Cilia move materials along the surface of a cell with a brushing motion. They are common on the surfaces of cells that line the airways and in certain ducts within the body.

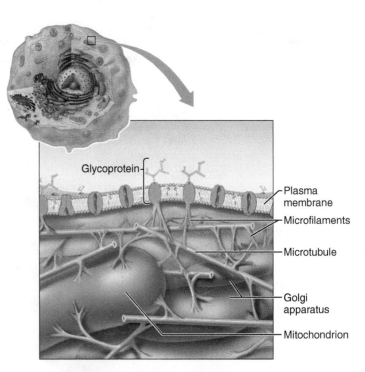

Figure 3.20 The cytoskeleton. The cytoskeleton consists of microtubules and microfilaments that attach to and support the cell's organelles and plasma membrane.

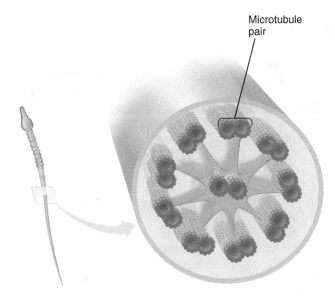

Figure 3.21 **Flagella.** A cross-sectional view of a flagellum showing that it is composed of nine pairs of microtubules surrounding a central pair.

In humans, flagella (approximately 200 microns long) are found only on sperm cells (Figure 3.21). The whiplike movement of the flagellum moves the entire sperm cell from one place to another.

Cilia and flagella are similar in structure. They are composed primarily of protein microtubules held together by connecting elements and surrounded by a plasma membrane. Nine pairs of fused microtubules surround two single microtubules in the center. The entire structure bends when temporary linkages form between adjacent pairs of microtubules, causing the pairs to slide past each other. The formation and release of these temporary bonds requires energy in the form of ATP.

Centrioles are involved in cell division

Centrioles are short, rodlike microtubular structures located near the nucleus. Centrioles are essential to the process of cell division because they participate in aligning and dividing the genetic material of the cell. We discuss centrioles when we describe how a cell divides in two (Chapter 17).

↩ Recap **The cytoskeleton forms a supportive framework for the cell. Cilia and flagella are specialized for movement, and centrioles are essential to cell division.** ▪

3.7 Cells use and transform matter and energy

Living cells can release the energy stored in the chemical bonds of molecules and use it to build, store, and break down still other molecules as required to maintain life. **Metabolism** is the sum of all of the chemical reactions in the organism.

a) **A linear pathway.**

b) **A cyclic pathway in which B through E repeat over and over again.**

Figure 3.22 **Types of metabolic pathways.**

In a single cell, thousands of different chemical reactions are possible at any one time. Some of these chemical reactions are organized as metabolic pathways in which one reaction follows after another in orderly and predictable patterns (Figure 3.22). Some metabolic pathways are linear, in which the **product** (or end material) from one chemical reaction becomes the **substrate** (starting material) for the next. Other metabolic pathways form a cycle in which substrate molecules enter and product molecules exit, but the basic chemical cycle repeats over and over again.

There are two basic types of metabolic pathways:

1. **Anabolism** (from the Greek *anabole*, meaning "a throwing up"): molecules are assembled into larger molecules that contain more energy, a process that requires energy. The assembly of a protein from many amino acids is an example of an anabolic pathway.
2. **Catabolism** (Greek *katabole*, meaning "a throwing down"): larger molecules are broken down, a process that releases energy. The breakdown of glucose into water, carbon dioxide, and energy is an example of a catabolic pathway.

Two facts are important about metabolic pathways. First, nearly every chemical reaction requires a specific enzyme. The cell regulates and controls the rates of chemical reactions through the specificity and availability of key enzymes. Second, the metabolic activities of a living cell require a lot of energy. Energy is required for building the complex macromolecules found only in living organisms, such as proteins, DNA, cholesterol, and so on. Energy is also used to power cellular activities such as active transport and muscle contraction.

Cells get their energy by catabolism of molecules that serve as chemical stores of energy. The most immediately useful source of energy, a sort of "energy cash" if you will, is ATP. The energy in ATP is locked in the chemical bond between the second and third phosphate group. Every time the third phosphate group is removed from an ATP molecule, energy is released that the cell can use to do work. The reaction is reversible, meaning that the application of energy to ADP in the presence of a phosphate group can

Health & Wellness

Do Antioxidant Supplements Slow the Rate of Cellular Aging?

The 100 trillion cells in your body are slowly aging. Some will live just a couple of months before they die and are replaced by newer cells. Others will live as long as you do, though they may show signs of aging. What causes cells to age? And most importantly, is there anything you can do to maintain your cells' good health and delay the aging process?

All cells produce waste products during the normal course of their metabolic activities. Some of these wastes are toxic. A predominant theory of cell aging is that these toxic substances may accumulate over time, eventually leading to an inability of the cell to function properly. One such group of toxic substances is *oxygen free radicals*—oxygen-containing molecules with an unpaired electron in the oxygen's outer shell. Because of that unpaired electron, oxygen free radicals (or just free radicals for short) are unstable molecules. They have a strong tendency to oxidize (remove electrons from) other molecules, damaging or destroying them in the process. Eventually an accumulation of molecular damage leads to a decline in cell function (aging).

Under normal circumstances certain enzymes produced within the cell and several vitamins defend our cells against free radicals. Collectively these enzymes and vitamins are called *antioxidants*. Some of the naturally occurring antioxidant enzymes are so powerful that they must be stored within peroxisomes in the cell so that they do not damage the cell itself. As their name implies, antioxidants inactivate free radicals (think of them as mopping up cellular garbage). The antioxidants include vitamins E, C, beta-carotene, and the enzyme superoxide dismutase.

The importance of the body's natural antioxidants in maintaining cellular health has led to the popular belief that taking high doses of antioxidants as dietary supplements could slow the cellular aging process and even the course of certain diseases, such as cancer. That's why there has been so much hype lately about the alleged health benefits of taking antioxidant vitamins or eating antioxidant-rich foods. (Try Googling the search term "antioxidants" and see how many hits you get.) But a word of caution should be interjected here. Animal studies have been encouraging but not definitive, and the few human studies have yielded mixed results. In its fact sheet on cancer and antioxidants, the National Cancer Institute describes in some detail how antioxidants "might" prevent cancer, but stops short of recommending antioxidant supplements for cancer treatment.[1]

So should you be taking antioxidant supplements, just in case? It's an open question with no real answer. The evidence is not yet convincing that you will live a healthier or longer life, but on the other hand there is no real evidence that moderate doses of antioxidants do any harm, either. Perhaps time and more research will tell us more, but we're just not there yet. ∎

[1]http://www.cancer.gov/cancertopics/factsheet/prevention/antioxidants

---

phosphorylate (add a phosphate group to) ADP again, re-creating ATP. The equation is written as:

$$ATP \leftrightarrow ADP + P_i + energy$$

In this equation, P_i is used as the abbreviation for the inorganic phosphate (PO_4^{-2}) to distinguish it from the chemical symbol for pure phosphorus (P).

Glucose provides the cell with energy

Cells can use a variety of fuels to make the ATP energy "cash" they need. The most readily available fuel generally is glucose, derived either from food recently eaten or from stored glycogen. However, if glucose is not available, cells may turn to stored fats and even proteins for fuel. Regardless of the fuel used, most of the ATP is produced by very similar metabolic pathways. Let's look at the use of glucose as a fuel source first, and then we'll describe briefly how other fuels are used.

Recall that glucose is a six-carbon sugar molecule with the chemical formula $C_6H_{12}O_6$. This seemingly simple little molecule packs a lot of potential energy in its chemical bonds. Just as a gallon of gas provides enough energy to power your car for 25 to 30 miles, a single glucose molecule provides the cell enough energy to produce approximately 36 molecules of ATP (Figure 3.23).

The production of ATP from glucose occurs in four stages, summarized in Figure 3.24:

1. *Glycolysis:* The six-carbon glucose molecule is split into two 3-carbon pyruvate molecules. Energy is required to get the process started.
2. *The preparatory step:* In preparation for the citric acid cycle, pyruvate enters a mitochondrion. A series of chemical reactions yields a two-carbon molecule called *acetyl CoA*, plus some energy.
3. *The citric acid cycle:* An acetyl CoA molecule is broken down completely by mitochondrial enzymes, and its energy is released. Most of the energy is captured by certain high-energy electron transport molecules.

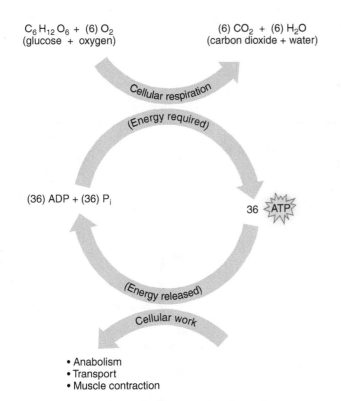

$C_6 H_{12} O_6$ + (6) O_2
(glucose + oxygen)

(6) CO_2 + (6) H_2O
(carbon dioxide + water)

Cellular respiration

(Energy required)

(36) ADP + (36) P_i

36 ATP

(Energy released)

Cellular work

- Anabolism
- Transport
- Muscle contraction

Figure 3.23 Glucose provides energy for the cell. The complete catabolism of glucose uses oxygen, produces carbon dioxide and water, and generates 36 molecules of ATP that can be used to do cellular work.

4. *The electron transport system:* Most of the energy derived from the original glucose molecule is used to phosphorylate ADP, producing high-energy ATP.

Glycolysis: Glucose is split into two pyruvate molecules Figure 3.25 illustrates **glycolysis**, the first stage in the complete breakdown of glucose (*glyco-* means "sweet," referring to sugar, and *-lysis* means "to break"). Glycolyis occurs within the cell's cytoplasm, not within mitochondria. In the first 5 of the 10 chemical reactions that constitute glycolysis, glucose is broken into two 3-carbon molecules called *glyceraldehyde-3-phosphate* (PGAL). Two of these steps require the input of energy (two molecules of ATP)—like putting a match to a bonfire.

Then, each of the two PGAL molecules is converted in a series of steps to *pyruvate*. This process requires several more enzymes. At several of these steps, enzymes carrying high-energy phosphate groups pass their phosphate groups directly to ADP, producing ATP. The process, called *substrate-level phosphorylation*, does not require oxygen. During glycolysis, four molecules of ATP are produced by substrate-level phosphorylation.

The rest of the potentially usable energy from glycolysis is released as high-energy hydrogen ions (H^+) and electrons (e^-). Most of these are picked up by a *coenzyme* called **NAD⁺** (nicotinamide adenine dinucleotide). A **coenzyme** is a small molecule that assists an enzyme by transporting small molecular groups. In this case NAD⁺ functions as an

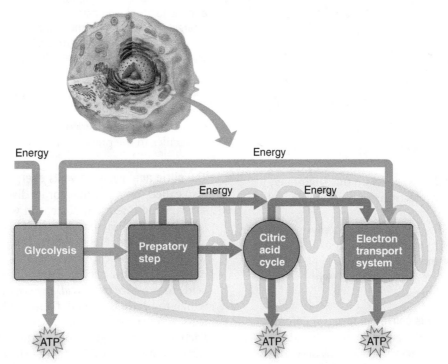

Energy

Energy

Energy

Energy

Glycolysis

Prepatory step

Citric acid cycle

Electron transport system

ATP

ATP

ATP

Figure 3.24 Cellular respiration: An overview. Glycolysis occurs in the cytoplasm. The products of glycolysis, two molecules of pyruvate, enter mitochondria. The preparatory step and the citric acid cycle result in the complete breakdown of the two pyruvate molecules but only limited ATP production. Most of the ATP is produced in the electron transport system, using energy harvested from the first three steps.

Figure 3.25 Glycolysis. This initial breakdown of glucose to two molecules of glyceraldehyde-3-phosphate (PGAL) requires energy. Thereafter, energy is generated as the two PGAL molecules are further degraded to two molecules of pyruvate.

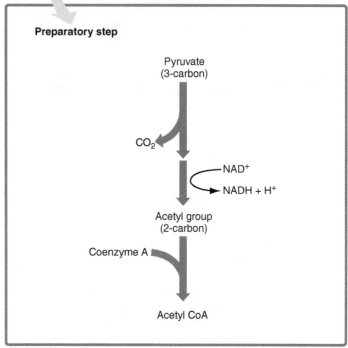

Figure 3.26 The preparatory step. Pyruvate is transported into a mitochondrion and catabolized to a two-carbon acetyl group. Energy is released, and the freed carbon is given off as carbon dioxide waste. The acetyl group combines with coenzyme A for delivery to the next step, the citric acid cycle.

energy-carrying molecule. NAD^+ picks up one high-energy H^+ ion and two high-energy electrons to become the higher-energy molecule **NADH**.

So far, then, the net energy yield from glycolysis is only two molecules of ATP (four were formed, but two were used to get the process started) and two molecules of NADH. The energy carried by NADH is used to make ATP within the mitochondria, as we'll see later.

The preparatory step: Pyruvate is converted to acetyl CoA At this point the pyruvate molecules enter the mitochondria, where all the rest of the ATP-generating reactions occur. In a series of steps preparatory to the citric acid cycle, a two-carbon *acetyl group* and a carbon dioxide (CO_2) waste molecule are formed from each pyruvate (**Figure 3.26**). Each acetyl group is then joined with another coenzyme (called *coenzyme A*) to

form acetyl CoA, which delivers the acetyl group to the *citric acid cycle*. A net gain of an additional two NADH molecules occurs from the conversion of two pyruvates to two acetyl CoA molecules in the preparatory step.

The citric acid cycle harvests energy The **citric acid cycle**, also called the *Krebs cycle* for its discoverer, Hans Krebs, is a series of eight sequential steps in which each acetyl group is completely disassembled to CO_2 waste and various high-energy products (**Figure 3.27**). The citric acid cycle begins when acetyl CoA combines with the four-carbon fragment left over from the previous turn of the cycle (oxaloacetic acid) to produce *citric acid,* the six-carbon molecule for which the cycle is named. Citric acid is the starting substrate for seven reactions that end with oxaloacetic acid again. Each reaction is regulated by a different enzyme. The two carbons that are lost during the citric acid cycle are given off as CO_2 waste, and one ATP molecule is produced directly by substrate-level phosphorylation. The high-energy hydrogen ions and electrons removed at various points in the cycle are harvested in the form of three molecules of NADH and one

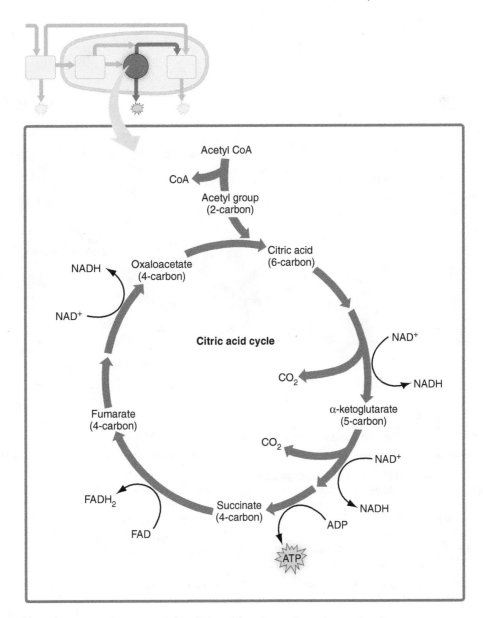

Figure 3.27 The citric acid cycle. A complete turn of the citric acid cycle produces two molecules of CO_2 waste, an ATP molecule, three molecules of NADH, and a molecule of $FADH_2$ for every 2-carbon acetyl group used as fuel. The cycle occurs twice for each molecule of glucose that undergoes glycolysis to produce two pyruvate molecules. The NADH and $FADH_2$ molecules carry high-energy hydrogen ions and electrons to the electron transport system, where their energy can be used to synthesize ATP.

molecule of another energy-carrying coenzyme called **FAD** (flavin adenine dinucleotide). FAD picks up two high-energy H^+ ions and two electrons to become **$FADH_2$**.

The electron transport system produces ATP So far, the glucose molecule has been completely dismantled and CO_2 has been generated as a waste product, but only four new ATP molecules have been generated. The rest of the energy is still in the electrons and hydrogen ions that are part of NADH and $FADH_2$.

At this point NADH and $FADH_2$ move to the inner membrane of the mitochondria and release their cargo to the **electron transport system** (Figure 3.28). Here, the energy-

rich electrons are transferred sequentially from one protein carrier molecule to another. The sequential transfer is important because it allows the energy in the electrons to be released in manageable quantities. The sequence of events is as follows:

1. NADH and $FADH_2$ release the H^+ and high-energy electrons they acquired in the citric acid cycle to a carrier protein of the electron transport system.
2. The electrons pass from one protein carrier molecule to the next in the electron transport system.
3. Each time an electron is transferred, the carrier molecule acquires some of its energy and the electron loses energy.

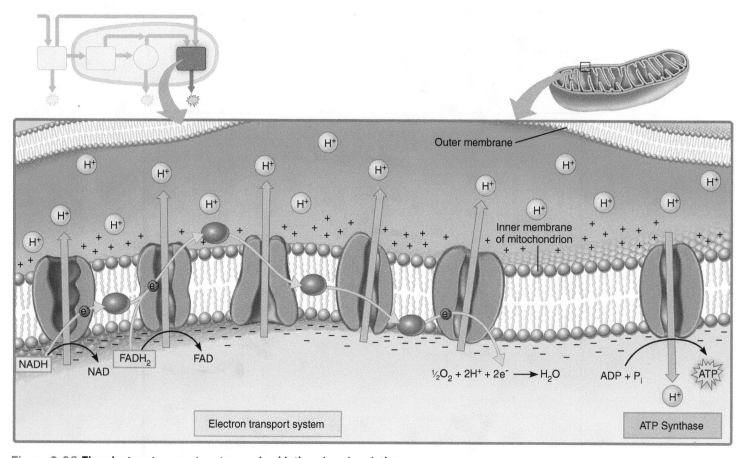

Figure 3.28 The electron transport system and oxidative phosphorylation. During electron transfer, the high-energy molecules of NADH (and FADH$_2$) give up electrons and hydrogen ions, releasing energy. The energy is used to transport hydrogen ions into the space between the two mitochondrial membranes. Diffusion of hydrogen ions back into the inner mitochondrial space provides the energy for the enzyme ATP synthase to synthesize ATP from ADP and inorganic phosphate (P$_i$). The process of using energy derived from the electron transport system to produce ATP by phosphorylation of ADP is called oxidative phosphorylation.

✓ *Explain in your own words what exactly is causing the ATP synthase to make ATP. Do NADH or FADH$_2$ interact directly with the ATP synthase?*

The carrier protein uses the energy to transport H$^+$ from the inner compartment of the mitochondria to the outer compartment.

The active transport of H$^+$ into the outer compartment of the mitochondria sets the stage for the actual production of ATP. Because the concentration of H$^+$ is now higher in the outer compartment than in the inner compartment, there is a concentration gradient that favors diffusion of H$^+$ back to the inner compartment. However, H$^+$ can diffuse only through special channels. These channels are actually an enzyme called **ATP synthase** that uses the energy derived from the diffusion of H$^+$ to catalyze the synthesis of ATP from ADP and P$_i$. Once it is formed, ATP leaves the inner compartment of the mitochondria via a special channel protein, to be used by the cell as an energy source.

As mentioned earlier, *phosphorylation* is the addition of a phosphate group. The process of producing ATP from

ADP plus P$_i$, using the energy obtained as electrons are transferred from one molecule to another in the electron transport system, is called **oxidative phosphorylation**. The term *oxidative* indicates that the process uses oxygen and that electrons have been removed.

By the time they have reached the end of the electron transport system, most of the energy of the electrons and H$^+$ has been spent. At this point the spent hydrogen ions and electrons combine with oxygen to form water, a waste product. The low-energy NAD$^+$ and FAD molecules, now lacking hydrogen ions and electrons, are recycled and used again. The ability to recycle NAD$^+$, FAD, and ADP increases cellular efficiency because it means that these do not need to be synthesized anew each time.

Cellular metabolic processes that use oxygen and produce carbon dioxide in the process of making ATP are collectively termed **cellular respiration**. Cellular respiration takes place entirely within mitochondria. Although some

ATP is made in the cytoplasm during glycolysis, glycolysis does not require oxygen. Indeed, glycolysis can proceed without oxygen because there are alternative metabolic pathways that pyruvate can take besides entering the preparatory step and citric acid cycle. In contrast, the citric acid cycle *is* considered to be part of cellular respiration, because although it does not use oxygen directly, it would soon come to a complete halt in the absence of oxygen.

✅**Quick Check** *If ATP synthase completely stopped working, could glycolysis or the citric acid cycle still produce any ATP? Explain.* ▪

Summary of energy production from glucose The most effective way to harvest the energy in any fuel, whether gasoline or glucose, is to release the energy *slowly*, under carefully controlled conditions. Holding a match to a gallon of gasoline results in a useless fire or even a potentially dangerous explosion, but burning it drop by drop in the pistons of your car allows the energy to be converted to mechanical work. Similarly, in a living cell, the whole point of glycolysis and cellular respiration is to release the energy in the chemical bonds of glucose *slowly* so that the energy can be harvested effectively.

That is exactly what the cell does (Figure 3.29). The complete breakdown of glucose during glycolysis, the

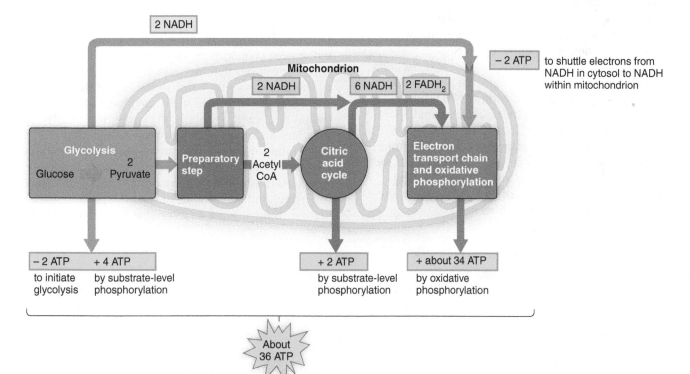

a) Most of the ATP generated during cellular respiration is synthesized in the electron transport system.

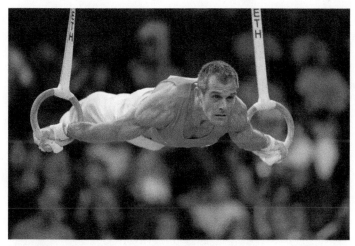

b) Cellular respiration powers the activities of humans and many other organisms.

Figure 3.29 **Cellular respiration: A recap.**

preparatory step, and the citric acid cycle are accomplished by a sequence of over 20 different chemical reactions, each controlled by an enzyme. The net yield of high-energy molecules (prior to the electron transport chain) is 4 molecules of ATP, 10 molecules of NADH, and 2 molecules of FADH$_2$. Each NADH carries sufficient energy to produce about 3 ATP molecules in the electron transport system. FADH$_2$ carries less energy, enters the electron transport chain at a lower energy point, and so produces only about 2 ATP molecules per FADH$_2$ molecule. Add it all up and you should get about 38 ATP molecules per glucose molecule.

But there's a catch. Two of the NADH (the two produced during glycolysis) were produced in the cytoplasm. Yet the electron transport system utilizes NADH located in the inner compartment of the mitochondria. Because the inner mitochondrial membrane is impermeable to NADH, the cytosolic NADH molecules release their H$^+$ ions and electrons, which are then transported across by transport proteins. Once inside, they may be picked up again by other NAD$^+$ molecules. But every transfer and active transport results in a small energy loss—in this case it's the equivalent of about two ATP molecules. Therefore, the net maximum yield of energy from a single glucose molecule is closer to 36 ATP molecules. In fact it may be even lower than that because some of the energy may be used directly to do other work for the cell, but for the sake of simplicity we'll settle on a number of 36.

Fats and proteins are additional energy sources

So far we have concentrated on the cellular catabolism of glucose. Normally the blood glucose concentration remains fairly constant even between meals because glycogen (the storage form of glucose in humans) is constantly being catabolized to replenish the glucose that is used by cells.

However, most of the body's energy reserves do not take the form of glycogen. In fact, the body stores only about 1% of its total energy reserves as glycogen; about 78% are stored as fats and 21% as protein. After glycogen, our bodies may utilize fats and proteins. Figure 3.30 illustrates the metabolic pathways for fat, glycogen, and protein.

Energy is constantly being transferred into and out of the body. Immediately after a meal, when plenty of glucose, lipids, and amino acids are readily available in the blood, we tend to use primarily glucose as an energy source. When we eat more calories than we can use immediately, some of the excess energy goes to replenish the body's stores of glycogen and the rest is converted to fat and stored in fat tissue. After we have not eaten for hours, the body uses first glycogen, then fats, and eventually even proteins for energy.

Pound for pound, fats carry more than twice the energy of carbohydrates such as glycogen. During fat catabolism, triglycerides (the storage form of fat) are first broken down to glycerol and fatty acids. The glycerol can be converted to glucose in the liver or it can be converted to pyruvic acid,

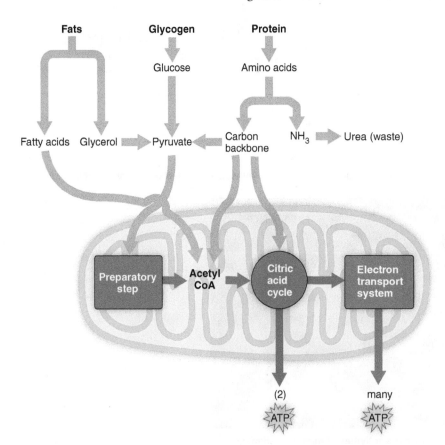

Figure 3.30 Metabolic pathways for fats, glycogen, and proteins as sources of cellular energy. All three sources produce pyruvate and acetyl groups. In addition, a few components of protein can enter the citric acid cycle directly.

which then enters the citric acid cycle. Enzymes break down the fatty acid tails to two-carbon acetyl groups, which also enter the citric acid cycle. Each molecule of triglyceride yields a great deal of ATP because the fatty acid tails are generally 16 to 18 carbons long and so generate many acetyl groups.

Proteins carry about the same amount of energy per pound as glycogen. Proteins are first broken down to amino acids, and the amine group ($—NH_2$) of each amino acid is removed. The carbon backbones then enter the citric acid cycle at various points, depending on the specific amino acid. The amine groups are converted to urea by the liver and then excreted in urine as waste.

Proteins serve primarily as enzymes and structural components of the body, not as a stored form of energy. Nevertheless, protein catabolism increases significantly during starvation. Prolonged protein catabolism causes muscle wasting, but at least it keeps the individual alive.

☑️**Quick Check** *If a person wants to lose weight, why is it better to reduce caloric intake moderately over a long period of time, rather than to just stop eating until the target weight is achieved?* ▪

Anaerobic pathways make energy available without oxygen

As we have seen, cellular respiration requires oxygen to complete the chemical reactions of the citric acid cycle and the electron transport chain. However, a small amount of ATP *can* be made in humans by anaerobic metabolism (without oxygen) for at least brief periods of time. Glycolysis, for example, is an anaerobic metabolic pathway. In the absence of oxygen, glucose is broken down to pyruvate (glycolysis occurs), but then the pyruvate cannot proceed through the citric acid cycle and electron transport chain (**Figure 3.31**). Instead, the pyruvate is converted to *lactic acid*. The buildup of lactic acid is what causes the burning sensation and cramps associated with muscle fatigue when not enough oxygen is available to muscle tissue. When oxygen becomes available again, the lactic acid is metabolized by aerobic pathways.

Figure 3.31 Anaerobic metabolism. In the absence of oxygen, glycolysis is the only ATP-producing step available. Glycolysis without oxygen results in lactic acid buildup.

Because glycolysis is the only step that can occur without oxygen, glucose (and glucose derived from glycogen) is the only fuel that can be used under anaerobic conditions. The amounts of ATP are very limited, however; only two molecules of ATP are produced per molecule of glucose instead of the usual 36.

↩️ **Recap** Metabolism refers to all of a cell's chemical processes. Metabolic pathways either create molecules and use energy (anabolism) or break them down and liberate energy (catabolism). The primary source of energy for a cell is ATP, produced within mitochondria by the complete breakdown of glucose to CO_2 and water. The process requires oxygen. A single molecule of glucose yields about 36 molecules of ATP. Fats and proteins can also be used to produce energy if necessary. ▪

Chapter Summary

Cells are classified according to their internal organization *p. 50*

- All cells have a plasma membrane that surrounds and encloses the cytoplasm.
- Eukaryotic cells have a nucleus.

Cell structure reflects cell function *p. 51*

- Limits to cell size are imposed by the mathematical relationship between cell volume and cell surface area.
- Various types of microscopes with magnifications up to 100,000-fold enable us to visualize cells and their structures.

A plasma membrane surrounds the cell *p. 53*

- The plasma membrane is a bilayer of phospholipids that also contains cholesterol and various proteins.

Molecules cross the plasma membrane in several ways *p. 54*

- Some molecules are transported across the plasma membrane passively (by diffusion), whereas others are transported by active processes requiring the expenditure of energy.
- Receptor proteins transfer information across the plasma membrane.
- The sodium-potassium pump is a plasma membrane protein with a critical role in the maintenance of cell volume.

Internal structures carry out specific functions *p. 61*

- The nucleus directs all of the cell's activities.
- Ribosomes, the endoplasmic reticulum, and the Golgi apparatus participate in the synthesis of life's molecules.
- Vesicles are membrane-bound spheres that transport, store, and ship cellular products and toxic or dangerous materials.
- Mitochondria make energy available for the cell in the form of the high-energy molecule ATP.

Cells have structures for support and movement *p. 66*

■ A cytoskeleton of microtubules and microfilaments serves as structural support and anchors the various organelles.

■ Cilia and flagella provide for movement in certain types of cells. Both cilia and flagella are made of pairs of protein microtubules.

Cells use and transform matter and energy *p. 67*

■ The creation and destruction of molecules either requires energy or liberates energy.

■ The most readily useful form of energy for cells is ATP.

■ The production of ATP from glucose requires four consecutive stages: glycolysis, a preparatory step, the citric acid cycle, and the electron transport system.

■ Cells can utilize glycogen, fats, or proteins for energy.

■ Only a small amount of ATP can be made in the absence of oxygen.

Terms You Should Know

active transport, *57*	metabolism, *67*
ATP synthase, *72*	mitochondria, *64*
citric acid cycle, *70*	NAD⁺, *69*
cytoskeleton, *66*	NADH, *70*
diffusion, *54*	osmosis, *55*
electron transport system, *71*	passive transport, *54*
endocytosis/exocytosis, *61*	plasma membrane, *50*
endoplasmic reticulum (ER), *63*	ribosome, *61*
glycolysis, *69*	sodium-potassium pump, *57*
Golgi apparatus, *63*	vesicle, *58*

Concept Review

Answers can be found in the Study Area in MasteringBiology.

1. Explain why being small is advantageous to a cell.
2. List the basic tenets of the *cell doctrine*.
3. Describe how phospholipids are oriented in the plasma membrane and why they orient naturally that way.
4. Define *passive transport* and name the three passive transport methods that are used to transport different molecules across the plasma membrane.
5. Compare and contrast endocytosis and exocytosis.
6. Describe the activity of the sodium-potassium pump and indicate its importance to the cell.
7. Explain what happens to cells placed in a high-salt or a low-salt environment, and why.
8. Define *vesicles* and name at least two different types of vesicles.
9. What are the four stages of ATP production from glucose, and which one yields the most ATP?
10. Describe what happens to a cell's ability to produce ATP when oxygen is not available.

Test Yourself

Answers can be found in Appendix A.

1. Which of the following adaptations would increase the surface area of a cell?
   a. increased number of mitochondria
   b. increased number of ribosomes
   c. presence of microvilli
   d. increased number of channel proteins
   e. changing a cell shape from cubical to spherical

2. Which of the following would be most likely to enter a cell by diffusion directly through the phospholipid bilayer?
   a. potassium ions
   b. steroid hormone
   c. hydrogen ions
   d. glucose
   e. sodium ions

3. Cells transport sodium ions out of the cell against the sodium concentration gradient. This is an example of:
   a. facilitated diffusion
   b. simple diffusion
   c. diffusion via channel proteins
   d. endocytosis
   e. active transport

4. Red blood cells placed into distilled water will:
   a. swell as water moves into the cells by osmosis
   b. shrink as sodium moves out of the cells by diffusion
   c. swell as water moves into the cells by active transport
   d. shrink as proteins move out of the cell by diffusion
   e. remain unchanged because of homeostatic mechanisms

5. Which organelles are most active during vigorous exercise?
   a. ribosomes
   b. endoplasmic reticulum
   c. mitochondria
   d. lysosomes
   e. cilia

6. Phagocytic white blood cells engulf and digest bacteria and cellular debris. Which organelles would be most involved in the digestion of the engulfed material?
   a. mitochondria
   b. lysosomes
   c. Golgi apparatus
   d. ribosomes
   e. endoplasmic reticulum

7. Some lymphocytes (white blood cells) synthesize and secrete defensive proteins known as antibodies. Which of the following represents the most likely path of these proteins from synthesis to secretion?
   a. endoplasmic reticulum—ribosomes—Golgi apparatus—vesicles—plasma membrane
   b. ribosomes—Golgi apparatus—vesicles—endoplasmic reticulum—plasma membrane
   c. ribosomes—Golgi apparatus—lysosome—endoplasmic reticulum—plasma membrane
   d. ribosomes—endoplasmic reticulum—Golgi apparatus—vesicles—plasma membrane
   e. ribosomes—lysosomes—endoplasmic reticulum—vesicles—Golgi apparatus

8. Which organelles would be active in liver cells that are detoxifying alcohol?
   a. Golgi apparatus
   b. lysosomes
   c. mitochondria
   d. endoplasmic reticulum
   e. peroxisomes

9. Cells lining the respiratory passages have numerous filamentous structures that sweep mucus and debris up and away from the lungs. These filamentous structures are:
   a. microtubules
   b. flagella
   c. cilia
   d. microfilaments
   e. microvilli

10. Which of the following is/are the most immediate source of energy for cellular work?
    a. glucose
    b. ATP
    c. glycogen
    d. triglycerides
    e. amino acid

11. All of the following cellular activities require energy except:
    a. facilitated transport
    b. active transport
    c. movement
    d. protein synthesis
    e. cell division

12. Which of the following can occur within a cell in the absence of oxygen?
    a. glycolysis
    b. lactate production
    c. citric acid cycle
    d. electron transport system
    e. both (a) and (b)

13. In which stage of cell respiration does oxygen play a role?
    a. glycolysis
    b. electron transport system
    c. citric acid cycle
    d. lactate production
    e. transport of pyruvate into the mitochondria

14. Which of the following is/are recycled during cellular respiration and do not appear in the net equation?
    a. NAD^+ and NADH
    b. ATP, ADP, and P_i
    c. glucose
    d. carbon dioxide
    e. oxygen

15. Most of the ATP produced during cell respiration is produced during:
    a. glycolysis
    b. citric acid cycle
    c. electron transport system
    d. lactate production
    e. anaerobic pathways

Apply What You Know

Answers can be found in the Study Area in MasteringBiology.

1. Imagine that you are shown two cells under the microscope. One is small, has lots of mitochondria, and contains numerous glycogen granules. The other is somewhat larger and has only a few mitochondria and no glycogen granules. Which cell do you think is more metabolically active? Explain your reasoning.

2. The sodium-potassium pump is a large protein molecule. Where do you think the sodium-potassium pumps are made in the cell, and how do you think they become inserted into the lipid bilayer of the plasma membrane?

3. Mitochondria resemble a bacterial cell in a number of ways. Some scientists hypothesize that mitochondria evolved from aerobic prokaryotes that were engulfed by anaerobic eukaryotes, and now both have evolved together in a mutually advantageous way. Can you think of an explanation for why it might have been advantageous for both cells to enter into such an arrangement?

4. You have decided that you need to lose a little weight. You have heard a lot about no-carbohydrate and low-carbohydrate diets, and you have decided to use one of these diet plans. Explain how a low-carbohydrate diet works. Can you think of any possible negative side effects of such a diet?

5. Recently a young man from Derby in the United Kingdom entered a contest and drank 26 pints of water in a very short time. He later died of complications due to hypotonic hydration, also known as water intoxication. How were his body's cells affected by the excess water, and how might that have contributed to his death?

6. You have been selected to serve on a jury for a trial involving a young man accused of public intoxication. His defense attorney argues that the alcohol found in his system was the result of natural fermentation; that he had just finished a grueling one-hour workout during which his body could not meet the oxygen demand, and that the excess lactic acid that was produced during the exercise was then converted to alcohol by the process of lactic acid fermentation. Should you believe the defense attorney? Explain why or why not.

BlogInFocus

Answer can be found in the Study Area in MasteringBiology.

1. What is a pluripotent stem cell, and why are scientists so interested in learning how to induce adult human cells into becoming pluripotent again? (For more on this topic, visit MJ's blog in the Study Area in MasteringBiology and look under "Pluripotent Stem Cells.")

MasteringBiology®

Go to MasteringBiology for practice quizzes, activities, eText, videos, current events, and more.

From Cells to Organ Systems

Dried skin cells on the surface of the skin.

Reshaping Your Body

By now you are familiar with the chemistry of lipids and the structure and function of fat cells. You understand that when your average daily caloric intake exceeds your average daily caloric expenditure, you gain weight. And yet all this knowledge hasn't helped, because you still have those annoying fat deposits in places where you don't want them! Perhaps you've tried dieting and exercise and still aren't happy with your body shape.

What if you could just melt away that unwanted fat? What if you could kill some of those pesky fat cells once and for all? What if you could sculpt your body into perfect shape without ever having to

diet or exercise again? What if you could sculpt your face just a little? It's a fantasy many of us have indulged in, and it's one of the reasons for the meteoric rise of several cosmetic procedures, including *Lipodissolve* and *High Intensity Focused Ultrasound (HIFU)*.

What Is Lipodissolve?

Lipodissolve, also called injection lipolysis, is described by its promoters as a safe, effective, nonsurgical way to sculpt the body into perfect shape. Usually the technique is performed as a series of six injections two weeks apart directly

into subcutaneous fat deposits. The injections contain two active ingredients: phosphatidylcholine (a phospholipid) and

A human fat cell (×3,000) filled with lipid droplets (yellow).

deoxycholate (a bile acid). The combination of these two drugs, known as PCDC (for phosphotidylcholine deoxycholate), allegedly works by dissolving the bonds between the three fatty acids and the glycerol backbone that comprise a triglyceride molecule, the primary molecular form of stored fat in the body. PCDC also is thought to disrupt the cell membranes of fat cells in the vicinity of an injection, resulting in death of the fat cells themselves. Some Lipodissolve cocktails also include vitamins and plant extracts.

And at the moment, the safety and effectiveness of Lipodissolve are not backed by scientific data. The Food and Drug Administration (FDA) has called Lipodissolve just another example of "unapproved drugs for unapproved uses." Nevertheless Lipodissolve clinics can legally administer Lipodissolve because of a loophole in our drug regulatory laws. According to the law, a licensed doctor can legally and ethically prescribe compounded drugs (drugs made from more than one ingredient) specifically for individual patients, as long as all of the *ingredients* are approved by the FDA. The intent is to protect the sanctity of the doctor–patient relationship, allowing the doctor to choose what is best for that particular patient. Both of the compounds in a Lipodissolve injection have been approved by the FDA as ingredients in other drugs, though neither was approved as a fat-dissolving drug.

Lipodissolve is injected directly into areas of excess fat.

Health clinics and spas have been quick to capitalize on the loophole, for at prices ranging from $400 to $1,500 per Lipodissolve treatment they stand to make a lot of money. Most patients who try the technique eventually sign up for treatment of several body parts. Women generally request treatment of their thighs and abdomen, whereas men are more likely to choose jaw lines and love handles. One of the distinct advantages of the technique is that because it does not involve surgery there is no recovery period. Not surprisingly, there are persistent rumors on various celebrity-watch Web sites that certain celebrities have tried the procedure or are thinking about it.

Is Lipodissolve Safe?

Critics of the Lipodissolve technique argue that the current law covering single doctor–patient relationships was never intended to allow mass marketing by chains of clinics or spas, or mass compounding of the PCDC drug combination. The American Society of Plastic Surgeons, The American Society of Aesthetic Plastic Surgery, and the American Society of Dermatologic Surgery have issued cautionary warnings against the technique, but that's understandable because all three societies represent surgeons who might be financially affected by Lipodissolve's increasing popularity.

Lipodissolve proponents, on the other hand, counter by pointing out that there have been only anecdotal reports of minor unwanted side effects associated with the technique, such as swelling, skin blistering, pain, and blackened skin in some patients. No deaths have been reported. However, because the technique has been performed in this country only since 2004, the long-term consequences of Lipodissolve therapy are still unknown. The procedure is not yet

regulated by the FDA, so physicians are free to try any combination of doses, injection intervals, and treatment sites they want.

Faced with the awkward and potentially dangerous situation of having patients flock to an unregulated procedure, the FDA decided to take action. Late in 2007 the FDA approved the first clinical trial of Lipodissolve—a double-blind, placebo-controlled prospective study that will follow patients for up to 46 weeks. The trial, to be conducted by the research arm of the American Society for Aesthetic Plastic Surgery, is expected to provide the first scientifically defensible data on the efficacy and safety of Lipodissolve. The results may not be known for several more years. In the meantime the FDA is keeping an eye on the situation. Consumers would be wise to remain skeptical about this procedure until more is known about it.

What About HIFU?

High Intensity Focused Ultrasound (HIFU) is a technique in which a high-intensity beam of ultrasound is focused on a particular tissue below the surface of the body. The high energy produced by the ultrasound waves generates heat, which destroys cells in the targeted area. HIFU was first used in the treatment of uterine fibroids and slow-growing prostate cancers. But lately, aesthetic medicine specialists have been adapting the technique for removal of fat deposits beneath the skin under the proprietary names Ultrashape, Liposonix, and Vaser. Patients are being promised non-invasive body sculpting without anesthesia or pain and with minimal recovery time. What's not to love about that?

Except that the technique has not been approved by the FDA for all of its current uses. It's only been approved for reduction in waist circumference so far.

QUESTIONS TO CONSIDER

1 Health clinics sometimes cite retrospective studies to support their claim that the Lipodissolve technique is safe. What is a "retrospective study"? How is it different from a controlled study?

2 How important is FDA approval and/or scientific evidence of safety to you? If someone were to pay for a Lipodissolve or Liposonix procedure for you, would you try it?

THE FACTS...

- Several nonsurgical cosmetic procedures for "melting away fat" are being heavily promoted by health clinics and spas.
- The procedures involve either a series of injections of fat-dissolving drugs directly into local fat deposits or the use of targeted high-intensity ultrasound.
- Neither technique has been fully approved by the FDA for all of its current uses in aesthetic medicine.

>> **In multicellular organisms, cells have specialized functions.** These functions evolved (along with multicellularity) because they benefit the entire organism.

>> **Groups of cells with a common function are called tissues.** The four main tissue types are epithelial, connective, muscle, and nervous.

>> **Organs and organ systems each perform one or more essential complex functions for the organism.** Humans have 11 different organ systems; examples are the male and female reproductive systems (reproduction), skeletal system (structural support), and muscular system (movement).

>> **Multicellular organisms must maintain homeostasis** (constancy) of their internal environments. The maintenance of a constant internal environment compatible with life allows each living cell, regardless of its specialized function, to live far away from the external environment.

>> **Homeostasis is maintained by negative feedback control systems.** In negative feedback systems, any deviation from the desired condition is detected and corrected.

For nearly two-thirds of the history of life, or more than two billion years, all organisms consisted of just one cell. Plenty of single-celled organisms exist today; in fact they far outnumber multicellular organisms. Theirs is a simple, uncomplicated life. They get their raw materials and energy from the fluid in which they are bathed, they dump their wastes into that same fluid, and they reproduce by dividing in two.

However, there are disadvantages to being a single cell. The single-celled organism is completely at the mercy of its immediate external environment for every requirement of life. If the pond in which it lives dries up, it will die. If salt levels in the water rise, if the temperature gets too hot, or if its food runs out, it dies. There must be another way!

There is another way, and that is for cells to join together. In this chapter we look at how cells are organized into the tissues, organs, and organ systems that make up your body. We consider the structure and function of your skin as an example of an organ system. And we discuss how your cells, tissues, and organs work together to maintain the health and stability of your body.

4.1 Tissues are groups of cells with a common function

A *multicellular organism* consists of many cells that collectively share the functions of life. Advantages to multicellularity include greater size (the better to eat, rather than be eaten) and the ability to seek out or maintain an environment conducive to life.

All cells in a multicellular organism have a specialized function that benefits the organism in some way. However, specialization is not enough. The specialized functions must be organized and integrated if they are to be useful. As an example, the activity of a single cell in your heart is insignificant because the cell is so small. The beating of your heart requires that hundreds of thousands of such cells be arranged end to end, so that their functions are coordinated to produce a single heartbeat.

Tissues are groups of specialized cells that are similar in structure and that perform common functions. There are four major types of tissues: epithelial, connective, muscle, and nervous.

4.2 Epithelial tissues cover body surfaces and cavities

Most **epithelial tissues** consist of sheets of cells that line or cover various surfaces and body cavities. Two epithelial tissues you know about are your skin and the lining of your mouth. Other epithelial tissues line the inner surfaces of your digestive tract, lungs, bladder, blood vessels, and the tubules of your kidneys.

Epithelial tissues are more than just linings. They protect underlying tissues. Often they are smooth to reduce friction; the smooth epithelial tissue lining your blood vessels helps blood flow more easily through your body, for instance. Some are highly specialized for transporting materials. Epithelial tissues (and cells) absorb water and nutrients across your intestines into your blood. They also secrete waste products across the tubules of your kidneys so that you can eliminate them in urine.

A few epithelial tissues are *glandular epithelia* that form the body's glands. **Glands** are epithelial tissues that are specialized to synthesize and secrete a product. **Exocrine glands** (*exo-* means "outside" or "outward") secrete their products into a hollow organ or duct. Examples of exocrine glands are the glands in your mouth that secrete saliva, sweat glands in your skin, and glands in your stomach that produce digestive acid. **Endocrine glands** (*endo-* means "within") secrete substances called *hormones* into the bloodstream. One endocrine gland is the thyroid gland, which secretes several hormones that help regulate your body's growth and metabolism. We describe various glands throughout the book where appropriate.

Epithelial tissues are classified according to cell shape

Biologists classify epithelial tissues into three types according to the shapes of the cells (Figure 4.1):

■ *Squamous epithelium* consists of one or more layers of flattened cells. (*Squama* means "platelike." Think of squamous epithelium as "squashed flat.") Squamous epithelium forms the outer surface of the skin and lines the inner surfaces of the blood vessels, lungs, mouth and throat, and vagina.

■ *Cuboidal epithelium* is composed of cube-shaped cells. Cuboidal epithelium forms the kidney tubules and also covers the surfaces of the ovaries.

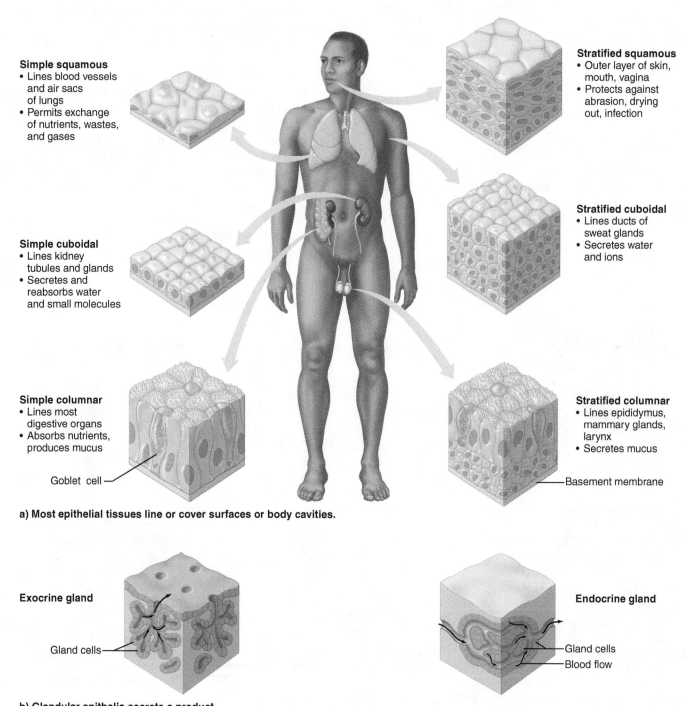

Simple squamous
• Lines blood vessels and air sacs of lungs
• Permits exchange of nutrients, wastes, and gases

Simple cuboidal
• Lines kidney tubules and glands
• Secretes and reabsorbs water and small molecules

Simple columnar
• Lines most digestive organs
• Absorbs nutrients, produces mucus

Goblet cell

Stratified squamous
• Outer layer of skin, mouth, vagina
• Protects against abrasion, drying out, infection

Stratified cuboidal
• Lines ducts of sweat glands
• Secretes water and ions

Stratified columnar
• Lines epididymus, mammary glands, larynx
• Secretes mucus

Basement membrane

a) Most epithelial tissues line or cover surfaces or body cavities.

Exocrine gland

Gland cells

Endocrine gland

Gland cells
Blood flow

b) Glandular epithelia secrete a product.

Figure 4.1 **Types of epithelial tissues.**

- *Columnar epithelium* is composed of tall, rectangular (column-shaped) cells. Columnar epithelium lines parts of the digestive tract, certain reproductive organs, and the larynx. Certain cells within columnar epithelium, called *goblet cells*, secrete mucus, a thick fluid that lubricates the tissues and traps bacteria, viruses, and irritating particles.

Epithelial tissues are classified not only by shape but also by the number of cell layers in the tissue. A *simple epithelium* is a single layer of cells, whereas a *stratified epithelium* consists of multiple layers (or strata). Simple epithelium is so thin that molecules can pass through it easily. Stratified epithelium is thicker and provides protection for underlying cells.

☑ **Quick Check** *What sort of epithelium would you expect to find lining a part of the digestive tract that absorbs food molecules and also secretes mucus? Explain your answer.* ■

The basement membrane provides structural support

Directly beneath the cells of an epithelial tissue is a supporting noncellular layer called the **basement membrane** (see Figure 4.1a), and beneath that is generally

Answers to ☑ questions can be found in Appendix A.

a layer of connective tissue (described later). You can think of the basement membrane as the mortar that anchors the epithelial cells to the stronger connective tissue underneath. The basement membrane is composed primarily of proteins secreted by the epithelial cells and their underlying connective tissue layer. It should not be confused with the plasma membrane that is a part of every living cell.

In addition to being attached to a basement membrane, epithelial cells may be connected to each other by several types of **cell junctions** made up of various proteins. Three different types of junctions may hold the cells together, depending on the type of epithelial tissue (Figure 4.2):

- *Tight junctions* seal the plasma membranes of adjacent cells so tightly together that nothing can pass between the cells. Tight junctions are particularly important in epithelial layers that must control the movement of substances into or out of the body. Examples include the cells that line the digestive tract (which bring in nutrients) and the bladder (which stores urine), and the cells that form the tubules of the kidneys (which remove waste products from the body).
- *Adhesion junctions*, sometimes called "spot desmosomes," are looser in structure. The protein filaments of adhesion junctions allow for some movement between cells so

a) Tight junctions form leak-proof seals between cells.

- Tight junction proteins
- Intercellular space

b) Adhesion junctions anchor two cells together, yet allow flexibility of movement.

- Protein filaments
- Intercellular space

c) Gap junctions provide for the direct transfer of water and ions between adjacent cells.

- Protein channel
- Intercellular space

Figure 4.2 Examples of junctions between cells. Only one type of junction is generally present in any given tissue.

☑ *Which type of junction would you expect to find between two cells that share ions or raw materials? Why?*

that the tissues can stretch and bend. Adhesion junctions in the epithelium of your skin, for instance, allow you to move freely.

- *Gap junctions* represent connecting channels made of proteins that permit the movement of ions or water between two adjacent cells. They are commonly found in the epithelial cells in the liver, heart, and some muscle tissues.

Recap Epithelial tissues line body surfaces and cavities, and form glands. They are classified according to cell shape (squamous, cuboidal, or columnar) and the number of cell layers (simple or stratified). ▪

4.3 Connective tissue supports and connects body parts

Connective tissue supports the softer organs of the body against gravity and connects the parts of the body together. It also stores fat and produces the cells of blood.

Unlike epithelial tissue, most connective tissues have few living cells. Most of their structure consists of nonliving extracellular material, the matrix that is synthesized by connective tissue cells and released into the space between them. The strength of connective tissue comes from the matrix, not from the living cells themselves. The few living cells rarely make contact with each other, and so direct cell-to-cell junctions are not present.

Connective tissues are so diverse that any classification system is really a matter of convenience (Table 4.1). Broadly, we can divide them into fibrous and specialized connective tissues.

Fibrous connective tissues provide strength and elasticity

Fibrous connective tissues connect various body parts, providing strength, support, and flexibility. Figure 4.3 shows the structural elements of fibrous connective tissue.

As indicated by their name, fibrous connective tissues consist of several types of fibers and cells embedded in a gel-like ground substance. **Collagen fibers**, made of protein, confer strength and are slightly flexible. Most fibrous connective tissues also contain thinner coiled **elastic fibers**, made primarily of the protein *elastin*, which can stretch without breaking. Some fibrous connective tissue also contains thinner fibers of collagen, called **reticular fibers**, that interconnect with each other. The reticular fibers often serve as an internal structural framework for some of the "soft" organs such as the liver, spleen, and lymph nodes.

The various fibers are embedded in a *ground substance* consisting of water, polysaccharides, and proteins that ranges

Table 4.1 Types of connective tissues

Type	Structure	Attributes	Locations
Fibrous Connective Tissue			
Loose	Mostly collagen and elastin fibers in no particular pattern; more ground substance	Flexible but only moderately strong	Surrounds internal organs, muscles, blood vessels
Dense	Mostly collagen in a parallel arrangement of fibers; less ground substance	Strong	In tendons, ligaments, and the lower layers of skin
Elastic	High proportion of elastin fibers	Stretches and recoils easily	Surrounds hollow organs that change shape or size regularly
Reticular (lymphoid)	Mostly thin, interconnecting reticular fibers of collagen	Serves as a flexible internal framework	In soft organs such as liver, spleen, tonsils, and lymph glands
Special Connective Tissues			
Cartilage	Primarily collagen fibers in a ground substance containing a lot of water	Maintains shape and resists compression	Embryonic tissue that becomes bone. Also the nose, vertebral disks, and the lining of joint cavities
Bone	Primarily hard mineral deposits of calcium and phosphate	Very strong	Forms the skeleton
Blood	Blood cells, platelets, and blood fluid called *plasma*	Transports materials and assists in defense mechanisms	Within cardiovascular system
Adipose tissue	Primarily cells called *adipocytes* filled with fat deposits	Stores energy in the form of fat	Under the skin, around some internal organs

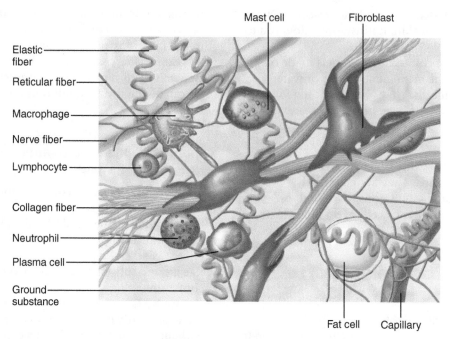

Figure 4.3 Fibrous connective tissue. The main elements are three types of fibers (collagen, elastic, and reticular) and a variety of cells (fibroblasts, fat cells, mast cells, and several types of white blood cells) in a ground substance of polysaccharides, proteins, and water. Blood vessels and nerves pass through or are associated with connective tissue. Fibrous connective tissues vary in their relative proportions of cells and fibers, and also in fiber orientation.

in consistency from gel-like to almost rubbery. The ground substance contains several types of cells, among them fat cells, mast cells, various white blood cells (macrophages, neutrophils, lymphocytes, and plasma cells), and most importantly, **fibroblasts**. The fibroblasts are the cells responsible for producing and secreting the proteins that compose the collagen, elastic, and reticular fibers. The fat cells, of course, store fat, and both the mast cells and white blood cells are involved in the body's immune system.

Fibrous connective tissues are subclassified according to the density and arrangement of their fiber types:

- *Loose connective tissue* (**Figure 4.4a**), also called *areolar connective tissue*, is the most common type. It surrounds many internal organs, muscles, and blood vessels. Loose connective tissue contains a few collagen fibers and elastic fibers in no particular pattern, giving it a great deal of flexibility but only a modest amount of strength.

a) Loose areolar connective tissue (× 160). In loose connective tissue the collagen and elastin fibers are arrayed in a random pattern.

b) Dense connective tissue (× 160). In dense connective tissue the fibers are primarily collagen fibers. In tendons and ligaments the fibers are oriented all in the same direction, with fibroblasts occupying narrow spaces between adjacent fibers.

Figure 4.4 **Examples of fibrous connective tissues.**

- *Dense connective tissue* (Figure 4.4b), found in tendons, ligaments, and lower layers of skin, has more collagen fibers. The fibers are oriented primarily in one direction, especially in the tendons and ligaments in and around our joints. Dense connective tissue is the strongest connective tissue when pulled in the same direction as the orientation of the fibers, but it can tear if the stress comes from the side. Very few blood vessels in dense connective tissue supply the few living cells. This is why, if you strain a tendon or ligament, it can take a long time to heal.
- *Elastic connective tissue* surrounds organs that have to change shape or size regularly. Examples include the stomach, which must stretch to accommodate food; the bladder, which stretches to store urine; and the vocal cords, which vibrate to produce sounds. Elastic connective tissue contains a high proportion of elastic fibers, which stretch and recoil easily.
- *Reticular connective tissue* (also called lymphoid tissue) serves as the internal framework of soft organs such as the liver and the tissues of the lymphatic system (spleen, tonsils, and lymph nodes). It consists of thin, branched reticular fibers (composed of collagen) that form an interconnected network.

✅**Quick Check** *People with a hereditary condition known as Ehlers-Danlos Syndrome (EDS) have hyperextensible joints that frequently dislocate, and extremely stretchy skin that tears easily. Develop a hypothesis for what type of tissue, and what protein in particular, might be the cause of EDS.* ▪

Specialized connective tissues serve special functions

The so-called *specialized connective tissues* are a diverse group that includes cartilage, bone, blood, and adipose tissue. Each is specialized to perform particular functions in the body.

Cartilage Cartilage is the transition tissue from which bone develops. It also maintains the shape of certain body parts (such as the soft tip of your nose) and protects and cushions joints. Disks of cartilage separate and cushion the vertebrae in your backbone, for instance, and cartilage forms the tough, smooth surfaces that reduce friction in some body joints.

Like dense connective tissue, cartilage consists primarily of collagen fibers. The two tissues differ in that the ground substance of cartilage, which is produced by cells called *chondroblasts*, contains a great deal more water. This is why cartilage functions so well as a cushion. As cartilage develops, the cells become enclosed in small chambers called *lacunae* (Figure 4.5a). There are no blood vessels in cartilage, so the mature cells (called *chondrocytes*) obtain their nutrients only by diffusion through the ground substance from blood vessels located outside the cartilage. Consequently, cartilage is slow to heal when injured.

Bone Like cartilage, **bone** is a specialized connective tissue that contains only a few living cells. Most of the matrix of bone consists of hard mineral deposits of calcium and phosphate. However, unlike cartilage, bone contains numerous blood vessels, and for this reason it can heal within four to six weeks after being injured. We discuss bone in more detail when we discuss the skeletal system.

Blood Blood consists of cells suspended in a fluid matrix called *plasma*. It is considered a connective tissue because all blood cells derive from earlier cells (called *stem cells*) located within bone. Red blood cells transport oxygen and nutrients to body cells and carry away the waste products of the cells' metabolism. White blood cells function in the immune system that defends the body, and platelets participate in the mechanisms that cause blood to clot following an injury. The composition and functions of blood are covered in more detail in a separate chapter.

a) **Cartilage from the trachea (× 300).** Mature cartilage cells, called chondrocytes, become trapped in chambers called lacunae within the hard, rubbery ground substance. Ground substance is composed of collagen fibers, polysaccharides, proteins, and water.

b) **Adipose tissue from the subcutaneous layer under the skin (× 140).** Adipose tissue consists almost entirely of fat cells. The fat deposit within a fat cell can become so large that the nucleus is pushed to the side.

Figure 4.5 Examples of special connective tissues.

Adipose tissue **Adipose tissue** is actually a loose connective tissue highly specialized for fat storage (Figure 4.5b). It has few connective tissue fibers and almost no ground substance. Most of its volume is occupied by **adipocytes** (fat cells). Adipose tissue is located primarily under the skin, where it serves as a layer of insulation. It also forms a protective layer around internal organs such as the kidneys. The number of adipocytes you have is partly determined by your genetic inheritance. When you eat more food than your body can use, some of the excess energy is stored in your adipocytes as fat (the fat cells get "fatter"). When you lose weight the fat cells slim down, too. In other words, weight loss reduces the volume of each fat cell but it does not necessarily reduce the number of fat cells. *Lipodissolve* is a controversial technique that disrupts and destroys fat cells chemically (review the Current Issue at the beginning of this chapter).

BlogInFocus (MB)

What are the FDA's concerns about how Lipodissolve is being promoted, and what is the agency doing about it? To learn more, visit MJ's blog in the Study Area in MasteringBiology and look under "FDA vs. Lipodissolve."

Recap Fibrous connective tissues provide strength and elasticity and hold body parts together. Among the specialized connective tissues, cartilage and bone provide support, blood transports materials throughout the body, and adipose tissue stores energy in the form of fat. ∎

4.4 Muscle tissues contract to produce movement

Muscle tissue consists of cells that are specialized to shorten, or contract, resulting in movement of some kind. Muscle tissue is composed of tightly packed cells called muscle *fibers.* The fibers are generally long and thin and aligned parallel to each other (Figure 4.6). The cytoplasm of a muscle fiber contains proteins, which interact to make the cell contract.

There are three types of muscle tissue: *skeletal, cardiac,* and *smooth.* They vary somewhat in body location, structure, and function, but they all do essentially the same thing—when stimulated, they contract. We devote an entire chapter to muscles as an organ system. For now, we'll focus solely on differences between the three types of muscle tissue.

Skeletal muscles move body parts

Skeletal muscle tissue connects to tendons, which attach to bones. When skeletal muscles contract, they cause body parts to move. The individual cells, also called fibers, are too small to be seen with the naked eye, but they may be as long as the entire muscle (Figure 4.6a). Each muscle cell has many nuclei, a phenomenon that happens because many young cells fuse end-to-end during development, producing one long cell.

a) **Skeletal muscle (× 100).** Skeletal muscle cells are very long and have many nuclei.

b) **Cardiac muscle (× 225).** Cardiac muscle cells interconnect with each other.

c) **Sheet of smooth muscle (× 250).** Smooth muscle cells are thin and tapered.

Figure 4.6 **Muscle tissue.**

A skeletal muscle may contain thousands of individual cells, all aligned parallel to each other. This parallel arrangement enables them to all pull in the same direction, shortening the muscle between its two points of attachment. Skeletal muscle is called *voluntary* muscle because we can exert conscious control over its activity. Skeletal muscle cells are activated only by nerves.

Cardiac muscle cells activate each other

Cardiac muscle tissue (Greek *kardia* means "the heart") is found only in the heart. The individual cells are much shorter than skeletal muscle fibers, and they have only one nucleus (Figure 4.6b). Like skeletal muscle, the cells are arranged parallel to each other. Cardiac muscle cells are short and blunt-ended, with gap junctions between the ends of adjoining cells. The gap junctions represent direct electrical connections between adjoining cells, so when one cell is activated it activates its neighbors down the line. Because of these gap junctions, the entire heart contracts in a coordinated fashion.

Cardiac muscle is considered involuntary because the heart can contract rhythmically entirely on its own, without any conscious thought on our part and without any stimulation by nerves.

✔Quick Check *Does skeletal muscle, like cardiac muscle, have gap junctions between adjacent cells? Why or why not?* ▪

Smooth muscle surrounds hollow structures

Smooth muscle tissue surrounds hollow organs and tubes, including blood vessels, digestive tract, uterus, and bladder. These slim cells are much smaller than skeletal muscle cells and have only one nucleus, like cardiac muscle (Figure 4.6c). The cells are aligned roughly parallel to each other. In blood vessels they are generally aligned in a circular fashion around the vessel. When smooth muscle cells shorten, the diameter of the blood vessel is reduced.

Smooth muscle cells taper at both ends, and there are gap junctions between adjacent cells so that when one contracts, nearby cells also contract. Like cardiac muscle, smooth muscle is involuntary in that we cannot control its contractions consciously.

⟲ Recap **The common feature of all muscle tissues (skeletal, cardiac, and smooth) is that they contract, producing movement.** ▪

4.5 Nervous tissue transmits impulses

Nervous tissue consists primarily of cells that are specialized for generating and transmitting electrical impulses throughout the body. It forms a rapid communication network for the body. Nervous tissue is located in the brain, the spinal cord, and the nerves that transmit information to and from various organs. An entire chapter is devoted to the nervous system, so we describe nervous tissue only briefly here.

Nervous tissue cells that generate and transmit electrical impulses are called **neurons** (Figure 4.7). Neurons can be as long as the distance from your spinal cord to the tip of your toe. Neurons typically have three basic parts: (1) the *cell body* where the nucleus is located; (2) *dendrites,* numerous cytoplasmic extensions that extend from the cell body and receive signals from other neurons; and (3) a long extension called an *axon* that transmits electrical impulses over long distances.

Nervous tissue also includes another type of cell called a **glial cell** that does not transmit electrical impulses. Glial cells play a supporting role by surrounding and protecting neurons and supplying them with nutrients.

Figure 4.7 Nervous tissue: a neuron (×170). The neuron is the functional unit of nervous tissue. The single neuron shown here is surrounded by numerous supporting cells called *glial cells*. The cell bodies of the glial cells do not stain well, but their nuclei are clearly visible.

⟲ Recap Nervous tissues serve as a communication network by generating and transmitting electrical impulses. ▪

4.6 Organs and organ systems perform complex functions

Many of the more complex functions of multicellular organisms (such as pumping blood or digesting food) cannot be carried out by one tissue type alone. **Organs** are structures composed of two or more tissue types joined together that perform a specific function or functions.

Your heart is an organ. Most of it consists of cardiac muscle, but there is also smooth muscle in the blood vessels that supply the cardiac muscle. The heart also contains nervous tissue that affects the rate at which the heart beats. It contains some connective tissue, primarily in the heart valves that open and close to control blood flow within the heart, and even a thin layer of epithelial tissue that lines the heart chambers. These tissues function together to pump blood, so together they constitute the organ known as the heart. Some organs have several functions. For example, the kidneys remove wastes and help control blood pressure.

The human body is organized by organ systems

Organ systems are groups of organs that together serve a broad function that is important to survival either of the individual organism (such as respiration, movement, or excretion of wastes) or of the species (reproduction). A good example is the organ system responsible for the digestion of food. Your *digestive system* includes your mouth, throat, esophagus, stomach, intestines, and even your liver, pancreas, and gallbladder. All of these organs must interact and be controlled and coordinated to accomplish their overall function.

The figures on pages 88 and 89 depict the 11 organ systems of the human body. Some organ systems perform several functions and so are discussed in several chapters in

Integumentary System
- Protects us from injury, infection, and dehydration
- Participates in temperature control
- Receives sensory input from the external environment

Skeletal System
- Protects, supports, and anchors body parts
- Provides the structural framework for movement
- Produces blood cells
- Stores minerals

Muscular System
- Produces movement or resists movement
- Generates heat

Nervous System
- Detects both external and internal stimuli
- Controls and coordinates rapid responses to these stimuli
- Integrates the activities of other organ systems

Endocrine System
- Produces hormones that regulate many body functions
- Participates with the nervous system in integrative functions

Digestive System
- Provides the body with water and nutrients
- (The liver) synthesizes certain proteins and lipids for the body
- (The liver) inactivates many chemicals, including hormones, drugs, and poisons

The 11 organ systems of the human body.

Circulatory System
- Transports materials to and from all cells
- Participates in the maintenance of body temperature
- Participates in mechanisms of defense against disease and injury

Lymphatic System
- Returns excess tissue fluid to the circulatory system
- Participates in both general and specific (immune) defense responses

Respiratory System
- Exchanges gases (oxygen and carbon dioxide) between air and blood
- Participates in the production of sound (vocalization)

Urinary System
- Maintains the volume and composition of body fluids
- Excretes some waste products

Reproductive System
- Female: Produces eggs
- Female: Nurtures the fertilized egg, developing embryo, and fetus until birth
- Male: Produces sperm
- Male: Participates in the delivery of sperm to the female

89

this book. For example, the lymphatic system has important functions related to defense against disease, the circulation of certain body fluids, and digestion. Other organ systems are covered in a single chapter.

Tissue membranes line body cavities

Some of the organs and organ systems are located in hollow cavities within the body (**Figure 4.8**). The large anterior cavity is divided into the thoracic cavity and abdominal cavity by the diaphragm between them. The thoracic cavity is in turn divided into two pleural cavities, each containing a lung, and the pericardial cavity, which encloses the heart. The lower part of the abdominal cavity is sometimes called the *pelvic cavity*. The smaller posterior cavity consists of the cranial cavity and the spinal cavity (vertebral canal). Many other smaller cavities exist as well, such as the synovial cavities in movable joints.

Tissue membranes consisting of a layer of connective tissue and (with one exception) a layer of epithelial cells line each body cavity and form our skin. There are four major types of tissue membranes:

- *Serous membranes.* Line and lubricate internal body cavities to reduce friction between internal organs.

- *Mucous membranes.* Line the airways, digestive tract, and reproductive passages that are open to the outside of the body. Goblet cells within the epithelial layer secrete *mucus*, which lubricates the membrane's surface and entraps foreign particles.
- *Synovial membranes.* Line the very thin cavities between bones in movable joints. These membranes secrete a watery fluid that lubricates the joint. Synovial membranes do not have a layer of epithelial cells.
- *Cutaneous membrane.* Our outer covering. You know it as skin, and it serves several functions discussed later in this chapter.

By now you may have noticed that "membrane" is a general term for a thin layer that covers or surrounds something. You have been introduced to three different membranes so far: the *plasma* membrane of phospholipids surrounding every cell, the *basement* membrane of extracellular material on which epithelial tissue rests, and *tissue* membranes that consist of several layers of tissue sandwiched together that cover or surround cavities, organs, and entire organ systems.

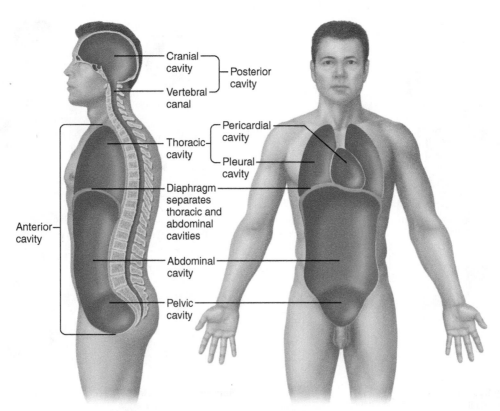

Figure 4.8 The main body cavities. The pelvic cavity and the abdominal cavity are continuous (not separated by a membrane).

✅**Quick Check** *What kind of membrane would you expect to find lining a pleural cavity? Explain.* ◾

Describing body position or direction

When describing parts of the body, biologists use precise terms to define position and direction. Generally speaking, an organ or even the entire body can be described by three planes known as the *midsagittal, frontal,* and *transverse* planes (Figure 4.9). These planes divide the body into left and right, front and back, and top and bottom, respectively. *Anterior* means "at or near the front" and *posterior* means "at or near the back." *Proximal* means "nearer (in closer proximity) to" any point of reference, usually the body trunk, and *distal* means "farther away." For example, your wrist is distal to your elbow. *Superior* means "situated above" or "directed upward," and *inferior* means "situated below" or "directed downward." Dozens of such terms, each with a precise meaning, are defined as they occur in this book.

↩ **Recap** **An organ consists of several tissue types that join together to perform a specific function. An organ system is a group of organs that share a broad function important for survival. The body's hollow cavities are lined by tissue membranes that support, protect, and lubricate cavity surfaces.** ◾

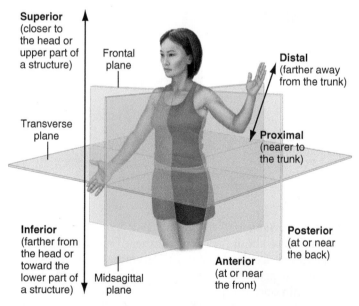

Figure 4.9 Planes of symmetry and terms used to describe position or direction in the human body. The frontal plane divides the body into anterior and posterior sections, the midsagittal plane divides it into left and right, and the transverse plane divides it into superior and inferior sections. Proximal and distal refer to points closer to or farther away from a point of reference, usually the trunk.

✅ *A friend who is an anatomist tells you that he has a blister on the inferior surface of his foot. He adds that it is posterior, not anterior. Where is the blister?*

4.7 The skin as an organ system

The proper name for the skin and its accessory structures such as hair, nails, and glands is the **integumentary system** (from the Latin *integere*, meaning "to cover"). We describe the skin here as a representative organ system; other organ systems are covered later in the book.

Skin has many functions

The skin has several different functions related to its role as the outer covering of the body:

- Protection from dehydration (helps prevent our bodies from drying out)
- Protection from injury (such as abrasion)
- Defense against invasion by bacteria and viruses
- Regulation of body temperature
- Synthesis of an inactive form of vitamin D
- Sensation: provides information about the external world via receptors for touch, vibration, pain, and temperature

Skin consists of epidermis and dermis

Recall that skin is a tissue membrane, and that tissue membranes contain layers of epithelial and connective tissue. The outer layer of the skin's epithelial tissue is the **epidermis**, and the inner layer of connective tissue is the **dermis** (Figure 4.10).

The skin rests on a supportive layer called the *hypodermis* (*hypo-* means "under"), consisting of loose connective tissue containing fat cells. The hypodermis is flexible enough to allow the skin to move and bend. The fat cells in the hypodermis insulate against excessive heat loss and cushion against injury.

Epidermal cells are replaced constantly The epidermis consists of multiple layers of squamous epithelial cells. A key feature of the epidermis is that it is constantly being replaced as cells near the base of the epidermis divide repeatedly, pushing older cells toward the surface.

Two types of cell make up the epidermis: keratinocytes and melanocytes. The more numerous of the two cell types are **keratinocytes**, which produce a tough, waterproof protein called *keratin*. Actively dividing keratinocytes located near the base of the epidermis are sometimes called *basal cells*. As keratinocytes derived from the basal cells move toward the skin surface, they flatten and become squamous. Eventually they die and dry out, creating a nearly waterproof barrier that covers and protects the living

Figure 4.10 The skin. The two layers of skin (epidermis and dermis) rest on a supportive layer (hypodermis). Although not part of the skin, the hypodermis serves important functions of cushioning and insulation.

cells below (**Figure 4.11**). The rapid replacement of keratinocytes allows the skin to heal quickly after injury.

One reason the outer layers of epidermal cells die is that the epidermis lacks blood vessels, so as mature cells are pushed farther from the dermis they can no longer obtain nutrients. The dead cells of the outer layers are shed over time, accounting for the white flakes you sometimes find on your skin or on dark clothing, especially when your skin is dry.

Less numerous cells, called **melanocytes**, are located near the base of the epidermis and produce a dark-brown pigment called *melanin*. Melanin accumulates inside keratinocytes and protects us against the sun's ultraviolet radiation. Exposure to sunlight increases the activity of melanocytes, accounting for the ability of some people to develop a suntan. (For more on tanning, see Health

& Wellness, *Suntans, Smoking, and Your Skin*.) Because all humans have about the same number of melanocytes, racial differences in skin color reflect either differences in melanocyte activity or differences in the rate of breakdown of melanin once it is produced.

✅ **Quick Check** *What would happen to your skin if your keratinocytes were to start dividing slightly more rapidly than usual?* ●

Fibers in dermis provide strength and elasticity The dermis is primarily dense connective tissue, consisting of collagen, elastic, and reticular fibers embedded in a ground substance of water, polysaccharides, and proteins. The fibers allow the skin to stretch when we move and give it strength to resist abrasion and tearing. Our skin becomes less flexible and more

Dead cells of epidermis

Keratinocyte containing melanin

Melanocyte containing melanin granules

Living cells of epidermis

Dividing keratinocyte (basal cell)

Basement membrane

Blood vessel

Dermis with blood vessel

Figure 4.11 The epidermis. Living cells near the base of the epidermis divide, pushing more mature cells toward the surface. As cells migrate toward the surface they die and dry out, forming a tough, waterproof barrier. The cells of the epidermis are supplied only by blood vessels located in the dermis.

wrinkled as we age because the number of fibers in the dermis decreases.

BlogInFocus MB

Is it okay to get skin sutures wet, or must they be kept covered and dry? To find out, visit MJ's blog in the Study Area in MasteringBiology and look under "skin sutures."

The surface of the dermis has many small projections called *papillae* that contain sensory nerve endings and small blood vessels. When the skin is rubbed excessively—such as when your shoes are too tight—the epidermis and dermis separate from each other and a fluid-filled blister develops between them.

The most abundant living cells in the dermis are the fibroblasts that produce the various fibers, but there are also mast cells, white blood cells, and occasional fat cells. Other structures in the dermis include:

- *Hair.* Each hair has a *shaft* above the skin's surface and a *root* below the surface. Hair is actually composed of several layers of cells enclosed in an outer layer of overlapping, dead, flattened keratinocytes. The root of a hair is surrounded by a sheath of several layers of cells called the *follicle*. The cells at the very base of the follicle are constantly dividing to form the hair root. As new hair cells are formed at the base, the hair root is pushed upward toward the skin's surface.
- *Smooth muscle.* Attached to the base of the hair follicle, it contracts when you are frightened or cold, causing your hair to become more erect.

Health & Wellness

Suntans, Smoking, and Your Skin

Many of us think suntans are attractive. A suntan indicates we have leisure time to spend basking in the sun, and it gives the skin a healthy looking "glow." But are suntans really healthy?

The answer is clearly "no," according to medical experts. Strong light rays can age your skin prematurely and increase your risk for skin cancer. The rays penetrate to the dermis and damage its collagen and elastin fibers. Elastin fibers clump together, leading at first to fine wrinkles and later to a wrinkled, leathery skin texture.

Prolonged exposure to light rays can also damage small blood vessels. Sometimes the vessels remain permanently dilated, leading to a condition called *telangiectasis*, or spider veins. Sunlight also damages the keratinocytes and melanocytes in the epidermis. The keratinocytes become rough and thickened and no longer fit together as a smooth interlocking layer. The melanocytes begin to produce melanin unevenly, leading to patches of darker pigmentation known as freckles, age spots, or liver spots.

What about tanning beds—are they okay? The tanning salon industry has been quite aggressive in trying to convince the public that tanning beds are not only safe, but that a healthy tan is good for you. Experts disagree. According to skin cancer researchers, repeated exposure to light rays, whether from sunlight or from tanning beds, is a risk factor for melanoma. In addition, your skin is likely to age more quickly as you get older. Although a minimal amount of sunlight is necessary to activate vitamin D, the amount is far below what is necessary to cause a tan.

Perhaps you have heard that ultraviolet (UV) rays consist of "good" UVA rays

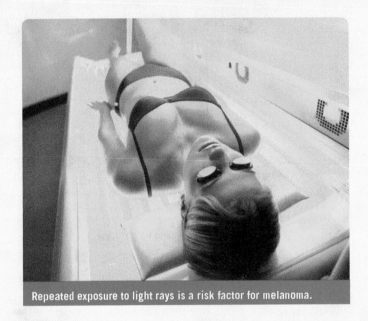

Repeated exposure to light rays is a risk factor for melanoma.

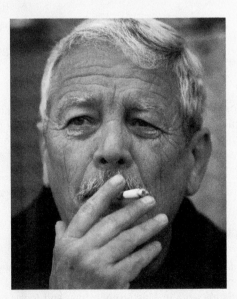

that tan your skin and "bad" UVB rays that cause sunburn. Tanning lotions with high SPF (sun protection factor) numbers are designed to block the UVB rays, which at least prevents the acute damage and pain of a sunburn. However, UVA rays are also bad for you. They penetrate more deeply than the UVB rays and in fact cause most of the long-term changes that age skin prematurely.

What about smoking? Heavy smokers are nearly five times more likely to develop premature wrinkles. Smoking damages and thickens the elastin fibers in the dermis. It also dehydrates keratinocytes in the epidermis, causing the epidermis to develop a rough texture. Finally, smoking narrows blood vessels, reducing blood flow to the skin. As a result, the skin of smokers heals more slowly from injury than the skin of nonsmokers. ■

- *Sebaceous glands.* Also known as oil glands, these secrete an oily fluid that moistens and softens hair and skin.
- *Sweat glands.* These produce sweat, a watery fluid containing dissolved ions, small amounts of metabolic wastes, and an antibiotic peptide called *dermicidin.* Sweat

helps regulate body temperature and protects against bacteria.
- *Blood vessels.* These supply the cells of the dermis and epidermis with nutrients and remove their wastes. The blood vessels also help regulate body temperature. They

dilate to facilitate heat loss when we are too hot and constrict to prevent heat loss when we are too cool. The dermis also contains lymph vessels, which drain fluids and play a role in the immune system.

- *Sensory nerve endings.* These provide information about the outside environment. Separate receptors exist to detect heat, cold, light touch, deep pressure, and vibration.

As mentioned earlier, the skin synthesizes an inactive form of vitamin D. It is not known which cell type in the skin is responsible. But we do know that a cholesterol-like molecule in the skin becomes an inactive form of vitamin D when it is exposed to the ultraviolet rays of sunlight. The inactive form must then be modified in the liver and kidneys before it becomes active.

Recap The skin is an organ because it consists of different tissues serving common functions. Functions of skin include protection, temperature regulation, vitamin D synthesis, and sensory reception. ▪

4.8 Multicellular organisms must maintain homeostasis

Although multicellularity offers many advantages to organisms, it presents certain disadvantages that must be overcome. For example, cells that are surrounded entirely by other cells can't obtain their nutrients directly from the organism's external environment and are constantly exposed to the waste products of neighboring cells.

The environment that surrounds the cells of a multicellular organism (their external environment) is the **internal environment** of the organism. The internal environment is a clear fluid called the **interstitial fluid** (the Latin noun *interstitium* means "the space between," in this case the space between cells). Every cell gets nutrients from the interstitial fluid around it and dumps wastes into it. In a multicellular organism, the interstitial fluid is the equivalent of the ocean, lake, or tiniest drop of fluid that surrounds and nourishes single-celled organisms.

Because every cell must receive all of its requirements for life from the surrounding interstitial fluid, the composition of this fluid must be kept fairly constant to sustain life. In the long run, nutrients consumed by the cell must be replaced and wastes must be removed or the cell will die.

Relative constancy of the conditions within the internal environment is called **homeostasis** (*homeo-* means "unchanging" or "the same," and *-stasis* means "standing"). The maintenance of homeostasis is so important for life that multicellular organisms, including human beings, devote a significant portion of their total metabolic activities to it. Although small changes in the internal environment do occur from time to time, the activities of cells, tissues, organs, and organ systems are carefully integrated and regulated to keep these changes within acceptable limits.

Homeostasis is maintained by negative feedback

In living organisms, homeostasis is maintained by **negative feedback** control systems (Figure 4.12). Negative feedback control systems operate in such a way that deviations

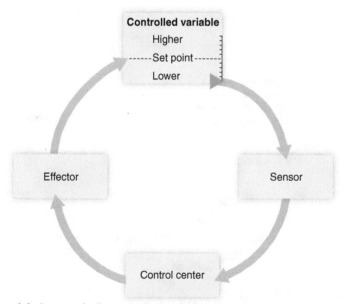

a) A *decrease* in the controlled variable causes events that *raise* the controlled variable toward its set point again.

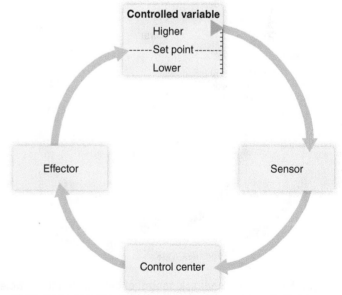

b) An *increase* in the controlled variable causes events that *lower* the controlled variable toward its set point again.

Figure 4.12 Components of a negative feedback control system. The focal point of the control system is the controlled variable. A sensor monitors the controlled variable and sends signals to a control center, which compares the current value of the controlled variable with its set point. If the controlled variable and set point do not match, the control center sends signals to effectors that take action to reverse the difference between the controlled variable and its set point.

from the desired condition are automatically detected and counteracted. A negative feedback control system has the following components:

- A **controlled variable**. The focal point of any negative feedback control loop is the *controlled variable*. A controlled variable is any physical or chemical property that might vary from time to time and that must be controlled to maintain homeostasis. Examples of controlled variables are blood pressure, body temperature, and the concentration of glucose in blood.
- A **sensor** (or *receptor*). The sensor monitors the current value of the controlled variable and sends the information (via either nerves or hormones) to the control center.
- A **control center**. The control center receives input from the sensor and compares it to the correct, internally set value of the controlled variable, sometimes called the **set point**. When the current value and the set point are not in agreement, the control center sends signals (again, via either nerves or hormones) to an effector.
- An **effector**. The effector takes the necessary action to correct the imbalance, in accordance with the signals it receives from the control center.

The cycle is called *negative feedback* because any change in the controlled variable triggers a series of events that ultimately opposes ("negates") the initial change, returning the variable to its set point. In other words, homeostasis is maintained.

✅ Quick Check *Your refrigerator's ability to maintain a relatively steady cool temperature is another example of a feedback system. Is it a negative or a positive feedback system? Identify the major components of the system.* ●

Negative feedback helps maintain core body temperature

A prime example of negative feedback is the maintenance of homeostasis of your body temperature. In this case, multiple organ systems participate in maintaining homeostasis (Figure 4.13).

The controlled variable is your core temperature, meaning the temperature near the center of your body. Temperature sensors in your skin and internal organs monitor core temperature. These sensors transmit signals via nerves to the control center, located in a region of your brain called the *hypothalamus*. The control center uses different combinations of effector mechanisms to raise or lower core temperature as needed.

When your core temperature falls *below* its set point, the hypothalamus:

- Sends more nerve impulses to blood vessels in the skin, causing the blood vessels to constrict. This restricts blood flow to your skin and reduces heat loss.

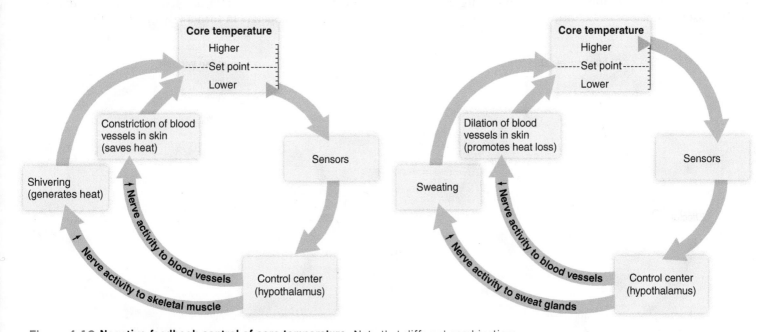

Figure 4.13 Negative feedback control of core temperature. Note that different combinations of effector mechanisms may be activated, depending on the direction of the initial change in core temperature.

✅ *In most people, hunger (and food intake) appears to be regulated in such a way that the amount of body fat stays surprisingly constant over time (despite people's efforts to lose weight). Draw a diagram showing how hunger and food intake might be regulated in a negative feedback system to keep body fat stores at a certain set point.*

- Stimulates your skeletal muscles, causing brief bursts of muscular contraction known as shivering. Shivering generates heat.

When your core temperature rises *above* its set point, the hypothalamus:

- Sends fewer nerve impulses to blood vessels in the skin, causing the blood vessels to dilate. This increases blood flow to your skin and promotes heat loss.
- Activates your sweat glands. As perspiration evaporates from your skin, you lose heat.

Even when your core temperature is normal, your hypothalamus is transmitting some nerve impulses to the blood vessels in your skin. Small changes in temperature, then, can be handled effectively just by increasing or decreasing the normal number of signals. Only when the variations in temperature are large is sweating or shivering called into play.

From this example, we can make the following points about negative feedback control:

- Many sensors may be active at once. In this case, sensors throughout the body monitor body temperature.
- The control center integrates all of this incoming information and comes up with an appropriate response.
- There can be multiple effectors as well as multiple sensors, and they may belong to different organ systems.

Both skin and muscles function in returning body temperature to its set point.

✅**Quick Check** *People who have fevers will often get "chills"— feeling as if they are cold and shivering—even though body temperature is actually above normal. Later, when the fever "breaks," they will suddenly start sweating. Explain why this happens.* ▪

Positive feedback amplifies events

Positive feedback control systems are relatively uncommon in living organisms. In positive feedback, a change in the controlled variable sets in motion a series of events that *amplify* the original change, rather than returning it to normal. The process of childbirth once labor has started is governed by positive feedback mechanisms.

Obviously something must terminate positive feedback events. The contractions of childbirth end when the child is born. The important point is that positive feedback is not a mechanism for maintaining homeostasis.

↺ **Recap All multicellular organisms must maintain homeostasis of their internal environment. In a negative feedback control system, any change in a controlled variable sets in motion a series of events that reverse the change, maintaining homeostasis.** ▪

Chapter Summary

Tissues are groups of cells with a common function *p. 80*

- The four main types of tissues are epithelial tissue, connective tissue, muscle tissue, and neural tissue.

Epithelial tissues cover body surfaces and cavities *p. 80*

- Epithelial tissues are sheets of cells that cover or line body surfaces and form the glands.
- Epithelial tissues are supported by a noncellular layer called the basement membrane.

Connective tissue supports and connects body parts *p. 83*

- Fibrous connective tissues contain several types of extracellular fibers and only a few living cells. They support and connect body parts.
- Cartilage, blood, bone, and adipose tissue are classified as special connective tissues.

Muscle tissues contract to produce movement *p. 86*

- Muscle tissue is composed of either skeletal, cardiac, or smooth muscle cells.
- Skeletal muscles are attached to bones by tendons.

Nervous tissue transmits impulses *p. 87*

- Neurons are specialized for conduction of electrical impulses.
- Glial cells surround and protect neurons and supply them with nutrients.

Organs and organ systems perform complex functions *p. 87*

- The human body is composed of 11 organ systems, each of which has at least one broad function.
- Membranes consisting of layers of epithelial and connective tissues line the body cavities.
- Positions of body parts are described on three planes: midsagittal, frontal, and transverse.

The skin as an organ system *p. 91*

- The skin functions as a protective barrier, participates in the maintenance of homeostasis, and provides us with sensory information about the external environment.
- Skin has two layers: an outer epithelial layer called the *epidermis* and an inner connective tissue layer called the *dermis*.
- Skin also contains nerves, blood vessels, glands, hair follicles, and smooth muscle.

Multicellular organisms must maintain homeostasis *p. 95*

- In a multicellular organism, the external environment of every cell is the internal environment of the organism.
- Relative constancy of the internal environment is called *homeostasis*.
- Homeostasis is maintained by negative feedback control systems.
- In a negative feedback control system, a change in the controlled variable sets in motion a sequence of events that tends to reverse (or negate) the initial change.
- In the regulation of body temperature, sensors located throughout the body send information about temperature to the control center, located in the hypothalamus of the brain.

■ Possible responses to a change in body temperature include dilating or constricting the blood vessels to the skin, shivering (if temperature is too low), and sweating (if temperature is too high).

Terms You Should Know

basement membrane, 82
cell junction, 82
connective tissue, 83
controlled variable, 96
dermis, 91
endocrine gland, 80
epidermis, 91
epithelial tissue, 80
exocrine gland, 80

homeostasis, 95
internal environment, 95
muscle tissue, 86
negative feedback, 95
nervous tissue, 87
neuron, 87
organ system, 87
set point, 96

Concept Review

Answers can be found in the Study Area in MasteringBiology.

1. Describe some advantages and disadvantages of multicellularity.
2. Name the four main types of tissues in the human body and list their main functions.
3. Describe the functions of the three types of cell junctions.
4. Distinguish between an organ and an organ system.
5. List the 11 organ systems of the body and give at least one function of each.
6. Define *interstitial fluid*.
7. Name the two cavities of the anterior body cavity that are separated from each other by the diaphragm.
8. Compare/contrast positive and negative feedback.
9. Discuss the purpose of *homeostasis* in the body.
10. Describe the function of a control center in a negative feedback control system.

Test Yourself

Answers can be found in Appendix A.

1. Collagen and elastin fibers are typically found in:
   a. connective tissue
   b. epithelial tissue
   c. intercellular junctions
   d. muscle tissue
   e. the epidermis

2. Cells in cardiac muscle are able to contract in a coordinated fashion because of communication made possible through:
   a. gap junctions
   b. spot desmosomes
   c. adhesion junctions
   d. tight junctions
   e. synapses

3. Which of the following membranes is not composed of cells?
   a. serous membrane
   b. synovial membrane
   c. cutaneous membrane
   d. basement membrane
   e. mucous membrane

4. Exocrine and endocrine glands are types of:
   a. loose connective tissue
   b. epithelial tissue
   c. squamous tissue
   d. fibrous connective tissue
   e. specialized connective tissue

5. The thoracic cavity is located _____ to the abdominal cavity.
   a. proximal
   b. superior
   c. inferior
   d. ventral
   e. distal

6. What property do all muscle tissues have in common?
   a. composed of collagen and elastin filaments
   b. under conscious control
   c. ability to form a communication network
   d. ability to contract
   e. cells are joined by tight junctions

7. Injury to bone heals more quickly than injury to cartilage because:
   a. bone marrow contains stem cells
   b. chondroblasts are only present during prenatal development
   c. the polysaccharides in cartilage ground substance can't be replaced
   d. there is a richer blood supply to bone
   e. bone has a higher mineral content

8. Which of the following tissues may be found in the skin?
   a. smooth muscle
   b. fibrous connective tissue
   c. nervous tissue
   d. epithelial tissue
   e. all of these tissues

9. Which of the following is responsible for skin pigmentation?
   a. melanin
   b. keratin
   c. collagen
   d. sebum
   e. dermicidin

10. When a decrease in blood pressure is detected by the central nervous system, the central nervous system triggers several changes that will return the blood pressure to its set point. This is an example of:
    a. positive feedback
    b. thermoregulation
    c. negative feedback
    d. reverse feedback
    e. set point feedback

11. The presence of a full bladder triggers the bladder to contract. As a little urine is released, this causes more contractions, which will completely empty the bladder. This is an example of:
    a. homeostatic regulation
    b. uroregulation
    c. negative feedback
    d. positive feedback
    e. reverse feedback

12. Which type of tissue stores triglycerides?
    a. muscle tissue
    b. loose connective tissue
    c. fibrous connective tissue
    d. columnar epithelial tissue
    e. adipose tissue

13. A substantial amount of nonliving extracellular material, also known as the matrix, characterizes all:
    a. muscle tissue
    b. epithelial tissue
    c. connective tissue
    d. nervous tissue
    e. membranes

14. All of the following organ systems may be involved in thermoregulation except the:
    a. integumentary system
    b. muscular system
    c. circulatory system
    d. skeletal system
    e. nervous system

15. Reducing food intake may lead to weight loss by:
    a. decreasing the number of muscle cells
    b. decreasing the amount of fibrous connective tissue
    c. decreasing the volume of adipocytes
    d. decreasing the volume of muscle cells
    e. decreasing the number of adipocytes

Apply What You Know

Answers can be found in the Study Area in MasteringBiology.

1. Your roommate says that the concept of homeostasis is being violated when the rate of respiration goes up during exercise, because the rate of respiration clearly is not being held constant. Explain to him where his thinking is faulty.

2. What do you think would be some of the problems associated with severe third-degree burns, in which both the epidermis and the dermis are severely damaged or destroyed?

3. Sherlock Holmes, the greatest fictional detective of all time, is talking to a woman in her late 40s, when he suddenly says, "I see, my dear madam, you must have enjoyed your cigarettes and your suntans." The woman is amazed, because she mentioned nothing about these two former favorite activities. What physical characteristics might Mr. Holmes have seen in this woman to indicate she was an avid sun-worshiper and cigarette smoker? How do these characteristics develop?

4. Dieting is difficult. People who do manage to lose weight can gain it back if they're not careful. Are techniques such as liposuction or Lipodissolve a good way to keep the weight off permanently? Why or why not?

5. Fibrous connective tissue consists of ground substance and fibers that provide strength, support, and flexibility. Concrete is used to make tough, durable structures in construction projects. How is a concrete structure like or unlike fibrous connective tissue?

6. By definition, an organ is a structure composed of two or more tissue types that perform a specific function. Performance of that function often requires coordination among many cells. Why is it so important that cardiac muscle cells of the heart be synchronized (coordinated) so that they beat nearly all at once?

BlogInFocus

Answers can be found in the Study Area in MasteringBiology.

1. What does the "SPF" on a suntan lotion product stand for? How high does the SPF number have to be for the product to be advertised as protective against cancer? (For more on this topic, visit MJ's blog in the Study Area in MasteringBiology and look under "SPF.")

MasteringBiology®

Go to MasteringBiology for practice quizzes, activities, eText, videos, current events, and more.

Blood

Two red blood cells, a white blood cell, and Staphylococcus bacteria.

Should You Bank Your Baby's Cord Blood?

When she was 15 and a sophomore in high school, Jaclyn Albanese was diagnosed with acute leukemia—a type of stem cell cancer in bone marrow. The usual treatment is chemotherapy and radiation to kill the cancer cells (and normal stem cells), and then a bone marrow transplant to repopulate the bone marrow with stem cells. Traditionally these stem cells have come from bone marrow donated by a family member or an unrelated volunteer whose marrow is compatible. Compatibility is crucial because, as you will learn in this chapter, the body's immune cells recognize and attack foreign cells. Jaclyn had hoped to

get a bone marrow transplant from one of her relatives, but none of them was a close enough match. Fortunately for Jaclyn, she found compatible units of cord blood from an unrelated donor. They saved her life. But, if her parents had banked the cord blood from her delivery when she was born, she wouldn't have needed to search for donors at all.

What Is Cord Blood?

During pregnancy, the fetus is cushioned by a temporary organ called the placenta and connected to its mother by the umbilical cord. Blood vessels in the umbilical cord and placenta filter out

Jaclyn Albanese.

Blood in the umbilical cord contains stem cells similar to those found in bone marrow.

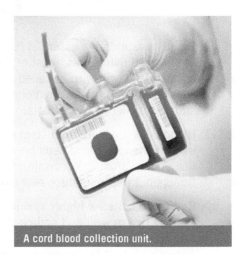

A cord blood collection unit.

HLA-DR, each of which comes in two forms. The ideal match would be for the patient to have the same six forms as the donor (a 6/6 match). Good matches between unrelated donors are rare—siblings of the same parents match only 25% of the time, and only about 10% of all patients who need a bone marrow transplant are able to find a compatible match from among unrelated donors.

This is why cord blood has become such a precious commodity. The immune cells in cord blood are less mature than those in bone marrow, so cord blood transplants are less likely to cause transfusion reactions, and even when reactions do occur, they tend to be less severe. As a result, the match between donor and recipient does not need to be a perfect 6/6—matches of 5/6 or even 4/6 are sufficient. This opens a much wider field of possibilities. Jaclyn Albanese could not find a single compatible bone marrow donor, but she was able to locate two units of compatible cord blood. She had a cord blood transplant in 1999 just prior to her junior year in high school, and today she is a college graduate. Jaclyn is one of approximately 6,000 patients who have benefited from cord blood transplants to date.

Banking Privately or Publicly

Should you bank your baby's cord blood privately, or donate it to a public cord blood bank?

Private blood banks say that banking your baby's cord blood privately is like taking out a medical insurance policy. They argue that you might want to use your baby's cord blood stem cells to treat a future disease (such as leukemia) in your child or a close family member. By banking your baby's cord blood, you ensure that your child always has access to the "perfect match"—his or her own stem cells. They also point out that scientists are working on stem-cell therapies for a variety of other conditions such as diabetes and heart disease. The implication is that in 30 or 40 years, by the time your

toxic substances, deliver nutrients from the mother, and remove waste products from the fetus. After the baby is delivered, the mother's body expels the placenta and umbilical cord. A health professional cuts the cord, and the baby's circulatory system begins to function on its own.

Until recently, the placenta and cord were discarded after birth. However, these structures still contain about 50 ml of cord blood. In addition to containing the usual components of blood, cord blood is rich in relatively immature stem cells from the fetus. These stem cells can be coaxed to divide repeatedly to produce immature blood cells, which in turn develop into platelets, red cells, and white cells.

Bone Marrow, Cord Blood, and Compatibility Issues

A good bone marrow transplant match between a donor and a patient involves three key antigens known as HLA-A, HLA-B, and

newborn is at greater risk of developing these chronic ailments, he or she may be able to use these stem cells for treatments as yet undreamed of. So far they have convinced many parents to have their baby's cord blood collected, processed, tested, and stored, at an average cost of $1,700 plus an annual storage fee of about $125.

Proponents of public blood banking argue that the likelihood of a baby born to a healthy family ever needing his or her stem cells are about 1 in 2,500. Is such an unlikely event worth banking your baby's blood privately? If you and your family are healthy, you might want to consider helping others by donating your child's cord blood to a public cord blood bank. To support public donations, in 2005 the federal government authorized $79 million in federal funds to collect and store cord blood from ethnically diverse donors. As a result, the National Marrow Donor Program now lists a national inventory of nearly 145,000 cord blood units—enough to be able to provide more than half of all patients with a 5/6 antigen match.

Jaclyn Albanese's parents did not have the choice of banking her cord blood privately when she was born. Fortunately, she was able to find the cord blood she needed through one of the few public cord blood banks in existence at the time.

QUESTIONS TO CONSIDER

1 Do you agree with the federal government's decision to allocate $79 million (about 40 cents per adult) for a public cord blood collection and storage network?

2 When (or if) you have a child, what will you do with its cord blood? Explain your decision.

THE FACTS...

- Cord blood—blood remaining in a newborn baby's placenta and umbilical cord—is rich in stem cells, similar to those found in bone marrow.
- Cord blood can benefit many patients who cannot find a suitable bone marrow donor.
- Private cord blood banks urge prospective parents to bank their baby's cord blood solely for their own child's future use.
- The federal government has established a public cord blood network for all Americans.

>> **Blood transports the essential requirements of life to all living cells.** Most of the blood consists of a watery fluid called plasma that contains ions, proteins, hormones, nutrients, and metabolic waste products.

>> **Blood cells originate from stem cells located in bone marrow.** Blood cells have a short lifespan, so stem cells continue to divide throughout life to produce new blood cells.

>> **Red blood cells are highly specialized for transporting oxygen and carbon dioxide.** Red blood cells contain a protein called *hemoglobin* that binds oxygen and carbon dioxide.

>> **White blood cells defend the body against injury and disease.** White blood cells are part of the body's immune system.

>> **Human blood types are A, B, AB, and O.** Blood type is determined by specific proteins called *antigens* on the surface of red blood cells. Your blood type determines what type of blood you can receive as a transfusion.

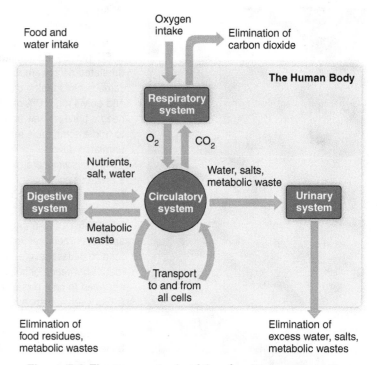

Figure 7.1 **The transport role of the circulatory system.** The cardiovascular system serves homeostasis by transporting nutrients and carrying off wastes from all parts of the body.

All cells in the body must obtain nutrients and get rid of wastes. How do they do these things? Diffusion to and from the fluid that surrounds them (interstitial fluid) is only part of the answer. If every cell drew its nutrients from interstitial fluid and there were no way to replenish the nutrients, the cells would soon starve. If every cell dumped its waste into the interstitial fluid and those wastes were not promptly removed, the cells would die in a sea of toxic waste. Cells need a system for keeping the oxygen content, the supply of nutrients, the concentrations of wastes, and the concentrations of every essential molecule and atom within acceptable limits. What they need is a system to maintain homeostasis of the interstitial fluid. In humans, that system is the circulatory system.

The **circulatory system** consists of the heart, the blood vessels, and the blood that circulates through them. As shown in Figure 7.1, the circulatory system plays a central role in supplying all cells with what they need and removing the substances they no longer need. The circulatory system ensures that blood flows throughout the entire body, bringing the necessary raw materials to the interstitial fluid surrounding every living cell and removing the waste. It picks up nutrients from the digestive system, exchanges gases with the respiratory system, and carries wastes and excess water and salts to the urinary system for removal from the body. It also carries some metabolic wastes to the liver for removal.

Whenever a substance is transported over any distance within the body, the circulatory system is at work.

In this chapter we concentrate on the composition and crucial functions of blood, the fluid that circulates within the heart and blood vessels. How the heart and blood vessels function together to transport blood throughout the body will be considered in a separate chapter.

7.1 The components and functions of blood

Blood consists of specialized cells and cell fragments suspended in a watery solution of molecules and ions. It is categorized as a specialized connective tissue because blood cells originate in the marrow of bone. Blood carries out three crucial tasks for the body:

- *Transportation.* Blood transports all substances needed anywhere by the body, including oxygen from the lungs, nutrients from the digestive system, and hormones from the endocrine glands. Blood also transports the waste products of cellular metabolism away from body tissues to the organs that eliminate them from the body.
- *Regulation.* Blood helps to regulate body temperature, the volume of water in the body, and the pH of body fluids.
- *Defense.* Blood contains specialized defense cells that help protect against infections and illness, and it has the ability to prevent excessive blood loss through the clotting mechanism.

Together these functions are crucial for maintaining homeostasis. Blood is so effective at performing these functions that so far scientists' efforts to develop an artificial blood substitute have not been very successful. If someone needs blood, a transfusion of human blood is often the only solution.

Adult men average 5 to 6 liters of blood (about 1.5 gallons), and adult women average 4 to 5 liters. Differences between men and women reflect differences in body size. In general, blood represents approximately 8% of your body weight.

Blood is thicker and stickier than water. This is because some components of blood are denser (heavier) than water and because blood is roughly five times more viscous (viscosity is a measure of resistance to flow). The old saying that blood is thicker than water is true.

Despite its uniform color, blood carries a rich array of components. Table 7.1 summarizes the components of blood and their functions. They fall into two major categories: the liquid component (plasma) and the cellular component or formed elements (*red cells, white cells,* and *platelets*). If you spin a blood sample in a centrifuge (a high-speed rotation device that mimics and magnifies gravitational forces), formed elements sink to the bottom of a test tube because they are denser than plasma (Figure 7.2). Red blood cells (RBCs), representing the bulk of the formed elements, settle to the bottom. White blood cells (WBCs) and platelets appear just above red blood cells in a thin, grayish-white layer.

Plasma consists of water and dissolved solutes

The top layer of a centrifuged blood sample, representing about 55% of the total volume, consists of a pale yellow liquid called **plasma**. Plasma is the transport medium for blood cells and platelets. About 90% of plasma is water. The rest is dissolved proteins, hormones, more than 100 different small molecules (including amino acids, fats, small carbohydrates, vitamins, and various waste products of metabolism), and ions.

The largest group of solutes in plasma consists of **plasma proteins**, which serve a variety of functions. Important plasma proteins include albumins, globulins, and clotting proteins.

Nearly two-thirds of plasma proteins are **albumins**, which primarily serve to maintain the proper water balance between blood and the interstitial fluid. Manufactured in the liver, albumins also bind to certain molecules (such as bilirubin and fatty acids) and drugs (such as penicillin) and assist in their transport in blood.

Globulins (designated alpha, beta, and gamma) are a diverse group of proteins that transport various substances in the blood. Many beta globulins bind to lipid (fat) molecules, such as cholesterol. When a protein attaches to one of these molecules, it creates a complex called a *lipoprotein*. Two medically important lipoproteins are the low-density lipoproteins (LDLs) and high-density lipoproteins (HDLs), and medical exams often include taking a blood sample to measure LDL and HDL relative proportions. The LDLs are sometimes called "bad cholesterol" because high blood levels of these lipoproteins are associated with increased risk of cardiovascular health problems. High levels of HDLs often indicate a lower risk of cardiovascular disease. We discuss lipoproteins and the health implications of high blood cholesterol levels when we discuss the heart and blood vessels.

Table 7.1 **Composition of blood**

Blood component	Examples and functions
Formed Elements (45%)	
Red blood cells	Transport oxygen to body tissues; transport carbon dioxide away from tissues.
White blood cells	Defend the body against invading organisms, abnormal cells.
Platelets	Take part in blood clotting as part of the body's defense mechanisms.
Plasma (55%)	
Water	The primary constituent of blood plasma.
Electrolytes (ions)	Sodium, potassium, chloride, bicarbonate, calcium, hydrogen, magnesium, others. Ions contribute to the control of cell function and volume, to the electrical charge across cells, and to the function of excitable cells (nerve and muscle). All ions must be kept at their normal concentrations for homeostasis to occur.
Proteins	Albumins maintain blood volume and transport electrolytes, hormones, and wastes. Globulins serve as antibodies and transport substances. Clotting proteins contribute to blood clotting.
Hormones	Insulin, growth hormones, testosterone, estrogen, others. Hormones are chemical messenger molecules that provide information needed to regulate specific body functions.
Gases	Oxygen is needed for metabolism; carbon dioxide is a waste product of metabolism. Both are dissolved in plasma as well as carried by RBCs.
Nutrients and wastes	Glucose, urea, many others. Nutrients, raw materials, and wastes (including heat) are transported by blood throughout the body.

a) Whole blood.

b) Blood after being spun in centrifuge.

c) A table-top centrifuge.

Plasma (55%)

Whole blood

Platelets and WBC (1%)

RBC (44%)

Figure 7.2 Blood. The formed elements sink to the bottom during centrifugation. The percentage of the blood that is red blood cells is called the hematocrit; in this sample the hematocrit is 44%.

Gamma globulins function as part of the body's defense system, helping to protect against infections and illness. We take a closer look at them when we discuss the immune system.

Clotting proteins, a third group of plasma proteins, play an important role in the process of blood clotting. As we see later in this chapter, blood clotting minimizes blood loss and helps maintain homeostasis after injury.

In addition to plasma proteins, plasma transports a variety of other molecules, including ions (also called electrolytes), hormones, nutrients, waste products, and gases. Electrolytes such as sodium and potassium contribute to the control of cell function and cell volume. Hormones, which are chemical "messengers" from the endocrine system, transport information throughout the body. Nutrients such as carbohydrates, amino acids, vitamins, and other substances are absorbed from the digestive tract or produced by cells' metabolic reactions. Waste products in plasma include carbon dioxide, urea, and lactic acid. Gases dissolved in plasma include oxygen, which is necessary for metabolism, and carbon dioxide, a waste product of metabolism.

✓ **Quick Check** *A medical researcher infuses a liter of blood plasma (whole blood minus the formed elements) into a patient. What do you think would be the effect of the infusion? What if he replaced all of the patient's blood with blood plasma?* ●

Red blood cells transport oxygen and carbon dioxide

Just under half of the volume of whole blood consists of its formed elements. The most abundant are **red blood cells (RBCs)**, also called **erythrocytes** ("red cells" in Greek). Red blood cells function primarily as carriers of oxygen and carbon dioxide. Each cubic millimeter of blood contains approximately 5 million red blood cells. They give blood its color and are the major reason why it is viscous.

Red blood cells offer a great example of how structure serves function. Red blood cells are small, flattened, doughnut-shaped disks whose centers are thinner than their edges (**Figure 7.3**). This is an unusual shape among human

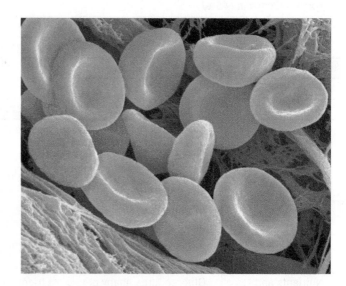

Figure 7.3 Red blood cells. Note that their flattened, biconcave shape gives them a sunken appearance.

cells, but it has several advantages for RBCs. It makes them flexible, so they can bend and flex to squeeze through tiny blood vessels. It also means that no point within an RBC's cytoplasm is ever far from the cell surface, which facilitates the process of gas exchange.

Red blood cells are highly specialized to transport oxygen. Mature RBCs have no nucleus and essentially no organelles. They are essentially fluid-filled bags of plasma membrane, crammed with nearly 300 million molecules of an oxygen-binding protein called **hemoglobin**. Hemoglobin consists of four polypeptide chains, each containing a heme group (Figure 7.4). At the center of each heme group is an iron atom, which can readily form a bond with an oxygen molecule (O_2). In total, a single red blood cell can carry up to 1.2 billion molecules of oxygen. RBCs lack mitochondria and generate ATP by anaerobic pathways. So, they don't consume any of the oxygen they carry; they just transport it.

Several factors influence the binding of hemoglobin to oxygen. Hemoglobin binds oxygen most efficiently when the concentration of oxygen is relatively high and the pH is fairly neutral. These are precisely the conditions that prevail in the lungs. In the lungs, oxygen diffuses into blood plasma and then into red blood cells, where it attaches readily to the iron atoms in hemoglobin. The binding of O_2 by hemoglobin removes some of the O_2 from the plasma, making room for more O_2 to diffuse from the lungs into the plasma. Hemoglobin, with four oxygen molecules attached, called *oxyhemoglobin*, has a characteristic bright red color.

Polypeptide chain ⎯⎯⎯

Heme group with ⎯⎯⎯
iron atom

Figure 7.4 A hemoglobin molecule. Hemoglobin consists of four polypeptide chains folded together, each with a heme group containing a single iron atom. There are nearly 300 million of these molecules in every red blood cell.

The bond hemoglobin forms with oxygen must be temporary so that the oxygen can be released to the cells that need it. In body tissues that use oxygen in the course of their metabolic activities, the concentration of dissolved oxygen and the pH are both lower. Under these conditions, hemoglobin readily releases oxygen into body tissues, making it available to cells. Increased body heat also increases the rate at which hemoglobin releases oxygen. Hemoglobin that has given up its oxygen is called *deoxyhemoglobin*. Deoxyhemoglobin is characteristically dark purple, but because venous blood returning from the cells contains a mixture of oxyhemoglobin and deoxyhemoglobin, venous blood generally has a dark red or maroon color that is between red and purple.

Hemoglobin also transports some carbon dioxide (CO_2), a waste product of cellular metabolism. In tissues, where carbon dioxide levels are high, about 25% of the CO_2 binds to hemoglobin (at different sites than O_2). In the lungs, CO_2 detaches from hemoglobin and is eliminated through respiration. Gas transport and exchange is covered in more detail in the chapter on the respiratory system.

✔ **Quick Check** *Suppose a patient has an unusually low body temperature and his blood pH is unusually basic. How might this affect oxygen delivery to the body tissues?* ▪

Hematocrit and hemoglobin reflect oxygen-carrying capacity

The percentage of blood that consists of red blood cells is called the **hematocrit** (review Figure 7.2). The hematocrit is a relative measure of the oxygen-carrying capacity of blood, and thus it is often of interest to the health care professional. The normal hematocrit range is 43–49% in men and 37–43% in women. A related number is the amount of hemoglobin in the blood, expressed in units of grams per 100 ml of blood (abbreviated Hb gm%). Normal values for hemoglobin are 14–18 gm% in men and 12–14 gm% in women.

An unusual hematocrit (or Hb gm%) may be cause for concern. A low hematocrit may signal *anemia* or other disorders of inadequate red blood cell production (see section 7.4). A high hematocrit can also be risky because excessive red blood cells thicken blood and increase the risk of blood clots. In rare cases a high hematocrit could signal *polycythemia*, a disorder of the bone marrow characterized by an overproduction of red blood cells. Polycythemia increases blood volume and blood viscosity, sometimes leading to headaches, blurred vision, and high blood pressure.

Some shifts in hematocrit (and hemoglobin) are normal and temporary. For example, if you visit the mountains on your next vacation and stay for at least several weeks, your hematocrit rises to compensate for lower levels of oxygen in the air you breathe. This is part of the normal homeostatic regulation of the oxygen-carrying capacity of the blood. After you return to your usual altitude, your hematocrit returns to normal.

> ☑ **Quick Check** *Is the blood sample in Figure 7.2 more likely to be from a man or a woman? Why?* ▪

All blood cells and platelets originate from stem cells

All blood cells and platelets originate from cells in the red marrow of certain bones. These cells, called **stem cells**, divide repeatedly throughout our lives, continually producing immature blood cells. These immature cells develop into platelets, and the various types of mature red and white blood cells described in Figure 7.5.

RBCs have a short life span

Some stem cells develop into immature cells called *erythroblasts* ("red" + "immature"). Erythroblasts become

filled with hemoglobin and develop into mature RBCs, or erythrocytes, in about a week. As they mature, these cells lose their nucleus and organelles, and so they cannot reproduce. Thus, all new RBCs must originate from dividing stem cells. Because they lack a nucleus and therefore cannot perform many standard cell activities (such as producing new proteins and phospholipids to renew their cell membranes), they wear out rather quickly. Red blood cells live for only about 120 days, but during that time they make nearly 3,000 round-trips a day, ferrying O_2 from the lungs to the tissues and CO_2 from the tissues back to the lungs. Because they live for such a short time, red blood cells must be produced throughout life—at the incredible rate of more than 2 million per second—just to keep the hematocrit constant.

Old and damaged RBCs are removed from the circulating blood and destroyed in the liver and spleen by large cells called **macrophages**. Macrophages are derived from *monocytes*, the largest of the white blood cells.

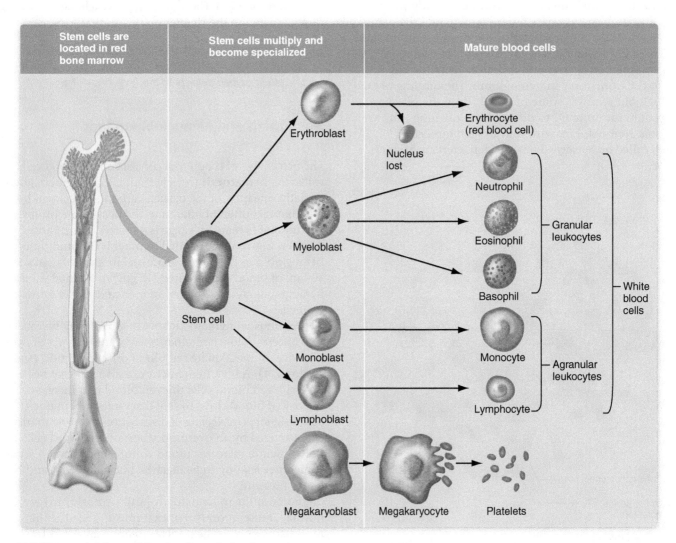

Figure 7.5 The production of blood cells and platelets. Blood cells have short life spans and must be continually replaced. Stem cells in the red marrow of bones continually divide and give rise to a variety of types of blood cells.

Macrophages surround, engulf, and digest the red blood cell. The process is called **phagocytosis**. The four peptide chains of the hemoglobin molecules are then dismantled into their constituent amino acids, and the amino acids are recycled to make new proteins. The iron atoms of the heme groups are returned to the red bone marrow, where they are used again in the production of new hemoglobin for new red blood cells. The heme groups (minus the iron) are converted by the liver to a yellowish pigment called *bilirubin*. If you've ever noticed how a bruise slowly changes color as it heals, from purple to blue to green to yellow, you have observed the chemical breakdown of the heme groups to bilirubin at the site of damage. Under normal circumstances, when hemoglobin is broken down in the liver, bilirubin mixes with bile secreted during digestion and passes into the intestines. This pigment contributes to the characteristic colors of urine and feces.

When the liver fails to secrete bilirubin into the bile properly or when the bile duct from the liver to the intestines is blocked, bilirubin may accumulate in blood plasma. High circulating levels of bilirubin make skin and mucous membranes look yellowish and can turn the whites of the eyes yellow. This condition is called *jaundice* (from *jaune*, French for "yellow"). Jaundice may also be caused by an increase in the rate of RBC breakdown.

RBC production is regulated by a hormone

Regulation of RBC production is a negative feedback control loop that maintains homeostasis (Figure 7.6). The number of RBCs is not regulated (there are no cells capable of counting the number of RBCs), only their effect—their ability to transport oxygen. Certain cells in the kidneys monitor the availability of oxygen. If oxygen availability falls for any reason, these cells cause the kidneys to secrete a hormone called **erythropoietin**. Erythropoietin is transported in the blood to the red bone marrow, where it stimulates stem cells to produce more red blood cells. When the oxygen-carrying capacity of blood returns to an appropriate level as monitored by kidney cells, the cells cut back on their production of erythropoietin, and RBC production returns to normal. Thus, the body maintains homeostasis of oxygen availability by adjusting the production rate of the RBCs that transport it.

Some people with kidney disease do not produce enough erythropoietin to regulate their RBC production properly. Fortunately, erythropoietin is now available commercially and can be administered to stimulate red cell production.

Some athletes have abused erythropoietin by injecting it to increase their RBC production and thus their blood oxygen-carrying capacity, a practice called **blood doping**. Three gold medalists at the 2002 Winter Olympics, Spain's Johann Mühlegg and Russia's Larissa Lazutina and Olga Danilova, were disqualified and stripped of their medals because of blood doping. All three skiers tested positive for

Figure 7.6 Negative feedback control of the availability of oxygen. Certain cells in the kidney are sensitive to the amount of oxygen available to them. When oxygen availability falls, these cells produce erythropoietin, a hormone that stimulates the bone marrow to produce red blood cells. The increase in red blood cells returns oxygen availability toward normal, which reduces the stimulus for further erythropoietin secretion. Ultimately, homeostasis of oxygen availability is achieved.

✅ *What might happen in this feedback loop if bone marrow is diseased and is unable to make enough red blood cells?*

darbepoetin, an erythropoietin-like drug that is 10 times more powerful than the natural hormone.

Blood doping can have serious health consequences. Excess red blood cells make blood more viscous, and so the heart must work harder to pump blood through the body. The dehydration that follows strenuous exercise can concentrate the blood even more, increasing the risk of blood clots, high blood pressure, heart attack, and stroke.

White blood cells defend the body

Approximately 1% of whole blood consists of **white blood cells (WBCs or leukocytes)**. Larger than red blood cells, they are also more diverse in structure and function. They have a nucleus but no hemoglobin. Because they are translucent, they are difficult to identify under the microscope unless they have been stained. Each cubic millimeter of blood contains only about 7,000 of them, and there is only one WBC for every 700 RBCs. White blood cells play a number of crucial roles in defending against disease and injury.

Like red blood cells, white blood cells arise from stem cells in the red bone marrow. As shown in Figure 7.5, stem cells produce immature blood cells that develop into the various WBCs. There are two major categories of white blood cells: *granular leukocytes* (granulocytes) and *agranular leukocytes* (agranulocytes). Both types contain granules (actually vesicles) in their cytoplasm that are filled with proteins and enzymes to assist their defensive work. However, the granules of the agranular leukocytes are not visible when the cells are stained for viewing ("a–" means "without").

Most WBCs have a short life span. Many granular leukocytes die within a few hours to nine days, probably because of injuries sustained while fighting invading microorganisms. Monocytes may survive for several months; lymphocytes for several days to many years. Dead and injured WBCs are continually removed from the blood by the liver and spleen.

Circulating levels of white blood cells rise whenever the body is threatened by viruses, bacteria, or other challenges to health. When activated by tissue injury or microbes, each type of WBC seems able to produce chemicals that stimulate the production of new WBCs from the bone marrow and also the release of stored WBCs from the spleen.

Red cells remain entirely within the vascular system except in cases of tissue injury, but some white cells leave the vascular system and circulate in the tissue fluid between cells, or in the fluid in the lymphatic system. Because they can change their shape, they can squeeze between the cells that form the capillary walls. White blood cells, part of the body's defense system, are discussed in more detail in the chapter on the immune system. In this chapter we describe the important characteristics of each type.

Granular leukocytes: Neutrophils, eosinophils, and basophils

The granular leukocytes include neutrophils, eosinophils, and basophils. These names are based on their staining properties:

- **Neutrophils,** the most abundant type of granulocyte, account for about 60% of WBCs. (Their name—which means "neutral-loving"—reflects the fact that their granules do not significantly absorb either a red or blue stain.) The first white blood cells to combat infection, neutrophils surround and engulf foreign cells (Figure 7.7). They especially target bacteria and some fungi, and their numbers can rise dramatically during acute bacterial infections such as appendicitis or meningitis.
- **Eosinophils** make up a relatively small percentage (2–4%) of circulating white blood cells. (Their name comes from their tendency to stain readily with an acidic red stain called *eosin*.) Eosinophils have two important functions. The first is to defend the body against large

Figure 7.7 A neutrophil attacks a *Bacillus* bacterium. In the first stage of phagocytosis, the neutrophil has approached the bacterium using the protuberances on its surface. Next it will engulf and destroy the bacterium (Color SEM × 8,000).

parasites such as worms (hookworms, tapeworms, flukes, and pinworms, among others). These parasites are too big to be surrounded and engulfed through phagocytosis. Instead, clusters of eosinophils surround each parasite and bombard it with digestive enzymes. The second function of eosinophils involves releasing chemicals that moderate the severity of allergic reactions.

- **Basophils**, the rarest white blood cells, account for only 0.5% of leukocytes. (They are named for their tendency to stain readily with basic blue stains.) The granules in the cytoplasm of basophils contain histamine, a chemical that initiates the inflammatory response. When body tissues are injured, basophils secrete histamine, causing adjacent blood vessels to release blood plasma into the injured area. The plasma brings in nutrients, various cells, and chemicals to begin the process of tissue repair. The swelling, itching, and redness associated with inflammation may not feel pleasant, but they are part of the immune system's defenses against molecules that are perceived as threatening.

Agranular leukocytes: Monocytes and lymphocytes The agranular leukocytes include monocytes and lymphocytes. The largest WBCs, **monocytes**, make up about 5% of circulating white blood cells. They can filter out of the bloodstream and take up residence in body tissues, where they differentiate into the macrophages that engulf invaders and dead cellular debris by phagocytosis. They also stimulate lymphocytes to defend the body. Monocytes seem especially active during chronic infections, such as tuberculosis, and against viruses and certain bacterial parasites.

Lymphocytes total about 30% of circulating white blood cells. They are found in the bloodstream, tonsils, spleen, lymph nodes, and thymus gland. They are classified into two types, *B lymphocytes* and *T lymphocytes* (or B cells and T cells). B lymphocytes give rise to *plasma cells* that produce *antibodies*, specialized proteins that defend against microorganisms and other foreign invaders. T lymphocytes target and destroy specific threats such as bacteria, viruses, and cancer cells. Both play a crucial role in the body's immune system.

☑ **Quick Check** *A friend sprains her ankle, and it soon becomes red, swollen, and sore. Which type of white blood cell is probably responsible for these symptoms, and what is its major function?* ▪

Platelets are essential for blood clotting

Less than 1% of whole blood consists of **platelets**. Platelets are derived from megakaryocytes, which are large cells derived from stem cells in the bone marrow (review Figure 7.5). Megakaryocytes never circulate—they remain in the bone marrow. Platelets are just small pieces of megakaryocyte cytoplasm and cell membrane. Because platelets are not living cells, they last only about five to nine days in the circulation.

When a blood vessel is injured and leaks blood, platelets participate in the clotting process, thereby limiting the vascular and tissue damage. We examine the clotting process in the next section. Once the bleeding is stopped, platelets also participate in the repair process by releasing proteins that promote blood vessel growth and repair.

↩ **Recap** **Blood consists of a watery fluid containing cells, proteins, nutrients, cellular waste products, and ions. Red blood cells are specialized for transporting oxygen and carbon dioxide; white blood cells protect against disease. Blood cells arise from stem cells in bone marrow. Platelets, important in blood clotting, are small pieces of bone marrow cells called** *megakaryocytes.* ▪

7.2 Hemostasis: Stopping blood loss

One of the most important properties of the circulatory system is its ability to limit blood loss following injury. **Hemostasis**, the natural process of stopping the flow or loss of blood, proceeds in three stages: (1) vascular spasm, or intense contraction of blood vessels in the area, (2) formation of a platelet plug, and (3) blood clotting,

also called *coagulation* (Figure 7.8). Once blood loss has stopped, tissue repair can begin.

Vascular spasms constrict blood vessels to reduce blood flow

When a blood vessel is damaged, smooth muscle in its wall undergoes spasms—intense contractions that constrict the vessels. If the vessels are medium-sized to large, the spasms

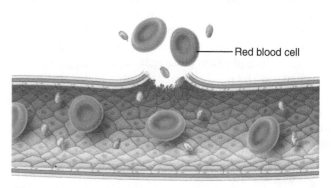

❶ **Vessel injury.** Damage to a blood vessel exposes the vessel muscle layers and the tissues to blood.

❷ **Vascular spasm.** The blood vessel contracts, reducing blood flow.

❸ **Platelet plug formation.** Platelets adhere to each other and to the damaged vessel.

❹ **Clot formation.** Soluble fibrinogen forms an insoluble mesh of fibrin, trapping RBCs and platelets.

Figure 7.8 **The stages of hemostasis.**

reduce immediate outflow of blood, minimizing the damage in preparation for later steps in hemostasis. If the vessels are small, the spasms press the inner walls together and may even stop the bleeding entirely. Vascular spasms generally last for about half an hour, long enough for the next two stages of hemostasis to occur.

Platelets stick together to seal a ruptured vessel

Normally, platelets circulate freely in blood. However, when the lining of a blood vessel breaks, exposing underlying proteins in the vessel wall, platelets swell, develop spiky extensions, and begin to clump together. They also become sticky and start adhering to the walls of the vessel and to each other. More platelets congregate and undergo these same changes. The result is a platelet plug that seals the injured area. If the rupture is fairly small, a platelet plug may be able to close it within several seconds. This may be enough to stop the bleeding. If damage is more severe, blood clotting occurs.

BlogInFocus (MB)

Based on the knowledge that platelets release proteins involved in the healing process, it has been proposed that a treatment called Platelet Rich Plasma (PRP) therapy might improve the healing time of slow-to-heal connective tissue injuries. (To learn more about this therapy, visit MJ's blog in the Study Area in MasteringBiology and look under "PRP Therapy.")

A blood clot forms around the platelet plug

The third stage in hemostasis is the formation of a blood clot, during which the blood changes from a liquid to a gel. This involves a series of chemical reactions that ultimately produce a meshwork of protein fibers within the blood. At least 12 substances, known as clotting factors, participate in these reactions. We will focus on three clotting factors: prothrombin activator, thrombin, and fibrinogen.

Damage to blood vessels stimulates the vessels and nearby platelets to release *prothrombin activator*. This activates the conversion of *prothrombin*, a plasma protein, into an enzyme called **thrombin**. This reaction requires the presence of calcium ions (Ca^{2+}). Thrombin in turn facilitates the conversion of a soluble plasma protein, *fibrinogen*, into long insoluble threads of a protein called **fibrin**. The fibrin threads wind around the platelet plug at the wound site, forming an interlocking net of fibers that traps and holds platelets, blood cells, and various molecules against the opening (see Figure 7.8).

The mass of fibrin, platelets, and trapped red blood cells coalesces into an initial *clot* that reduces the flow of blood at the site of injury (Figure 7.9). This initial fibrin clot can form in less than a minute. Shortly thereafter, platelets in the clot

start to contract, tightening the clot and pulling the vessel walls together. Generally the entire process of blood clot formation and tightening takes less than an hour.

If any step in this process is blocked, even a minor cut or bruise can become life threatening. Consider *hemophilia*, an inherited condition caused by a deficiency of one or more clotting factors. People with the most common form of the condition, hemophilia A, lack a protein known as *clotting factor VIII*. When a vessel is breached, blood clots slowly or not at all. Even if the skin is not broken, severe bruising can spread into joints and muscles (Figure 7.10). Fifty years ago

Figure 7.9 Magnified view of a developing clot, showing red blood cells trapped in a network of fibrin fibers.

Figure 7.10 Complications of hemophilia. People with hemophilia can suffer severe bruising (hemorrhaging) from only minor bumps or scrapes.

Donating Blood

A rapid loss of 30% or more of blood volume strains the body's ability to maintain blood pressure and deliver oxygen to cells throughout the body. When this happens, survival may depend on receiving a gift of donated blood. In addition, blood is often needed for certain planned surgical procedures. Approximately 15 million units of blood are donated every year, and almost 5 million people receive donated blood. Most people who donate blood get nothing more (and nothing less) than the satisfaction of knowing they have helped someone in need.

To donate blood you must be at least 17 years old (16 in some states) and weigh at least 110 pounds. You'll be given a physical examination and asked for your health history, including a confidential questionnaire about your sexual history and recent international travel. This is not done to embarrass you, but to ensure that it is safe for you to give blood and that your blood will be safe for others. You will not be allowed to donate if you are pregnant, for example, and you may not be allowed to donate if you have traveled recently to a malaria-infected area or if you have ever received a blood transfusion in (or were born in) certain

countries. For more specific information, consult the American Red Cross.

The blood withdrawal procedure itself is relatively painless (a needle is inserted into an arm vein) and takes about 10–20 minutes. All needles used are brand-new and sterile—you cannot catch AIDS or any other bloodborne disease by donating blood. Afterward you'll be advised to drink and eat something, and avoid rigorous physical exercise for the rest of the day. This is not the best day to go mountain climbing, but just about anything less strenuous is OK.

Most donors are allowed to give only one unit of blood (1 pint, about 10% of your blood volume). This is not enough to affect you adversely. Usually the donated blood volume is replaced within several hours by any fluids that you drink. The liver replaces the lost plasma proteins within two days, and stem cells in bone marrow replace the lost RBCs in about a month.

What happens to the blood you give? Sometimes it is stored as whole blood, but more often it is separated into three components: packed cells, platelets, and plasma. Each component may be given to different recipients, meaning that your single "gift of life" can benefit several people. ■

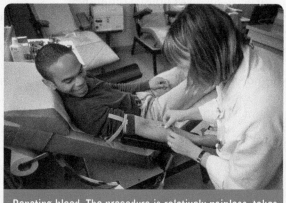

Donating blood. The procedure is relatively painless, takes only a short time, and can save lives.

most people with hemophilia did not survive to adulthood, but today many bleeding episodes can be controlled by administering clotting factor VIII. Because clotting factor VIII was initially purified from donor blood, which at that time could not be tested for the HIV virus, in the past some hemophiliacs contracted AIDS. Today all blood is screened for HIV. In addition, the use of donor blood as a source of factor VIII has decreased because genetic engineering techniques have made it possible to produce factor VIII in the laboratory.

Certain medications can also interfere with hemostasis. If you cut yourself after taking aspirin, for example, you

may notice that you bleed more than usual. This is because aspirin blocks platelet clumping and slows the formation of a platelet plug. If you plan to have surgery, your doctor will probably advise you to avoid taking aspirin for at least 7–10 days before the surgery.

↻ **Recap** **Damage to blood vessels causes the vessels to spasm (contract). Nearby platelets become sticky and adhere to each other, limiting blood loss. In addition, a series of chemical events causes the blood in the area to clot, or coagulate (form a gel).** ■

7.3 Human blood types

Blood transfusions—the administration of blood directly into the bloodstream of another person—may seem like a miracle of modern medicine, but the concept is not new. For over a century, physicians have tried to counteract severe blood loss by transfusing blood from one living person into another. Sometimes these attempts were successful. More often they were not, resulting in severe illness or even death for the recipient. Why did they save some lives but not others?

Today we know the success of blood transfusions depends largely on **blood type**, based primarily on the ABO blood group system. If you ever donate or receive blood, you will undergo testing to determine your blood type. If you receive blood from someone who does not belong to a compatible blood type, you could suffer a severe reaction.

To understand the concept of blood typing, we must first be familiar with antigens and antibodies. Our cells have certain surface proteins that the immune system can recognize and identify as "self"—in other words, belonging to us. These are like passwords that cause our immune system to ignore our own cells. Foreign cells carry different surface proteins, which the immune system recognizes as "nonself." An **antigen** (*anti* means "against," and the Greek word *gennan* means "to generate") is a nonself cell protein that stimulates the immune system of an organism to defend the organism. As part of this defense, the immune system produces an opposing protein called an **antibody** ("against" + "body").

Produced by lymphocytes, antibodies belong to the class of plasma proteins called gamma globulins, mentioned earlier. Antibodies mount a counterattack on antigens they recognize as nonself (Figure 7.11). There are many antibodies, each one specialized to attack one particular antigen. This response has been compared to a lock and key: only a specific antibody key can fit a specific antigen lock. Antibodies float freely in the blood and lymph until they encounter an invader with the matching antigen. They bind to the antigen molecule to form an antigen-antibody complex that marks the foreigner for destruction. The formation of an antigen-antibody complex often causes the foreign cells to clump together, effectively inactivating them (Figure 7.11b).

Antigens and antibodies are discussed in more detail in the chapter on the immune system. Let's look at how their interactions relate to blood type and blood transfusions.

ABO blood typing is based on A and B antigens

Like other cells, red blood cells have proteins on the outer surface of their cell membranes that allow the body to identify them as "self." The interactions between these antigens, and the development of antibodies against the antigens of foreign red blood cells, underlie the reactions that can occur after blood transfusions.

Red blood cells are classified according to the ABO blood group system, in which nearly all individuals belong to one of four types: A, B, AB, or O. Type A blood has A antigens, type B blood has B antigens, type AB blood has *both* A and B antigens, and type O blood has neither (think of the O as a "zero"). In addition, all individuals have circulating antibodies (and the ability to make more antibodies) against any surface antigens different from their own; type A blood has type B antibodies, type B blood has type A antibodies, type O blood has both type A and B antibodies, and type

a) Antibody binds to antigen. Antibodies ignore the "self" surface proteins but bind to the antigen of the foreign cell, forming an antigen-antibody complex.

b) Antigen-antibody complexes clump together. Clumping effectively inactivates the foreign cells.

Figure 7.11 How antibodies recognize and inactivate foreign cells.

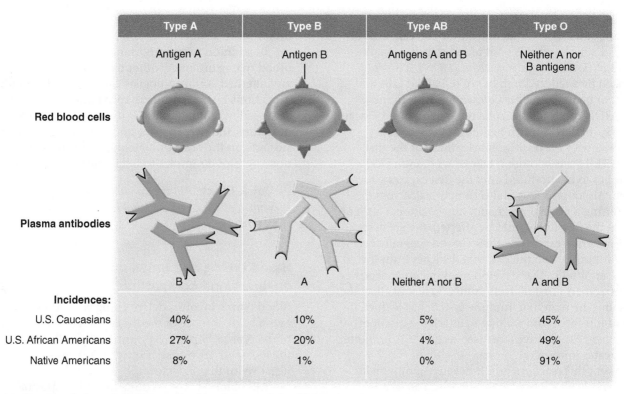

	Type A	Type B	Type AB	Type O
Red blood cells	Antigen A	Antigen B	Antigens A and B	Neither A nor B antigens
Plasma antibodies	B	A	Neither A nor B	A and B
Incidences:				
U.S. Caucasians	40%	10%	5%	45%
U.S. African Americans	27%	20%	4%	49%
Native Americans	8%	1%	0%	91%

Figure 7.12 Characteristics of the four major blood types of the ABO typing system, showing their RBC surface antigens, antibodies, and relative incidences among various populations.

☑ *In which population—Caucasian, African American, or Native American—would it be least risky to do an emergency blood transfusion without blood typing either the donor or the recipient?*

AB blood has neither antibody. Figure 7.12 shows these various blood types and also indicates the relative incidences of each type in various populations. The antibodies appear early in life, regardless of whether a person has ever received a blood transfusion. These antibodies attack red blood cells with foreign antigens, damaging them and causing them to *agglutinate*, or clump together. If agglutination is extreme, the clumps may block blood vessels, causing organ damage or even death. In addition, hemoglobin released by damaged red blood cells can block the kidneys, leading to kidney failure. Any adverse effect of a blood transfusion is called a *transfusion reaction*.

If you have type A blood, you are restricted to receiving transfusions of either type A or type O blood because neither of them has a foreign (type B) antigen. A transfusion of type B or type AB blood would provoke your antibodies to mount an attack against the B antigen of the donated RBCs, causing them to agglutinate. Similarly, if you're type B, you cannot receive any blood with type A antigens (A or AB). People with type AB blood can generally receive transfusions not only from other AB individuals but from all three of the other blood types as well. People with type AB blood, however, can donate only to other type AB individuals. Type O persons can give blood to persons of A, B, or AB type, but they can receive blood only from type O. Notice that it is the antibodies of the recipient that generally cause the

transfusion reaction. Though the donor blood may have antibodies against the recipient's RBCs, they rarely cause transfusion reactions because the volume of blood given is generally small compared to the volume of the recipient's blood.

☑ **Quick Check** *Suppose a man has a rare mutation in his blood cell antigens, such that he has only a single unique blood antigen, "C." Nobody else in the world has the type C antigen and nobody else has antibodies that will react to it. Can he donate blood safely to anybody else? Explain.* ●

Rh blood typing is based on Rh factor

Another red blood cell surface antigen, called **Rh factor** because it was first discovered in rhesus monkeys, is also important in blood transfusions. Approximately 85% of Americans are *Rh-positive*, meaning they carry the Rh antigen on their red blood cells. About 15% are *Rh-negative*—they do not have the Rh antigen, and consequently their immune systems respond to any foreign Rh antigen by making antibodies against it.

The Rh factor is a particular concern for Rh-negative women who wish to have children. If an Rh-negative woman becomes pregnant by an Rh-positive man, the fetus may be Rh-positive. If some of the fetus's Rh-positive blood cells leak into the mother's blood, the mother starts producing anti-Rh antibodies. These maternal antibodies can cross the placenta and attack the fetus's red blood cells. The result may be *hemolytic disease of the newborn (HDN)*, a disorder characterized by a reduced number of red blood cells and toxic levels of hemoglobin breakdown products in the newborn. HDN can lead to mental retardation or even death.

The risk of HDN is much higher for the second and all subsequent Rh-positive fetuses than for the first (Figure 7.13). This is because it takes days or even weeks for antibodies to be produced after the first exposure to an antigen. Although a few fetal cells may leak across the placenta during a normal pregnancy and so present a slight chance that the first fetus could be affected, the greatest chance of maternal exposure to fetal blood generally occurs right at childbirth, when the placenta detaches from the uterus. The antibodies that develop from maternal exposure during the woman's first delivery come too late to affect the first fetus. But the maternal immune system has learned its lesson, and it is ready and waiting to attack the blood of any subsequent Rh-positive fetus (see section 9.7, Immune memory creates immunity).

To prevent this reaction, an Rh-negative mother who *may* be carrying an Rh-positive child is given an injection of anti-Rh antibodies (RhoGAM) at 28 weeks of gestation, just in case. Then, if the newborn *is* Rh-positive, the mother is given a second injection no later than three days after childbirth. The injected antibodies quickly destroy any of the newborn's red blood cells that may have entered the woman's circulation during childbirth, before her immune system has time to react to them. The injected antibodies disappear in a short time.

In addition to its important medical applications, blood typing has many other uses. Because blood types are inherited, anthropologists can track early population migrations by tracing inheritance patterns. Blood typing is also used in criminal investigations to compare the blood of victims and perpetrators, and to eliminate or identify suspects on the basis of matching antigens. DNA tests can be done on blood samples to help determine paternity.

✅ **Quick Check** *Will the immune system of an Rh-positive woman attack blood cells from an Rh-negative baby? Why or why not?* ▪

Blood typing and cross-matching ensure blood compatibility

Blood typing involves determining your ABO type and the presence or absence of the Rh factor. For example, if your blood type is "B-pos" (B+), you are type B and positive for the Rh factor. If you are "O-neg" (O−), you are type O and negative for the Rh factor.

ABO blood typing is done by adding plasma containing small amounts of anti-A and anti-B antibodies to diluted blood, and then placing a drop of the blood on a glass slide. If the blood agglutinates, then it must contain the antigens that match the antibodies (Figure 7.14).

AB+ individuals were once called *universal recipients* because they can generally receive blood from any other

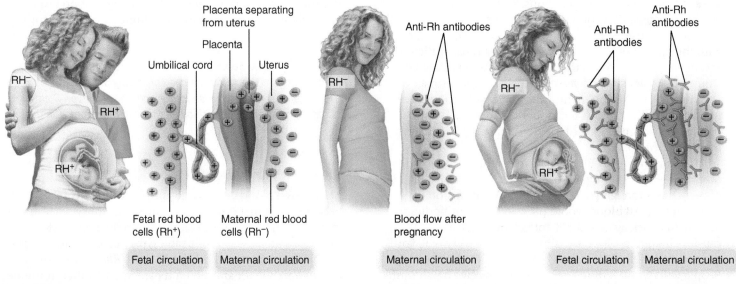

a) **When an Rh-positive man fathers a child by an Rh-negative woman, the fetus may inherit the Rh-positive antigen.**

b) **During pregnancy or more commonly at childbirth, a small amount of fetal blood enters the mother's circulation.**

c) **Over the next several weeks the woman develops antibodies and an immune memory against the Rh antigen.**

d) **When the woman becomes pregnant with her second Rh-positive child, her immune system quickly produces antibodies that attack the fetus's red blood cells.**

Figure 7.13 **How Rh factor incompatibility can affect a fetus.**

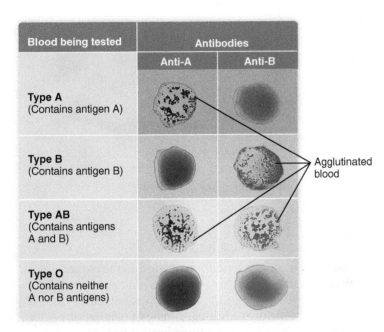

Blood being tested	Antibodies	
	Anti-A	Anti-B
Type A (Contains antigen A)		
Type B (Contains antigen B)		
Type AB (Contains antigens A and B)		
Type O (Contains neither A nor B antigens)		

Agglutinated blood

Figure 7.14 Blood typing for ABO blood types. Anti-A and Anti-B antibodies are added to a drop of diluted blood. If the red blood cells have the surface antigen that matches the antibody, the blood agglutinates (the red cells clump together). Type O blood does not agglutinate in response to either antibody.

☑ *Draw two more pictures illustrating what Rh-positive and Rh-negative blood will look like if they are each mixed with Rh antibodies.*

type. Type O− individuals were formerly called *universal donors* because their blood can usually be donated to any other type. However, because transfusion reactions can occur unexpectedly, the terms are now considered outdated. Why do transfusion reactions occur occasionally even when blood has been adequately typed for ABO blood type and the Rh factor? The reason is that there are over 100 other less common blood antigens in the human population, in addition to the very common A, B, and Rh antigens. Fortunately, most of them are fairly rare. To ensure that blood transfusions are absolutely safe, however, medical laboratories generally do blood typing and *cross-matching*. Cross-matching involves mixing small samples of donor blood with recipient plasma, and recipient blood with donor plasma, and examining both combinations for agglutination. If agglutination does not occur in either combination, the bloods are assumed to be a good match.

↺ **Recap** Blood types A, B, AB, and O are defined by the presence (or absence) of type A and/or type B surface antigens on red blood cells. In addition to blood type, all persons are classified according to the presence or absence of another red blood cell surface antigen called the Rh factor. Antibodies to the Rh factor can cause a serious immune reaction of a mother to her own fetus under certain circumstances. ■

7.4 Blood substitutes

Although it might seem that whole blood would always be the best choice for a patient who needs blood, there are a number of reasons why this might not always be so: 1) Human blood can carry transmissible diseases, though these days the risk is small. 2) Blood must be typed and cross-matched to the recipient in order to avoid transfusion reactions. The right blood may not always be available for every patient. 3) Whole blood can only be stored for several months and must be stored under refrigerated conditions. Refrigeration during storage and transport is not always possible in some countries. 4) Demand for blood is rising more quickly than the supply.

For all of these reasons, the development of a good blood substitute has been an area of active research for over 70 years. Two types of blood substitutes are currently under investigation. Both are more properly called *oxygen-carrying* blood substitutes because they focus on only the oxygen-carrying function of blood. One type is based on various forms of modified hemoglobin in aqueous (watery) solutions. Generally the hemoglobin comes from animals or is produced by genetic engineering in bacteria, so there are still the issues of limited supply and of possible disease transmission. In addition, hemoglobin protein in aqueous solution (not enclosed in a red blood cell membrane) is toxic to kidneys. Therefore the hemoglobin must first be "packaged" in some way (encapsulated, cross-linked, or polymerized) before it can be used as an oxygen-carrying alternative to whole red blood cells.

The other type of oxygen-carrying blood substitute seeks to take advantage of the high oxygen-carrying capacity of *perfluorocarbons* (PFCs), a group of colorless liquids containing only carbon and fluorine. PFCs are not soluble in water, so they must be dispersed (emulsified) as small droplets in water. Each droplet is about 1/40th the size of a red blood cell, making them small enough to travel through the smallest blood vessels. An aqueous solution containing PFC can carry several times more oxygen than whole blood, and because PFCs are completely man-made and can be heat-sterilized, they carry virtually no risk of transmitting disease. They could also be manufactured in unlimited quantities and stored for prolonged periods without refrigeration. However, a distinct disadvantage of the PFCs is that they are removed from the bloodstream within two days by exhalation and evaporation via the lungs. PFCs currently are used only as a temporary substitute for blood.

Several commercial hemoglobin-based and PFC-based products have been developed and tested in clinical trials, only to be withdrawn due to safety concerns. The bottom line is that there is still no ideal substitute for whole blood. Research into blood substitutes continues, however, so don't be surprised if there is a viable blood substitute in commercial use in your lifetime.

↺ **Recap** Blood substitutes currently under investigation include modified hemoglobin products and perfluorcarbons. ■

7.5 Blood disorders

Blood disorders include infections, several types of cancers, and disorders that affect the ability of the blood to deliver oxygen to the tissues or to clot properly when injury occurs. The effects of blood disorders are often widespread because blood passes through every organ in the body.

Mononucleosis: Contagious viral infection of lymphocytes

Mononucleosis is a contagious infection of lymphocytes in blood and lymph tissues caused by the Epstein-Barr virus, a relative of the virus that causes herpes. Most common during adolescence, "mono" is nicknamed the "kissing disease" because it's frequently spread through physical contact.

Symptoms of mononucleosis can mimic those of the flu: fever, headache, sore throat, fatigue, and swollen tonsils and lymph nodes. A blood test reveals increased numbers of monocytes and lymphocytes. The disease is called mononucleosis because many of the lymphocytes enlarge and begin to resemble monocytes. There is no known cure for mononucleosis, but almost all patients recover on their own within four to six weeks. Extra rest and good nutrition help the body overcome the virus.

It has been proposed that an innovative way to cleanse blood of infectious bacteria might be to draw them out with magnets. (To learn more about this still clinically untested idea, visit MJ's blog in the Study Area in MasteringBiology and look under "Cleansing Blood with Magnets.")

Blood poisoning: Bacterial infection of blood

Although blood normally is well defended by the immune system, occasionally bacteria may invade the blood, overwhelm its defenses, and multiply rapidly in blood plasma. The bacteria may be toxic themselves, or they may secrete toxic chemicals as by-products of their metabolism. A bacterial infection of blood is called *blood poisoning*, or *septicemia*.

Blood poisoning may develop from infected wounds (especially deep puncture wounds), severe burns, urinary system infections, or major dental procedures. To help prevent it, wash wounds and burns thoroughly with soap and water. Consult your doctor immediately when an infection is accompanied by flushed skin, chills and fever, rapid heartbeat, or shallow breathing. An early sign of some blood poisonings is the sudden appearance of red streaks on healthy skin near the site of an infection (Figure 7.15). The red streaks are due to inflammation of veins or lymph vessels in the area, indicating that the infection is spreading towards the systemic circulation. Although blood poisonings can be very dangerous (even fatal) if left untreated, in most cases they can be treated effectively with antibiotics.

Figure 7.15 Blood poisoning.

Anemia: Reduction in blood's oxygen-carrying capacity

Anemia is a general term for reduction in the oxygen-carrying capacity of blood. All causes of anemia produce similar symptoms: pale skin, headaches, fatigue, dizziness, difficulty breathing, and heart palpitations—the uncomfortable feeling that one's heart is beating too fast as it tries to compensate for the lack of oxygen delivery. Major types of anemia include:

- **Iron-deficiency anemia.** Recall that every hemoglobin molecule contains four molecules of iron. When the body is deficient in iron, hemoglobin cannot be synthesized properly. The result is fewer hemoglobin molecules per red blood cell, and thus a decreased ability to transport oxygen. Iron-deficiency anemia is the most common form of anemia worldwide. Usually it is due to too little iron in the diet, but it can also be caused by an inability of the digestive tract to absorb iron properly. Generally it can be treated by taking pills that contain iron, or by eating foods rich in iron such as leafy green vegetables and meat.
- **Hemorrhagic anemia.** Anemia due to blood loss (hemorrhage) may be caused by injuries, bleeding ulcers, excessive menstrual flow, and even certain parasites. Treatment includes finding and treating the underlying cause of blood loss, if possible, and making sure one has enough iron in the diet to replenish the lost red blood cells.
- **Pernicious anemia.** Pernicious anemia is caused by a deficiency of vitamin B_{12} absorption by the digestive tract. Vitamin B_{12} is important for the production of normal red blood cells. Pernicious anemia can be treated by injections of B_{12}.
- **Hemolytic anemia.** Hemolytic anemia is the result of rupture (lysis) or early destruction of red blood cells. One cause is sickle-cell disease, an inherited disorder in which the red blood cells take on an abnormal sickle shape when the oxygen concentration is low. Because of their abnormal shape, sickled red blood cells become damaged as they travel through small blood vessels. Once damaged, they are destroyed by the body. Sickle-cell anemia is most prevalent in Africans who live near the equator and in African Americans. Another common cause of hemolytic anemia is the parasite that causes malaria.

- **Anemia due to renal failure.** When the kidneys fail, they do not produce enough erythropoietin to maintain normal red blood cell production. In this case the anemia is secondary to the renal failure and the attendant decline in erythropoietin, not the primary problem. This type of anemia is easily corrected by treatment with exogenous erythropoietin, called EPO, which maintains their red blood cell production within normal limits.

☑ **Quick Check** *Why does exogenous erythropoietin (EPO) effectively treat anemia due to renal failure, but is ineffective in treating the other four types?* ▪

Leukemia: Uncontrolled production of white blood cells

Leukemia refers to any of several types of blood cancer. Their common characteristic is uncontrolled proliferation of abnormal or immature white blood cells in the bone marrow. Overproduction of abnormal WBCs crowds out the production of normal white blood cells, red cells, and platelets. Huge numbers of leukemia cells enter and circulate in the blood, interfering with normal organ function.

There are two major categories of leukemia: acute, which develops rapidly, and chronic. Both are thought to originate in the mutation of a white blood cell (a change in genetic structure) that results in uncontrolled cell division, producing billions of copies of the abnormal cell. Possible causes for the original mutation include viral infection or exposure to radiation or harmful chemicals. Genetic factors may also play a role.

Leukemia can produce a wide range of symptoms. Tissues may bruise easily because of insufficient production of platelets. Anemia may develop if the blood does not contain enough red blood cells. Bones may feel tender because the marrow is packed with immature white blood cells. Some people experience headaches or enlarged lymph nodes.

Treatment can cure leukemia in some cases and prolong life in others. Treatment generally involves radiation therapy and chemotherapy to destroy the rapidly proliferating cancer cells. This kills the normal stem cells as well, so transplants of bone marrow tissue are required to provide new stem cells. Cord blood transplants may be another option (see "Current

Issue: Should You Bank Your Baby's Cord Blood?"). As with blood transfusions, all tissue must undergo testing to make sure the donor's antigens are compatible with those of the patient.

Multiple myeloma: Uncontrolled production of plasma cells

Like leukemia, *multiple myeloma* is a type of cancer. In this case, abnormal plasma cells in the bone marrow undergo uncontrolled division. Plasma cells are a type of lymphocyte responsible for making a specific antibody. The proliferating plasma cells manufacture too much of an abnormal, frequently incomplete antibody, impairing production of other antibodies and leaving the body vulnerable to infections. Bones become tender as healthy bone marrow is crowded out by malignant plasma cells. Levels of calcium in the blood soar as bone tissue is destroyed. Treatment includes anticancer drugs and radiation therapy.

Thrombocytopenia: Reduction in platelet number

Thrombocytopenia is a reduction in the number of platelets in the blood. Thrombocytopenia can occur for a number of reasons, such as viral infection, anemia, leukemia, other blood disorders, exposure to X-rays or radiation, and even as a reaction to certain drugs. Sometimes platelet levels decline for no apparent reason, in which case they often rise again after several weeks.

Symptoms include easy bruising or bleeding, nosebleeds, bleeding in the mouth, blood in urine, and heavy menstrual periods. Treatment of the underlying cause generally improves the condition. If it persists, surgical removal of the spleen often helps.

↩ **Recap** **Blood poisoning and mononucleosis are types of blood infection. Several factors, including iron deficiency or hemorrhage, can lead to a reduction in oxygen-carrying capacity of blood. Leukemia and multiple myeloma are blood cell cancers that arise when abnormal cells in the bone marrow divide uncontrollably. Thrombocytopenia, a disease of too few platelets, is characterized by easy bleeding or bruising.** ▪

Chapter Summary

The components and functions of blood *p. 142*

- Blood consists of formed elements and plasma. Blood has transport, regulatory, and protective functions.
- Plasma contains numerous plasma proteins involved in transport, regulation of water balance, and protection. It also contains ions, hormones, nutrients, wastes, and gases.
- Erythrocytes (RBCs) are highly specialized for the transport of oxygen, but they also transport some carbon dioxide.

- Hemoglobin is the primary protein in red blood cells and gives blood its oxygen-carrying capacity.
- The formed elements of blood all originate from stem cells in red bone marrow.
- Leukocytes (WBCs) defend the body against disease and the effects of injury.
- RBCs and WBCs have short life spans and must continually be replaced. RBC production is stimulated when the body detects low oxygen levels in the blood.
- Platelets are cell products that participate in blood hemostasis.

Hemostasis: Stopping blood loss *p. 149*

- Hemostasis is a three-phase process that prevents blood loss through damaged vessels. The phases are (1) vascular spasm, (2) the formation of a platelet plug, and (3) blood clotting.
- During the formation of a blood clot, substances released by damaged blood vessels cause soluble proteins called *fibrinogen* to become insoluble protein threads called *fibrin*. The threads form an interlocking mesh of fibers, trapping blood cells and sealing ruptured vessels.

Human blood types *p. 152*

- Successful transfusion of blood from one person into another depends on compatibility of their blood types, which is determined by antibodies in plasma and surface antigens on red blood cells.
- Blood types are classified primarily on the basis of the ABO system and the presence or absence of the Rh factor.
- Rh factor in particular can affect certain pregnancies adversely.

Blood substitutes *p. 155*

- Hemoglobin-based blood substitutes are made from modified hemoglobin derived from animals or genetically engineered bacteria.
- Perfluorocarbon-based blood substitutes are emulsions of colorless liquids with a high oxygen-carrying capacity, called perfluorocarbons (PFCs).

Blood disorders *p. 156*

- Mononucleosis is a contagious viral disease of lymphocytes and lymphatic tissue.
- *Blood poisoning* is a general term for infection of blood plasma by various microorganisms.
- Anemia is a reduction in blood oxygen-carrying capacity for any number of reasons, including insufficient red blood cell or hemoglobin production, and excessive blood loss.
- Leukemia is a cancer characterized by uncontrolled production of abnormal leukocytes (white blood cells).

Terms You Should Know

anemia, *156*	leukocyte (WBC), *147*
blood type, *152*	phagocytosis, *147*
erythrocyte (RBC), *144*	plasma, *143*
erythropoietin, *147*	plasma proteins, *143*
fibrin, *150*	platelet, *149*
hematocrit, *145*	Rh factor, *153*
hemoglobin, *145*	stem cell, *146*
hemostasis, *149*	

Concept Review

Answers can be found in the Study Area in MasteringBiology.

1. Describe the functions of blood.
2. Describe the role of hemoglobin in the transport of oxygen and carbon dioxide.
3. Explain how the production of red blood cells is regulated to maintain homeostasis of the oxygen-carrying capacity of blood.

4. Define *hematocrit*, and explain why it is important.
5. Describe how damaged or dead RBCs and the hemoglobin they contain are removed from the blood.
6. Describe the difference between the actions of neutrophils and eosinophils.
7. Describe the mechanism of hemostasis.
8. List the four ABO blood types. For each one, list its red blood cell surface antigen(s) and plasma antibody (antibodies).
9. Describe the Rh factor and its implications for pregnancy.
10. Compare and contrast the various causes of anemia.

Test Yourself

Answers can be found in Appendix A.

1. All of the following proteins are associated with blood. Which of these is found specifically inside red blood cells?
   a. prothrombin
   b. fibrinogen
   c. albumin
   d. hemoglobin

2. Which of the following blood components protects the individual from a variety of infectious agents such as bacteria and viruses?
   a. white blood cells
   b. platelets
   c. albumin
   d. red blood cells

3. Which of the following make(s) up the greatest volume of whole blood?
   a. platelets
   b. red blood cells
   c. plasma
   d. white blood cells

4. Which of the following influence(s) the bonding of oxygen to hemoglobin?
   a. pH
   b. oxygen concentration
   c. temperature
   d. all of the above

5. Jason has just spent four weeks in Rocky Mountain National Park, studying plants that grow above 10,000 feet elevation. Which of the following would be a likely change in his blood because of time spent at high elevation?
   a. increased number of red blood cells
   b. increased number of white blood cells
   c. increased number of platelets
   d. increased amount of globulins in the plasma

6. A person with Type A− (A-negative) blood will have:
   a. type A plasma antibodies
   b. type A antigens on the red blood cells
   c. Rh antigens on the red blood cells
   d. all of the above

7. A deficiency of platelets would result in:
   a. fatigue and dizziness
   b. bleeding and bruising
   c. increased susceptibility to infections
   d. all of the above

8. Which donor blood type would be most appropriate for transfusing an O− recipient?
   a. A−
   b. B−
   c. O−
   d. Any of these blood types could be successfully used for this recipient.

9. What do erythroblasts, myeloblasts, lymphoblasts, and megakaryoblasts have in common?
   a. They are immature cells that develop into white blood cells.
   b. They are immature cells that develop into red blood cells.
   c. They are found in the circulating blood.
   d. They are immature cells found in the bone marrow.

10. Jaundice is caused by the presence of _____ in the blood plasma, which is a breakdown product of _____.
    a. hemoglobin…red blood cells
    b. bilirubin…hemoglobin
    c. albumin… white blood cells
    d. prothrombin…platelets

11. Which white blood cells are present in the greatest number in the blood and are the body's first responders to infection?
    a. neutrophils
    b. lymphocytes
    c. platelets
    d. monocytes

12. The steps in the hemostasis process are (1) platelets become sticky and form a platelet plug, (2) prothrombin is converted to thrombin by prothrombin activator, (3) walls of a damaged blood vessel undergo spasms, (4) a clot forms from fibrin, platelets, and trapped red blood cells, and (5) fibrinogen is converted to fibrin. Which of the following choices represents the correct order of these steps?
    a. 1-3-2-4-5
    b. 3-1-2-5-4
    c. 3-2-1-4-5
    d. 3-5-4-1-2

13. Hemophilia results from:
    a. an insufficient number of red blood cells
    b. an insufficient number of platelets
    c. a lack of one or more plasma proteins involved in blood clotting
    d. an abnormal type of hemoglobin

14. Which of the following can lead to anemia?
    a. insufficient iron in the diet
    b. insufficient Vitamin B_{12} absorption from the digestive tract
    c. spending several weeks at a high altitude
    d. both (a) and (b)

15. Which property do red blood cells and platelets have in common?
    a. Both lack a nucleus.
    b. Both transport oxygen.
    c. They are found in approximately equal numbers in the circulating blood.
    d. Both are derived from erythroblasts.

Apply What You Know

Answers can be found in the Study Area in MasteringBiology.

1. A 35-year-old white male is sent by his physician for a blood test. The lab results indicate his white blood cell count (number of WBCs per milliliter of blood) is 18,000. The typical WBC count for a man his age is 6,000–9,000, meaning his white blood cell count is considerably higher than normal. What may this mean?

2. One treatment for certain types of leukemia is to try to kill all of the stem cells in bone marrow through radiation and chemotherapy and then to give a bone marrow transplant from another person (a donor). Can just anyone be the donor? Who is most likely to be a good donor? Explain.

3. In the not too distant past, people with type O-negative blood were considered to be universal blood donors, and their blood was sought out during times of need. Explain what was meant by the term *universal donor*, why O-negative persons were considered to be universal donors, and why universal donor is now considered an outdated term.

4. The text states that when red blood cells reach actively metabolizing tissues, they release their cargo of oxygen because both the oxygen concentration and the pH are lower in metabolically active tissues than in the general circulation. The oxygen concentration is lower because actively metabolizing tissues are using oxygen at a rapid rate. But what causes the pH to fall? And how might a fall in pH cause the hemoglobin to release oxygen?

   Can you think of any other variables that might also lead to the release of oxygen by hemoglobin?

5. The term has just ended. Over the past three weeks you wrote three term papers, studied for finals, and went to work at your part-time job. You passed all your courses and never missed a day of work. Of course, you spent the last three weeks living on soda, frozen pizza, and Ramen noodles (who has time for real food with all this work?).

   Now that the term is over you notice that you are very tired, your skin is pale, you are experiencing headaches and dizziness, and even your breathing is difficult. You go to your doctor who diagnoses you with anemia. What type of anemia do you most likely have, how is it different from other forms of anemia, and what treatment will your doctor most likely suggest?

6. Coumadin is an anticoagulant drug that is sometimes given to patients who have just suffered a deep vein thrombosis, a pulmonary embolism, or a heart attack, or to patients with artificial heart valves. It helps reduce the chance of future clots and the further risk of embolism. The active ingredient in Coumadin is warfarin, a rat poison. How do you think the same compound can be used for these two very different purposes?

BlogInFocus

Answers can be found in the Study Area in MasteringBiology.

1. A drug has been discovered that prevents newly formed blood clots from breaking down. What sorts of patients or medical conditions might be helped with such a drug? (Hint: Visit MJ's blog in the Study Area in MasteringBiology and look under "Drug Reduces Bleeding.")

MasteringBiology®

Go to MasteringBiology for practice quizzes, activities, eText, videos, current events, and more.

Heart and Blood Vessels

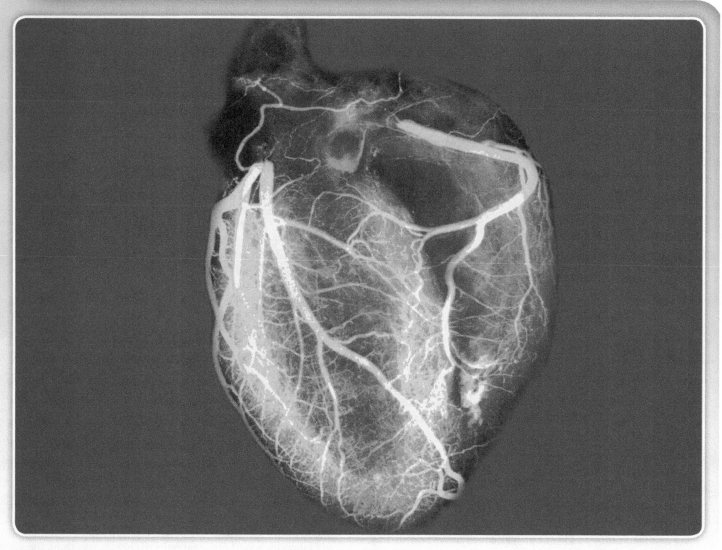

A colored arteriogram of a healthy heart.

Comparative Effectiveness Research

Mr. Reynolds has a heart problem. An angiogram shows that a short section of one of the main arteries supplying the left ventricle of his heart is narrowed, restricting blood flow to his heart muscle. His doctor tells him that he is at serious risk of a heart attack. The doctor explains that there are at least three techniques that could be used to restore blood flow to his heart: 1) balloon angioplasty, 2) placement of a coronary artery stent, or 3) a coronary artery bypass graft (CABG). Which would be best for Mr. Reynolds? They go over the options together, but to Mr. Reynolds it seems like comparing

apples to oranges, and he isn't sure he understands. He leaves the decision to his physician, whom he has known for 25 years. In the end the physician chooses the technique that has worked best for his previous patients.

The body of medical literature is now so vast and expanding so rapidly that even the best physicians can't know it all. This is where a relatively new field of medical science called "Comparative Effectiveness Research" (CER) comes in. CER focuses solely on analyzing the medical literature already available, in order to reach scientifically sound judgments about the value (or

lack of value) of specific medical tests, treatments, and disease prevention strategies. In essence, CER seeks to determine the best practices in medicine based on our current knowledge.

Changing How Medicine Is Practiced

Consider how CER might benefit Mr. Reynolds's physician (and Mr. Reynolds, of course). By reviewing CER data, Mr. Reynolds's physician might learn that a stent is considered most effective for a middle-aged white male, but that there's an age-related tipping point; if the patient is over 55, balloon angioplasty is the better option. (Hmmm, how old *is* Mr. Reynolds this year?) CER might also be able to tell the physician whether the treatment of choice depends on the severity of the narrowing. If the degree of narrowing of a coronary artery is greater than 80%, for example, then the best option (again, for a middle-aged white male) would be a coronary artery bypass graft rather than balloon angioplasty. (What is the degree of narrowing in Mr. Reynolds, anyway?) Toss in other factors like gender, race, physical condition, body weight, smoker-versus-nonsmoker, and you can begin to see the full power of CER. In theory, CER could analyze multiple factors at once to arrive at the best treatment option for patients who are described by a particular combination of factors. Even the most experienced physicians don't carry *that* much information around in their heads!

Some politicians believe that little investment in CER now could pay for itself in reduced health care expenditures in the future. To jump-start a national CER program, Congress passed the "Comparative Effectiveness Research Act of 2009" and funded it with $1.1 billion as part of the economic stimulus package. To keep the program free of bias, the prestigious Institute of Medicine of the National Academies of Science was asked to come up with a list of 100 top priority topics for CER funding. Among the topics are comparisons of the most effective practices to treat or prevent a number of cardiovascular diseases and risk factors, including high blood pressure, coronary artery disease, heart failure, and abnormalities of heart electrical rhythm. This is not surprising, because cardiovascular diseases are the number one cause of death in the United States (cancer is second).

Who Will Make Health Care Decisions?

CER could become a powerful tool for improving health care quality and lowering

Doctoring, 1948.

costs. Nevertheless, the CER Act of 2009 has stirred strong feelings among physicians, patients, politicians, and the health care industry because of the ways it could change how medicine is practiced. Physicians and patient advocacy groups worry that if "best practices" become defined by CER, doctors and patients could begin to lose the right to make decisions regarding treatment options. They fear that health care decisions may be dictated primarily by bureaucrats and insurance companies. In recognition of this concern, the legislation included language to the effect that the outcomes of CER research are not to be used to develop required or mandated guidelines when it comes to treatment decisions, payment, or insurance coverage, including Medicare/Medicaid coverage. In other words, physicians and patients can still use their best judgment in deciding upon the appropriate treatment option, regardless of what CER shows, at least for now.

But therein lies the big question: Will physicians and patients continue to be the decision makers in medical treatment decisions? Or is it inevitable that the old way of practicing medicine is going to change? Do we really believe that health insurance companies, group health plans,

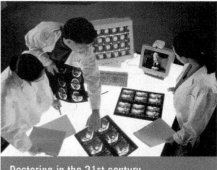
Doctoring in the 21st century.

and even Medicare/Medicaid will *not* find a way to use CER data to "influence" reimbursement policies, and hence treatment decisions? Would it be a good thing or a bad thing if they did?

Flash forward 25 years. It's you in the doctor's office now, and the doctor is telling you that your cardiac scan shows a 63% narrowing of a section of your left-anterior descending coronary artery. She swings around to her computer, taps a few keys, and reports that according to the latest data analysis from the Comparative Effectiveness Research Institute, the current most effective method for repair of your coronary artery is "Robotic Artificial Vessel Extension" (RAVE), and that your government-supported health insurance will pay for it. A few more taps and she informs you that there is an opening on the hospital's surgical schedule on Tuesday and that Dr. Sloan is available to do your surgery. She adds that 99.7% of Dr. Sloan's surgeries of this type have been successful, and that 94% of all patients with your condition are discharged from the hospital on the same day as the surgery. You go home to your wife with the good news, and tell her to go ahead and book that vacation to London next month.

QUESTIONS TO CONSIDER

1 Who do you want to help you decide which treatment options would be best for you? If it's not a specific person or position (doctor, patient representative, health insurance specialist), what information would you like to have available to you?

2 Do you think cost-effectiveness should be a part of any comparative effectiveness analysis of treatment or diagnostic options? Why or why not?

THE FACTS...

- **The medical literature is expanding so rapidly that even the best physicians can no longer keep up with it.**

- **Recognizing this, the government will spend $1.1 billion on Comparative Effective Research (CER) to determine the best practices in medicine based on our current knowledge, and to make that information available to everyone.**

- **CER could also slow down rising health care costs.**

- **A legitimate concern is that CER recommendations will eventually influence third-party payer reimbursement policies, so that patients and doctors will lose the ability to make treatment choices.**

>> **The structure of blood vessels reflects their function.** Thick-walled arteries and arterioles transport blood to the tissues under high pressure; capillaries allow fluid exchange between blood and interstitial fluid; large thin-walled veins store most of the blood and return it to the heart.

>> **The heart is a pump comprised primarily of muscle.** The heart has no bones; its ability to pump blood depends on one-way valves and coordination of muscle contraction.

>> **Arterial blood pressure is held fairly constant by homeostatic control mechanisms.** Maintenance of a nearly constant arterial blood pressure allows local blood flow to each tissue to be regulated by local mechanisms.

>> **Cardiovascular disorders are the number one cause of death in the United States.** Cardiovascular disorders include heart attack, heart failure, stroke, and cardiac arrhythmias.

>> **Your risk of developing cardiovascular disease is affected by your lifestyle choices.** Risk factors include smoking, a lack of exercise, obesity, and chronic stress.

The heart is a pump, but it's a very special pump indeed. The heart is constructed entirely of living cells and cellular materials, yet it is capable of greater reliability than some of the best pumps ever built by humans. It can easily withstand 80–100 years of continuous service without ever stopping for repairs. Its output is also fully adjustable on demand, over a range of about 5–25 liters of blood per minute.

The heart and blood vessels are known collectively as the **cardiovascular system** (from the Greek *kardia*, heart, and the Latin *vasculum*, small vessel). The heart provides the power to move the blood, and the vascular system represents the network of branching conduit vessels through which the blood flows. The cardiovascular system is essential to life because it supplies every region of the body with just the right amount of blood. It is essential to maintaining homeostasis. We consider the blood vessels first.

8.1 Blood vessels transport blood

A branching network of blood vessels transports blood to all parts of the body. The network is so extensive that if our blood vessels were laid end to end, they would stretch 60,000 miles!

We classify the body's blood vessels into three major types: *arteries, capillaries,* and *veins.* Thick-walled arteries transport blood to body tissues under high pressure. Microscopic capillaries participate in exchanging solutes and water with the cells of the body. Thin-walled veins store blood and return it to the heart. Figure 8.1 illustrates the structures of each type of blood vessel, described in more detail below.

Arteries transport blood away from the heart

As blood leaves the heart it is pumped into large, muscular, thick-walled **arteries**. Arteries transport blood away from the heart. The larger arteries have a thick layer of muscle because they must be able to withstand the high pressures generated by the heart. Arteries branch again and again, so the farther blood moves from the heart, the smaller in diameter the arteries become.

Large and medium-sized arteries are like thick garden hoses, stiff yet somewhat elastic (distensible). Arteries stretch a little in response to high pressure but are still strong enough to withstand high pressures year after year. The ability to stretch under pressure is important because a second function of arteries is to store the blood that is pumped into them with each beat of the heart and then provide it to the capillaries (at high pressure) even between heartbeats. The elastic recoil of arteries is the force that maintains the blood pressure between beats. Think of the arteries as analogous to a city's water system of branching, high-pressure pipes that provide nearly constant water pressure to every home.

The structure of the walls of large and medium-sized arteries is ideally suited to their functions. The vessel wall is a sandwich of three distinct layers surrounding the *lumen,* or hollow interior of the vessel:

1. The thin inner layer, the *endothelium,* is a layer of flattened, *squamous* epithelial cells. It is a continuation of the lining of the heart. The flattened cells fit closely together, creating a slick surface that keeps friction to a minimum and promotes smooth blood flow.

2. Just outside the endothelium is a layer composed primarily of smooth muscle with interwoven elastic connective tissue. In most arteries this is the thickest layer of the three. Tonic contraction of the smooth muscle of large and medium-sized arteries stiffens the arteries and helps them resist the high pressures within, but it does not constrict them enough to alter blood flow. The elastic tissue makes large and medium-sized arteries slightly distensible so they can stretch passively to accommodate the blood that enters with each heartbeat.

3. The outermost layer of large and medium-sized arteries consists of a tough supportive layer of connective tissue, primarily collagen. This sturdy casing anchors vessels to surrounding tissues and helps protect them from injury.

The fact that arteries are constantly under high pressure places them at risk of injury. If the endothelium becomes damaged, blood may seep through the injured area and work

Figure 8.1 The structures of blood vessels in the human body.

its way between the two outer layers, splitting them apart. The result is an *aneurysm*, or ballooning of the artery wall. Some aneurysms cause the smooth muscle and endothelial layers to bulge inward as they develop, narrowing the lumen enough to reduce blood flow to an organ or region of the body. Others force the outer connective tissue layer to bulge outward. Sometimes aneurysms cause severe chest pain, but in other cases they are completely symptomless until they rupture or "blow out," causing massive internal bleeding and often death. If you've ever seen a water line burst, you know how quickly it can be devastating. Aneurysms of the aorta (see section 8.2) kill an estimated 25,000 Americans every year. Actor John Ritter's sudden death in 2003 was caused by a ruptured aneurysm.

Aneurysms often take years to develop. During this time many can be detected and repaired surgically. Some physicians recommend that anyone with a family history of aneurysm should be examined, even if there are no symptoms. Doctors can sometimes detect inward-bulging aneurysms with a stethoscope (an instrument for listening to sounds inside the body) because flowing blood produces characteristic sounds as it passes through the narrowed area. A computerized tomography (CT) scan may also locate aneurysms before they rupture.

Arterioles and precapillary sphincters regulate blood flow

Eventually blood reaches the smallest arteries, called **arterioles** (literally, "little arteries"). The largest artery in the body, the *aorta*, is about 2.5 centimeters (roughly 1 inch) wide. In contrast, arterioles have a diameter of 0.3 millimeter or less, about the width of a piece of thread.

By the time blood flows through the arterioles, blood pressure has fallen considerably. Consequently, arterioles can be simpler in structure. Generally they lack the outermost layer of connective tissue, and their smooth muscle layer is not as thick. In addition to blood transport and storage, arterioles have a third function not shared by the larger arteries: they help regulate the amount of blood that flows to each capillary. They do this by contracting or relaxing the smooth muscle layer, altering the diameter of the arteriole lumen.

Right where an arteriole joins a capillary is a band of smooth muscle called the **precapillary sphincter** (**Figure 8.2**). The precapillary sphincters serve as gates that control blood flow into individual capillaries.

Contraction of vascular smooth muscle is called *vasoconstriction*. Vasoconstriction of arterioles and precapillary sphincters reduces their diameter and so reduces blood flow to the capillaries. Conversely, relaxation of vascular smooth muscle is called *vasodilation*. Vasodilation of arterioles and precapillary sphincters increases their diameter and so increases blood flow to the capillaries.

A wide variety of external and internal factors can produce vasoconstriction or vasodilation, including nerves, hormones, and conditions in the local environment of the arterioles and precapillary sphincters. If you go outside on a cold day, you may notice that your fingers start to look pale. This is because vasoconstriction produced by nerves is narrowing your vessels to reduce heat loss from your body. On the other hand, hot weather will make your skin appear flushed as vasodilation occurs to speed up heat loss and cool you off. Emotions can also have an impact: vasodilation is partly responsible for the surge in blood flow that causes the penis or clitoris to become erect when we are sexually aroused. Later in this chapter we will talk more about how the cardiovascular system is regulated to maintain homeostasis.

Capillaries: Where blood exchanges substances with tissues

Arterioles connect to the smallest blood vessels, called **capillaries**. Capillaries are thin-walled vessels that average only about one-hundredth of a millimeter in diameter—not much wider than the red blood cells that travel through them. In fact, they are so narrow that RBCs often have to pass through them in single file or even bend to squeeze through.

Extensive networks of capillaries, called *capillary beds*, can be found in all areas of the body, which is why you are likely to bleed no matter where you cut yourself. The branching design of capillaries and their thin, porous walls allow blood to exchange oxygen, carbon dioxide, nutrients, and waste products with tissue cells. Capillary walls consist of a single layer of squamous epithelial cells. Microscopic pores pierce this layer, and the cells are separated by narrow slits. These openings are large enough to allow the exchange of fluid and other materials between blood and the interstitial fluid (the fluid that surrounds every living cell), yet small enough to retain red blood cells and most plasma proteins in the capillary (**Figure 8.3**). Some white blood cells can also squeeze between the cells in capillary walls and enter the tissue spaces.

In effect, capillaries function as biological strainers that permit selective exchange of substances with the interstitial fluid. In fact, capillaries are the *only* blood vessels that can exchange materials with the interstitial fluid.

Figure 8.4 illustrates the general pattern of how water and substances move across a capillary. At the beginning of a capillary, fluid is filtered out of the vessel into the interstitial fluid, accompanied by oxygen, nutrients, and raw materials needed by the cell. The filtered fluid is essentially like plasma except that it contains very little protein because most protein molecules are too large to be filtered. Filtration of fluid is driven by the blood pressure generated by the heart. Waste materials such as carbon dioxide and urea diffuse out of the cells and back into the blood.

Most of the filtered fluid is reabsorbed by diffusion back into the last half of the capillary before it joins a vein. The force for this reabsorption is the presence of protein in the blood but not in the interstitial fluid. In other words,

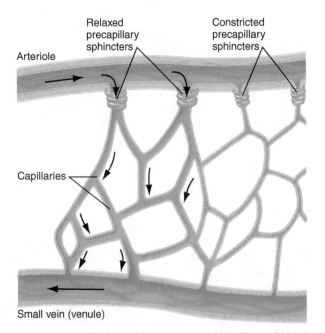

Figure 8.2 Precapillary sphincters control the flow of blood into individual capillaries. In this diagram the two precapillary sphincters on the right are vasoconstricted, reducing flow in that region. Arrows indicate direction of blood flow.

a) **A medium-magnification view showing a rich network of capillaries surrounding and interconnecting small arteries and veins.**

b) **A higher magnification showing a single branching capillary.** Notice the red blood cells traveling single file in the capillary.

c) **The structure of a capillary.**

Figure 8.3 **Capillaries.**

Figure 8.4 **The general pattern of movement between capillaries, the interstitial fluid, and cells.** For simplicity, only a single tissue cell is shown, but a single capillary may supply many nearby cells.

✅ *Why does most of the fluid that was filtered out of the proximal (beginning) end of the capillary move back into distal (far) end?*

water diffuses from an area of high water concentration (interstitial fluid) to an area of lower water concentration (blood plasma). However, the diffusional reabsorption of water does not quite match the pressure-induced filtration of water, so a small amount of filtered fluid remains in the interstitial space as excess interstitial fluid.

✅**Quick Check** *Why doesn't exchange of gases and nutrients with the interstitial fluid occur in arteries and arterioles too, instead of just in capillaries? Put another way, what about the structure of an artery or an arteriole prevents such exchange from occurring?* ▪

Lymphatic system helps maintain blood volume

Although the imbalance between the amount of plasma fluid filtered by the capillaries and the amount reabsorbed is not large, over the course of a day it would amount to about two or three liters. This excess plasma fluid must be returned to the cardiovascular system somehow, or soon all the plasma would end up in the interstitial fluid.

The excess plasma fluid is absorbed by blind-ended capillaries that join together into a collection system of larger vessels, collectively called the *lymphatic system*. The lymphatic system is somewhat similar to (and nearly parallel to) the venous system of blood vessels, except that the fluid it contains (called *lymph*) does not contain plasma proteins or red blood cells. In addition to absorbing excess interstitial fluid, the capillaries of the lymphatic system also pick up objects in the interstitial fluid that are too large to diffuse into the blood capillaries, such as lipid droplets absorbed during digestion and invading microorganisms. The lymphatic system transports the lymph back to veins near the heart, where it rejoins the venous blood.

Aside from its role in returning excess fluid and large objects to the blood, the lymphatic system also plays a major role in

Answers to ✅ **questions can be found in Appendix A.**

our immune defenses. You'll hear more about the lymphatic system when we discuss the immune system. For now, just be aware that the lymphatic system, though technically not part of the cardiovascular system, plays a vital role in maintaining the proper volumes of blood and interstitial fluid.

✅ **Quick Check** *There are certain parasitic worms that can enter the lymphatic system and completely block the lymphatic capillaries draining an arm or a leg. Predict what would happen to the arm or leg if this occurs.* ■

Veins return blood to the heart

From the capillaries, blood flows back to the heart through *venules* (small veins) and **veins** (see Figures 8.1 and 8.4). Like the walls of arteries, the walls of veins consist of three layers of tissue. However, the outer two layers of the walls of veins are much thinner than those of arteries. Veins also have a larger diameter lumen than arteries.

The anatomical differences between arteries and veins reflect their functional differences. As blood moves through the cardiovascular system, the blood pressure becomes lower and lower. The pressure in veins is only a small fraction of the pressure in arteries, so veins do not need nearly as much wall strength (provided by muscle and connective tissue) as arteries. The larger diameter and high distensibility of veins allows them to stretch (like thin balloons) to accommodate large volumes of blood at low pressures.

In addition to their transport function, then, veins serve as a blood volume reservoir for the entire cardiovascular system. Nearly two-thirds of all the blood in your body is in your veins. Thanks to their blood reservoir function, even if you become dehydrated or lose a little blood, your heart will still be able to pump enough blood to keep your blood pressure fairly constant.

The distensibility of veins can lead to problems in returning blood to the heart against the force of gravity. When you stand upright, blood tends to collect in the veins of your legs and feet. People who spend a lot of time on their feet may develop *varicose veins*, permanently swollen veins that look twisted and bumpy from pooled blood. Varicose veins can appear anywhere, but they are most common in the legs and feet. In severe cases the skin surrounding veins becomes dry and hard because the tissues are not receiving enough blood. Often varicose veins can be treated by injecting an irritating solution that shrivels the vessels and makes them less visible. This should not affect blood flow because surrounding undamaged veins take over and return blood to the heart.

Fortunately, three mechanisms assist the veins in returning blood to the heart: (1) contractions of skeletal muscles, (2) one-way valves inside the veins, and (3) movements associated with breathing. Let's look at each in turn.

Skeletal muscles squeeze veins On their path back to the heart, veins pass between many skeletal muscles. As we move and these muscles contract and relax, they press against veins and collapse them, pushing blood toward the heart. You may have noticed that you tire more easily when you stand still than when you walk around. This is because walking improves the return of blood to your heart and prevents fluid accumulation in your legs. It also increases blood flow and the supply of energy to your leg muscles.

One-way valves permit only one-way blood flow Most veins contain valves consisting of small folds of the inner layer that protrude into the lumen. The structure of these valves allows blood to flow in one direction only: toward the heart. They open passively to permit blood to move toward the heart and then close whenever blood begins to flow backward. Together, skeletal muscles and valves form what is called the "skeletal muscle pump" (Figure 8.5). Once blood has been pushed toward the heart by skeletal muscles or drained in that direction by gravity, it cannot drain back again because of these one-way valves. The opening and closing of venous valves is strictly dependent on differences in blood pressure on either side.

Valve (open)

One-way valves (closed)

Calf muscles relaxed

Calf muscles contracted

Figure 8.5 The skeletal muscle pump. With the calf muscle relaxed, blood accumulates in the vein. Backflow is prevented by one-way valves. When the calf muscle contracts, skeletal muscles press on the vein, forcing blood toward the heart through the upper one-way valve. The lower one-way valve remains closed, preventing backflow.

Pressures associated with breathing push blood toward the heart The third mechanism that assists blood flow involves pressure changes in the thoracic (chest) and abdominal cavities during breathing. When we inhale, abdominal pressure increases and squeezes abdominal veins. At the same time, pressure within the thoracic cavity decreases, dilating thoracic veins. The result is to push blood from the abdomen into the chest and toward the heart. This effect is sometimes called the "respiratory pump."

↻ **Recap** A branching system of thick-walled arteries distributes blood to every area of the body. Arterioles regulate blood flow to local regions, and precapillary sphincters regulate flow into individual capillaries. Capillaries consisting of a single layer of cells exchange materials with the interstitial fluid. The lymphatic system removes excess fluid. The thin-walled veins return blood to the heart and serve as a volume reservoir for blood. ▪

8.2 The heart pumps blood through the vessels

The heart, a muscular, cone-shaped organ slightly larger than your fist, is located in the thoracic cavity between the lungs and behind the sternum, or breastbone. The heart consists mostly of a special type of muscle called *cardiac muscle*. Unlike skeletal muscle, cardiac muscle does not connect to bone. Instead, it pumps ceaselessly in a squeezing motion to propel blood through the blood vessels.

Your heart pumps about 75 times every minute—and this does not include the times it speeds up to supply extra blood during exertion or stress. It never rests for more than two-thirds of a second. Over 70 years, this adds up to about 2.8 billion heartbeats, truly an impressive performance for any muscle. Under normal circumstances the heart's rate of pumping is controlled by the brain, but it can also beat on its own without any instructions from the brain at all.

The heart is mostly muscle

A human heart is shown in **Figure 8.6**. In its natural position within the chest cavity the heart is enclosed in a tough fibrous sac called the *pericardium* (not shown in Figure 8.6). The pericardium protects the heart, anchors it to surrounding structures, and prevents it from overfilling with blood. Separating the pericardium from the heart is a space called the *pericardial cavity*. The pericardial cavity contains a film of lubricating fluid that reduces friction and allows the heart and the pericardium to glide smoothly against each other when the heart contracts.

In cross section we see that the walls of the heart consist of three layers: the epicardium, myocardium, and endocardium (**Figure 8.7**). The outermost layer, the *epicardium*, is a thin layer of epithelial and connective tissue.

Figure 8.6 A human heart.

The middle layer is the **myocardium**. This is a thick layer consisting mainly of cardiac muscle that forms the bulk of the heart. The myocardium is the layer that contracts every time the heart beats. The structure of cardiac muscle cells allows electrical signals to flow directly from cell to cell. An electrical signal in one cardiac muscle cell can spread to adjacent cells, enabling large numbers of cells to contract as a coordinated unit. Every time the myocardium contracts, it squeezes the chambers inside the heart, pushing blood outward into the arteries. The innermost layer of the heart, the *endocardium*, is a thin endothelial layer resting on a layer of connective tissue. The endocardium is continuous with the endothelium that lines the blood vessels.

BlogInFocus MB

Damaged heart muscle cells normally are not replaced fast enough help the body recover from heart disease. What's being done to try to solve this problem? Visit MJ's blog in the Study Area in MasteringBiology and look under "Replacing Damaged Heart Cells."

Occasionally, one of the layers of the heart wall becomes inflamed. These conditions are named according to the location of the problem; *–itis* is a suffix that means "inflammation." Thus *pericarditis* refers to inflammation of

Aorta

Superior vena cava

Left pulmonary artery

Right pulmonary artery

Pulmonary trunk

Left pulmonary veins

Left atrium

Aortic semilunar valve

Pulmonary semilunar valve

Right atrium

Left atrioventricular (AV) valve

Left ventricle

Right atrioventricular (AV) valve

Chordae tendineae

Right ventricle

Papillary muscles

Septum

Epicardium

Inferior vena cava

Myocardium

Endocardium

Figure 8.7 A view of the heart showing major blood vessels, chambers, and valves.

the pericardium, *endocarditis* to an inflamed endocardium, and so on. A variety of factors can lead to inflammation in or around the heart wall, including infections, cancer, injuries, or complications from major surgery. Depending on the underlying cause, many cases respond well to antibiotic and anti-inflammatory drugs.

The heart has four chambers and four valves

Taking a closer look at the details of the structure of the heart, we see that it consists of four separate chambers (see Figure 8.7). The two chambers on the top are the **atria** (singular: *atrium*), and the two more-muscular bottom chambers are the **ventricles**. A muscular partition called the **septum** separates the right and left sides of the heart.

Blood returning to the heart from the body's tissues enters the heart at the *right atrium*. From the right atrium, the blood passes through a valve into the *right ventricle*. The right ventricle is more muscular than the right atrium because it pumps blood at considerable pressure through a second valve and into the artery leading to the lungs.

Blood returning from the lungs to the heart enters the *left atrium* and then passes through a third valve into the

left ventricle. The very muscular left ventricle pumps blood through a fourth valve into the body's largest artery, the aorta. From the aorta, blood travels through the arteries and arterioles to the systemic capillaries, venules, and veins and then back to the right atrium again.

The left ventricle is the most muscular of the heart's four chambers because it must do more work than any other chamber. The left ventricle must generate pressures higher than aortic blood pressure in order to pump blood into the aorta. (We'll see how high aortic pressure is in a minute.) The right ventricle has a thinner wall and does less work because the blood pressure in the arteries leading to the lungs is only about one-sixth that of the aorta.

Four heart valves enforce the heart's one-way flow pattern and prevent blood from flowing backward. The valves open and shut passively in response to changes in the pressure of blood on each side of the valve. The right and left **atrioventricular (AV) valves** located between the atria and their corresponding ventricle prevent blood from flowing back into the atria when the ventricles contract. The AV valves consist of thin connective tissue flaps (cusps) that project into the ventricles. The right AV valve is called the *tricuspid valve* because it has three flexible flaps. The left AV valve has two flaps, so it is referred to as the *bicuspid* or *mitral valve*. These valves are supported by strands of connective tissue called *chordae tendineae* that connect to muscular extensions of the ventricle walls called *papillary muscles*. Together, the chordae tendineae and papillary muscles prevent the valves from everting (opening backward) into the atria when the ventricles contract.

Two **semilunar valves** (the pulmonary and the aortic) prevent backflow into the ventricles from the main arteries leaving the heart when the heart relaxes. Each semilunar valve consists of three pocketlike flaps. The valves' name reflects the half-moon shape of these flaps (*semi* means "one-half"; *luna* comes from the Latin word for "moon").

Next, let's follow the overall pattern of blood flow through the body.

The pulmonary circuit provides for gas exchange

Figure 8.8 shows the general structure of the entire cardiovascular system. Note that the heart is pumping blood through the lungs (the **pulmonary circuit**) and through the rest of the body to all the cells (the **systemic circuit**) simultaneously. Each circuit has its own set of blood vessels. Let's follow the pulmonary circuit first:

1. When blood returns to the heart from the veins, it enters the right atrium. The blood that returns to the heart is deoxygenated—it has given up oxygen to tissue cells and taken up carbon dioxide.
2. From the right atrium, blood passes through the right atrioventricular valve into the right ventricle.
3. The right ventricle pumps blood through the pulmonary semilunar valve into the pulmonary trunk (the main pulmonary artery) leading to the lungs. The pulmonary trunk divides into the right and left pulmonary arteries, which supply the right and left lungs, respectively.
4. At the pulmonary capillaries, blood gives up carbon dioxide and receives a fresh supply of oxygen from the air we inhale. It is now oxygenated.
5. The freshly oxygenated blood flows into the pulmonary veins leading back to the heart. It enters the left atrium and flows through the left atrioventricular valve into the left ventricle.

The deoxygenated blood in the right side of the heart never mixes with oxygenated blood in the left. Deoxygenated blood leaving the right side of the heart must pass through the pulmonary circuit (where it picks up oxygen) before it reaches the left side of the heart.

✓**Quick Check** *Do the pulmonary arteries carry oxygenated blood or deoxygenated blood? What features of the pulmonary arteries make them arteries rather than veins?* ■

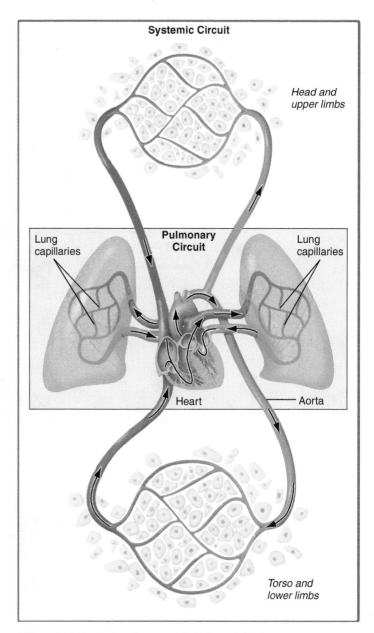

Figure 8.8 A schematic representation of the human cardiovascular system showing the separate pulmonary and systemic circuits. The systemic circuit includes the circulations of the head, torso, limbs, and internal organs, including the heart and some tissues in the lungs.

The systemic circuit serves the rest of the body

When blood enters the left ventricle, it begins the *systemic circuit*, which takes it to the rest of the body.

1. The left ventricle pumps blood through the aortic semilunar valve into the **aorta**, the largest artery.
2. From the aorta, blood travels through the branching arteries and arterioles to the capillaries, where it delivers oxygen and nutrients to all of the body's tissues and organs and removes waste products.
3. From the capillaries, blood flows to the venules, veins, and then back again to the right atrium.

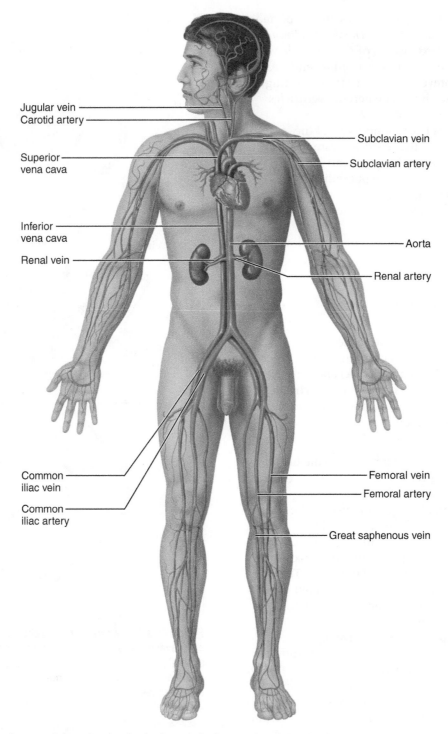

Jugular vein

Carotid artery

Subclavian vein

Superior vena cava

Subclavian artery

Inferior vena cava

Aorta

Renal vein

Renal artery

Common iliac vein

Femoral vein

Femoral artery

Common iliac artery

Great saphenous vein

Figure 8.9 Some of the major arteries and veins in the human body. For simplicity, the lungs and most of the internal organs have been omitted.

Figure 8.9 shows some of the major arteries and veins of the human body. Arteries and veins serving the same vascular region often (but not always) have the same name and generally are located very near to each other. For example, a common iliac artery supplies blood to each leg, and a common iliac vein returns blood from the leg to the heart. However, carotid arteries supply the head, but jugular veins return the blood from the head.

As you might expect of such a hard-working muscle, the heart requires a great deal of oxygen and nutrients to fuel its own operations. Although the heart represents only about 1/200 of your body's weight, it requires roughly 1/20

Cholesterol and Atherosclerosis

As you probably already know, cholesterol is a key component of all cell membranes and the precursor molecule for several hormones. All cells require a certain amount of it for normal functioning. However, too much cholesterol in the blood can lead to a condition called *atherosclerosis*—a thickening of an arterial vessel wall due to the buildup of fatty materials containing cholesterol. Left untreated, atherosclerosis contributes to heart attacks, strokes, aneurysms, and peripheral vascular disease.

Most of the cholesterol in the blood is bound to certain carrier proteins. Together, the cholesterol and the protein are called a *lipoprotein*. There are two types of lipoproteins, based on their densities. One of them, called *low-density lipoprotein (LDL)*, is considered "bad" in terms of atherosclerosis. When present in normal amounts, LDL transports cholesterol throughout the body and makes it available to cells. However, when there is too much LDL it begins to attach to the cells lining the arterial blood vessel wall and then makes its way into the cells. Once inside the cell, LDL triggers an inflammatory response that ultimately results in the buildup of fatty deposits called atherosclerotic *plaques* within the blood vessel wall. Eventually these plaques may rupture, causing blood clots to form that can occlude arteries and cause heart attacks and strokes.

High-density lipoproteins (HDLs), on the other hand, are considered "good" because they target cholesterol for removal. HDLs pick up free cholesterol and carry it to the liver, where it is detached from the protein, mixed with bile, and secreted into the small intestine. Some of the cholesterol in bile is excreted from the body with the feces, although some is reabsorbed, to be used again.

Risk factors for atherosclerosis include factors that raise blood cholesterol (obesity, sedentary lifestyle, and a high-fat diet), smoking, diabetes, hypertension, and a family history of atherosclerosis. Before age 45 men have a 10 times greater risk than women; however, women's risk rises after menopause.

According to the American Heart Association, a total cholesterol of under 200 mg/dl is considered desirable. Ideally, HDL should be greater than 60 mg/dl and LDL should be less than 100 mg/dl. A total cholesterol of greater than 240 mg/dl along with a high LDL and/or low HDL would be cause for concern.

If you're having trouble remembering which lipoprotein is bad for you and which is good, just remember that cholesterol is a lipid, and lipids are less dense than protein or water. So "low-density means more cholesterol," and therefore low-density lipoprotein (LDL) is the "bad" one.

Some degree of atherosclerosis is common with advancing age. However, lifestyle can make a big difference in how rapidly atherosclerosis develops and whether it becomes severe. At the end of this chapter we look at what you can do to lower your risk of atherosclerosis and other cardiovascular conditions. ■

a) Cross section of an artery narrowed by atherosclerotic plaque.

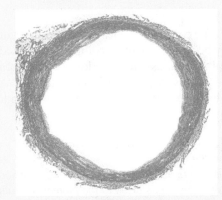

b) The same photo with the atherosclerotic plaque removed, showing how a normal artery would look.

Atherosclerosis.

of your total blood flow at rest. And although the heart is almost continuously filled with blood, the myocardium is too thick to be served by diffusion of oxygen and nutrients from the blood passing through. Thus the heart has its own set of blood vessels called the **coronary arteries** that supply the heart muscle (**Figure 8.10**). The coronary arteries branch from the aorta just above the aortic semilunar valve and encircle the heart's surface (the word coronary comes from the Latin *corona*, meaning "encircling like a crown"). From the surface they send branches inward to supply the myocardium. *Cardiac veins* collect the blood from the capillaries in the heart muscle and channel it back to the right atrium.

Figure 8.10 **Blood vessels of the heart.**

The coronary arteries are relatively small in diameter. If they become partially or completely blocked, perhaps as a result of atherosclerosis, serious health problems can result. Later in this chapter and in the **Health & Wellness** feature we look at what happens when circulation to the heart is impaired.

✅ **Quick Check** *Some babies are born with a heart defect in which the ventricles are connected to the wrong arteries—that is, the right ventricle sends blood to the aorta, and the left ventricle sends blood to the pulmonary trunk. What is the problem with this arrangement?* ●

The cardiac cycle: The heart contracts and relaxes

The pumping action of the heart is pulsatile rather than continuous, meaning that it delivers blood in separate and distinct pulses. A complete cardiac cycle involves contraction of the two atria, which forces blood into the ventricles, followed by contraction of the two ventricles, which pumps blood into the pulmonary artery and the aorta, followed by relaxation of the entire heart. The term **systole** refers to the period of contraction and **diastole** refers to the period of relaxation. The entire sequence of contraction and relaxation is called the **cardiac cycle**.

Every cardiac cycle consists of three steps, as shown in Figure 8.11. Start with the heart as it first begins to contract:

1. *Atrial systole.* As contraction starts, the heart is already nearly filled with blood that entered the ventricles and atria passively during the previous diastole. Contraction of the heart begins with the atria. During atrial systole, both atria contract, raising blood pressure in the atria and giving the final "kick" that fills the two ventricles to capacity. Atrial systole also momentarily stops further inflow from the veins. Both atrioventricular valves are still open, and both semilunar valves are still closed.

2. *Ventricular systole.* The contraction that began in the atria spreads to the ventricles, and both ventricles contract simultaneously. The rapidly rising ventricular pressure produced by contraction of the ventricles causes the two AV valves to close, preventing blood from flowing backward into the atria and veins. At this time the atria relax and begin filling again. The pressure within the ventricles continues to rise until it is greater than the pressure in the arteries, at which point the pulmonary and aortic semilunar valves open and blood is ejected into the pulmonary trunk and the aorta. With each ventricular systole, about 60% of the blood in each ventricle is forcibly ejected.

3. *Diastole.* Both atria and both ventricles are relaxed throughout diastole. At this point pressure within the ventricles begins to fall. As soon as ventricular pressures fall below arterial pressures during early diastole, the pulmonary and aortic semilunar valves close, preventing backflow of arterial blood. Once ventricular pressure falls below blood pressure in the veins, the AV valves open and blood begins to flow passively into the heart.

A complete cardiac cycle occurs every 0.8 second or so. These cycles repeat, from birth to death, without ever stopping. Atrial systole lasts about 0.1 second; ventricular systole, about 0.3 second. During the remaining 0.4 second, the heart relaxes in diastole.

As each surge of blood enters the arteries during systole, the artery walls are stretched to accommodate the extra volume, and arterial pressure rises. Arteries recoil passively during diastole as blood continues to flow out of them through the capillaries. You can feel this cycle of rapid expansion and recoil in the wall of an artery if it's located close to the skin's surface. This is called a *pulse.* A good place to detect a pulse is the radial artery (inside your wrist, just below the base of the thumb).

The heart is composed primarily of cardiac muscle, and like our skeletal muscles it benefits from regular exercise. During sustained (aerobic) exercise the heart beats more rapidly and more powerfully to sustain blood pressure in the face of increased blood flow to hard-working skeletal muscles. Over time this causes the heart to increase in size (hypertrophy) slightly.

Right atrium

Pulmonary semilunar valve

Right AV valve

Right ventricle

Left atrium

Aortic semilunar valve

Left AV valve

Left ventricle

0.1 second

a) Atrial systole. Both atria contract, forcing blood into the ventricles. The AV valves are open, and the semilunar valves are closed.

Diastole

0.4 second

Systole

Aorta

Pulmonary trunk

0.3 second

c) Diastole. The ventricles relax and begin to fill passively with blood through the open AV valves. The semilunar valves are closed, and the atria remain relaxed.

b) Ventricular systole. Both ventricles contract, causing the AV valves to close and the semilunar valves to open. Blood is ejected into the pulmonary trunk and aorta. The atria relax.

Figure 8.11 **The cardiac cycle.**

✓ *What makes the AV and semilunar valves open and close?*

However, it is important not to overdo any exercise training regimen. If it is over-exercised, the heart may become starved for oxygen, and heart muscle may become damaged. The usual guideline for safe but effective exercise training is to perform an activity that raises your heart rate to its "target heart rate" for at least 20 minutes, three times a week or more.

BlogInFocus (MB)

During aerobic exercise you are generally advised to maintain a "target heart rate," the ideal heart rate for exercising your heart strenuously, but not too strenuously. According to new research, the target heart rate is different for women than for men. To review the new findings, visit MJ's blog in the Study Area in MasteringBiology and look under "Maximum Heart Rate for Women."

Heart sounds reflect closing heart valves

There is probably no more basic rhythm to which humans respond than the familiar "lub-DUB–lub-DUB" of the heart beating. We probably experience it, at least subconsciously, even before we are born. These *heart sounds* reflect events that occur during the cardiac cycle—specifically the closing of the heart valves. The "lub" signals the closure of the two AV valves during ventricular systole. The slightly louder "DUB" occurs when the aortic and pulmonary semilunar valves close during ventricular diastole. The sounds are due to vibrations in the heart chambers and blood vessels caused by the closing of the valves.

Blood flows silently as long as it flows smoothly. However, if blood encounters an obstruction, the disturbed flow can create unusual heart sounds called *murmurs*. Many murmurs result from incomplete closing of the heart valves due to unusually shaped valve flaps or stiffening of the flap tissue. If a valve does not close completely, some blood is

a) A pulmonary semilunar valve.

b) An artificial heart valve.

Figure 8.12 **Heart valves.**

forced through it during the cardiac cycle, creating a swishing noise that can be detected through a stethoscope. Murmurs are not necessarily a sign of disease, but physicians can diagnose a variety of heart conditions, including leaking or partially blocked valves, from their sound and timing. Even serious murmurs can often be treated with surgery to replace the defective valve with an artificial valve (Figure 8.12).

☑**Quick Check** *Do any sounds occur at the moment when the atria contract? When the ventricles contract? Explain.* ▪

Cardiac conduction system coordinates contraction

The coordinated sequence of the cardiac cycle is due to the *cardiac conduction system,* a group of specialized cardiac muscle cells that initiate and distribute electrical impulses throughout the heart. These impulses stimulate the heart muscle to contract in an orderly sequence that spreads from atria to ventricles. The cardiac conduction system consists of four structures: sinoatrial node, atrioventricular node, atrioventricular bundle and its two branches, and Purkinje fibers.

The stimulus that starts a heartbeat begins in the **sinoatrial (SA) node**, a small mass of cardiac muscle cells located near the junction of the right atrium and the superior vena cava. The muscle cells of the SA node look just like cardiac muscle cells elsewhere in the heart. What sets them apart is that they initiate electrical signals spontaneously and repetitively, without the need for stimulation from other cells. Electrical impulses initiated by the SA node travel from cell to cell across both atria like ripples on a pond, stimulating waves of contraction (Figure 8.13). Cell-to-cell electrical transmission is made possible by the presence of gap junctions between adjacent cells. The SA node is properly called the *cardiac pacemaker* because it initiates the heartbeat. However, the cardiac pacemaker can be influenced by the brain to speed up or slow down, as we'll see in a minute.

The electrical impulse traveling across the atria eventually reaches another mass of muscle cells called the

Sinoatrial (SA) node

Atrioventricular (AV) node

AV bundle

Bundle branches

Purkinje fibers

Figure 8.13 **The cardiac conduction system.** Electrical activity of the heart normally starts at the SA node, spreads across the atria to the AV node, and then progresses down the AV bundle and its branches to the Purkinje fibers.

atrioventricular (AV) node, located between the atria and ventricles. The muscle fibers in this area are smaller in diameter, causing a slight delay of approximately 0.1 second, which temporarily slows the rate at which the impulse travels. This delay gives the atria time to contract and empty their blood into the ventricles before the ventricles contract.

From the AV node, the electrical signal sweeps to a group of conducting fibers in the septum between the two ventricles called the **atrioventricular (AV) bundle**. These fibers branch and extend into **Purkinje fibers**, smaller fibers that carry the impulse to all cells in the myocardium of the ventricles. Because the electrical impulse travels down the septum to the lower portion of the ventricles and then spreads rapidly upward through the Purkinje fibers, the lower part of the ventricles contract before the upper part. This lower-to-upper squeezing motion pushes blood into the pulmonary trunk and aorta.

Electrocardiogram records the heart's electrical activity

Because the body is largely water and water conducts electrical activity well, we can track the electrical activity of the heart as weak differences in voltage at the surface of the body. An **electrocardiogram (ECG** or **EKG)** is a record of the electrical impulses in the cardiac conduction system. An ECG involves placing electrodes on the skin at the chest, wrists, and ankles. The electrodes transmit the heart's electrical impulses, which are recorded as a continuous line on a screen or moving graph.

A healthy heart produces a characteristic pattern of voltage changes. A typical ECG tracks these changes as a series of three formations: P wave, QRS complex, and T wave. First is the small P wave, representing the electrical impulse traveling across the atria (see Figure 8.13). Second is the QRS complex, representing the spread of the electrical impulse down the septum and around the two ventricles in the Purkinje fibers. It occurs just before the ventricles start to contract. Finally, the T wave is the result of the *end* of the electrical activity in the ventricles. At this time the ventricles relax.

If something goes wrong with the cardiac conduction system or if the heart muscle becomes damaged, abnormal heart electrical impulses and contractions may occur. An abnormality of the rhythm or rate of the heartbeat is called an *arrhythmia*. Arrhythmias take many forms. Occasional skipped heartbeats, for example, are fairly common and usually of no consequence. However, a type of rapid irregular ventricular contraction known as *ventricular fibrillation* (or "V-fib") is very quickly fatal unless treated immediately. Ventricular fibrillation is the leading cause of cardiac death in otherwise healthy people. In a hospital, ventricular fibrillation is treated by "cardioversion," in which a strong electrical current is applied to the chest to eliminate the abnormal fibrillating pattern and restore the normal rhythm.

Arrhythmias produce characteristic ECG tracings, and the ECG is a valuable tool for identifying the cause, type, and location of arrhythmias. Figure 8.14 shows a patient undergoing an ECG, a normal ECG recording, and a recording from a patient in ventricular fibrillation. Arrhythmias less life-threatening than ventricular fibrillation can sometimes be treated with medications. In some cases an artificial pacemaker (a small generating unit that automatically stimulates the heart at set intervals) can be surgically implanted under the chest skin to normalize the heart rate.

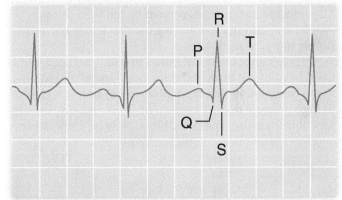

a) An ECG being recorded.

b) A normal ECG recording.

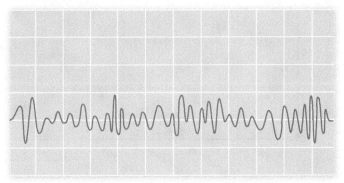

c) Ventricular fibrillation.

Figure 8.14 **The ECG is a tool for diagnosing heart arrhythmias.**

⟲ **Recap** The heart wall consists of three layers: the epicardium, the myocardium, and the endocardium. The heart contains four chambers and four one-way valves. The right atrium and right ventricle pump blood to the lungs; the left atrium and left ventricle pump blood to the rest of the body. Each cardiac cycle is a repetitive sequence of contraction (systole) and relaxation (diastole). Contraction of the heart is coordinated by modified cardiac muscle cells that initiate and transmit electrical impulses through a specialized conduction system. An electrocardiogram (ECG) is a recording of the heart's electrical activity taken from the surface of the body. ▪

8.3 Blood exerts pressure against vessel walls

Blood pressure is the force that blood exerts on the wall of a blood vessel as a result of the pumping action of the heart.

Blood pressure is not the same in all blood vessels. Figure 8.15 compares the pressures in the various segments of the vascular system. You can see from the highs and lows shown here that pressure is pulsatile in the arteries; that is, it varies with each beat of the heart. The highest pressure of the cycle, **systolic pressure**, is the pressure reached during ventricular systole when the ventricles contract to eject blood from the heart. The lowest pressure, **diastolic pressure**, occurs during ventricular diastole when the ventricles relax. Arteries store the energy generated by the heart during systole, and during diastole they use that stored energy to supply blood to the tissues.

Maintenance of arterial blood pressure is crucial to drive the flow of blood throughout the body and all the way back to the heart. Recall that fluid always flows from a region of high pressure toward a region of lower pressure. By the time it reaches the capillaries, blood flow is steady rather than pulsatile, and pressure continues to fall as blood flows through venules and veins. The differences in the blood pressure of arteries, capillaries, and veins keep blood moving through the body.

Measuring Blood Pressure

When health professionals measure your blood pressure, they are assessing the pressure in your main arteries. From a clinical standpoint, blood pressure gives valuable clues about the relative volume of blood in the vessels, the condition or stiffness of the arteries, and the overall efficiency of the cardiovascular system. Trends in blood pressure over time are a useful indicator of cardiovascular changes.

Blood pressure is recorded as mm Hg (millimeters of mercury, because early equipment used a glass column filled with mercury to measure the pressure). In young, healthy individuals, systolic pressures of less than 120 mm Hg and diastolic pressures of less than 80 mm Hg are considered desirable. With advancing age there is a slight tendency for systolic blood pressure in particular to increase slightly, as a consequence of age-related stiffening of the arteries.

Blood pressure is measured with a *sphygmomanometer* (*sphygmo* comes from the Greek word for "pulse"; a manometer is a device for measuring fluid pressures). An inflatable cuff is placed over the brachial artery in your upper arm and connected to a pressure-measuring device (Figure 8.16). When the cuff is inflated to a pressure above systolic pressure, blood flow through the brachial artery stops because the high cuff pressure collapses the artery. The cuff is then deflated slowly while a health professional listens with a stethoscope for the sounds of blood flowing in your artery. As soon as pressure in the cuff falls below the peak of systolic pressure, some blood spurts briefly through the artery during the high point of the pressure pulse, making a characteristic light tapping sound that is audible through the stethoscope. The cuff pressure at which this happens is recorded as systolic pressure. As the cuff continues to deflate, eventually blood flow through the artery becomes continuous and the tapping sound ceases. The point where the sound disappears is your diastolic pressure. This procedure yields two numbers, corresponding to your systolic and diastolic pressures. These represent the high and low points of blood pressure during the cardiac cycle.

Hypertension: High blood pressure can be dangerous

Blood pressure higher than normal is called **hypertension** (*hyper* comes from the Greek for "excess"). Table 8.1 presents the systolic and diastolic readings health professionals use to classify blood pressure as normal or hypertensive. Hypertension is a significant risk factor for cardiovascular disease, because the greater the pressure, the greater the strain on the cardiovascular system. Blood vessels react to the pounding by becoming hardened and scarred, which makes them less able to stretch during systole. Hypertension also

Figure 8.15 Blood pressure in different segments of the vascular system.

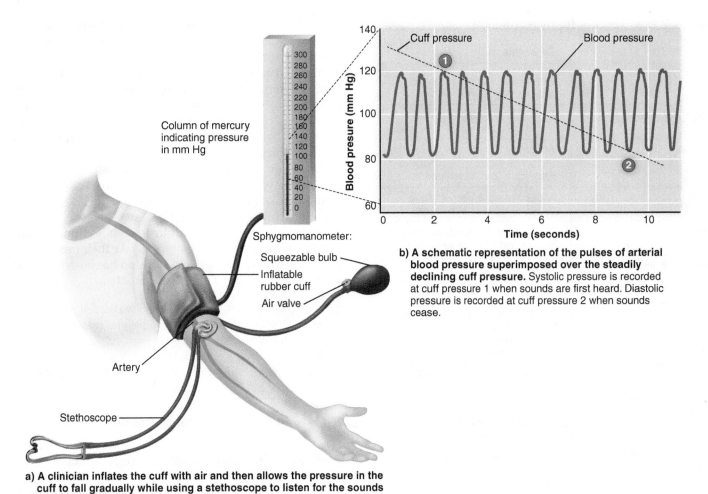

Column of mercury indicating pressure in mm Hg

Sphygmomanometer:

Squeezable bulb

Inflatable rubber cuff

Air valve

Artery

Stethoscope

b) A schematic representation of the pulses of arterial blood pressure superimposed over the steadily declining cuff pressure. Systolic pressure is recorded at cuff pressure 1 when sounds are first heard. Diastolic pressure is recorded at cuff pressure 2 when sounds cease.

a) A clinician inflates the cuff with air and then allows the pressure in the cuff to fall gradually while using a stethoscope to listen for the sounds of blood movement through the artery.

Figure 8.16 **How blood pressure is measured.**

✓ *Explain in your own words why the tapping noise is only heard when the cuff pressure is between systolic and diastolic pressure. In other words, what's making the noise?*

Table 8.1 **Systolic and diastolic blood pressure**

Blood pressure category	Systolic (mm Hg)		Diastolic (mm Hg)
Normal	Less than 120	and	Less than 80
Prehypertension	120–139	or	80–89
Hypertension, Stage 1	140–159	or	90–99
Hypertension, Stage 2	160 or higher	or	100 or higher

Source: National Institutes of Health, National Heart, Lung, and Blood Institute, March 2003.

places a greater strain on the heart, because the work it must do is directly proportional to the arterial pressure against which it must pump.

Hypertension is called "the silent killer" because usually it has no symptoms. The American Heart Association estimates that approximately 50 million Americans have hypertension and a third of them don't even realize it. If left untreated, hypertension increases the risk of serious health problems such as heart attack, heart failure, stroke, kidney damage, even damage to the tissues inside the eyes.

What causes hypertension? Many times it happens because blood vessels become narrowed from atherosclerosis. Certain other factors also increase the risk, as summarized in Table 8.2. The only sure way to diagnose it is to have your blood pressure measured.

Table 8.2 Risk factors for hypertension

Risk factor	Comments
Heredity	Family history of hypertension raises risk.
Age	Blood pressure tends to rise throughout life.
Race	African Americans have twice the incidence found in Caucasian Americans and Asian Americans.
Sex	Males are more likely than females to develop hypertension.
Obesity	The heart must pump harder to push blood through vessels.
High salt intake	In some individuals (but not others) a high salt intake raises blood pressure slightly.
Smoking	Smoking raises the blood concentration of epinephrine, a hormone that stimulates the heart.
Sedentary lifestyle	Not well understood. May be due to higher blood lipids or weight gain.
Persistent emotional stress	Emotional stress activates portions of the nervous system that elevate pressure.
Diabetes mellitus	Diabetics have a higher incidence of hypertension, for reasons not yet known.
Heavy alcohol consumption	Mechanisms unknown.
Oral contraceptives and certain medications	Mechanisms vary by medication.

Blood pressure varies from minute to minute even in healthy individuals. Simply getting up in the morning raises it, as do exercise, emotions, smoking cigarettes, eating, drinking, and many other factors. Even having your blood pressure measured can make you nervous enough for your blood pressure to rise—a situation that health professionals call "white coat hypertension." This is why physicians generally have you sit quietly while measuring your blood pressure.

If hypertension is suspected, your physician will probably measure your blood pressure on at least three different occasions before making a firm diagnosis. True hypertension is a *sustained* elevation in blood pressure above normal levels—a systolic pressure of 140 mm Hg or greater or a diastolic pressure of 90 mm Hg or greater. Even blood pressure that is consistently just below the hypertensive level (prehypertension) may carry a slightly higher risk of health complications.

Generally, if systolic pressure is high, diastolic pressure will be, too. However, sometimes systolic pressure can register at above-normal levels while diastolic pressure remains normal, a condition called *isolated systolic hypertension*. Most common in older adults, it is diagnosed as a systolic pressure of 160 mm Hg or higher with a diastolic reading of less than 90 mm Hg. Like the more common form of hypertension, isolated systolic hypertension is associated with increased health problems.

At the end of this chapter we discuss what you can do to lower your risk of hypertension as well as other cardiovascular problems. If hypertension does develop, however, a number of medical treatments are available to lower blood pressure to a healthy level. It is important for people on antihypertensive drugs to take their medication consistently; even though hypertension has no symptoms, it increases the risk of related health problems.

✅ **Quick Check** *A nurse taking blood pressure in a patient hears a tapping sound begin when the cuff pressure is 141 mm Hg, and the sound ends when cuff pressure is 95 mm Hg. What are the systolic and diastolic pressures of this patient, and is this enough to tell you if this patient has normal blood pressure?* ∎

Hypotension: When blood pressure is too low

It is also possible for blood pressure to fall below normal levels, a condition called *hypotension* (*hypo* comes from the Greek for "under"). Generally hypotension is a problem only if blood pressure falls enough to reduce blood flow to the brain, causing dizziness and fainting. Drops in blood pressure can follow abrupt changes in position, such as standing up suddenly. Other causes include severe burns or injuries involving heavy blood loss.

↩ **Recap** Blood pressure is the force that blood exerts on the wall of a blood vessel. It is measured as two numbers corresponding to systolic and diastolic pressures. Hypertension (high blood pressure) is a serious risk factor for cardiovascular disease and other health problems. ∎

8.4 How the cardiovascular system is regulated

The overall function of the cardiovascular system is to provide every cell with precisely the right blood flow to meet its needs at all times. This might seem like a complicated process because different types of tissues have different needs, which change according to circumstances. In principle, however, the system is rather simple.

Consider for a minute how your community provides water to every house according to the needs of the occupants. Basically, municipal water systems provide constant water *pressure* to every house. With steady water pressure available, each household simply adjusts the *flow* of water into the house by turning faucets on and off.

The human cardiovascular system is based on similar principles. Consider the following key points:

- Homeostatic regulation of the cardiovascular system centers on *maintaining a constant arterial blood pressure*.
- A constant arterial blood pressure is *achieved* by regulating the heart rate and force of contraction (adjusting flow *into* the arteries) and by regulating the diameters of all the body's arterioles as a whole (adjusting overall flow *out* of the arteries).
- With arterial blood pressure held relatively constant, local blood flows are adjusted to meet local requirements.

As we will see, this overall regulation is achieved with nerves, hormones, and local factors coupled to metabolism.

Baroreceptors maintain arterial blood pressure

There is probably no more important regulated variable in the entire body than blood pressure. Without a relatively constant blood pressure as the driving force for supplying blood to the capillaries, homeostasis simply would not be possible. Blood pressure does vary, but always within a range consistent with being able to provide blood to all cells.

To regulate blood pressure, the body must have some way of measuring it. In fact, several of the large arteries, including the aorta and the two carotid arteries, have certain regions called **baroreceptors** (the Greek *baro* denotes pressure). The baroreceptors regulate arterial blood pressure in the following manner:

1. When blood pressure rises, arterial blood vessels are stretched passively.
2. Stretch of baroreceptors in the carotid arteries and aorta causes them to send signals via nerves to an area of the brain called the *cardiovascular center*.
3. The cardiovascular center responds by sending signals via nerves to the heart and blood vessels.
4. The effect on the heart is to lower heart rate and the force of contraction. This reduces **cardiac output**, the amount of blood that the heart pumps into the aorta each minute.
5. The effect on arterioles is vasodilation, an increase in arteriole diameter. Vasodilation increases blood flow through all tissues.
6. The net effect of both reducing cardiac output and increasing flow through the tissues is to return arterial pressure to normal.

Exactly the opposite sequence of events occurs when arterial pressure falls *below* normal. When pressure falls and the arteries stretch less than normal, the baroreceptors send fewer nerve signals to the brain. The brain correctly interprets this as a fall in pressure and sends nerve signals that increase cardiac output and constrict arterioles, raising arterial blood pressure again.

All day long—every time you stand up, sit down, get excited, run for the bus—your blood pressure fluctuates up or down. But it is quickly brought back within normal range by a negative feedback loop initiated by baroreceptors.

Nerves and hormones adjust cardiac output

As mentioned before, cardiac output is the amount of blood pumped into the aorta in one minute. We calculate cardiac output by multiplying *heart rate* (number of heartbeats per minute) by *stroke volume* (volume of blood pumped out with each heartbeat). For a healthy adult at rest, the heart rate averages about 75 beats per minute, and the stroke volume averages about 70 milliliters per beat. Resting cardiac output, then, is about 5.25 liters per minute. Because our normal blood volume is only about 5 liters, in essence the entire blood supply passes through the heart every minute.

Regulation of cardiac output is centered in an area of the brain called the *medulla oblongata*, which is where the cardiovascular center is located. The medulla oblongata receives nerve signals from the baroreceptors, from receptors in muscles and joints, and from areas of the brain involved in emotions. In response to the inputs it receives, the cardiovascular center sends nerve signals to the heart in two sets of nerves. *Sympathetic nerves* stimulate the heart and cause it to beat faster, and *parasympathetic nerves* inhibit the heart and cause it to beat more slowly.

The hormones *epinephrine* (also called *adrenaline*) and *norepinephrine* stimulate the heart as well. Epinephrine and norepinephrine are secreted by the adrenal glands whenever the sympathetic nervous system is activated.

Sympathetic nerves also help to maintain blood pressure by controlling blood vessel diameters. Most blood vessels are under a constant state of partial constriction by the sympathetic nerves. An increase in sympathetic nerve activity further constricts blood vessels and raises blood pressure. Conversely, a decrease in sympathetic nerve activity dilates blood vessels and lowers pressure. Most blood vessels do not have parasympathetic nerves, so activation or deactivation of the parasympathetic nervous system has little effect on overall blood vessel diameters.

☑ **Quick Check** *A young girl with an allergy to peanuts suffers a severe allergic reaction that includes a sudden drop in blood pressure. How will her body attempt to restore the blood pressure over the next few seconds and minutes?* ▪

Local requirements dictate local blood flows

With arterial blood pressure held relatively constant, the flow of blood through each precapillary sphincter (and hence each capillary) can be adjusted according to need, just like turning a faucet on or off. How is the flow adjusted? When a particular tissue is metabolically active, such as when a muscle is contracting, it consumes more oxygen and nutrients. Increased metabolism also raises the production of carbon dioxide and other waste products. One or more

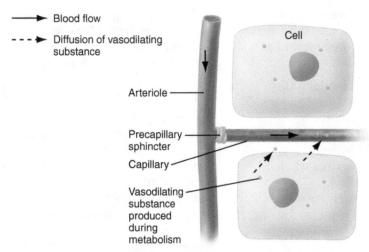

→ Blood flow

- - -► Diffusion of vasodilating substance

Cell

Arteriole

Precapillary sphincter

Capillary

Vasodilating substance produced during metabolism

a) At rest, very little of the vasodilating substance would be produced, and flow would be minimal.

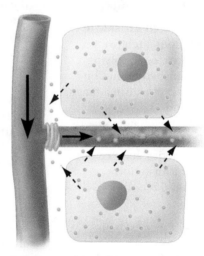

b) With increased metabolic activity, the presence of more of the substance in the interstitial space would cause the arteriole and precapillary sphincter to vasodilate, increasing flow.

Figure 8.17 **How an increase in metabolism increases local blood flow.**

of these changes associated with increased metabolism cause precapillary sphincters within the tissue to vasodilate, increasing flow. Scientists do not yet know the precise mechanisms of this vasodilation or the identity of all the chemical substances that influence the vasodilation, but we do know that it occurs. Figure 8.17 shows how an increase in cellular metabolism within a tissue increases the local blood flow to that tissue.

Look at the overall process and you can see how together these control mechanisms deliver blood efficiently to all tissues. First, nerves and hormones adjust cardiac output and the rate of blood flow through the vascular system as a whole, in an effort to maintain relatively constant arterial blood pressure. Second, any cell or part of the body that is not receiving enough blood can override the system locally and get exactly what it needs—no more, no less.

Some tissues and organs need a more consistent blood supply than others. This is taken into account by our control system. Consider what would happen if you lost a substantial volume of blood due to injury, producing a precipitous fall in blood pressure. The negative feedback control of arterial blood pressure would stimulate your heart and constrict your arterioles, reducing flow to most organs in an effort to raise blood pressure. However, organs whose survival depends critically on a constant blood supply (your brain and heart, for example) can override the generalized vasoconstriction with their local control mechanisms. Organs whose metabolic activities are not required for their immediate survival (such as your kidneys and digestive tract) just remain vasoconstricted for a while. In effect, the limited available blood supply is shunted to essential organs.

You may wonder why, if these homeostatic controls are working properly, people ever develop hypertension. Every time blood pressure went up a little, wouldn't feedback mechanisms bring it back to normal? This is the great mystery of hypertension. Although scientists don't fully understand it yet, for some reason the body seems to adjust to high pressure once it has been sustained for a long time. Apparently the feedback system slowly resets itself to recognize the higher pressure as normal. The reason may be that hypertension tends to develop slowly over decades, so there is never a single defining moment when pressure registers as too high.

Exercise: Increased blood flow and cardiac output

During exercise the metabolic activity of the active skeletal muscles goes up dramatically. As a result the production of vasodilator waste products increases, and the local concentration of oxygen falls. Both of these contribute to dilation of the blood vessels. Consequently, blood flow through the active skeletal muscles increases.

To sustain blood pressure in the face of increased blood flow, the heart must increase its output. From what you know, you might guess that an increase in blood flow to muscle would cause a fall in blood pressure, which in turn would cause a baroreceptor-mediated reflex increase in cardiac output. However, blood pressure doesn't fall very much (if at all) during exercise—if anything, it rises a little. During exercise, the primary cause of increased cardiac output is sensory input from moving muscles and joints. This sensory input signals the cardiovascular center to stimulate the heart and increase cardiac output even before blood pressure can fall very much. In other words, during exercise the body anticipates the need for increased cardiac output and prevents blood pressure from falling in the first place.

In nonathletic people, cardiac output reaches a maximum of about 20–25 liters per minute during heavy exercise. However, trained athletes whose heart muscles have hypertrophied as a result of exercise training can reach cardiac outputs of up to 35 liters per minute, or almost seven times their resting cardiac output.

Recap Homeostatic regulation of the cardiovascular system centers on maintaining a relatively constant arterial blood pressure. Arterial pressure is sensed by baroreceptors located in the carotid arteries and aorta. Two opposing sets of nerves (sympathetic and parasympathetic) and a hormone (epinephrine) adjust cardiac output and arteriole diameters to maintain arterial blood pressure fairly constant. Local factors regulate blood flow into individual capillaries by altering the diameters of precapillary sphincters. ∎

8.5 Cardiovascular disorders: A major health issue

Disorders affecting the cardiovascular system are a major health problem in Western countries. Cardiovascular disorders cause more than 700,000 deaths per year in the United States alone. They are the number one killer in the United States, far ahead of the number two killer, cancer (approximately 550,000 deaths per year).

We have already discussed hypertension and aneurysms, and atherosclerosis. In the rest of this chapter we look at several other conditions, including arrhythmias, angina, heart attack, heart failure, embolism, and stroke. Finally, we examine what you can do to reduce your own risk of cardiovascular health problems.

Angina: Chest pain warns of impaired blood flow

As a hard-working muscle, the heart requires a constant source of blood. Normally the coronary arteries and their branches provide all the blood the heart needs, even during sustained exercise. However, if these arteries become narrowed, blood flow to the heart may not be sufficient for the heart's demands. This may lead to *angina*, a sensation of pain and tightness in the chest. Often angina is accompanied by shortness of breath and a sensation of choking or suffocating (*angina* comes from the Latin word for "strangling"). Many angina episodes are triggered by physical exertion, emotional stress, cold weather, or eating heavy meals, because the heart requires more blood and oxygen at these times.

Angina is uncomfortable but usually temporary. Stopping to rest and taking several deep breaths can often relieve the discomfort. However, angina should never be ignored, because it is a sign of insufficient circulation to the heart. *Angiography* is a procedure that enables blood vessels to be visualized after they are filled with a contrast medium (a substance that is opaque to X-rays). Angiography allows health professionals to take X-ray pictures of blood vessels (called *angiograms*) and assess their condition (Figure 8.18).

Certain medications can increase blood flow to the heart muscle. Another treatment for narrowed coronary arteries is *balloon angioplasty*, which involves threading into the blocked artery a slender flexible tube with a small balloon attached. When the balloon reaches the narrowest point of the vessel, it is inflated briefly so that it presses against the fatty plaques that narrow the vessel lumen, flattening them and widening the lumen. Balloon angioplasty has a high success rate, although in some cases the vessel narrows again over time, requiring repeat treatments. A coronary artery bypass graft (see the next section) can yield longer-lasting benefits.

Heart attack: Permanent damage to heart tissue

If blood flow to an area of the heart is impaired long enough, the result is a **heart attack**—sudden death of an area of heart tissue due to oxygen starvation. (The clinical

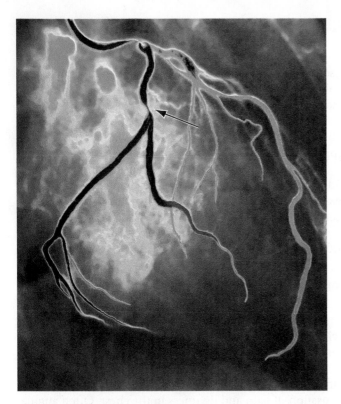

Figure 8.18 A coronary angiogram. A contrast medium (similar in function to a dye) is injected into the coronary arteries, causing them to become visible on an X-ray photograph. Note the area of narrowing in the coronary artery indicated by the arrow.

Aorta

Vein grafts

Plaque blocking blood flow

Figure 8.19 Coronary artery bypass grafts. This is an example of a "triple CABG," in which three vein grafts have been placed to bypass three areas of atherosclerotic plaque. Arrows indicate additional blood flow to the area beyond the restricted artery.

term is *myocardial infarction*; infarction refers to tissue death from inadequate blood supply.) Many people who suffer a heart attack have a previous history of angina. The classic symptoms of a major heart attack, especially in men but also in women, include intense chest pain, a sense of tightness or pressure on the chest that makes it hard to breathe, and pain that may radiate down the left arm. Women tend to experience nausea and jaw and back pain more frequently than men, but as these symptoms do not seem as immediately life-threatening, women's heart attacks are not diagnosed as soon as men's based on symptoms alone. The symptoms may come and go for several minutes at a time, leading many people to delay seeking medical attention.

A heart attack causes permanent damage to the heart. Because the body cannot replace cardiac muscle cells, damage to the heart impairs its ability to function. Most heart attack fatalities occur because of ventricular fibrillation, the serious heart arrhythmia brought about by damage to heart muscle.

Prompt treatment is crucial for recovery from a heart attack. If a heart attack is even suspected, the person should be rushed immediately to a hospital. The diagnosis of a heart attack is generally made on the basis of the ECG and the presence in the blood of certain enzymes that are released from dead and damaged heart cells. Health professionals can

often control cardiac arrhythmias and other complications and administer clot-dissolving drugs to unblock vessels. The sooner treatment begins, the more successful it is likely to be.

Later (or even before a heart attack has occurred, if the narrowing of coronary vessels has been diagnosed by angiography), a *coronary artery bypass graft (CABG)* can be performed to improve coronary blood flow. In this procedure, a piece of blood vessel is removed from somewhere else in the body (often a leg vein is used) and grafted onto the blocked artery to bypass the damaged region (Figure 8.19). Over time the grafted vein thickens and takes on the characteristics of an artery.

Thanks to these and other treatments, the heart attack survival rate has risen dramatically. Eighty percent of heart attack survivors are back at work within three months.

Heart failure: The heart becomes less efficient

Generally our bodies maintain adequate arterial pressure because of the tight control mechanisms described earlier. However, if the heart muscle becomes damaged for any reason, the heart may become weaker and less efficient at pumping blood, a condition called **heart failure**.

When the heart begins to pump less blood, blood backs up in the veins and pressure in the veins and capillaries rises. The high capillary blood pressure causes more fluid than usual to filter out of the capillaries and into the interstitial space, causing fluid congestion. When that happens a person is said to have **congestive heart failure**. ("Congestive" refers to the buildup of interstitial fluid.)

People with congestive heart failure get out of breath when walking or climbing even a short flight of stairs. They may even have trouble breathing while lying down because the horizontal position results in even higher venous pressure and fluid accumulation in the lungs. Other symptoms include swollen ankles and legs, swollen neck veins, and weight gain from the extra fluid.

There are several reasons why a heart might begin to fail. Aging is one factor, but certainly not the only one because older people do not necessarily develop heart failure. Other possible causes include past heart attacks, leaking heart valves, heart valves that fail to open normally, uncontrolled hypertension, or serious arrhythmias. Lung conditions such as emphysema can raise blood pressure in the lungs and strain the heart.

Treatments for congestive heart failure focus on improving cardiac performance and efficiency while preventing the accumulation of interstitial fluid. Regular mild exercise promotes more efficient blood flow, and frequent resting with the feet elevated helps fluid drain from leg veins. Physicians may prescribe diuretics (drugs that help the body get rid of excess fluid), vasodilating drugs to expand blood vessels, or medications to help the heart muscle beat more forcefully.

BlogInFocus (MB)

> Wouldn't it be great if we could create a beating heart in the laboratory? It's been done (with certain limitations) in mice. To find out how it was done, visit MJ's blog in the Study Area in MasteringBiology and look under "Creating a Beating Heart."

Embolism: Blockage of a blood vessel

Embolism refers to the sudden blockage of a blood vessel by material floating in the bloodstream. Most often the obstacle (an *embolus*) is a blood clot that has broken away from a larger clot elsewhere in the body (often a vein) and lodged in an artery at a point where arterial vessels branch and get smaller in diameter. Other possible emboli include cholesterol deposits, tissue fragments, cancer cells, clumps of bacteria, or bubbles of air.

Embolism conditions are named according to the area of the body affected. A *pulmonary embolism* blocks an artery supplying blood to the lungs, causing sudden chest pain and shortness of breath. A *cerebral embolism* impairs circulation to the brain, possibly causing a stroke. A *cardiac embolism* can cause a heart attack.

Stroke: Damage to blood vessels in the brain

To function normally, the brain requires a steady blood supply—about 15% of the heart's output at rest. Any impairment of blood flow to the brain rapidly damages brain cells. **A stroke** (*cerebrovascular accident*) represents damage to part of the brain caused by an interruption to its blood supply. In effect, it is the brain equivalent of a heart attack. Strokes are the most common cause of brain injury and a leading cause of death in Western nations. The two most common causes are an embolism blocking a vessel and rupture of a cerebral artery.

Symptoms of strokes appear suddenly and vary according to the area of the brain affected. They may include weakness or paralysis on one side of the body, fainting, inability to speak or slurred speech, difficulty in understanding speech, impaired vision, nausea, or a sudden loss of coordination.

Immediate medical care is crucial. If the stroke resulted from a cerebral embolism, clot-dissolving drugs or an embolectomy (surgery to remove the embolus) can save a life. Eliminating the clot as quickly as possible (within minutes or hours) can also limit the area of damage and reduce the severity of the permanent injury. If a ruptured artery is responsible, health providers may be able to surgically drain the excess blood.

Although some people recover well from a stroke or suffer only minor permanent effects, others do not recover much lost function at all despite intensive physical therapy over many months. The reason for generally poor recovery rates is that the body does not grow new nerve cells to replace damaged ones. Nevertheless, rehabilitation with skilled health professionals generally offers the best chance of at least a partial recovery. Recovery involves retraining nerve pathways that already exist so they can take over the functions of damaged nerve cells.

↺ **Recap** Cardiovascular disorders are the number one killer in the United States. Most disorders are caused either by conditions that result in failure of the heart as a pump or by conditions in which damage to blood vessels restricts flow or ruptures vessels. ▪

8.6 Replacing a failing heart

Sometimes heart failure is so complete that it becomes necessary to replace the heart entirely. For most patients the only option is a heart transplant, using a heart from a human cadaver. Heart transplants are expensive (nearly $700,000), but the chances of success are fairly good; currently the average length of survival after a heart transplant is about 15 years. The main problem is a shortage of healthy hearts from recently deceased human donors. About a third of all patients on heart transplant lists die before they get a suitable heart.

a) The SynCardia heart.

b) The AbioCor heart.

Figure 8.20 **Artificial hearts.**

When a human heart is not available soon enough or the patient is not eligible for one, the only short-term solution may be an artificial heart. Several different artificial hearts are currently under development, but only two have been approved by the FDA so far. Each is approved only for specific purposes. The SynCardia heart (Figure 8.20a) is approved only for temporary use, that is, until a suitable donor can be found. So far, nearly a thousand patients have received the SynCardia heart. About 80% of them survived until they received a human heart transplant. The other, called the AbioCor Replacement Heart (Figure 8.20b), is only approved to extend the lives of patients who by virtue of their medical condition are not eligible for a heart transplant. According to the manufacturer (AbioMed), 14 patients received the Abiocor heart during clinical trials. The longest survivor lived 512 days.

Another option being explored is a *xenotransplant* (an organ from another species), most likely from pigs or baboons. These are less than ideal because tissue incompatibility can lead to transplant rejection by the immune system, and also because these species do not live as long as humans, raising the question of whether the hearts would last long enough. If these issues could be resolved, xenotransplants could save thousands of lives a year.

There's work to be done before either artificial hearts or xenotransplants are considered viable alternatives to human hearts from cadavers. From the simple perspective of pumping blood adequately, artificial hearts actually perform rather well. If we could overcome the occasional mechanical failures, infections, and the twin problems of blood clotting or excessive bleeding, then an artificial heart might become a permanent replacement for a failed heart, not just a temporary fix.

Recap The best solution for a failed heart is a heart transplant from a human cadaver. The current generation of artificial hearts is only a temporary solution. Xenotransplants are still in the research stage, not approved for human use. ▪

8.7 Reducing your risk of cardiovascular disease

Cardiovascular disorders are among the most preventable of chronic health conditions. Although some factors are beyond your control—such as sex, race, age, and genetic inheritance—your lifestyle choices can also affect your risk. Things you can do to reduce your risk include:

- Don't smoke, or if you do, quit. Smokers have more than twice the risk of heart attack that nonsmokers do, and smokers who suffer a heart attack are nearly four times as likely to die from it. Some researchers think secondhand smoke poses a risk as well.
- Watch your cholesterol levels. Cardiovascular risk rises with the blood cholesterol level. There is also evidence that high cholesterol increases risk even more when it is combined with other factors such as hypertension and tobacco smoke.
- Keep moving (Figure 8.21). Regular, moderate exercise lowers the risk of cardiovascular disease. This is not surprising because the heart is, after all, a muscle. Most physicians recommend exercising for at least 20 to 30 minutes, at least three times per week. Physical activity tends to lower blood pressure and cholesterol and makes it easier to maintain a healthy body weight. Always consult your physician before starting an exercise program.

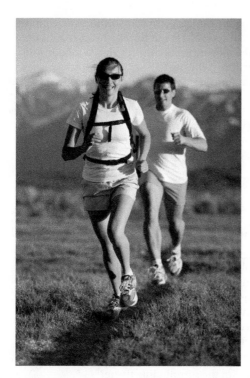

Figure 8.21 Moderate, regular exercise improves cardiovascular performance and lowers the risk of cardiovascular disease.

- If your blood pressure is on the high side, seek treatment. As discussed earlier, untreated hypertension damages blood vessels and increases the workload on the heart.

In addition to these major risks, at least three other factors are associated with cardiovascular disease, although the precise link has not yet been determined. This is why doctors recommend the following:

- Maintain a healthy weight. It's not clear how obesity contributes to cardiovascular problems, but overweight people have a higher rate of heart disease and stroke even if they do not have other risk factors. One hypothesis is that increased weight strains the heart. Increased weight also has adverse effects on other risk factors such as blood cholesterol and hypertension.
- Keep diabetes under control. Diabetes mellitus is a disorder of blood sugar levels. Untreated diabetes damages blood vessels, but effective treatments reduce cardiovascular damage significantly. (Diabetes will be described in more detail when we discuss the endocrine system.)
- Avoid chronic stress. Again the mechanism is unclear, but there is an association between a person's perceived stress and behavior patterns and the development of cardiovascular disease. Stress may also affect other risk factors, for example how much a smoker smokes or whether a person starts smoking.

Recap You can reduce your risk of developing cardiovascular disease by not smoking, exercising regularly, watching your weight and cholesterol, and avoiding prolonged stress. If you have diabetes and/or hypertension, try to keep these conditions under control. ■

Chapter Summary

Blood vessels transport blood *p. 162*

- The primary function of blood vessels is to bring blood into close proximity with all living cells.
- Thick-walled arteries transport blood to the capillaries at high pressure.
- Small arterioles and precapillary sphincters regulate the flow of blood into each capillary.
- Thin-walled capillaries are the only vessels that exchange fluids and solutes with the interstitial fluid.
- Distensible venules and veins store blood at low pressure and return it to the heart.

The heart pumps blood through the vessels *p. 167*

- The heart is composed primarily of cardiac muscle. Structurally, it consists of four separate chambers and four one-way valves. Its primary function is to pump blood.

- The heart pumps blood simultaneously through two separate circuits: the pulmonary circuit, where blood picks up oxygen and gets rid of carbon dioxide, and the systemic circuit, which supplies the rest of the body's cells.
- The heart contracts and relaxes rhythmically. Contraction is called *systole*, and relaxation is called *diastole*.
- The coordinated contraction of the heart is produced by a system of specialized cardiac muscle cells that initiate and distribute electrical impulses throughout the heart muscle.
- An electrocardiogram, or ECG, records electrical activity of the heart from the surface of the body. An ECG can be used to diagnose certain cardiac arrhythmias and disorders.

Blood exerts pressure against vessel walls *p. 176*

- The heart generates blood pressure, and the arteries store the blood under pressure during diastole.
- Systolic and diastolic arterial blood pressures can be measured with a sphygmomanometer.
- High blood pressure, called *hypertension*, is a major risk factor for cardiovascular disease.

How the cardiovascular system is regulated *p. 178*

- The most important controlled variable in the cardiovascular system is arterial blood pressure.
- Arterial blood pressure is monitored by stretch receptors located in certain large arteries.
- Cardiac output and the diameters of the arterioles are regulated (controlled) to keep arterial blood pressure relatively constant.
- With pressure held constant, local blood flows can be adjusted according to the metabolic needs of the tissues and cells in that area of the body.

Cardiovascular disorders: A major health issue *p. 181*

- The heart muscle is always working. Impairment of blood flow to the heart can lead to a sense of pain and tightness in the chest (angina) and/or permanent damage to heart tissue (myocardial infarction, or heart attack).
- Slowly developing, chronic failure of the heart as a pump can lead to excessive interstitial fluid, a condition known as *congestive heart failure.*
- An embolism is the sudden blockage of a blood vessel by any object.
- Strokes, also called *cerebrovascular accidents,* can be caused by either embolisms or rupture of blood vessels. The result is damage to a part of the brain when its blood supply is interrupted.

Replacing a failing heart *p. 183*

- The best solution for a patient with a failed heart is a heart transplant from a human cadaver.
- Currently, artificial hearts are only intended as temporary solutions for heart failure.

Reducing your risk of cardiovascular disease *p. 184*

- Your chances of developing a cardiovascular disorder depend on certain risk factors. Some risk factors you cannot change, whereas others depend on the choices you make in life.

Terms You Should Know

artery, *162*	pulmonary circuit, *169*
atrioventricular (AV) valves, *168*	semilunar valves, *169*
atrium, *168*	sinoatrial (SA) node, *174*
capillary, *164*	systemic circuit, *169*
diastole, *172*	systole, *172*
myocardium, *167*	vein, *166*
precapillary sphincter, *164*	ventricle, *168*

Concept Review

Answers can be found in the Study Area in MasteringBiology.

1. Why is it so important that the heart always get a consistent and adequate blood supply?
2. Compare and contrast the structures and functions of the three types of blood vessels.
3. Describe how arterial blood pressure is measured by the body.
4. Describe the function of the heart valves.
5. Compare the functions of the pulmonary circuit and the systemic circuit.

6. Describe the cardiac cycle of relaxation and contraction, and explain what causes each of the two heart sounds during the cycle.
7. Describe the function of the SA and AV nodes as they control contraction of the heart.
8. Of what functional value is the distensibility of veins? In other words, why not have them just as thick and stiff as arteries?
9. Name the one hormone that has a stimulatory effect on the heart (increases heart rate).
10. List ways to reduce the risk of cardiovascular disease.

Test Yourself

Answers can be found in Appendix A.

1. _____ carry blood away from the heart and _____ carry blood toward the heart.
   a. veins…arteries
   b. arteries…arterioles
   c. veins…capillaries
   d. arteries…veins
   e. arteries…capillaries

2. Which blood vessel is best suited for exchange of gases and nutrients with the surrounding tissue?
   a. artery
   b. vein
   c. capillary
   d. arteriole

3. Which of the choices represents the order of vessels through which blood passes after leaving the heart?
   a. artery – arteriole – capillary – venule – vein
   b. artery – capillary – arteriole – venule – vein
   c. vein – venule – capillary – arteriole – artery
   d. artery – vein – capillary – arteriole – venule

4. All of the following mechanisms assist in returning venous blood to the heart except:
   a. an increase in heart rate
   b. pressure changes in the abdominal and thoracic cavities due to breathing
   c. contraction of skeletal muscles in the legs
   d. one-way valves located inside veins

5. Which of the following represents the order of structures beginning inside the ventricle and traveling outward?
   a. pericardium – epicardium – myocardium – endocardium
   b. epicardium – myocardium – endocardium – pericardium
   c. endocardium – myocardium – epicardium – pericardium
   d. endocardium – pericardium – myocardium – epicardium

6. Which vein(s) carry oxygenated blood?
   a. superior vena cava and inferior vena cava
   b. right and left pulmonary veins
   c. aorta
   d. both (a) and (b)

7. Which of the following statements regarding the cardiac cycle is false?
   a. When the ventricles contract, the atrioventricular valves close.
   b. When the ventricles relax, the semilunar valves close.
   c. When the atria contract, the semilunar valves open.
   d. When the atria contract, the atrioventricular valves open.

8. A pacemaker is used to correct:
   a. coronary artery disease
   b. cardiac arrhythmias
   c. heart murmurs
   d. hypertension

9. As the blood travels through the circulatory system, the greatest drop in pressure occurs in:
   a. arteries
   b. arterioles
   c. capillaries
   d. venules

10. All of the following are part of the cardiac conduction system except:
    a. the chordae tendineae
    b. the Purkinje fibers
    c. the sinoatrial node
    d. the atrioventricular bundle

11. Which of the following is/are involved in regulating blood pressure?
    a. heart
    b. baroreceptors
    c. cardiovascular center in medulla oblongata
    d. all of the above

12. Which of the following would be an appropriate homeostatic response to a drop in blood pressure below what is normal?
    a. heart rate decreases
    b. vasoconstriction of arterioles
    c. force of cardiac contraction decreases
    d. both (a) and (b)

13. Which of the following might cause the heart rate to increase from 68 beats/min to 120 beats/min?
    a. epinephrine
    b. stimulation via parasympathetic nerves
    c. stimulation via sympathetic nerves
    d. both (a) and (c)

14. Which of the following might be treated appropriately by administering clot-dissolving drugs?
    a. hypertension
    b. hypotension
    c. pulmonary embolism
    d. a hemorrhagic stroke

15. A heart attack occurs as a result of:
    a. prolonged hypotension
    b. narrowing or blockage of the coronary arteries
    c. improper closure of semilunar valves
    d. disruption of the cardiac conduction system

Apply What You Know

Answers can be found in the Study Area in MasteringBiology.

1. During exercise, arterial blood pressure changes very little. However, cardiac output may double and blood flow to exercising muscle may go up 10-fold, while at the same time the blood flow to kidneys may decline by nearly 50%. Explain possible mechanisms that might account for these very different changes.

2. When a coronary artery bypass graft (CABG) is performed, the vessels used for the bypass grafts are usually veins taken from the patient's legs. Over time the grafted veins take on many of the characteristics of arteries; that is, they become thicker and stiffer. What might this suggest about the possible cause(s) of the structural differences between arteries and veins? Hypothesize what might happen if you took a section of artery and implanted it into a vein.

3. Soldiers have to stand in formation at full attention for long periods of time. Sometimes this can cause otherwise very fit and healthy young people to pass out during long inspections. What would cause this?

4. Workers who spend hours per day standing can develop circulation problems in their legs. A recommended solution is to wear graduated compression stockings. These stockings are tighter around the ankles and less tight higher up on the legs. Why does standing for long periods sometimes lead to circulatory problems, and how can wearing something tight on the legs help prevent this?

5. Inflammation of the pericardium can lead to a condition called *pericardial effusion*, in which fluids collect in the space surrounding the heart. What effect would this have on the functioning of the heart? How might the condition be treated?

6. Ventricular fibrillation is a potentially fatal condition where the cells of the heart are no longer coordinated in their contractions. Why is it important that contraction of the heart muscle occurs nearly all at once?

7. VSD or ventricular septal defect is a condition that accounts for half of all congenital cardiovascular anomalies. In this condition a hole exists in the septum, the muscular wall between the ventricles, which allows blood from the right and left side of the heart to mix. What sort of problems might this condition cause?

8. Last night you and your roommate were sound asleep when the phone rang. Your roommate, startled awake, jumped from her bed and rushed for the phone across the room. Before she reached the phone she suddenly felt dizzy and had to sit down to avoid fainting. What happened?

BlogInFocus

Answers can be found in the Study Area in MasteringBiology.

1. Based on what you know, do you think that lowering "prehypertensive" blood pressures to "normal" might be cost-effective in preventing cardiovascular disease? (To view a research paper that relates tangentially to this question, visit MJ's blog in the Study Area in MasteringBiology and look under "Treating Prehypertension.")

MasteringBiology®

Go to MasteringBiology for practice quizzes, activities, eText, videos, current events, and more.

The Immune System and Mechanisms of Defense

Colorized TEM (× 25,000) of a mast cell containing granules of histamine (dark purple).

AIDS: A Crisis in Africa, a Challenge for the World

Africa is in the midst of an AIDS epidemic. What is AIDS, how bad is the epidemic, how will it affect us, and what (if anything) are we willing to do about it?

In Africa, AIDS Is Out of Control

AIDS stands for *acquired immune deficiency syndrome*. It is caused by a virus that attacks the immune system, called *human immunodeficiency virus* (*HIV*). Approximately two-thirds of the world's HIV-infected people live in sub-Saharan Africa. The United Nations estimates that 22.9 million people there are already infected with HIV. The region accounts for nearly three-quarters of the world's AIDS deaths.

Patterns of AIDS infection and transmission in Africa differ from those of industrialized countries. In the United States, more men than women are infected with HIV, which is often transmitted via homosexual sex. In Africa, however, an estimated 60% of HIV-infected persons are women who have contracted the virus heterosexually. Studies in several African nations have found that females aged 15–19 are four to five times more likely to be infected than males their age. According to one report, in Africa older HIV-infected men coerce or pay impoverished girls to have sex in the mistaken belief that sex with a virgin will cure AIDS.

The problem of AIDS in sub-Saharan Africa is made worse by political, economic, and social instability. Almost a third of all sub-Saharan African nations are at war or are suffering intense internal conflict. In many of these countries the economies are weak, sanitation is poor, and even rudimentary medical services are often lacking. Malnutrition and starvation are widespread. Approximately 11 million children in sub-Saharan Africa have been orphaned by AIDS, war, or famine. Many of them are abandoned and impoverished, fending for themselves without adult supervision.

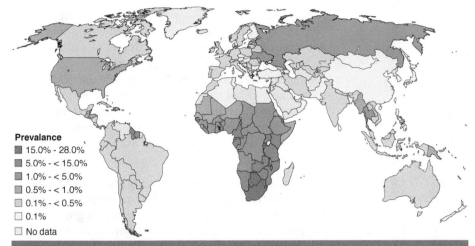

Prevalance

- 15.0% - 28.0%
- 5.0% - < 15.0%
- 1.0% - < 5.0%
- 0.5% - < 1.0%
- 0.1% - < 0.5%
- 0.1%
- No data

Over two-thirds of all people living with HIV live in sub-Saharan Africa.

This AIDS drug manufactured in Thailand costs less than $400/year.

What can be done to help sub-Saharan Africa? Possibilities include:

- Providing accurate information on HIV transmission and helping people understand how their sexual practices may contribute to the spread of the disease.
- Seeking AIDS treatments and preventive measures that are inexpensive enough to be used effectively in poor countries.
- Providing economic assistance and encouraging political stability.
- Improving the delivery of health care.

These are all good ideas, of course. But any solution to the growing AIDS crisis in African countries must recognize that their problems are different from ours.

Roadblocks to Effective HIV Treatment

Strategies for treating HIV infection and preventing AIDS in sub-Saharan Africa face some significant obstacles not seen in North America. For example, improving the delivery of health care is difficult in rural areas without roads and bridges and in nations with too few medical personnel. Then there is the problem of identifying AIDS patients in the first place. In North America, people who are suspected of having AIDS generally are tested for HIV, and health professionals

maintain careful records documenting their patients' symptoms and treatments. In contrast, most African nations do not require that suspected AIDS patients be tested for HIV, and health professionals often can't monitor patients effectively or even pay for the tests to diagnose HIV infection. The diagnosis is made more difficult by the fact that other regional health problems, such as malnutrition, tuberculosis, and malaria, have symptoms that can resemble those of AIDS.

What about education? The type of public information campaigns used in North America to curb the transmission of sexually transmitted diseases may not be possible in countries with less developed media networks. Furthermore, social norms are different, and misinformation and denial are widespread. Sex education for both boys and girls and strategies to change men's sexual behavior are sorely needed. Providing male and female condoms at low cost might also help. In Thailand, a national program to promote condom use lowered the prevalence of HIV among 21-year-old military conscripts from 4% in the mid-1990s to less than 1% by 2002.

A final hurdle is the cost of treatment. Recent advances in AIDS treatment depend on new *antiretroviral* drugs (ARVs) that can cost up to $2,500 per month—more than

many Africans earn in a year. High prices for new AIDS drugs reflect the enormous research and development costs that are required by U.S. law to ensure drugs' safety and effectiveness. Foreign firms can manufacture and sell AIDS medicines at a fraction of the U.S. price because they do not have to recover the cost of drug development. In addition to selling the low-cost drugs abroad, foreign manufacturers sometimes smuggle them into North America. U.S. pharmaceutical firms claim that the knockoff ARVs endanger future research and the development of even better HIV treatments. They have struck back by taking legal action against distributors and purchasers of illegal AIDS medications.

The global economic downturn of 2009 only made things worse. AIDS treatment programs suffered financially along with the rest of the economy. In addition, increased poverty usually leads to poorer nutrition, even less access to health care, and risky social behaviors such as trading sex for money.

The result of all of these problems is that in sub-Saharan Africa, fewer than half of all HIV-infected people currently receive treatment. Furthermore, only 60% of all patients who begin HIV treatment are still receiving it two years later. This is unfortunate, because ARVs should be taken for the rest of the patient's life in order to fully protect against the development of AIDS.

The challenge of AIDS in sub-Saharan Africa is likely to remain with us for some time. We can deal with it now or we can deal with an even larger problem later.

QUESTIONS TO CONSIDER

1 Should foreign pharmaceutical companies be allowed to manufacture ARVs at low cost and sell them to needy nations?

2 As a matter of public health, should governments ensure that AIDS medicines are available to those who need them?

THE FACTS...

- Two-thirds of the world's HIV-infected people live in sub-Saharan Africa.
- In sub-Saharan Africa, girls aged 15–19 are four to five times more likely to be HIV-infected than boys.
- Attempts to solve the AIDS crisis in Africa are hampered by poor infrastructure; inadequate health care; poor medical record keeping; and educational, political, and social issues.
- Many African nations cannot afford the high cost of current AIDS treatment drugs.

>> The health risk of a **pathogen** (disease-causing organism) is determined by its **transmissibility** (how *easily* it can be passed from person to person), **mode of transmission** (*how* it is transmitted; through air, food, blood, etc.), and **virulence** (how *damaging* the disease is when one catches it).

>> **The immune system** has **nonspecific** (against many pathogens) and **specific** (against one pathogen) defense mechanisms.

>> **Nonspecific defense mechanisms** include immune system cells that engulf and digest foreign cells, chemicals that are toxic to foreign cells, proteins that interfere with viral reproduction, and the development of a fever.

>> **Specific defense mechanisms involve the production of antibodies and T cells** that recognize and inactivate one specific pathogen. Specific defense mechanisms have a memory component that is the basis of immunity.

>> **Inappropriate immune system activity** can lead to allergies and autoimmune diseases.

>> **AIDS (Acquired Immune Deficiency Syndrome) is caused by a virus that targets certain cells of the immune system,** thereby rendering the body incapable of fending off other infections.

The world is swarming with living organisms (bacteria) and even some nonliving entities (viruses and prions) too small to be seen with the naked eye. They're found on doorknobs, the money we handle, and our clothes. They're in the food we eat and the air we breathe. Most are harmless—indeed, some are highly beneficial. The ones that cause disease are called **pathogens** (from the Greek *pathos*, meaning "disease," plus *gennan*, meaning "to produce").

Pathogens come from outside the body. As a group they account for a large fraction of all human disease and suffering, but there are other challenges to our health that come from within. Mutations (alterations to a cell's DNA) may cause some of our own cells to become abnormal and may even lead to cancer. Fortunately, our bodies can recognize cells that become abnormal and dispatch most of them before they ever have the chance to develop further.

What ways do we have to protect ourselves? Our body's immune system and other general defense mechanisms include:

■ *Barriers to entry or ways of expelling or neutralizing pathogens before they can do harm.* These include skin, stomach acid, tears, and such actions as vomiting and defecation.

■ *Nonspecific defense mechanisms.* Nonspecific defenses help the body respond to generalized tissue damage and many of the more common or obvious pathogens, including most bacteria and some viruses.

■ *Specific defense mechanisms.* These enable the body to recognize and kill specific bacteria and other foreign cells and to neutralize viruses. Our specific defense mechanisms employ sophisticated weaponry indeed. The specific defense mechanisms are also the basis of immunity from future disease.

All three mechanisms are operating night and day to protect us. Crucial to the nonspecific and specific defense mechanisms is the **immune system**, a complex group of cells, proteins, and structures of the lymphatic and circulatory systems. However, even the immune system is not perfect; it can only kill or neutralize pathogens or abnormal cells that it can recognize. This has implications for how the human body deals with certain pathogens.

What is the immune system on alert for? We start by looking at some of the kinds of pathogens that can invade our bodies.

9.1 Pathogens cause disease

Pathogens include bacteria, viruses, fungi, a few protozoa, and possibly prions. Larger parasites, including various worms, can also be pathogens, although they are relatively rare in industrialized countries. Because bacteria and viruses are by far the most numerous and problematic pathogens in Western nations, we focus on them as we describe how we protect and defend ourselves. We'll also discuss prions as a newly discovered class of pathogens.

Bacteria: Single-celled living organisms

Bacteria (singular: *bacterium*) are single-celled organisms that do not have a nucleus or membrane-bound organelles. All the DNA in most bacteria is contained in just one chromosome, which usually forms a continuous loop that is anchored to the plasma membrane. Bacterial ribosomes are smaller than ours and float freely in the cytoplasm. The outer surface of bacteria is covered by a rigid cell wall that gives bacteria their distinctive shapes, including spheres, rods, and spirals (Figure 9.1).

Judging by their variety and numbers, bacteria are among the most successful organisms on Earth. Although they are smaller than the typical human cell, their small size is actually an advantage. Like all living organisms, bacteria need energy and raw materials to maintain life and to grow and divide. Their small size means that they have a high surface-to-volume ratio, a decided advantage when it comes to getting raw materials and getting rid of wastes by diffusion.

Like our own cells, bacteria use ATP as a direct energy source and amino acids for making proteins. They store energy as carbohydrates and fats. Where do they obtain

a) SEM (× 2,000) of *Streptococcus*, a spherical bacterium that causes sore throats.

b) SEM (× 5,600) of *Escherichia coli*, a common intestinal bacteria that is usually harmless.

c) SEM (× 12,000) of *Campylobacter jejuni*, a spiral-shaped bacterium that causes food poisoning.

Figure 9.1 Electron micrographs of the three common shapes of bacteria.

those raw materials? Anywhere they can. Some bacteria break down raw sewage and cause the decomposition of dead animals and plants, thereby playing an essential role in the recycling of energy and raw materials. Others obtain nutrients from the soil and air.

Humans have learned to harness bacteria to produce commercial products, including antibiotic drugs, hormones, vaccines, and foods ranging from sauerkraut to soy sauce. Some bacteria even live within our digestive tract, drawing energy from the food we eat in exchange for manufacturing vitamins or controlling the populations of other, more harmful bacteria. Life as we know it would not be possible without these little organisms.

A few bacteria are pathogens, however. Pathogens rely on living human cells for their energy supply, and in the process they damage or kill the human cells. They cause pneumonia, tonsillitis, tuberculosis, botulism, toxic shock syndrome, syphilis, Lyme disease, and many other diseases. Although we concentrate on pathogens in this chapter, do keep in mind that most bacteria are harmless, and many are even beneficial.

Bacterial infections are generally treated with **antibiotics**—chemotherapeutic agents that inhibit or abolish the growth of bacteria, fungi, and protozoa.

Viruses: Tiny infectious agents

Viruses are extremely small infectious agents, perhaps one-hundredth the size of a bacterium and one-thousandth the size of a typical eukaryotic cell (**Figure 9.2**). Structurally a virus is very simple, consisting solely of a small piece of

Mitochondrion

Nucleus

Golgi apparatus

Plasma membrane

Endoplasmic reticulum

Relative size of a bacterium

Relative size of a virus

Ribosomes

DNA

Cell wall

Plasma membrane

RNA

DNA

Protein coat

a) Eukaryotic cell. Eukaryotic cells have a membrane-bound nucleus and well-defined membrane-bound organelles.

b) Bacterial cell. Bacteria have a single strand of DNA and free-floating small ribosomes within their cytoplasm. Their plasma membrane is surrounded by a rigid cell wall.

c) Viruses. Viruses consist of a protein coat surrounding either RNA or DNA.

Figure 9.2 Size and structural differences between a eukaryotic cell, a bacterium (prokaryotic cell), and viruses.

genetic material (either RNA or DNA) surrounded by a protein coat. They have no organelles of their own, so they don't grow and they can't reproduce on their own.

Are viruses alive? Biologists are divided on this question. Most would say that they are not because they cannot reproduce on their own. Viruses have no observable activity associated with life when they are not in contact with another living cell. However, when they enter a living cell, they take it over and use the cell's organelles to make more viruses.

Viruses have several ways of gaining entry into living cells. Most viruses that infect human cells are taken into the cell cytoplasm by endocytosis; once inside the cell, the protein coats are dissolved and the viral genetic material is released for incorporation into the cell's genetic material. Other viruses merge their outer coat with the cell membrane and release their genetic contents into the cell's cytoplasm. Still other viruses attach to the outer surface of the cell membrane and inject just their genetic material into the cell, much as a needle and syringe inject drugs into the body. Regardless of the method of entry, the presence of the viral genetic material causes the cell to begin producing thousands of copies of the virus instead of carrying out its own metabolic activities. Sometimes the newly formed viruses are released by a type of budding from the cell membrane while the cell is still alive. In other cases the cell becomes so packed with viruses that it dies and bursts, releasing a huge number of viruses all at once.

Diseases caused by viruses range from serious—AIDS, hepatitis, encephalitis, rabies—to annoying—colds, warts, or chicken pox. Viral infections can be minor for some people but serious for others. An otherwise healthy person may be ill for only a few days with a viral infection, whereas someone who is very young, very old, or in poor health may die.

Antibiotics generally don't work against viral infections. The best ways to cure a viral infection are either to prevent the viruses from entering living cells or to stop the host cell from producing more viruses once it's infected.

Prions: Infectious proteins

In 1986, scientists identified a disease in British cattle that destroyed nerve cells in the animals' brain and spinal cord, causing the animals to stagger, jerk, tremble, and exhibit other bizarre behaviors. The press nicknamed it "mad cow disease." Then between 1994 and 1996, 12 Britons ages 19 to 39 developed signs of a new human disease called *variant Creutzfeldt-Jakob disease (vCJD)*. Alarmingly, researchers found that all of the vCJD patients had eaten beef from animals suspected of having mad cow disease. Later they confirmed that a *prion* was responsible for both the mad cow disease and the 12 cases of vCJD.

A **prion** is a misfolded form of a normal brain cell protein. But it is not just a misfolded protein—it is misfolded protein that can trigger the misfolding of nearby *normal* forms of the protein as well. Once prions enter a nerve cell, the misfolding process becomes self-propagating—one prion produces another, which produces another, and so on. Eventually so many prions accumulate within infected brain cells that the cells die and burst, releasing prions to infect other brain cells. The death of nerve cells accounts for the debilitating neurological symptoms and progressive degeneration seen in both mad cow disease and human vCJD.

BlogInFocus MB

Is it possible that other neurodegenerative diseases such as Alzheimer's disease and Parkinson's disease are also caused by prions? Visit MJ's blog in the Study Area in MasteringBiology and look under "Neurodegenerative Diseases."

Prions are resistant to cooking, freezing, and even drying. There is no known cure for prion infection. Because infection occurs when humans (or cattle) eat prion-infected cattle tissues, the best way to prevent vCJD in humans is to limit the spread of mad cow disease in cattle. Global cooperation is making this possible. In 1994 the European Union banned the use of mammalian meat and bone meal products as cattle feed, and since that time the number of cases of mad cow disease has fallen dramatically.

✓**Quick Check** *Suppose you are studying a mysterious disease, and you discover that it is caused by a tiny pathogen that contains some nucleic acid and some protein, but does not have a plasma membrane. Is it most likely a bacterium, a virus, or a prion? Explain your answer.* ■

Transmissibility, mode of transmission, and virulence determine health risk

Some pathogens are clearly more risky to human health than others. Factors that determine the danger of a particular pathogen include transmissibility (how easily it is passed from one person to another), mode of transmission (how it is transmitted), and virulence (how damaging the resulting disease is).

For instance, the viruses that cause the common cold are easily transmitted from hands to mucous membranes, as well as in the fluid particles spread by a sneeze. However, these viruses tend not to be very virulent. The HIV virus that causes AIDS, by contrast, is only moderately transmissible. Its mode of transmission is limited to exchange of body fluids (blood, semen, breast milk, or vaginal secretions).

Answers to ✓ **questions can be found in Appendix A.**

However, the HIV virus is tremendously virulent, and this is what makes it so dangerous.

Imagine what would happen if a disease as transmissible as the flu and as virulent as AIDS were to arise in the human population. In fact, there have been such diseases, and they have caused deadly epidemics. Between 1348 and 1350, the **bubonic plague**, a bacterial infection, killed an estimated 25–40% of the European population. A 1918 outbreak of influenza killed more than 20 million people worldwide.

Pathogens continue to challenge human defenses. A prime example is the Ebola virus that arose in Africa in 1976 and still presents a threat today. It is one of the most virulent pathogens known, killing more than 80% of an exposed population in less than two weeks.

Recap Like all cells, bacteria draw their energy and raw materials from their environment. Pathogenic bacteria get the materials they need from living cells, damaging or killing the cells in the process. A virus consists of a single strand of DNA or RNA surrounded by protein. Viruses use their DNA or RNA to force a living cell to make more copies of the virus. Prions are infectious proteins that cause normal proteins to misfold. ▪

9.2 The lymphatic system defends the body

As noted in the chapter on blood, the **lymphatic system** is closely associated with the cardiovascular system. The lymphatic system performs three important functions:

- It helps maintain the volume of blood in the cardiovascular system.
- It transports fats and fat-soluble vitamins absorbed from the digestive system to the cardiovascular system.
- It defends the body against infection.

We briefly described how the lymphatic system helps to maintain blood volume and interstitial fluid volume when we discussed the cardiovascular system. We'll discuss its role in transporting fats and vitamins when we describe the digestive system. In this chapter we turn to the third function: the role of the lymphatic system in protecting us from disease. Most of the cells of the immune system are housed in the lymphatic system, although they can also circulate in blood and enter the interstitial fluid. Here we describe the structural components of the system; in later sections we discuss how specific immune system cells carry out their function.

The basic components of the lymphatic system are a network of lymph vessels throughout the body, the lymph nodes, the spleen, the thymus gland, and the tonsils and adenoids (Figure 9.3).

Lymphatic vessels transport lymph

The lymphatic system begins as a network of small, blind-ended *lymphatic capillaries* in the vicinity of the cells and blood capillaries. Lymph capillaries have wide spaces between overlapping cells. Their structure allows them to take up substances (including bacteria) that are too large to enter a blood capillary.

The fluid in the lymphatic capillaries is *lymph*, a milky body fluid that contains white blood cells, proteins, fats, and the occasional bacterium and virus. Lymphatic capillaries merge to form the *lymphatic vessels*. Like veins, lymphatic vessels have walls consisting of three thin layers, and they contain one-way valves to prevent backflow of lymph. Also like veins, flow in lymphatic vessels is aided by skeletal muscle contractions and pressure changes in the chest during respiration. The lymphatic vessels merge to form larger and larger vessels, eventually creating two major lymphatic ducts: the *right lymphatic duct* and the *thoracic duct*. The two lymph ducts join the subclavian veins near the shoulders, thereby returning the lymph to the cardiovascular system.

Lymph nodes cleanse the lymph

Located at intervals along the lymphatic vessels are small organs called **lymph nodes**. Lymph nodes remove microorganisms, cellular debris, and abnormal cells from the lymph before returning it to the cardiovascular system. There are hundreds of lymph nodes, clustered in the areas of the digestive tract, neck, armpits, and groin (Figure 9.4). They vary in diameter from about 1 millimeter to 2.5 centimeters. Each node is enclosed in a dense capsule of connective tissue pierced by lymphatic vessels. Inside each node are connective tissue and two types of white blood cells, *macrophages* and *lymphocytes*, which identify microorganisms and remove them. (Macrophages and lymphocytes are discussed in greater detail in later sections.)

The lymphatic vessels carry lymph into and out of each node (see Figure 9.3). Valves within these vessels ensure that lymph flows only in one direction. As the fluid flows through a node, the macrophages destroy foreign cells by phagocytosis, and the lymphocytes activate other defense mechanisms. The cleansed lymph fluid flows out of the node and continues on its path to the veins.

The spleen cleanses blood

The largest lymphatic organ, the **spleen**, is a soft, fist-sized mass located in the upper-left abdominal cavity. The spleen is covered with a dense capsule of connective tissue interspersed with smooth muscle cells. Inside the organ are two types of tissue, called *red pulp* and *white pulp*.

The spleen has two main functions: it controls the quality of circulating red blood cells by removing the old and damaged ones, and it helps fight infection. The red pulp contains macrophages that scavenge and break down microorganisms as well as old and damaged red blood

Figure 9.3 The lymphatic system. The lymphatic system consists of a network of lymphatic vessels throughout the body, lymph nodes, the thymus gland, tonsils and adenoids, and the spleen.

Figure 9.4 Lymph node. Color scanning electron micrograph (× 1,000) of a section through a lymph node, showing macrophages (pink) and lymphocytes (yellow) lying in wait to attack and destroy foreign and damaged cells. A few red blood cells (red) are also present.

cells and platelets. The cleansed blood is then stored in the red pulp. Your body can call on this reserve for extra blood in case of blood loss or a fall in blood pressure, or whenever you need extra oxygen-carrying capacity. The white pulp contains primarily lymphocytes searching for foreign pathogens; it does not store blood. Notice that the main distinction between the spleen and lymph nodes is *which* fluid they cleanse—the spleen cleanses the blood, and the lymph nodes cleanse lymph. Together, they keep the circulating body fluids relatively free of damaged cells and microorganisms.

A number of diseases, such as infectious mononucleosis and leukemia, cause the spleen to enlarge. The swollen spleen can sometimes be felt as a lump in the upper-left abdomen. A strong blow to the abdomen can rupture the spleen, causing severe internal bleeding. In this case surgical removal of the spleen may be necessary to forestall a fatal hemorrhage. We can live without a spleen because its functions are shared by the lymph glands, liver, and red bone marrow. However, people who have had their spleen removed are often a little more vulnerable to infections.

Thymus gland hormones cause T lymphocytes to mature

The **thymus gland** is located in the lower neck, behind the sternum and just above the heart. Encased in connective tissue, the gland contains lymphocytes and epithelial cells. The thymus gland secretes two hormones, thymosin and thymopoietin, that cause certain lymphocytes called *T lymphocytes* (T cells) to mature and take an active role in specific defenses.

The size and activity level of the thymus gland vary with age. It is largest and most active during childhood. During adolescence it stops growing and then slowly starts

to shrink. By that time our defense mechanisms are typically well established. In old age the thymus gland may disappear entirely, to be replaced by fibrous and fatty tissue.

Tonsils protect the throat

The *tonsils* are masses of lymphatic tissue near the entrance to the throat. Lymphocytes in the tonsils gather and filter out many of the microorganisms that enter the throat in food or air.

We actually have several tonsils, and some are not readily visible. The familiar tonsils at the back of the throat are the largest and most often infected. When they become infected, the resulting inflammation is called *tonsillitis*. If the infection becomes serious, the tissues can be surgically removed.

Lymphatic tissue called the *adenoids* lies at the back of the nasal passages. The adenoids tend to enlarge during early childhood, but in most people they start to shrink after age 5 and usually disappear by puberty. In some cases they continue to enlarge and obstruct airflow from nose to throat. This can cause mouth breathing, a nasal voice, and snoring. Like the tonsils, the adenoids can be surgically removed if they grow large enough to cause problems.

Recap The lymphatic system helps protect us from disease. Macrophages and lymphocytes within the lymph nodes identify microorganisms and remove them. The spleen removes damaged red blood cells and foreign cells from blood. The thymus gland secretes hormones that help T lymphocytes mature. Cells in the tonsils gather and remove microorganisms that enter the throat. ▪

9.3 Keeping pathogens out: The first line of defense

Our bodies have several ways to prevent entry of pathogens. We also have ways to neutralize them, inhibit their growth, or expel them when they do get in. Here are some of the body's defense strategies.

Skin: An effective deterrent

The most important barrier against entry of any pathogen into our bodies is the skin. Skin has four key attributes that make it such an effective barrier: (1) its structure, (2) the fact that it is constantly being replaced, (3) its acidic pH, and (4) the production of an antibiotic by sweat glands.

Regarding structure, the outermost layers of the skin's epidermis consist of dead, dried-out epithelial cells. These cells contain a fibrous protein called *keratin*, which is also a primary component of fingernails and hair. Once the cells have died and the water has evaporated, the keratin forms a dry, tough, somewhat elastic barrier to the entry of microorganisms. Second, skin is continually being renewed throughout life. Dead cells shed from the surface are replaced by new cells at the base of the epidermis. Any pathogens deposited on the surface are shed along with the dead cells. Third, healthy skin has a pH of about 5 to 6, primarily because of the sweat produced by sweat glands. This relatively low (acidic) pH makes skin a hostile environment for many microorganisms. Finally, sweat glands produce a natural antibiotic peptide called *dermicidin* that can kill a range of harmful bacteria.

For further proof of skin's effectiveness as a barrier to infection, look at what happens when you get a tiny cut or scratch in your skin. If the damage reaches the moist layers of living cells underneath the skin, you may see signs of infection in the area within a few days. One of the most critical problems in treating patients with extensive burns is the infections that often result from the loss of the barrier function of skin.

Impeding pathogen entry in areas not covered by skin

Most successful pathogens enter the body at places where we do not have skin. They enter through the mucous membranes that line the digestive, urinary, respiratory, and reproductive tracts, where they can take advantage of moist surfaces in direct contact with living cells. They enter around the eyes or in the ears. However, even these areas have ways to impede pathogen entry. Defenses include tears, saliva, earwax, digestive and vaginal acids, and mucus, which impede entry; the ability to remove pathogens by vomiting, urination, and defecation; and even competition created by nonpathogenic bacteria that normally live in (and on) the body.

Tears, saliva, and earwax Although we may not think of tears as a defense mechanism, they perform a valuable service by lubricating the eyes and washing away particles. Tears and saliva both contain **lysozyme**, an enzyme that kills many bacteria. In addition, saliva lubricates the delicate tissues inside the mouth so that they do not dry out and crack. It also rinses microorganisms safely from the mouth into the stomach, where most of them are killed by stomach acid. Earwax traps small particles and microorganisms.

Mucus Mucus is a thick, gel-like material secreted by cells at various surfaces of the body, including the lining of the digestive tract and the branching airways of the respiratory system. Microorganisms that come into contact with the sticky mucus become mired and cannot gain access to the cells beneath. In addition, the cells of the airways have tiny hairlike projections called *cilia* that beat constantly in a wavelike motion to sweep mucus upward into the throat. There we get rid of the mucus by coughing or swallowing it. Sometimes we remove mucus and microorganisms by sneezing, which is also one of the primary ways we pass microorganisms to other people (Figure 9.5).

Digestive and vaginal acids Undiluted digestive acid is strong enough to kill nearly all pathogens that enter the digestive

Figure 9.5 Sneezing removes mucus and microorganisms from the body. Sneezing also promotes the transmission of certain respiratory infections from person to person.

tract on an empty stomach. Only one strain of bacteria, *Helicobacter pylori*, has actually evolved to thrive in the highly acidic environment of the stomach. *H. pylori* is now known to contribute to many cases of stomach ulcers (see Chapter 14).

Vaginal secretions are slightly acidic, too, though not nearly as acidic as stomach secretions.

Vomiting, urination, and defecation Vomiting, though unpleasant, is certainly an effective way of ridding the body of toxic or infected stomach contents.

Generally speaking, the urinary system does not have a resident population of bacteria. Urine is usually slightly acidic, and in addition the constant flushing action of urination tends to keep bacterial populations low. Urine pH can vary from fairly acidic to slightly basic, depending on diet. Some physicians advise patients with bladder or urethral infections to drink cranberry juice, which is acidic. The increased acidity of the urine inhibits bacterial growth, and the increased urine volume flushes the bacteria out.

The movement of feces and the act of defecation also help remove microorganisms from the digestive tract. When we become ill, the muscles in the intestinal wall may start to contract more vigorously, and the intestine may secrete additional fluid into the feces. The result is *diarrhea*—increased fluidity, frequency, or volume of bowel movements. Unpleasant though diarrhea may be, mild cases serve a useful function by speeding the removal of pathogens.

Resident bacteria Certain strains of beneficial bacteria normally live in the mucous membranes lining the vagina and the digestive tract. They help control population levels of more harmful organisms by competing successfully against them for food. They may also make the body less vulnerable to pathogens. For example, *Lactobacillus* bacteria in the vagina produce a substance that lowers vaginal pH to levels that many fungi and bacteria cannot tolerate.

One might ask how any beneficial bacteria ever get to the small and large intestine if they have to pass through the stomach first. The answer is that following a meal the stomach contents are not so acidic because food both dilutes and buffers the stomach acid, so some bacteria pass through the stomach with the food we eat.

⟲ Recap **Various mechanisms create an inhospitable environment for pathogenic microorganisms. Skin is a dry outer barrier. Tears, saliva, earwax, and mucus trap pathogens or wash them away. Acidic conditions kill them or inhibit their growth; urination, defecation, and vomiting forcibly expel them; and resident bacteria compete with pathogens for food. ▪**

9.4 Nonspecific defenses: The second line of defense

If pathogens manage to breach our physical and chemical barriers and start to kill or damage cells, we have a problem of a different sort. Now the body must actively seek out the pathogens and get rid of them. It must also clean up the injured area and repair the damage.

Our second line of defense includes a varied group of defense mechanisms. We refer to them as *nonspecific* because they do not target specific pathogens. Instead, they appear in response to all types of health challenges without discriminating between them. Table 9.1 summarizes nonspecific defenses, which include phagocytes, natural killer cells, the inflammatory response, the complement system, interferons, and fever.

Phagocytes engulf foreign cells

As noted in the chapter on blood, *phagocytes* are white blood cells that destroy foreign cells through the process of **phagocytosis**. A phagocyte first captures a bacterium with its cytoplasmic extensions (Figure 9.6). Then it draws the bacterium in, eventually engulfing it (endocytosis) and enclosing it in a membrane-bound vesicle. Inside the cell, the vesicle containing the bacterium fuses with lysosomes, and the powerful enzymes in the lysosomes dissolve the bacterial membranes. Once digestion is complete, the phagocyte jettisons the bacterial wastes by exocytosis.

Some white blood cells can slip through the walls of blood vessels into tissue spaces, attracted by substances released by injured cells at the site of infection. Other phagocytes reside permanently in connective tissues of the lymph nodes, spleen, liver, lungs, and brain.

Neutrophils are the first white blood cells to respond to infection. They digest and destroy bacteria and some fungi in the blood and tissue fluids. Other white blood cells, known as *monocytes*, leave the vascular system, enter the tissue fluids, and develop into **macrophages** (from the Greek for "large eater") that can engulf and digest large numbers of foreign cells, especially viruses and bacterial parasites. Macrophages serve a cleanup function by scavenging old blood cells,

Table 9.1 The second line of defense: Nonspecific defense

Defense	Functions
Phagocytes	Neutrophils and macrophages engulf and digest foreign cells.
	Eosinophils bombard large parasites with digestive enzymes and phagocytize foreign proteins.
Natural killer cells	Release chemicals that disintegrate cell membranes of tumor cells and virus-infected cells.
Inflammatory response	Four components include redness, warmth, swelling, and pain.
	Attracts phagocytes and promotes tissue healing.
Complement system	A group of proteins that assists other defense mechanisms; enhances inflammation and phagocytosis, kills pathogens.
Interferons	Stimulate the production of proteins that interfere with viral reproduction.
Fever	Modest fever makes internal environment less hospitable to pathogens, fosters ability to fight infections.

dead tissue fragments, and cellular debris. They also release chemicals that stimulate the production of more white blood cells. Technically, macrophages are no longer white blood cells because they are no longer in blood.

When invaders are too big to be engulfed and digested by phagocytosis, other white blood cells called **eosinophils** take action. Eosinophils cluster around large parasites such as flukes and pinworms and bombard them with digestive enzymes. Eosinophils also engulf and digest certain foreign proteins.

When the body is actively fighting an infection, the mortality rate of white blood cells rises dramatically. Tissue fluid, dead phagocytes and microorganisms, and cellular debris accumulate at the infection site, producing a characteristic discharge called *pus*. If pus becomes trapped and cannot drain, the body may wall it off with connective tissue. The result is an *abscess*. Common places for abscesses to form include the breast (mastitis), the gums (dental abscesses), and more rarely the liver or brain. Many abscesses subside after being drained, whereas others require antibiotic drugs or surgical removal.

Inflammation: Redness, warmth, swelling, and pain

Any type of tissue injury—whether infection, burns, irritating chemicals, or physical trauma—triggers a series of related events collectively called the *inflammatory response*, or

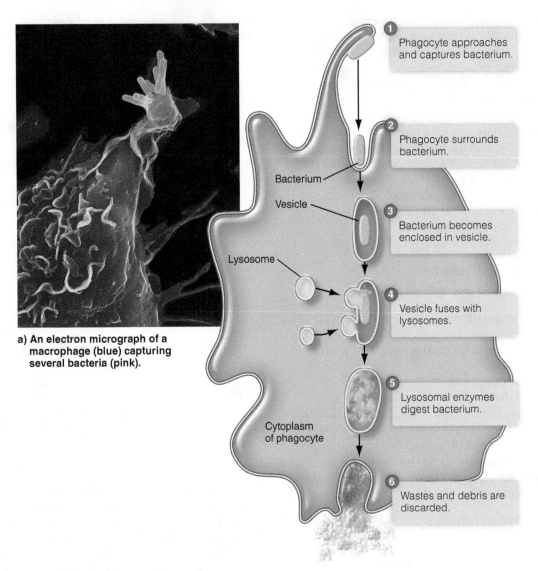

a) An electron micrograph of a macrophage (blue) capturing several bacteria (pink).

1 Phagocyte approaches and captures bacterium.

2 Phagocyte surrounds bacterium.

Bacterium

Vesicle

3 Bacterium becomes enclosed in vesicle.

Lysosome

4 Vesicle fuses with lysosomes.

5 Lysosomal enzymes digest bacterium.

Cytoplasm of phagocyte

6 Wastes and debris are discarded.

b) Steps in the process.

Figure 9.6 **Phagocytosis.**

inflammation. Inflammation has four outward signs: redness, warmth, swelling, and pain. Although these may not sound like positive developments, the events that cause these signs prevent the damage from spreading, dispose of cellular debris and pathogens, and set the stage for tissue-repair mechanisms.

The inflammatory response starts whenever tissues are injured (Figure 9.7). The release of chemicals from damaged cells sounds the alarm for the process to begin. These chemicals stimulate **mast cells**, which are connective tissue cells specialized to release **histamine**. Histamine promotes vasodilation of neighboring small blood vessels. White blood cells, called **basophils**, also secrete histamine.

Recall that most white blood cells are too large to cross capillary walls. As histamine dilates blood vessels, however, the endothelial cells in vessel walls pull slightly apart, and the vessels become more permeable. This allows additional phagocytes to squeeze through capillary walls into the interstitial fluid. There they attack foreign organisms and damaged cells. After destroying pathogens, some phagocytes travel to the lymphatic system, where their presence activates lymphocytes to initiate specific defense mechanisms (discussed later).

Vasodilation brings more blood into the injured area, making it red and warm. The rising temperature increases phagocyte activity. The increased leakiness of capillary walls allows more fluid to seep into tissue spaces, causing swelling. The extra fluid dilutes pathogens and toxins and brings in clotting proteins that form a fibrin mesh to wall off the damaged area from healthy tissue. As a bonus, the fluid carries in extra oxygen and nutrients to promote tissue healing and carries away dead cells, microorganisms, and other debris from the area.

Swollen tissues press against nearby nerve endings. This swelling, plus the sensitizing effects of inflammatory chemicals, creates the sensation of pain that accompanies

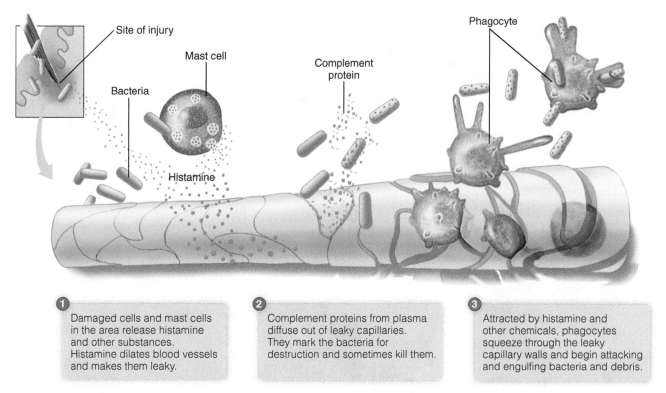

1. Damaged cells and mast cells in the area release histamine and other substances. Histamine dilates blood vessels and makes them leaky.

2. Complement proteins from plasma diffuse out of leaky capillaries. They mark the bacteria for destruction and sometimes kill them.

3. Attracted by histamine and other chemicals, phagocytes squeeze through the leaky capillary walls and begin attacking and engulfing bacteria and debris.

Figure 9.7 The inflammatory response.

inflammation. However, even pain can be positive. The discomfort hinders active movement and forces the injured person to rest, facilitating the healing process.

✅ **Quick Check** *Antihistamines are drugs that block the effect of histamine. Why do antihistamines help alleviate the "stuffy nose" and nasal congestion of a cold?* ▪

Natural killer cells target tumors and virus-infected cells

Natural killer (NK) cells are a group of white blood cells (lymphocytes) that destroy tumor cells and cells infected by viruses. NK cells are able to recognize certain changes that take place in the plasma membranes of tumor cells and virus-infected cells. The name "natural killer" reflects the fact that NK cells are nonspecific killers, unlike other killer cells discussed later in this chapter that target only specific enemies.

NK cells are not phagocytes. Instead, they release chemicals that break down their targets' cell membranes. Soon after an NK attack, the target cell's membrane develops holes, and its nucleus rapidly disintegrates. NK cells also secrete substances that enhance the inflammatory response.

The complement system assists other defense mechanisms

The **complement system**, or *complement*, comprises at least 20 plasma proteins that circulate in the blood and

complement, or assist, other defense mechanisms. Normally these proteins circulate in an inactive state. When activated by the presence of an infection, however, they become a potent defense force. Once one protein is activated it activates another, leading to a cascade of reactions. Each protein in the complement system can activate many others, creating a powerful "domino effect."

Some activated complement proteins join to form large protein complexes that create holes in bacterial cell walls. Fluids and salts leak in through these holes, until eventually the bacterium swells and bursts (Figure 9.8). Other activated complement proteins bind to bacterial cell membranes, marking them for destruction by phagocytes. Still others stimulate mast cells to release histamine or serve as chemical attractants to draw additional phagocytes to the infection.

Interferons interfere with viral reproduction

One of the most interesting defense mechanisms is an early warning system between virus-infected and still-healthy cells. As mentioned earlier, viruses cannot reproduce on their own. Instead, they invade body cells and use the cells' machinery to make more viruses.

Cells that become infected by viruses secrete a group of proteins called **interferons**. Interferons diffuse to nearby healthy cells, bind to their cell membranes, and stimulate the healthy cells to produce proteins that interfere with the synthesis of viral proteins, making it harder for the viruses to infect the protected cells.

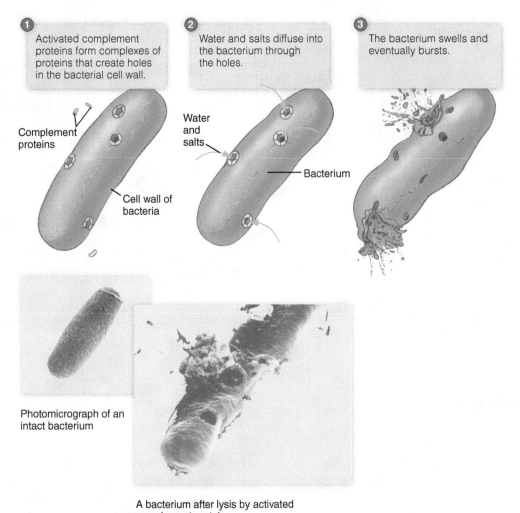

① Activated complement proteins form complexes of proteins that create holes in the bacterial cell wall.

Complement proteins

Cell wall of bacteria

② Water and salts diffuse into the bacterium through the holes.

Water and salts

Bacterium

③ The bacterium swells and eventually bursts.

Photomicrograph of an intact bacterium

A bacterium after lysis by activated complement proteins

Figure 9.8 **How activated complement proteins kill bacteria.**

Interferons are now being produced in pharmaceutical laboratories. At least one interferon protein (*alpha interferon*) has shown promise against certain viral diseases, including genital warts, hepatitis B, and one form of leukemia.

Fever raises body temperature

A final weapon in our second line of defense is **fever**, an abnormally high body temperature. Your body's "thermostat" is set to approximately 98.6°F (37°C), with a normal range of about 97–99°F (36–37.2°C). When macrophages detect and attack bacteria, viruses, or other foreign substances, they release certain chemicals into the bloodstream. These chemicals, called *pyrogens*, cause the brain to reset your thermostat to a higher temperature.

There is a tendency to treat all fevers as if they were a problem. But a modest fever may be beneficial because it makes our internal environment less hospitable to pathogens and enhances the body's ability to fight infections. Fever increases the metabolic rate of body cells, speeding up both defense mechanisms and tissue-repair processes. When the infection is gone, the process reverses. Macrophages stop releasing pyrogens, the thermostat setting returns to normal, and your fever "breaks."

However, high fevers can be dangerous. Because the chemical bonds that give a protein its shape are relatively weak, they may be broken by high temperatures. If that happens, the shape of the protein will change and the protein may not function normally. It's a good idea to monitor the course of any fever, particularly in children and older adults. Health professionals recommend seeking medical advice for any fever that lasts longer than two days or rises above 100°F.

Recap Nonspecific defense mechanisms involve a general attack against all foreign and damaged cells. Neutrophils and macrophages engulf and digest bacteria and damaged cells, and eosinophils bombard larger organisms (too large to be engulfed) with digestive enzymes. The inflammatory response attracts phagocytes and promotes tissue healing. Interferons interfere with viral reproduction, and a modest fever enhances our ability to fight infections. ∎

9.5 Specific defense mechanisms: The third line of defense

Even if foreign cells manage to bypass physical and chemical barriers and overcome nonspecific defenses, they must still cope with the body's third line of defense, the most sophisticated weapon of all. The *immune system* comprises cells, proteins, and the lymphatic system, all working together to detect and kill particular pathogens and abnormal body cells. The activities of the immune system are collectively called the **immune response**. Because the immune system targets specific enemies, we refer to these operations as *specific defense mechanisms*.

The immune response has three important characteristics:

- It recognizes and targets specific pathogens or foreign substances.
- It has a "memory," the capability to store information from past exposures so that it can respond more quickly to later invasions by the same pathogen.
- It protects the entire body; the resulting immunity is not limited to the site of infection.

The key to specific defenses is the body's ability to distinguish between its own cells and those of foreign invaders. Among its own cells, it must also be able to distinguish between those that are healthy, those that are abnormal (such as cancer cells), and those that are dead or dying.

The immune system targets antigens

An **antigen** is any substance that mobilizes the immune system and provokes an immune response. Generally antigens are large protein or polysaccharide molecules. In much the same way that a key fits a lock, each antigen has a unique shape, and every bacterium or virus has a different one. The immune system responds to each uniquely shaped antigen by producing specific *antibodies* to attack and inactivate the antigen (and the cell carrying it).

All antigens are located only on the outer surface of a cell or virus. Hence the immune system cannot detect viruses (or viral DNA/RNA) once they are safely inside a living human cell.

Human cells also have surface proteins that can act as antigens under the right circumstances. Your cells have a unique set of proteins on their surfaces that your immune system uses to recognize that the cells belong to you. These *self markers* are known as **major histocompatibility complex (MHC) proteins**. Your MHC proteins are unique to you by virtue of your unique set of genes. Normally they signal your immune system to bypass your own cells. They are a sort of password, the equivalent of a cellular fingerprint. Your immune system "reads" the password and leaves your cells alone.

However, the same MHC proteins that define your cells as belonging to you would be read as *nonself markers* in another person. In other words, your MHC proteins would be antigens in another person. Abnormal and cancerous cells in your own body also have MHC proteins that are not recognized as "self." The immune system targets all antigens, including those on pathogens and foreign and damaged human cells, for destruction.

✅ **Quick Check** *Why does pregnancy pose a problem for the mother's immune system?* ■

Lymphocytes are central to specific defenses

Lymphocytes play crucial roles in our specific defense mechanisms. As described in the chapter on blood, lymphocytes are white blood cells originating from stem cells in bone marrow. They are fairly small white blood cells with a single nucleus that fills nearly the entire cell. They total about 30% of circulating white blood cells. Lymphocytes are found in the bloodstream, tonsils, spleen, lymph nodes, and thymus gland.

There are two types: B lymphocytes and T lymphocytes, also called **B cells** and **T cells**. (Their names are based on where they mature: B cells mature in bone marrow; T cells in the thymus gland.) Although both types of lymphocytes can recognize and target antigen-bearing cells, they go about this task in different ways.

B cells are responsible for **antibody-mediated immunity**. B cells produce **antibodies**—proteins that bind with and neutralize specific antigens. They release antibodies into the lymph, bloodstream, and tissue fluid, where they circulate throughout the body. Antibody-mediated immunity works best against viruses, bacteria, and foreign molecules that are soluble in blood and lymph.

T cells are responsible for **cell-mediated immunity**, which depends on the actions of several types of T cells. Unlike B cells, T cells do not produce antibodies. Instead, some T cells directly attack foreign cells that carry antigens. Other T cells release proteins that help coordinate other aspects of the immune response, including the actions of T cells, B cells, and macrophages. Cell-mediated immunity protects us against parasites, bacteria, viruses, fungi, cancerous cells, and cells perceived as foreign (including, unfortunately, transplanted tissue— see section 9.8, Tissue rejection: A medical challenge). T cells can identify and kill infected human cells even before the cells have a chance to release new bacteria or viruses into the blood.

✅ **Quick Check** *Suppose a baby was born without a functional thymus gland. Could this child still produce antibodies? Explain your answer.* ■

B cells: Antibody-mediated immunity

In adults, B cells mature in the bone marrow. As they mature, they develop unique surface receptors (with the same structure as an antibody) that allow them to recognize specific antigens. Then they travel in the bloodstream to the lymph nodes, spleen, and tonsils, where they remain inactive until they encounter a foreign cell with that particular antigen. When a B cell with just the right surface receptor encounters the appropriate antigen, its surface receptors bind to the antigen (Figure 9.9). This activates the B cell to grow and then multiply rapidly, producing more B cells exactly like the original and bearing the same surface receptors. The resulting identical cells, all descended from the same cell, are called *clones*.

Although the B cells themselves tend to remain in the lymphatic system, most of the cells of the clone are called **plasma cells** because they begin to secrete their antibodies into the lymph fluid and ultimately into the blood plasma. A typical plasma cell can make antibody molecules at a staggering rate—about 2,000 molecules per second. A plasma cell maintains this frantic pace for a few days and then dies, but its antibodies continue to circulate in blood and lymph.

When the antibodies encounter matching antigens, they bind to them and create an *antigen-antibody complex*. Antibodies specialize in recognizing certain proteins; thus one particular antibody can bind to one particular antigen (Figure 9.10). The formation of an antigen-antibody complex marks the antigen (and the foreign cell that carries it) for destruction either by activated complement proteins or by phagocytes. Some antibodies also inactivate pathogens by causing the cells to agglutinate (clump together), preventing them from entering human cells and causing disease.

Some of the clone cells become memory cells, long-lived cells that remain inactive until that same antigen reappears in the body at some future date. Memory cells store information about the pathogen; if there is a second exposure, the immune response is even faster than the first time. Upon exposure, these memory cells quickly become plasma cells and start to secrete antibodies. Memory cells are the basis for long-term immunity.

The five classes of antibodies

Antibodies belong to the class of blood plasma proteins called *gamma globulins*. Because they play such a crucial role in immunity, the term **immunoglobulin (Ig)** is often used. There are five classes of immunoglobulins, each designated by a different letter: IgG, IgM, IgA, IgD, and IgE. Each type has a different size, location in the body, and function:

- *IgG (75% of immunoglobulins)*. This is the most common class. Found in blood, lymph, intestines, and tissue fluid, the long-lived IgG antibodies activate the complement system and neutralize many toxins. They are the only antibodies that cross the placenta during pregnancy and pass on the mother's acquired immunities to the fetus.

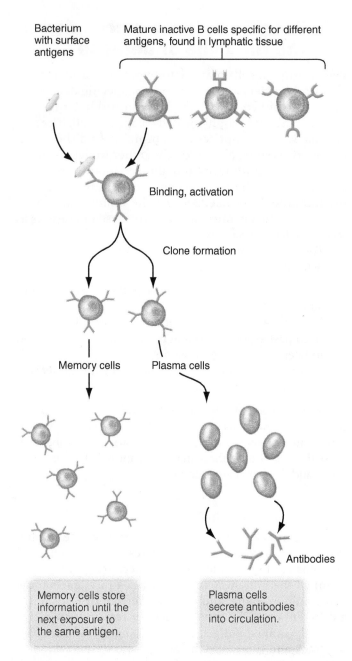

Figure 9.9 The production of antibodies by B cells. The surface antigen of a pathogen binds to the matching receptor on a mature, inactive B cell in lymphatic tissue. The B cell becomes activated and grows larger. The enlarged cell begins to divide rapidly, forming a clone. Some of the clone cells become memory cells; others become plasma cells. Memory cells lie in wait for the next exposure to the antigen. Plasma cells secrete antibodies into the lymph fluid.

- *IgM (5–10%)*. IgM antibodies are the first to be released during immune responses. Found in blood and lymph, they activate the complement system and cause foreign cells to agglutinate. ABO blood cell antibodies belong to this class.
- *IgA (15%)*. IgA antibodies enter areas of the body covered by mucous membranes, such as the digestive, reproductive, and respiratory tracts. There they neutralize infectious

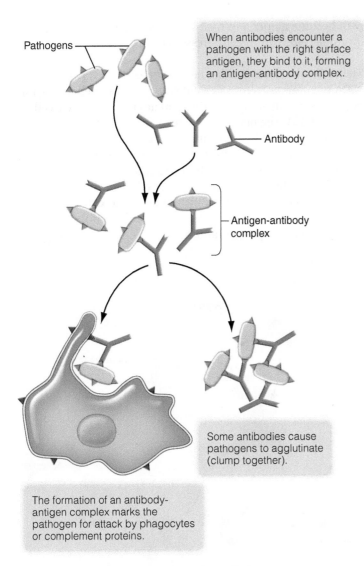

When antibodies encounter a pathogen with the right surface antigen, they bind to it, forming an antigen-antibody complex.

Pathogens

Antibody

Antigen-antibody complex

Some antibodies cause pathogens to agglutinate (clump together).

The formation of an antibody-antigen complex marks the pathogen for attack by phagocytes or complement proteins.

Figure 9.10 How antibodies inactivate pathogens.

pathogens. They are also present in mother's milk and are transmitted to the infant during breast-feeding.

- *IgD (less than 1%)*. IgD antibodies are in blood, lymph, and B cells. Their function is not clear, but they may play a role in activating B cells.
- *IgE (approximately 0.1%)*. The rarest of the immunoglobulins, IgE antibodies are in B cells, mast cells, and basophils. They activate the inflammatory response by triggering the release of histamine. They are also the troublemakers behind allergic responses (covered in section 9.9).

Antibodies' structure enables them to bind to specific antigens

An antigen provides all the information the immune system needs to know about a foreign substance. Essentially, antigens are the locks on an enemy's doors. The immune system can identify the lock, produce the antibody key, and

then send in immune system cells to open the door and neutralize the invader. How does this happen?

All antibodies share the same basic structure, represented by an IgG antibody (**Figure 9.11**). Each IgG antibody (or surface receptor, if it is attached to a B cell) consists of four linked polypeptide chains arranged in a Y shape. The two larger chains are called "heavy" chains, and the two smaller ones are called "light" chains. Each of the four chains has a constant region that forms the trunk and two branches and a variable region that represents the antigen-binding site. Because it has a unique amino acid sequence, each variable region has a unique shape that fits only one specific antigen.

The constant regions are similar for all antibodies in one class, although they differ from those of other classes. The IgG antibody depicted in Figure 9.11 is a single Y-shaped molecule with two binding sites. Larger antibodies in the IgM class consist of five Y-shaped molecules linked together, with 10 binding sites.

☑ **Quick Check** *Explain, in terms of details of antibody structure, why a memory cell that protects you against hepatitis cannot protect you against the common cold.* ▪

T cells: Cell-mediated immunity

There are two basic functional differences between B cells and T cells. First, B cells produce circulating antibodies; T cells either release chemicals that stimulate other cells of the immune system, or they directly attack the foreign cell and kill it. Second, T cell receptors cannot recognize whole antigens—they only react to small fragments of antigens. Thus it is

Antigen

Antigen-binding site

Variable regions

Constant regions

Light chain

Heavy chain

Figure 9.11 Structure of an antibody (or B cell surface receptor). An antibody consists of four peptide chains linked together to form a Y shape. Only the lighter-colored ends of each chain vary. These variations determine the specificity of each antibody for only one antigen.

necessary for a certain amount of antigen processing to occur before T cells can do their job. The antigen must be presented to them in a form that they can recognize.

Certain cells—including macrophages and activated B cells—fulfill this role by acting as **antigen-presenting cells (APCs)** that engulf foreign particles, partially digest them, and display fragments of the antigens on their surfaces (Figure 9.12). After an APC engulfs a pathogen, it partially degrades the antigen inside a vesicle. The vesicle containing antigen fragments joins with another vesicle containing MHC molecules, the molecules that become the cell's self markers. The MHC binds to the antigen pieces and moves to the cell surface, to be displayed as an antigen-MHC complex. Essentially, the cell "presents" a fragment of the antigen for T cells to recognize, along with its own cell-surface self marker.

T cells develop from stem cells in bone marrow but migrate to the thymus gland, where they become mature but remain inactive. During maturation they also develop one of two sets of surface proteins, CD4 or CD8. These proteins determine what type of T cell they will become. CD4 T cells

will become helper and memory cells, and CD8 T cells will become cytotoxic and suppressor cells.

Helper T cells stimulate other immune cells When a T cell with CD4 receptors encounters an antigen-presenting cell displaying a fragment of an antigen, it differentiates into a **helper T cell** (Figure 9.13). The new helper T cell undergoes mitosis (see Chapter 17), quickly producing a clone of identical helper T cells. Because all the cells in the clone carry the same receptors, they all recognize the same antigen.

Most of the cells in the helper T cell clone begin secreting a class of signaling molecules called **cytokines**. Among them are proteins that stimulate the actions of T cells and macrophages, and substances that promote

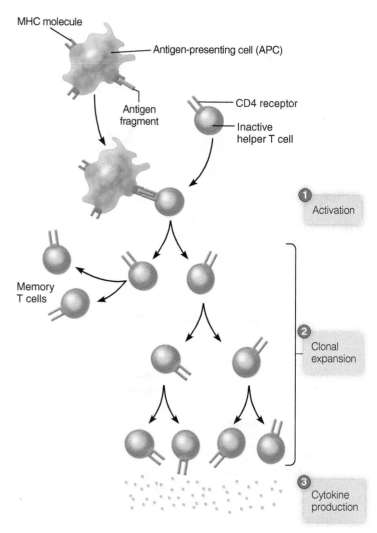

Figure 9.13 The activation and clonal expansion of helper T cells. Activation occurs when a mature but inactive helper T cell comes in contact with an antigen-presenting cell displaying the appropriate antigen fragment. After clonal expansion, the clones produce cytokines. A few activated clones become memory T cells.

✔ *Why does the clonal expansion occur? That is, why can't the activated T cells simply start producing cytokines without undergoing clonal expansion?*

Figure 9.12 labels and steps:

Major histocompatibility complex protein (MHC)
Antigen
Pathogen
Lysosome
Vesicle with MHC molecules
Antigen-MHC complex

1. The macrophage engulfs a pathogen.
2. Lysosomes partially digest the pathogen.
3. A vesicle containing MHC molecules binds to the digestive vesicle.
4. The MHC molecules and a fragment of the antigen form an antigen-MHC complex.
5. The antigen-MHC complex is displayed on the surface of the cell when the vesicle fuses with the cell membrane and releases its digestive products.

Figure 9.12 How a macrophage acts as an antigen-presenting cell (APC).

development of other immune cells. Cytokines released by helper T cells stimulate other immune cells such as phagocytes, natural killer cells, and T cells with CD8 receptors. They also attract other types of white blood cells to the area, enhancing nonspecific defenses. They even activate B cells, creating an important link between antibody-mediated and cell-mediated immunity.

The role of helper T cells and their cytokines in directing the activities of other immune cells is crucial to an effective immune response—without them the immune response would be severely impaired or nonexistent. The reason AIDS is so devastating is that HIV destroys helper T cells, and thus weakens the body's ability to mount a cell-mediated immune response to a wide variety of other diseases. (See section 9.10, Immune deficiency: The special case of AIDS.)

Cytotoxic T cells kill abnormal and foreign cells When a mature T cell with CD8 receptors meets an antigen-producing cell that displays an antigen fragment, the T cell begins to produce a clone of **cytotoxic T cells** (also called *killer T cells*). These are the only T cells that directly attack and destroy other cells (**Figure 9.14**).

Once activated, cytotoxic T cells roam throughout the body. They circulate through blood, lymph, and lymphatic tissues in search of cells that display the antigens they recognize. Or they may migrate to a tumor or site of infection, where they release chemicals that are toxic to abnormal cells.

Figure 9.15 illustrates cytotoxic T cells in action. When a cytotoxic T cell locates and binds to a target cell, secretory vesicles release a protein called *perforin* into the space between the two cells. The perforin molecules assemble

Figure 9.14 The activation and clonal expansion of cytotoxic T cells. Following activation and clonal expansion, the clones directly attack and kill cells carrying the antigen fragment they recognize.

a) **Cytotoxic T cells (blue) attaching to a target cell (pink).**

b) **How cytotoxic T cells kill a target cell.**

Figure 9.15 Cell-mediated immunity in action.

themselves into a pore in the target cell, allowing water and salts to enter. That alone should eventually kill the cell in much the same way that activated complement protein does (review Figure 9.8). But just to make sure, the cytotoxic T cell also releases granzyme, a toxic enzyme that is small enough to pass through the pore. The cytotoxic T cell then detaches from the target cell and goes off in search of other prey.

Several promising medical treatments involve harnessing the defensive capabilities of cytokines, specifically interferons. Genetically engineered gamma interferon is used to treat the chronic viral disorder hepatitis C. Another type of interferon has been moderately successful for treating multiple sclerosis, and a third is being used to treat certain types of cancer.

☑ **Quick Check** *What causes memory T cells (both helper and cytotoxic type) to begin clonal expansion?* ▪

Memory T cells reactivate during later exposures Some activated T cells become memory cells, retaining receptors for the antigen that originally stimulated their production. If that antigen is presented to them again, the memory cells are reactivated. Some form new helper T cells that multiply quickly to marshal an immune response. Others form a new army of cytotoxic T cells to attack and destroy. Like memory B cells, memory T cells are an important factor that distinguishes specific defenses from nonspecific defense mechanisms.

Table 9.2 summarizes the various cells and proteins involved in specific defense mechanisms.

Table 9.2 Cells and proteins involved in specific defenses

Cell/Protein	Function
B cells	Mature in bone marrow. Responsible for antibody-mediated immunity.
Plasma cells	Produce and secrete specific antibodies.
Memory B cells	Store information. Upon subsequent exposure, become plasma cells and secrete antibodies.
Immunoglobu-lins	Five classes of antibodies. Every antibody has a unique shape that fits one specific antigen.
T cells	Mature in thymus. Responsible for cell-mediated immunity.
Helper T cells	Produce cytokines. Enhance immune responses by stimulating other immune cells.
Cytotoxic T cells	Attack and destroy abnormal cells.
Memory T cells	Store information. Upon subsequent exposure, become helper and cytotoxic T cells.
Cytokines	A class of signaling molecules that stimulate various immune system activities.

↺ **Recap** An antigen is any substance that provokes an immune response. When activated by first exposure to a specific antigen, lymphocytes called B cells quickly produce antibodies against the antigen. They also produce a few long-lived memory cells that remain inactive until the next exposure to the same antigen. Other lymphocytes called T cells mature in the thymus gland. Helper T cells stimulate other immune cells, cytotoxic T cells attack abnormal and foreign cells, and memory T cells store information until the next exposure to the same antigen. ▪

9.6 Immune memory creates immunity

When you are first exposed to an antigen, your immune system protects you with the wealth of defense mechanisms described so far. Your first exposure to a particular antigen generates a *primary immune response*. As we have seen, this involves recognition of the antigen, and production and proliferation of B and T cells.

Typically the primary immune response has a lag time of three to six days after the antigen first appears. During this period B cells specific to that antigen multiply and develop into plasma cells. Antibody concentrations rise, typically reaching their peak about 10–12 days after first exposure. Then they start to level off (Figure 9.16).

However, as you have learned, B and T cells create a population of memory cells. The presence of these memory cells is the basis for **immunity** from disease. (The Latin word *immunis* means "safe" or "free from.") Subsequent exposure to the pathogen elicits a *secondary immune response* that is faster, longer lasting, and more effective than the first. Within hours after second exposure to an antigen, memory cells bind to the pathogen. New armies of T and plasma cells form, and within a few days antibody concentrations rise rapidly to much higher levels than in the primary response. Notice that antibody levels remain much higher in the body after second exposure.

Memory cells are long-lived, and many retain their ability to generate a secondary immune response over a lifetime. The secondary immune response can be so effective that you don't even realize you've been exposed to the pathogen a second time. At worst, you may experience only a fleeting sensation of feeling unwell. Other memory cells, such as the ones for the bacterial infection that causes tetanus, need to be reactivated every 10 years or so.

Given this immunity, though, why is it possible to get a cold or the flu over and over, sometimes several times a year? One reason is that there are more than 100 different viruses that can cause colds and flu. Even if your latest respiratory ailment feels like the previous one, it may actually be due to an entirely different pathogen. Furthermore, the viruses that cause colds and flu evolve so rapidly that they are essentially different each year. Their antigens change enough that each one requires a different antibody, and each exposure triggers a primary

Figure 9.16 The basis of immunity. The antibody response to a first exposure to antigen (the primary immune response) declines in about a month. A second exposure to the same antigen results in a response that is more rapid in onset, larger, and longer lasting. On this graph the abscissa scale is broken because it may be months or even years before second exposure. Note that the concentration of antibody during a secondary response may be 100 times higher than the primary response.

✅ *Suppose a person lacks the capability to produce any memory cells, but otherwise has a normal immune system. Sketch new lines on each of the graphs showing what this person's antibody responses will look like during a first exposure and a second exposure.*

response. Rapid evolution is their survival mechanism. Our survival mechanism is a good immune system.

🔄 **Recap** First exposure to a specific antigen generates a primary immune response. Subsequent exposure to the same antigen elicits a secondary immune response that is faster, longer lasting, and more effective than the primary immune response. ▪

9.7 Medical assistance in the war against pathogens

Our natural defenses against pathogens are remarkable. Nevertheless, we humans have taken matters into our own hands by developing the science of medicine. We have been able to conceive of and produce other sophisticated weaponry to help us combat pathogens. Important milestones in human health include the development of active and passive methods of immunization, which help the body resist specific pathogens; the production of monoclonal antibodies; and the discovery of antibiotics.

Active immunization: An effective weapon against pathogens

It is said that an ounce of prevention is worth a pound of cure, and this is certainly true when dealing with pathogens. The best weapon against them is to give the body a dose of the antigen in advance so that the immune system will mount a primary immune response against it. Then, if exposed to that microorganism in the environment, the body is already primed with the appropriate antibodies and memory cells. The immune system can react swiftly with a secondary response, effectively shielding you from the danger of the disease and discomfort of its symptoms.

The process of activating the body's immune system in advance is called **active immunization**. This involves administering an antigen-containing preparation called a **vaccine**. Most vaccines are produced from dead or weakened pathogens. An example is the oral polio vaccine (the Sabin vaccine), made from weakened poliovirus. Other vaccines are made from organisms that have been genetically altered to produce a particular antigen.

Of course, vaccines created from dead or weakened pathogens have their limitations. First, there are issues of safety, time, and expense. Living but weakened pathogens generally make better vaccines because they elicit a greater immune response. However, a vaccine that contains weakened pathogens has a slight potential to cause disease itself. This has happened, although rarely, with the polio vaccine. It takes a great deal of time, money, and research to verify the safety and effectiveness of a vaccine. Second, a vaccine confers immunity against only one pathogen, so a different vaccine is needed for every virus. This is why doctors may recommend getting a flu vaccine each time a new flu strain appears (nearly every year). Third, vaccines are not particularly effective after a pathogen has struck; that is, they do not cure an already existing disease.

Nonetheless, vaccines are an effective supplement to our natural defense mechanisms. Active immunization generally produces long-lived immunity that can protect us for many years. The widespread practice of vaccination has greatly reduced many diseases such as polio, measles, and whooping cough.

In the United States, immunization of adults has lagged behind that of children. It's estimated that more than 50,000 Americans die each year from infections, including pneumonia, hepatitis, and influenza, that could have been prevented with timely vaccines.

In many countries, vaccines are too costly and difficult to administer: generally they must be injected by a health care worker with some basic level of training. To get around this problem, some researchers are developing potatoes or bananas that are genetically modified to produce vaccines against diseases such as hepatitis B, measles, and the diarrhea-causing Norwalk virus. An oral vaccine against Norwalk virus has already undergone limited testing in humans.

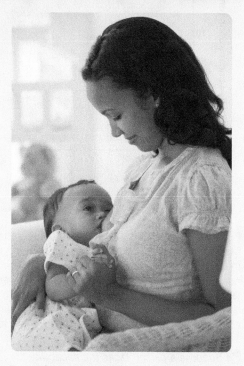

The Case for Breast Milk

When human infants are born their immune systems are still very immature. At birth they still don't have a sufficient number of phagocytes (to engulf foreign cells) or lymphocytes (that produce antibodies). Normally the populations of these cells begin to increase shortly after birth in response to colonization of the infant's gut by bacteria. But it takes time, and so newborns are more vulnerable than adults to relatively minor ailments such as middle ear infections, diarrhea, and respiratory and urinary tract infections.

Human milk has several benefits at this early stage beyond its nutritional value. Human milk contains both phagocytes and lymphocytes, which boost the infant's population of these immune cells until the infant's immune system is more fully developed. Human milk is also loaded with antibodies of the IgA type. These antibodies offer protection against essentially all of the microbes that inhabit the mother's gut, many of which will eventually colonize the infant's gut as well. In addition, human milk has a high concentration of a protein called *lactoferrin*, which stimulates the immune system and kills bacteria while at the same time preventing an inflammatory response. Together, human IgA and lactoferrin account for about 30% of the proteins in human milk, compared to just 5% in cow's milk. Finally, some of the oligosaccharides (long sugar molecules) in human milk also serve a protective function. By virtue of their shape, the oligosaccharides prevent certain harmful bacteria from binding to the infant's gut, thereby preventing an infection from developing.

Human milk has some long-term benefits as well. Children that were breastfed are better protected against certain infections than non-breastfed children, even for several years after breastfeeding has stopped. They also seem to respond to some vaccinations with better T cell and antibody responses. Precisely how human milk encourages the development and maturation of the infant's immune system is still under investigation.

Finally, a word of caution: Substances not so good for the infant can also be transferred via breastfeeding, including heroin, cocaine, prescription medications, caffeine, and alcohol. ■

Passive immunization can help against existing or anticipated infections

To fight an existing or even anticipated infection, a person can be given antibodies prepared in advance from a human or animal donor with immunity to that illness. Usually this takes the form of a *gamma globulin* shot (serum containing primarily IgG antibodies). The procedure is called **passive immunization**. In essence, the patient is given the antibodies that his/her own immune system might produce if there were enough time.

Passive immunization has the advantage of being somewhat effective against an existing infection. It can be administered to prevent illness in someone who has been unexpectedly exposed to a pathogen, and it confers at least some short-term immunity. However, protection is not as long-lasting as active immunization following vaccine administration because the administered antibodies disappear from the circulation quickly. Passive immunization also can't confer long-term immunity against a second exposure, because the person's own B cells aren't activated and so memory cells for the pathogen do not develop.

Passive immunization has been used effectively against certain common viral infections, including those that cause hepatitis B and measles, bacterial infections such as tetanus, and Rh incompatibility. Passive immunization of the fetus and newborn also occurs naturally across the placenta and through breast-feeding.

✓**Quick Check** *In New York City in the late 1800s, children ill with diphtheria were often given an extract from the blood of horses that had previously had diphtheria. Was this an example of active or passive immunization, and did it provide permanent or temporary protection?* ■

Monoclonal antibodies: Laboratory-created for commercial use

An antibody preparation used to confer passive immunity in a patient is actually a mixture of many different antibody molecules, because a single pathogen can have many different antigens on its surface. **Monoclonal antibodies**, on the other hand, are antibodies produced in the laboratory from cloned descendants of a single hybrid B cell. As such, monoclonal antibodies are relatively pure preparations of antibodies specific for a single antigen. Monoclonal antibodies are proving useful in research, testing, and cancer treatments because they are pure and they can be produced cheaply in large quantities.

Figure 9.17 summarizes a technique for preparing monoclonal antibodies. Typically, B cells are removed from a mouse's spleen after the mouse has been immunized with a specific antigen to stimulate B cell production. The B cells are fused with myeloma (cancer) cells to create *hybridoma* (hybrid cancer) cells that have desirable traits of both parent cells: they each produce a specific antibody, and they proliferate with cancer-like rapidity. As these hybridoma cells grow in culture, those that produce the desired antibody are separated out and cloned, producing millions of copies. The antibodies they produce are harvested and processed to create preparations of pure monoclonal antibodies. (The

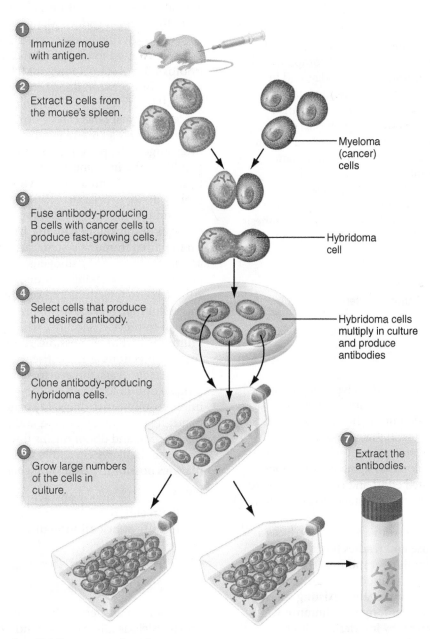

1. Immunize mouse with antigen.

2. Extract B cells from the mouse's spleen.

Myeloma (cancer) cells

3. Fuse antibody-producing B cells with cancer cells to produce fast-growing cells.

Hybridoma cell

4. Select cells that produce the desired antibody.

Hybridoma cells multiply in culture and produce antibodies

5. Clone antibody-producing hybridoma cells.

6. Grow large numbers of the cells in culture.

7. Extract the antibodies.

Figure 9.17 How monoclonal antibodies are produced.

term *monoclonal* means these antibody molecules derive from a group of cells cloned from a single cell.)

Monoclonal antibodies have a number of commercial applications, including home pregnancy tests, screening for prostate cancer, and diagnostic testing for hepatitis, influenza, and HIV/AIDS. Monoclonal antibody tests tend to be more specific and more rapid than conventional diagnostic tests. In the future it may be possible to use monoclonal antibodies to deliver anticancer drugs directly to cancer cells. The first step would be to bond an anticancer drug to monoclonal antibodies prepared against the cancer. Upon injection into the patient, the antibodies would deliver the drug directly to the cancer cells, sparing nearby healthy tissue.

Antibiotics combat bacteria

Literally, *antibiotic* means "against life." Antibiotics kill bacteria or inhibit their growth. The first antibiotics were derived from extracts of molds and fungi, but today most antibiotics are synthesized by pharmaceutical companies.

There are hundreds of antibiotics in use today, and they work in dozens of ways. In general, they take advantage of the following differences between bacteria and human cells: (1) bacteria have a thick cell wall, human cells do not; (2) bacterial DNA is not safely enclosed in a nucleus, human DNA is; (3) bacterial ribosomes are smaller than human ribosomes; and (4) bacterial rate of protein synthesis is very rapid as they grow and divide. So penicillin focuses on the difference in cell walls and blocks the synthesis of bacterial cell walls, and streptomycin inhibits bacterial protein synthesis by altering the shape of the smaller bacterial ribosomes.

BlogInFocus (MB)

An innovative approach to fighting bacterial infections is to use "good" bacteria to fight the "bad" ones. To learn more, visit MJ's blog in the Study Area in MasteringBiology and look under "Using Bacteria to Fight Bacteria."

Some antibiotics combat only certain types of bacteria. Others, called *broad-spectrum antibiotics*, are effective against several groups of bacteria. By definition, however, antibiotics are ineffective against viruses. Recall that viruses do not reproduce on their own; they replicate only when they are inside living cells. Using antibiotics to fight viral infections such as colds or the flu is wasted effort and contributes to the growing health problem of bacterial resistance to antibiotics.

↩ **Recap** Active immunization with a vaccine produces a primary immune response and readies the immune system for a secondary immune response. Administration of prepared antibodies (passive immunization) can be effective against existing infections but does not confer long-term immunity. Most antibiotics kill bacteria by interfering with bacterial protein synthesis or bacterial cell wall synthesis. ▪

9.8 Tissue rejection: A medical challenge

Because the goal of the immune system is to protect the body from invasion by nonself cells, it is not surprising that the immune system attacks foreign human tissues with vigor. This phenomenon is called *tissue rejection*. A very common type of tissue rejection is rejection of transfused blood by the recipient patient. It's called a *transfusion reaction*, and it can be fatal.

Surgical techniques for performing many organ transplants are really not that difficult. Historically, the major stumbling block to widespread transplantation of most organs has been the effectiveness of the immune system in rejecting foreign tissue. In the normal immune response, cytotoxic T cells swiftly attack and destroy any and all foreign cells. Before a transplant is even attempted, then, the donor's and recipient's ABO and other blood group antigens must first be determined. Next, donor and recipient tissues are tested to compare MHC antigens, because cytotoxic T cells target foreign MHC proteins. The closer the relationship between donor and recipient the better, because their MHC antigens are likely to be similar. Although successful transplants can be done between unrelated people, at least a 75% match between tissues is essential. After surgery the patient must take *immunosuppressive drugs* that block the immune response, such as corticosteroid drugs to suppress inflammation or cytotoxic medications that kill rapidly dividing cells (to block activated lymphocytes).

Immunosuppressive therapy can dramatically prolong the lives of transplant patients, but it brings other risks. An impaired immune system cannot protect the body as effectively against pathogens and abnormal cells, so patients who are taking immunosuppressive drugs are more vulnerable to infections and certain cancers. The key to a successful transplant is to suppress the immune system enough to prevent rejection, while preserving as much immune function as possible. Antibiotic drugs can help control infections as they arise.

In recent years, three factors have made organ transplants a viable option for many people: (1) improvements in immunosuppressive drugs, (2) better techniques for cross-matching (or "typing") tissue, and (3) national sharing of information and donor organs through organ-bank systems. The organ-bank system allows patients to receive the best matches possible regardless of where they live.

↩ **Recap** The major obstacle to organ transplantation is the recipient's immune response, as cytotoxic T cells usually attack all foreign cells. ▪

9.9 Inappropriate immune system activity causes problems

Conditions characterized by inappropriate immune system activity include allergies and autoimmune disorders such as lupus erythematosus and rheumatoid arthritis.

Allergies: A hypersensitive immune system

Many of us—perhaps 10% of North Americans—suffer from allergies. Some allergies are relatively minor; others are quite severe. Examples include hay fever, poison ivy rashes, and severe reactions to specific foods or drugs. Some allergic reactions even require hospitalization.

An **allergy** is an inappropriate response of the immune system to an **allergen** (any substance that causes an allergic reaction). The key word is *inappropriate*: the allergen is not a dangerous pathogen, but the body reacts as if it were.

Recall that there are five classes of immunoglobulins. As shown in Figure 9.18, the culprits involved in allergic reactions are those in the IgE group. At some point, exposure to an allergen triggers a primary immune response, causing

B cells to produce specific IgE antibodies. The IgE antibodies bind to mast cells (found primarily in connective tissue) and to circulating basophils.

When the same allergen enters the body a second time, it binds to the IgE antibodies on mast cells and basophils, causing them to release histamine. The result is an allergic reaction, a typical inflammatory response that includes warmth, redness, swelling, and pain in the area of contact with the allergen. Histamine also increases secretion of mucus in the region. Every time the body is exposed to this allergen, the body reacts as if it has an injury or infection, even though it doesn't.

Some allergens affect only the areas exposed. Other allergens, including food allergens and bee sting venom,

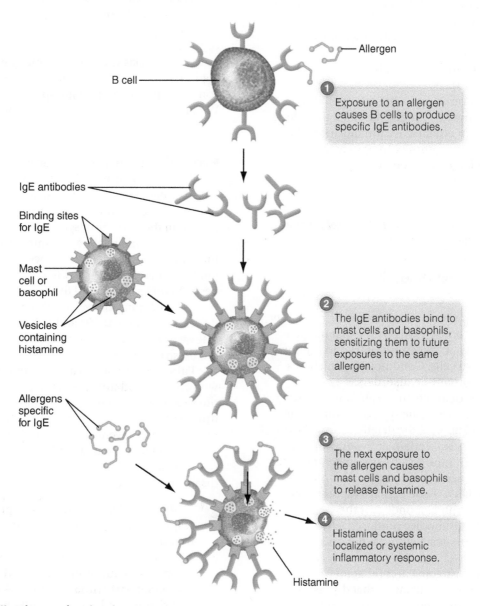

Figure 9.18 **How an allergic reaction develops.**

are absorbed or injected into the bloodstream. These substances are carried quickly to mast cells throughout the body, including connective tissue in the respiratory, digestive, and circulatory systems. Such allergens often elicit a *systemic response*, meaning they affect several organ systems. Systemic responses include constriction of smooth muscle in the lungs and digestive system and dilation of blood vessels.

Symptoms of a severe systemic allergic reaction can include difficulty breathing (caused by constricted airways), severe stomach cramps (muscle contractions), swelling throughout the body (increased capillary permeability), and circulatory collapse with a life-threatening fall in blood pressure (dilated arterioles). This is known as *anaphylactic shock*. Anyone who appears to be suffering from anaphylactic shock should be rushed to a hospital, because the reaction can be fatal. The symptoms often begin suddenly, and doctors advise people with a history of strong allergic reactions to carry an emergency kit with them at all times. The kit contains a self-injected hypodermic syringe of epinephrine, a hormone that dilates the airway and constricts peripheral blood vessels, preventing shock.

Most allergies, however, are more annoying than dangerous. Antihistamines—drugs that block the effects of histamine—are often effective treatments for mild to moderate reactions. Allergy shots can help by causing the body to produce large numbers of IgG antibodies, which combine with the allergen and block its attachment to IgE.

☑ **Quick Check** *Why do allergic reactions often get worse with each successive exposure to the antigen?* ▪

Autoimmune disorders: Defective recognition of "self"

On rare occasions, the immune system's remarkable ability to distinguish self from nonself fails. When that happens, the immune system may produce antibodies and cytotoxic T cells that target its own cells. Conditions in which this happens are called **autoimmune disorders**.

Approximately 5% of adults in North America, two-thirds of them women, have some type of autoimmune disorder. We don't yet know all the details of how these diseases arise. In some cases, certain antigens simply are never exposed to the immune system as it undergoes fetal development. These antigens were never programmed into the system as self, so when tissue damage exposes them, the mature immune system responds as if they are foreign. In other cases, antibodies produced against a foreign antigen may cross-react with the person's own tissues.

At the moment there are no cures for autoimmune disorders. Treatments include therapies that depress the body's defense mechanisms and relieve the symptoms. Autoimmune conditions include a wide range of diseases,

including multiple sclerosis, a progressive disorder of the central nervous system (see Chapter 11), and Type 1 diabetes mellitus, which targets cells in the pancreas (see Chapter 13). We will look at two more conditions: lupus erythematosus and rheumatoid arthritis.

Lupus erythematosus: Inflamed connective tissue Lupus erythematosus (or *lupus*) is an autoimmune disorder in which the body attacks its own connective tissue. One type of lupus, called *discoid lupus erythematosus*, primarily affects areas of the skin exposed to sunlight. More serious is systemic lupus erythematosus, which may affect various tissues and organs including the heart, blood vessels, lungs, kidneys, joints, and brain.

Lupus often starts as a red skin rash on the face or head. Other symptoms include fever, fatigue, joint pain, and weight loss. Spreading inflammation can lead to osteoarthritis (see Chapter 5), pericarditis (see Chapter 8), or pleurisy (inflammation of the lining of the lungs).

Lupus affects nine times as many women as men. Typically it occurs during childbearing age and is more common in certain racial groups such as African Americans, West Indians, and Chinese. Medications can reduce the inflammation and alleviate the symptoms.

Rheumatoid arthritis: Inflamed synovial membranes Rheumatoid arthritis is a type of arthritis involving inflammation of the synovial membrane that lines certain joints (see Chapter 5). In rheumatoid arthritis, B cells produce antibodies against a protein in the cartilage of synovial membranes. The resulting immune response releases inflammatory chemicals that cause further tissue damage. At first, fingers, wrists, toes, or other joints become painful and stiff. Over time the inflammation destroys joint cartilage and the neighboring bone. Eventually, bony tissue begins to break down and fuse, resulting in deformities (Figure 9.19) and reduced range of motion. The disease is intermittent, but with each recurrence the damage is progressively worse.

Pain-relieving medications can help many people with rheumatoid arthritis, as can regular mild exercise and physical therapy to improve range of motion. Powerful drugs that neutralize chemicals in the inflammatory response can prevent joints from becoming deformed. Surgery to replace damaged joints with artificial joints can restore the ability to move, and prevent painful disabilities.

↩ **Recap An allergy is an inappropriate inflammatory response. An autoimmune disorder occurs when the immune system fails to distinguish self from nonself cells and begins to attack the body's own cells. Examples of autoimmune disorders are lupus erythematosus (inflammation of connective tissue) and rheumatoid arthritis (inflammation of synovial membranes).** ▪

with protein spikes. It has no nucleus and no organelles. Like other viruses, HIV infects by entering a cell and using the cell's machinery to reproduce. HIV targets helper T cells, gaining entry by attaching to CD4 receptors.

HIV belongs to a particular class of viruses, called *retroviruses*, that have a unique way of replicating (Figure 9.21). Retroviruses first attach to the CD4 receptor of a helper T cell. The attachment fuses the retrovirus's envelope with the cell's membrane, releasing the viral RNA and enzymes into the cell. Under the influence of the viral enzymes and using the viral RNA as a template (a pattern), the host cell is forced to make a single strand of DNA complementary to the viral RNA, and from it a second strand of DNA complementary to the first. The new double-stranded DNA fragment is then inserted into the cell's DNA. The cell, not recognizing the DNA as foreign, uses it to produce more viral RNA and proteins, which are then assembled into thousands of new viruses within the cell. The sheer magnitude of viral replication so saps the T cell's energy that eventually it dies and ruptures, releasing the viral copies. The new viruses move on to infect other helper T cells.

HIV is transmitted in body fluids

HIV is a fragile virus that cannot survive dry conditions for even a short time. This means that it cannot be transmitted through the air, by casual contact, or by doorknobs or toilet seats. However, HIV can be transmitted in at least four body fluids—blood, semen, breast milk, and vaginal secretions. It is not known to be transmitted by contact with urine, feces, saliva, perspiration, tears, or nasal secretions unless those fluids contain blood.

Most commonly, HIV is transmitted by sexual contact or contaminated hypodermic needles. In addition, infected mothers can pass it to their children during pregnancy, labor and delivery, or when breast-feeding. It has been estimated, for example, that a healthy newborn who is breastfed by an infected mother has about a 20% chance of contracting HIV from its mother's milk. A significant number of cases of HIV infection resulted from blood transfusions until the mid-1980s, when it became routine to test blood for HIV antibodies.

Figure 9.19 Rheumatoid arthritis.

9.10 Immune deficiency: The special case of AIDS

Immune deficiency is a general term for an immune system that is not functioning properly. One immune deficiency disease is *severe combined immunodeficiency disease (SCID)*. For the rare person who inherits SCID, even a minor infection can become life-threatening. People with SCID have too few functional lymphocytes to defend the body against infections.

The most common and best-known severe immune deficiency condition is **AIDS (acquired immune deficiency syndrome)**. A *syndrome* is a medical term for a group of symptoms that occur together, and *acquired* means that one catches it—in this case by becoming infected with the virus called **HIV (human immunodeficiency virus)**.

HIV targets helper T cells of the immune system

Figure 9.20 shows the structure of HIV. The virus consists of nothing more than single-stranded RNA and enzymes, wrapped in two protein coats and a phospholipid membrane

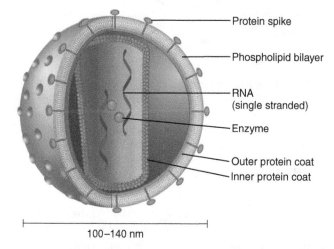

100–140 nm

Figure 9.20 The structure of HIV.

Labels: Protein spike; Phospholipid bilayer; RNA (single stranded); Enzyme; Outer protein coat; Inner protein coat

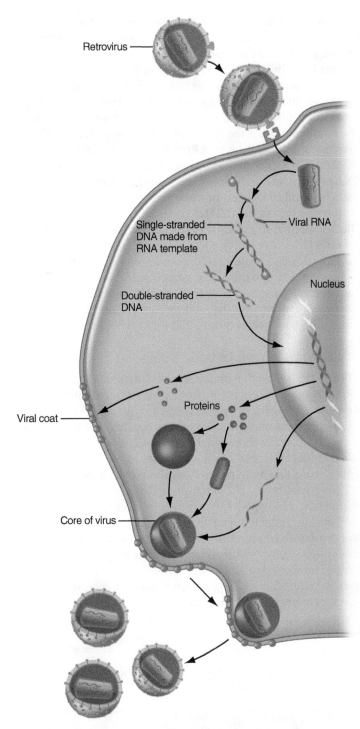

Figure 9.21 How HIV replicates. After binding to a helper T cell's CD4 receptor, the virus injects its RNA and enzymes into the cell and uses them to force the cell to make single- and then double-stranded DNA. The DNA is inserted into the cell's own DNA within the nucleus, where it directs the cell to make more protein coat and viral RNA and protein core. The coats and cores join, exiting the cell as new viruses.

Because transmission of HIV generally requires direct contact with body fluids, HIV is considered relatively hard to transmit from person to person (at least when compared to such common diseases as the flu). However, unlike the flu,

HIV is extremely virulent unless it is aggressively treated with an expensive regimen of drugs. Over 90% of all U.S. citizens diagnosed with AIDS by 1988 (before effective drugs were available) are now dead.

AIDS develops slowly

The symptoms of HIV infection and the subsequent development of full-blown AIDS progress slowly. The course of the disease falls into three phases (Figure 9.22).

Phase I Phase I lasts anywhere from a few weeks to a few years after initial exposure to the virus. There is a brief spike in HIV in the blood, followed by typical flulike symptoms of swollen lymph nodes, chills and fever, fatigue, and body aches. The immune system's T cell population may decline briefly then rebound as the body begins to produce more cells and antibodies against the virus. The presence of antibodies against the virus is the basis for a diagnosis of HIV infection, and a person having these antibodies is said to be "HIV-positive." However, he or she will not yet have the disease syndrome called *AIDS*.

Unless they suspect they have been exposed to HIV, most people would not associate Phase I symptoms with HIV infection and so would not think to be tested. The antibodies do not destroy the virus entirely because many of the virus particles remain inside cells, where antibodies and immune cells cannot reach them.

Phase II In Phase II the virus begins to do its damage, wiping out more and more of the helper T cells. The loss of T cells makes the person more vulnerable to *opportunistic infections*—infections that take advantage of the weakened immune system to establish themselves in the body. During Phase II people *may* have persistent or recurrent flulike symptoms, but they may have no symptoms at all if they do not have an opportunistic infection. If they have not been tested for HIV antibodies they may not even know they are infected.

Two-thirds to three-quarters of all people who test positive for antibodies to HIV do not exhibit symptoms associated with AIDS. During Phases I and II, many people pass the virus on to others without realizing it. Those they infect may transmit the virus to still others. Phase II can occur within 6 months, but on average it takes about 10 years to progress to Phase III. Left untreated, 95% of people in Phase II progress to Phase III.

Phase III Once the number of helper T cells of an HIV-positive person falls below 200 per cubic millimeter of blood *and* the person has an opportunistic infection or type of cancer associated with HIV infection, the person is said to have AIDS. Infections and cancers associated with AIDS include pneumonia, meningitis, tuberculosis, encephalitis, Kaposi's sarcoma, and non-Hodgkin's lymphoma, among others.

Notice that AIDS may not appear until years after initial HIV infection. Untreated AIDS is nearly always fatal.

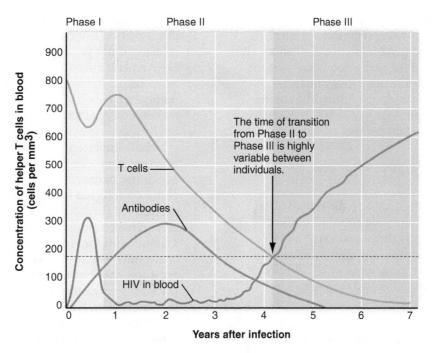

Figure 9.22 Time course of the progression toward AIDS after HIV infection. Phase I is characterized by flulike symptoms followed by apparent recovery. There is a brief spike in HIV in the blood. Within six months HIV-specific antibodies appear. In Phase II there is a slow decline in the number of T cells. Most of the HIV is harbored inside cells. Phase III (AIDS) is characterized by a T cell count of less than 200 per cubic millimeter of blood, a decline in HIV-specific antibodies, a rise in HIV in blood, opportunistic infections, and certain cancers.

The AIDS epidemic: A global health issue

AIDS was first described in 1981 when the Centers for Disease Control in Atlanta began to notice a disturbing similarity between cases involving a strange collection of symptoms (this illustrates the advantage of having a central clearinghouse for information). It is now believed that HIV first infected humans in the 1960s in Africa after "jumping species" from other primates to humans.

The worldwide damage done by HIV so far is truly astonishing. Today, more than 34 million people are living with HIV infection or AIDS, representing nearly 1% of the adult population worldwide. So far, nearly 30 million people have died of AIDS, and approximately 7,400 people are newly diagnosed with HIV every day.

And yet, there is a glimmer of hope on the horizon. The number of new HIV infections worldwide in 2010 was 21% below the number of new infections in the peak year of 1997. Worldwide deaths from AIDS totaled 1.8 million per year in 2010, down from a peak of 2.2 million in the mid-2000s. And although the vast majority of new cases of HIV infections still occur in sub-Saharan Africa, the rate of new infections and the death rate from AIDS in sub-Saharan Africa are both beginning to decline slightly.

The picture is even better in the United States, thanks to a well-developed AIDS reporting system and the availability of good health care. Although the number of persons living with AIDS continues to climb, the number of deaths from AIDS in the United States has stabilized at about 16,000

per year after peaking sharply in 1995 at nearly 60,000 per year. Most of the decline in death rates since 1995 is due to new drugs that suppress the active component of an HIV infection and keep infected people alive much longer. However, to be completely effective the drugs need to be taken for the rest of the patient's lifetime.

Although the death rate from AIDS has stabilized in the United States, the number of persons living with HIV/AIDS continues to climb. **Figure 9.23** shows only those currently

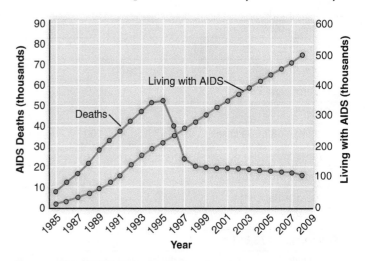

Figure 9.23 HIV/AIDS in the United States. AIDS deaths and the number of people living with AIDS each year since 1985.

Source: Centers for Disease Control and Prevention (CDC).

living with AIDS. An additional 700,000 persons are HIV-infected but are not yet showing symptoms of AIDS. About 20% of all HIV-infected persons do not even know they are infected. Treatment of the rising number of persons living with HIV/AIDS is likely to place a heavy financial burden on our health care system in the future. The current cost of treating an HIV-infected person with HIV suppressive drugs is about $14,000 to $20,000 per year.

Risky behaviors increase your chances of getting AIDS

Table 9.3 shows how HIV is contracted in the United States among adults and adolescents (people above 12 years of age). In the United States, nearly three-quarters of all HIV-infected persons in 2009 were men. The riskiest behaviors for both men and women are engaging in sex with HIV-infected men and sharing needles during injected drug use.

Making sex safer

The only sure way to eliminate the risk of contracting HIV/AIDS completely is to eliminate sexual contact altogether. Some people do choose abstinence for ethical, practical, or professional reasons or at certain times in their lives. However, most persons do not remain abstinent throughout their lives. Given the risks of contracting HIV/AIDS, anyone who is sexually active should think seriously about how to make their sexual contacts as safe as possible. Below are several *safer sex guidelines* and some evidence for them. The suggestions do not guarantee complete safety, which is why they are called recommendations for "safer" rather than "safe" sex.

Table 9.3 Persons living with HIV infection in the United States in 2009, by sex and exposure category

Exposure category	Percent of total
Males	
Sex with other men	54
Injected drug use	14
Sex with other men and injected drug use	6
Heterosexual contact	9
Other*	17
Male total: 483,969 cases	**100**
Females	
Injected drug use	19
Heterosexual contact	51
Other*	30
Female total: 176,851 cases	**100**

*Other includes hemophilia, blood transfusion, perinatal exposure, and risk factors not reported or not identified.

Source: Centers for Disease Control and Prevention, HIV/AIDS Surveillance Report, 2009.

- *Reduce the number of sexual partners.* Evidence shows that this is particularly effective among homosexual men. The evidence is not yet conclusive regarding the relationship between HIV infection and number of partners in heterosexual transmission, perhaps because the median number of partners is generally lower. Nevertheless, it makes sense that fewer partners translates to lower risk.

- *Choose a sexual partner with low-risk behavior.* This is especially important. A partner who has a history of injecting drugs or a man who has sex with other men is a high-risk partner. One study reported that choosing a partner who is not in any high-risk group lowers the risk of AIDS almost 5,000-fold.

- *Avoid certain high-risk sexual practices.* Any sexual behavior that increases the risk of direct blood contact, such as anal-genital sex, should be considered risky. Oral-genital sex is less risky but not risk-free.

- *Use latex or polyurethane condoms or other barriers.* In laboratory tests, latex or polyurethane condoms prevent the passage of HIV. How effective they are in actual use is not certain, but because they are about 90% effective as a birth control method, a reasonable hypothesis (not yet tested) is that they reduce the risk of HIV by about the same amount. Condoms are effective only if used consistently and correctly. Natural skin condoms are not as safe as latex condoms. The use of dental dams is recommended for oral-vaginal sex.

- *Use nonoxynol-9, a spermicidal agent.* In laboratory tests, nonoxynol-9 has been shown to inhibit the growth of HIV. Be aware, however, that the evidence is conflicting regarding whether nonoxynol-9 offers any protection during sexual contact.

- *Get tested (and have your partner tested).* Notice, however, that the HIV tests currently available are designed to detect the human *antibodies* to HIV, not the virus itself. It can take up to six months after exposure to produce enough antibodies for the antibody test to become positive. For this reason, retesting at least six months after the last possible exposure is a good idea. Evidence shows that close to 90% of HIV-infected persons will have a positive HIV antibody test result within six months. A negative test at six months indicates substantially lower risk, but it does not provide complete assurance. A few individuals may not test positive for three or more years.

New treatments offer hope

As yet there is no cure for AIDS, but researchers are investigating more than a hundred drugs to treat the condition. In general, AIDS drugs work by interfering with HIV replication at one of the steps in the virus's life cycle:

- **Interference with viral entry into the cell.** If the virus can't enter the cell it can't take over the cell's metabolic machinery and force it to make more viruses. These drugs, called *entry inhibitors,* work by blocking the ability of the virus to lock onto receptors on the cell's surface, a necessary first step to entry.

- **Inhibition of enzymes required for replication of viral RNA.** Called *reverse transcriptase inhibitors*, these drugs prevent the virus from taking over the cell's metabolic pathways that lead to replication of viral RNA after the virus has gained entry to the cell.
- **Prevention of insertion of the viral genome into the cell's DNA.** These drugs, called *integrase inhibitors*, block viral enzyme required to insert the viral RNA into the host cell's DNA.
- **Inhibition of enzymes required to assemble viral proteins.** Called *protease inhibitors*, these drugs prevent the virus from being assembled within an infected cell, even though the virus may already have forced the cell to replicate its RNA and proteins.

Because each class of drugs works by an entirely different mechanism, more effective treatment can sometimes be achieved by taking several different drugs in combination. However, no combination of drugs has yet been found that completely cures an HIV infection. People who are HIV-positive have to be prepared to take AIDS drugs throughout their lives.

With an ever-expanding arsenal of AIDS drugs at their disposal, doctors are now starting to treat people who are infected with HIV but who don't yet show the symptoms of AIDS. The hope is that early treatment of an HIV infection will prevent the widespread destruction of the immune system that precedes the onset of AIDS symptoms. People who are at-risk for HIV infections are advised to be tested so that asymptomatic cases can be detected and treated.

Are there any pills or drugs that could be taken by a healthy person in advance of exposure to HIV that would prevent HIV infection? Visit MJ's blog in the Study Area in MasteringBiology and look under "Pills to Prevent HIV Infection" to find out.

Some researchers believe that safe and effective vaccines offer the only real hope of conquering HIV. Several dozen potential vaccines are already being tested on human volunteers around the world, but so far none has proved effective enough to warrant widespread use. The production of vaccines is complicated by the fact that HIV mutates rather quickly. There are already several strains of the virus, each of which would need a separate vaccine. In addition, HIV is so dangerous that it is considered too risky to produce vaccines from whole but weakened viruses, the way many other vaccines are produced. Most HIV vaccines currently under investigation are produced from other viruses engineered to contain pieces of the HIV virus, or from pieces of the HIV viral genetic material.

Recap AIDS (acquired immune deficiency syndrome) is a devastating disorder of the immune system caused by a virus (HIV) that attacks helper T cells. HIV is transmitted in body fluids, typically through sexual contact, blood transfusions, contaminated needles, or breast-feeding.

Chapter Summary

Pathogens cause disease *p. 190*

- Pathogens include bacteria, viruses, fungi, protozoa, worms, and possibly prions.
- Bacteria have very little internal structure and are covered by a rigid outer cell wall.
- Viruses cannot reproduce on their own. Viral reproduction requires a living host cell.
- Prions are misfolded proteins that replicate by causing a normal protein to misfold.
- The danger from a particular pathogen depends on *how* it is transmitted, how *easily* it is transmitted, and how *damaging* the resulting disease is.

The lymphatic system defends the body *p. 193*

- The lymphatic system consists of vessels, lymph nodes, the spleen, the thymus gland, and the tonsils.
- The lymphatic system helps protect us against disease.
- Phagocytic cells in the spleen, lymph nodes, and tonsils engulf and kill microorganisms.
- The thymus gland secretes hormones that help T lymphocytes mature.

Keeping pathogens out: The first line of defense *p. 195*

- Skin is an effective barrier to the entry of microorganisms.
- Tears, saliva, mucus, and earwax trap organisms and/or wash them away.
- Digestive acid in the stomach kills many microorganisms.
- Vomiting, defecation, and urination physically remove microorganisms after entry.

Nonspecific defenses: The second line of defense *p. 197*

- Phagocytes surround and engulf microorganisms and damaged cells.
- Inflammation has four outward signs: redness, warmth, swelling, and pain.
- Natural killer cells kill their targets by releasing damaging chemicals.
- Circulating proteins of the complement system either kill microorganisms directly or mark them for destruction.
- Interferons are proteins that interfere with viral reproduction.
- Fever raises body temperature, creating a hostile environment for some microorganisms.

Specific defense mechanisms: The third line of defense *p. 201*

- Cells of the immune system can distinguish foreign or damaged cells from our own healthy cells.
- All cells have cell-surface markers called *MHC proteins* that identify the cells as "self."

- An antigen is a substance that stimulates the immune system and provokes an immune response.
- B cells produce antibodies against foreign antigens.
- T cells of several types release chemicals that enhance the immune response and kill foreign cells directly.

Immune memory creates immunity p. 206

- Information about an antigen is stored in memory cells after first exposure.
- The second exposure to the antigen produces a much greater immune response than the first.
- The rapidity of the second response is the basis of immunity from disease.

Medical assistance in the war against pathogens p. 207

- Vaccines immunize the body in advance against a particular disease.
- Injected antibodies provide temporary immunity and are of some benefit against an existing infection.
- Monoclonal antibodies are used primarily in medical tests.
- Antibiotics are effective against bacteria, but not against viruses.

Tissue rejection: A medical challenge p. 210

- The phenomenon of tissue rejection is a normal consequence of the body's ability to recognize self from nonself.
- Immunosuppressive drugs, the ability to test for various antigens, and organ donor matching programs have increased the success rate of organ transplantation in humans.

Inappropriate immune system activity causes problems p. 210

- Allergies occur when the immune system responds excessively to foreign particles that are not otherwise harmful.
- Autoimmune disorders develop when a person's immune system attacks the person's own cells as if they were foreign.

Immune deficiency: The special case of AIDS p. 213

- AIDS is caused by a virus (HIV).
- The disease can take years to develop after initial HIV infection, but it is nearly always fatal.
- Worldwide, the number of cases of HIV infection and of AIDS is still rising rapidly.
- The chances of contracting AIDS can be reduced (but never eliminated completely) by practicing "safer" sex.

Terms You Should Know

active immunization, *207*	immune response, *201*
AIDS (acquired immune deficiency syndrome), *213*	inflammations, *198*
	interferons, *199*
antibiotics, *191*	macrophage, *197*
antibody, *201*	monoclonal antibodies, *209*
antibody-mediated immunity, *201*	passive immunization, *208*
	pathogen, *190*
antigen, *201*	phagocytosis, *197*
bacteria, *190*	prion, *192*
B cell, *201*	T cell, *201*
cell-mediated immunity, *201*	vaccine, *207*
cytokines, *204*	viruses, *191*
HIV (human immunodeficiency virus), *213*	

Concept Review

Answers can be found in the Study Area in MasteringBiology.

1. Define the term *pathogen* and give some examples.
2. Describe what is unusual about viruses that cause some people to question whether they are living things.
3. Explain how prions affect human health.
4. Describe the functions of organs of the lymphatic system.
5. List the four components of an inflammatory response.
6. Describe in general terms the distinction between *nonspecific* and *specific* defense mechanisms.
7. Describe the concept of an antigen and how it relates to self and nonself markers.
8. Describe how cells that belong to a particular individual are identified so that the individual's immune system doesn't attack them.
9. Explain how cytotoxic T cells kill target cells.
10. Describe how a vaccine produces immunity from a specific disease.

Test Yourself

Answers can be found in Appendix A.

1. In which of the following ways are bacterial cells similar to human cells?
   a. Bacterial cells have cell walls.
   b. Bacterial cells have a single, circular chromosome.
   c. Bacterial cells use ATP to fuel cellular activities.
   d. Bacterial cells lack mitochondria.

2. Which of the following statements about viruses is true?
   a. Viruses require a host cell in which to reproduce.
   b. Viruses are very small bacteria.
   c. Viral infections can generally be controlled with antibiotics.
   d. Viruses are composed of protein only.

3. Which of the following pathogenic agents causes a self-propagating misfolding of proteins in nerve cells?
   a. bacteria
   b. prions
   c. viruses
   d. helminths (worms)

4. Consider the following group of diseases: hepatitis, chicken pox, warts, and measles. What do these diseases have in common?
   a. They are all caused by bacteria.
   b. They are readily treated with antibiotics.
   c. They are all caused by viruses.
   d. They are very common in patients infected with HIV.

5. Which of the following is true regarding prion diseases?
   a. They are caused by a deadly type of virus.
   b. They can readily be treated with antibiotics.
   c. They can be prevented by vaccinations.
   d. They cause accumulation of misfolded proteins in brain cells.

6. Which of the following is a benefit of resident bacteria?
   a. Resident bacteria cause the stomach to be acidic.
   b. Resident bacteria produce antiviral compounds that prevent viral infections.
   c. Resident bacteria can out-compete harmful bacteria and lower the incidence of infection.
   d. Resident bacteria digest cellulose within the human digestive tract.

7. DiGeorge syndrome is a congenital disease that results in a poorly developed, non-functioning thymus gland. Which of the following would be a likely problem experienced by a baby with DiGeorge syndrome?
   a. lack of B cells
   b. lack of antibodies
   c. lack of T cells
   d. lack of macrophages

8. The following are steps in phagocytosis: (1) Bacterium is digested by lysosomal enzymes, (2) phagocyte approaches bacterium, (3) phagocytic vesicle fuses with lysosome, and (4) phagocyte engulfs bacterium, forming a phagocytic vesicle. In which order do these steps occur?
   a. 4-2-3-1
   b. 2-4-3-1
   c. 2-3-4-1
   d. 4-1-3-2

9. In which of the following choices is the cell correctly matched with its function?
   a. eosinophil: produces antibodies
   b. B lymphocyte: directly attacks foreign cells
   c. basophil: secretes histamine
   d. T lymphocyte: phagocytizes bacteria

10. Each of the following processes helps combat infection except:
    a. inflammation
    b. fever
    c. autoimmunity
    d. antibody production

11. The primary immune response is:
    a. faster than the secondary immune response
    b. longer lasting than the secondary immune response
    c. less effective than the secondary immune response
    d. due to the presence of memory cells

12. Compared to active immunization, passive immunization:
    a. provides immediate protection
    b. is longer lasting
    c. creates a large number of memory cells
    d. may occasionally cause the disease it is intended to prevent

13. Which of the following increases the likelihood of successful organ transplant?
    a. matching the ABO blood group antigens
    b. matching the MHC tissue antigens
    c. administration of immunosuppressive drugs
    d. all of these choices

14. Which of the following does not belong with the others?
    a. lupus erythematosus
    b. rheumatoid arthritis
    c. anaphylactic shock
    d. Type I diabetes mellitus

15. Which of the following statements about HIV is true?
    a. Latex condoms are 100% effective in blocking transmission of HIV.
    b. Most individuals who progress to Phase II of HIV infection remain in Phase II and never progress to Phase III (AIDS).
    c. HIV specifically impairs the cell-mediated immune response.
    d. Anti-HIV medications such as AZT and maraviroc can cure HIV infection.

Apply What You Know

Answers can be found in the Study Area in MasteringBiology.

1. When you get a minor infection in a small cut in the skin, sometimes soaking it in hot water speeds the healing process. How might the heat help?
2. Explain why antibiotics don't work against viruses.
3. Everyone knows that bacteria can cause disease. Suppose that we could actually remove all bacteria from our bodies all at once. Would that be a good thing or a bad thing?
4. In 1918 a pandemic of a deadly flu strain killed upward of 30 million people. If that same flu strain were to come around again, would we be better off or worse off than those who were alive in 1918?
5. Researchers have been working on an effective vaccine for gonorrheal infections for some years. One promising vaccine is delivered via a spray into the nasal cavity. This is clearly not the site of gonococcal infection. Why would one administer a vaccine meant to protect the reproductive tract into the nasal cavity?
6. Why is it that most people get the chicken pox only once, but they can get a cold or the flu over and over again throughout a lifetime?
7. The immune system is supposed to defend us from harmful microorganisms. Why doesn't it always work? In other words, why do some people still get sick and die?

BlogInFocus

Answers can be found in the Study Area in MasteringBiology.

1. The FDA recently approved the first treatment for scorpion stings. The antivenom is given after a sting has occurred. Based on what you know, is it a form of active immunization, or is it passive immunization? (To learn more, visit MJ's blog in the Study Area in MasteringBiology and look under "Antivenom Against Scorpion Stings.")

2. Researchers have been trying to develop a vaginal gel that would be effective against HIV infection, without much success so far. Why do you suppose there's so much interest in a vaginal gel? Can you think of any advantage that the gel might have over condoms, which are nearly 100% effective? (Hint: Think about who decides to use each method, or visit MJ's blog in the Study Area in MasteringBiology and look under "Vaginal Gel Against HIV Infection.")

MasteringBiology®

Go to MasteringBiology for practice quizzes, activities, eText, videos, current events, and more.

The Nervous System: Integration and Control

Colored SEM (× 2,700) of two nerve cells from the cerebellum of the human brain.

Head Trauma in Young Athletes

Late in the first half of a middle school football game in 2006, Zackery Lystedt went down hard and banged his head against the ground. He struggled to his feet holding his head in pain. In the second half he returned to the game, forcing a fumble by the opposing team on the goal line and preserving the victory for his team. But in the process he banged his head again. After the game he said to his dad, "Dad, my head hurts," and then "I can't see." Then he lapsed into a coma.

A Single Blow to the Head Can Cause a Concussion

Zackery most likely suffered a mild *concussion* after the first impact. A concussion is a trauma-induced change

in mental status, often accompanied by headache, confusion, dizziness, double vision, lack of coordination, confused speech, and (occasionally) loss of consciousness. Concussion is a description of symptoms. The medical term for the underlying cause is Mild Traumatic Brain Injury (MTBI). The brain is actually a fairly soft and fragile tissue, which is precisely why it is encased in a bony skull for protection. A strong blow to the head jars the brain against the inside of the hard skull, causing temporary disruption of function of higher brain centers (a concussion), followed by mild brain swelling. In most cases the swelling and the concussive symptoms go away with time, and the person recovers completely.

Zackery might have recovered from the first impact, except that he suffered a second impact soon after the first. That set the stage for a more serious condition known as "second impact syndrome," in which the brain swelling is more severe. Zackery experienced the most extreme condition of all, an acute intracranial hemorrhage. He was in a coma for 30 days, didn't speak for nearly nine months, and today still relies on a wheelchair.

In response to his accident, in 2009 Zackery's home state of Washington passed one of the toughest laws in the country for protecting young athletes from brain injuries. Under Washington law, athletes under the age of 18 who are suspected of having sustained a concussion *must* be removed from the game (or practice), and are not allowed to return until they have written authorization-to-play from a medical professional trained to diagnose and manage head injuries. Other states quickly followed suit. By 2011 least 31 states had passed what have become known as Lystedt Laws.

Concussions and other acute brain injuries are more common among young athletes than you might think. Approximately one in five high school football players suffer a concussion or a more serious brain injury in just four years. The second most dangerous high school sport in terms of head injuries is girls' soccer. It used to be thought that younger athletes bounced back quickly from "getting their bell rung" (a blow to the head), but neuroscientists now have evidence that it's just the opposite. The effects of acute concussions are longer lasting in adolescents than in adults, and the cognitive deficits are more severe. Fortunately, increased awareness is leading to improvements in safety in contact sports, including better helmets, changes in game rules, increased parental and coach staff awareness of the symptoms of a concussion, and more medical supervision.

The Long-Term Effects of Repetitive Head Trauma

Until recently, the potential long-term risks of repetitive head trauma were completely unknown. New evidence raises the possibility that athletes who compete in high head-impact sports may be at risk for permanent degenerative brain disease later in life, even if they never suffer an obvious concussion. Medical doctors call it Chronic Traumatic Encephalopathy (CTE), permanent pathological changes in the brain brought about by repeated blows to the head. Impact sensors inside football helmets show that when two professional football linemen collide helmet-to-helmet, the head impact force is the equivalent of hitting your

head against the windshield in a car crash at 25 miles per hour. Do these repetitive "minor" impacts have an additive effect?

What little information we have so far is cause for concern. In 2007 the National Football League (NFL) commissioned a telephone survey of more than 1,000 retired professional football players who had played at least three seasons in the NFL. The University of Michigan researchers who conducted the survey found that 6.1% of the players over 50 reported that they had been diagnosed with a dementia-related condition, more than five times higher than the national average for their age group. For players aged 30 to 49, it was *nineteen times* the age-matched

Zackery Lystedt in physical therapy after his accident.

national average. (*Dementia* is the term for the loss of function—including memory, language, judgment, behavior, and thinking—associated with *permanent* brain damage, as opposed to acute injury.)

Telephone surveys are not the most reliable way to collect data, so these findings should be interpreted with caution. To complicate matters, most professional football players probably also played football in college and in high school, so there's no telling when their injuries were sustained. Nevertheless, former NFL players have filed numerous lawsuits against the NFL over damages allegedly caused by repeated head injuries sustained during their professional football careers.

It would be a shame if an inability to protect our athletes from injuries ultimately led to a decline in contact sports. More information is needed about acute and chronic head injuries. We need to know how and why the injuries are occurring and what can be done to prevent them. We owe it to the athletes to make contact sports as safe as possible.

Zackery graduated from high school in 2011. He and his parents continue to campaign for new rules that will increase the safety of football.

QUESTIONS TO CONSIDER

1 Does your state have a Lystedt Law or its equivalent? In your state, who decides when a player may return to the game after an injury?

2 What do you think could feasibly be done to find out if repetitive head trauma leads to brain damage and dementia later in life?

THE FACTS...

- A high-impact blow to the head can cause a concussion. The medical consequences of concussions are greater in young athletes than in adults.

- Most states have passed laws recently requiring approval of a medical professional before an injured athlete may return to a game or practice.

- Preliminary data suggests (but does not prove) that repetitive head trauma over many years may lead to permanent brain damage and dementia later in life.

>> **The nervous system is the body's main control system.** The nervous system receives input from a variety of sources. It controls our body's physical movements, maintains homeostasis of many internal variables, and even initiates our higher thought processes and emotions.

>> **The unit of function in the nervous system is a neuron** (nerve cell). Neurons generate and transmit electrical impulses called *action potentials*.

>> **Neurons communicate with each other chemically.** Information is passed from one neuron to another via the release of chemical substances called *neurotransmitters*.

>> **The brain has the capacity for long-term memory.** Long-term memory involves permanent chemical and physical changes within the brain.

>> **Psychoactive drugs** (drugs that affect states of consciousness, emotions, or behavior) all act by altering communication between neurons in the brain. They do so by influencing the concentrations or actions of neurotransmitters.

You're on your way to class. It is cold, but you are not wearing your coat, and you are hungry. Your mind is elsewhere as you think about your psychology exam coming up. As you cross the street you see a doughnut shop and you smell doughnuts and coffee in the air. Suddenly you hear sounds—the screech of a skidding truck behind you and the blaring of the truck's horn. Quickly you whirl around, glance at the approaching truck, and leap to safety on the sidewalk. The doughnuts and the psychology exam are forgotten momentarily.

Your nervous system is constantly receiving input from all kinds of sources. It's also sorting through a huge amount of stored information in your brain's large memory banks, looking for the probable meaning of all sensory inputs, which in this scenario includes the meaning of screeching truck tires. The nervous system adds up and makes sense of this seemingly unrelated information quickly and enables you to react. How does this happen?

Here are four characteristics of the nervous system:

- The nervous system receives information from many different senses simultaneously.
- The nervous system integrates information. Integration is the process of taking different pieces of information from many different sources and assembling the pieces into a whole that

makes sense. This process entails sifting through mountains of data and coming up with a plan or course of action.

- The nervous system is very fast. It can receive information, integrate it, and produce a response within tenths of a second. In this chapter we learn about the special properties of the nervous system that give it such speed.
- The nervous system can initiate specific responses, including muscle contraction, glandular secretion, and even conscious thought and emotions.

Most of the functions of the nervous system are completely automatic and can be carried on simultaneously without requiring our attention or conscious decision making. However, the nervous system can also bring selected information to the level of conscious awareness. Working with the endocrine system (Chapter 13), the nervous system maintains homeostasis. It also allows us to feel emotions, to be aware of ourselves, and to exert conscious control over the incredible diversity of our physical movements.

11.1 The nervous system has two principal parts

The nervous system includes the **central nervous system (CNS)** and the **peripheral nervous system (PNS)** (Figure 11.1). The CNS consists of the brain and the spinal cord. It receives, processes, stores, and transfers information. The PNS includes the components of the nervous system that lie outside the CNS. The PNS has two functional subdivisions: the sensory division of the PNS carries information to the brain and spinal cord, and the motor division of the PNS carries information from the CNS to other parts of the body.

The motor division of the peripheral nervous system is further subdivided along functional lines. The *somatic division* of the PNS controls skeletal muscles, and the *autonomic division* of the PNS controls smooth muscles, cardiac muscles, and glands. In turn, the autonomic division has two subdivisions called the *sympathetic* and *parasympathetic* divisions. In general, the actions of the sympathetic and parasympathetic divisions oppose each other. They work antagonistically to accomplish the automatic, subconscious maintenance of homeostasis.

We examine each of these components in more detail later in this chapter. But first, we discuss the structure and function of neurons and of the neuroglial cells that accompany and support them.

⟲ **Recap** The nervous system has two major subdivisions: the central nervous system (CNS), consisting of the brain and spinal cord, and the peripheral nervous system (PNS), which includes all parts of the nervous system that lie outside the CNS. The motor division of the PNS has a somatic division, which controls skeletal muscles, and an autonomic division, which controls smooth muscles, cardiac muscles, and glands. ∎

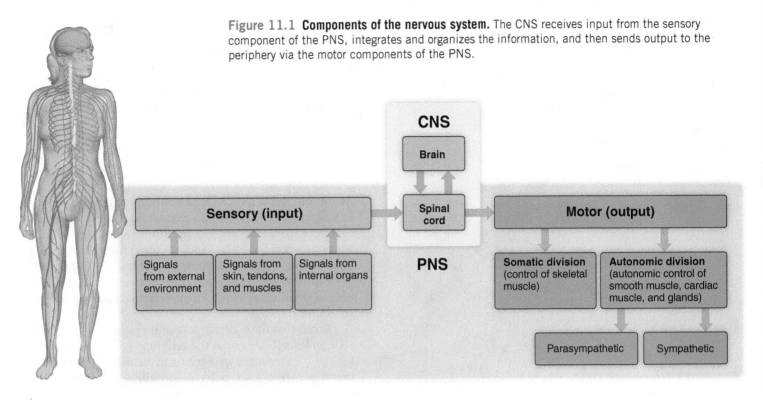

Figure 11.1 Components of the nervous system. The CNS receives input from the sensory component of the PNS, integrates and organizes the information, and then sends output to the periphery via the motor components of the PNS.

11.2 Neurons are the communication cells of the nervous system

Neurons are cells specialized for communication. They generate and conduct electrical impulses, also called *action potentials*, from one part of the body to another. The longest neurons extend all the way from your toes to your spinal cord. These are single cells, remember.

There are three types of neurons in the nervous system, as shown in Figure 11.2.

■ **Sensory neurons** of the PNS are specialized to respond to a certain type of stimulus, such as pressure or light. They transmit information about this stimulus to the CNS in the form of electrical impulses. In other words, sensory neurons provide input to the CNS.

■ **Interneurons** within the CNS transmit impulses between components of the CNS. Interneurons receive input from sensory neurons, integrate this information, and influence the functioning of other neurons.

■ **Motor neurons** of the PNS transmit impulses away from the CNS. They carry the nervous system's output, still in the form of electrical impulses, to all of the tissues and organs of the body.

All neurons consist of a cell body, one or more dendrites, and an axon. The main body of a neuron is called the **cell body**. The nucleus, with its content of DNA, is located in the cell body, as are the mitochondria and other cell organelles.

Slender extensions of the cell body, called **dendrites**, receive information from receptors or incoming impulses from other neurons (see Figure 11.2). Interneurons and motor neurons have numerous dendrites that are fairly short and extend in many directions from the cell body. Sensory neurons are an exception, because their dendrites connect directly to an axon.

An **axon** is a long, slender tube of cell membrane containing a small amount of cytoplasm. Axons are specialized to conduct electrical impulses. Axons of sensory neurons originate from a dendrite, whereas the axons of interneurons and motor neurons originate from the point of union with the cell body, called the *axon hillock* (see Figure 11.2). At its other end, the axon branches into slender extensions called *axon terminals*. Each axon terminal ends in a small, rounded tip called an *axon bulb*.

Typically, an interneuron or motor neuron receives incoming information from other neurons at its dendrites or cell body. If the incoming information is of the right kind and is strong enough, the neuron responds by generating an electrical impulse of its own at its axon hillock. In contrast, in a sensory neuron the impulse is initiated where the dendrite joins the axon. The impulse is then transmitted from one end of the axon to the other, bypassing the cell body entirely. We talk more about different types of receptors in the chapter on sensory mechanisms (Chapter 12).

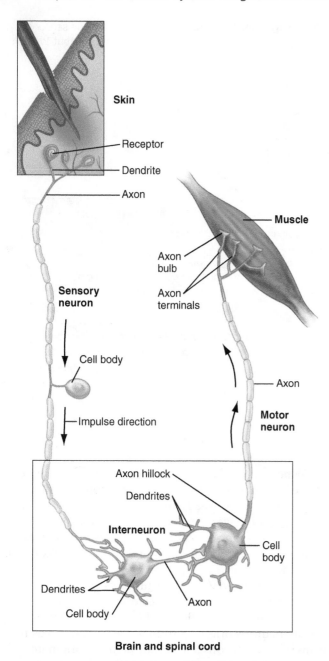

Figure 11.2 Types of neurons in the nervous system. The flow of information begins at a receptor near a dendritic ending of a sensory neuron and ends at the axon bulbs of a motor neuron. In this example the receptors are in skin. Interneurons are located entirely within the central nervous system and typically have short axons.

Recap Neurons generate and transmit electrical impulses from one part of the body to another. Sensory neurons transmit impulses to the CNS. Interneurons transmit impulses between components of the CNS. Motor neurons transmit impulses away from the CNS to muscles and glands. ▪

11.3 Neurons initiate action potentials

The function of a neuron is to transmit information from one part of the body to another in the form of electrical impulses. Next, we look at how a neuron initiates and conducts an impulse.

Sodium-potassium pump maintains resting potential

As you learned when you studied the structure and function of cells, the sodium-potassium pump is essential to the control of cell volume by virtue of its ability to remove osmotic particles (sodium ions) from the cell. The same sodium-potassium pump is also essential for the development and maintenance of an electrical charge across the cell membrane. How does it help to create and maintain an electrical charge?

Recall that the sodium-potassium pump transports three sodium ions (Na^+) out of the cell for every two potassium ions (K^+) transported in. Each time the sodium-potassium pump goes through a cycle, the net effect is the removal of one osmotic particle (a Na^+ ion) and also one positive charge (because the Na^+ ion is positively charged). In other words, the sodium-potassium pump removes both osmotic particles and positive charges from the cell at the same time. As a result of the activity of the sodium-potassium pumps and also the presence of negatively charged protein molecules trapped within the cell, the cell cytoplasm has a slight excess of negative charge compared to the interstitial fluid. The difference in charge results in a small but measurable difference in voltage across the cell membrane, called the *membrane potential*.

In a neuron capable of action potentials but not generating one at the moment, the normal membrane potential at rest is its **resting (membrane) potential**. The resting potential of a neuron is about –70 millivolts (mV), meaning that the inside of the neuron is negatively charged compared to the outside. Figure 11.3 illustrates the role of the sodium-potassium pump and the processes of diffusion of Na^+ and K^+ (through channels) in maintaining the resting potential.

The concentration of sodium is much higher in the interstitial fluid than it is in the cytoplasm, whereas the inverse is true for potassium. Because sodium is always leaking into the cell and potassium is leaking out by passive diffusion, you might think that the concentration differences between the inside and outside would disappear over time. This doesn't happen because the active transport of sodium and potassium by the pump in the opposite directions exactly balances the rates of leakage. At rest, the ionic concentration differences are maintained and the membrane potential stays at –70 mV, inside negative. As we'll see in a moment, the large

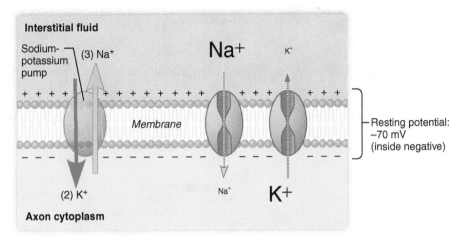

Figure 11.3 Maintenance of the resting membrane potential. The sodium-potassium pump actively transports three Na$^+$ ions out of the cell in exchange for two K$^+$ ions. Most of the K$^+$ leaks out again. However, the inward leak of sodium is so slow that the pump effectively is able to exclude most Na$^+$ from the cell. The exclusion of positive ions (Na$^+$) from the cell creates a voltage difference (an electrical potential) across the cell membrane of about −70 mV (inside negative). The relative concentrations of Na$^+$ and K$^+$ in the interstitial fluid and the cytoplasm are indicated by the sizes of the letters associated with the diffusion channels.

concentration differences for sodium and potassium across the axon membrane enable the neuron to generate impulses simply by opening and closing ion channels.

✅ **Quick Check** *Suppose that a neuron has unusual Na/K pumps that move four Na$^+$ out for every two K$^+$ in. Predict whether the resting potential of this neuron will be more negative, less negative, or the same as a normal cell, and explain your reasoning. ▪*

Graded potentials alter the resting potential

The resting potential of a neuron undergoes a change when an impulse arrives from another neuron. Every incoming impulse produces, in a series of steps discussed in a moment, a small transient change in the resting potential in a local area of the membrane. Depending on the type of signal and its strength, the change might be to *depolarize* the membrane (move the voltage closer to zero), or *hyperpolarize* it (make it even more negative). These transient local changes in resting potential are called **graded potentials** because they can vary in size. They occur only at a single region on the membrane, fading away at increasing distances from that region like the ripples made by a raindrop on water. A neuron may receive hundreds of incoming signals from other neurons, so hundreds of these graded potentials may occur at the same time.

A key feature of graded potentials is that they can add up in space and time, meaning that many

incoming signals from other neurons produce a bigger change in membrane potential than does one impulse alone. This is known as **summation**.

An action potential is a sudden reversal of membrane voltage

If the sum of all graded potentials is sufficiently strong to reach a certain triggering membrane voltage called the **threshold**, an action potential results. An **action potential** is a sudden, temporary reversal of the voltage difference across the cell membrane. Once an action potential is initiated, it sweeps rapidly down the axon at a constant amplitude and rate of speed until it reaches the axon terminals.

Figure 11.4 depicts the resting membrane potential, graded potentials and how they summate, and an action potential.

Functionally, an action potential (also known as an *electrical impulse*) is the only form in which information is transmitted long distance by the nervous system. An action potential is like a single monotonic "beep" in a touch-tone phone or a single on-off pulse of current. Its meaning is provided only by where it came from and where it goes—that is, by how the nervous system is wired.

Action potentials occur because the axon membrane contains voltage-sensitive ion channels that open and

Figure 11.4 The resting membrane potential, graded potentials, and an action potential in a neuron. Stimulation by other neurons is indicated by the arrows. Note that graded potentials can either depolarize or hyperpolarize the membrane and that they can summate. If the sum of all graded potentials is sufficient to depolarize the membrane to threshold, an action potential occurs.

✅ *Extend the graph to draw what you think will happen if this neuron now receives an even stronger depolarizing stimulus (say, a series of four depolarizing graded potentials) that results in another action potential. Will this new action potential be higher and/or longer lasting than the first one?*

close sequentially once threshold has been reached. An action potential occurs as a sequence of three events: (1) depolarization, (2) repolarization, and (3) reestablishment of the resting potential (**Figure 11.5**).

1. *Depolarization: sodium moves into the axon.* When threshold is exceeded, voltage-sensitive Na⁺ channels in the axon's membrane open briefly and Na⁺ ions diffuse rapidly into the cytoplasm of the axon. This influx of positive ions causes *depolarization*, meaning that the membrane potential shifts from negative (–70 mV) to positive (about +30 mV).

2. *Repolarization: potassium moves out of the axon.* After a short delay the Na⁺ channels close automatically. But the reversal of the membrane polarity triggers the opening of K⁺ channels. This allows more K⁺ ions than usual to diffuse rapidly out of the cell. The loss of positive ions from the cell leads to *repolarization*, meaning that the interior of the axon becomes negative again.

3. *Reestablishment of the resting potential.* Because the K⁺ channels are slow to close, there is a brief overshoot of membrane voltage during which the interior of the axon is slightly hyperpolarized. Shortly after the K⁺ channels close, the resting potential is reestablished. At this point the axon is prepared to receive another action potential. The entire sequence of three steps takes about 3 milliseconds.

While an action potential is under way, an axon can't generate another action potential. This period is called the *absolute refractory period*. The presence of an absolute refractory period ensures that

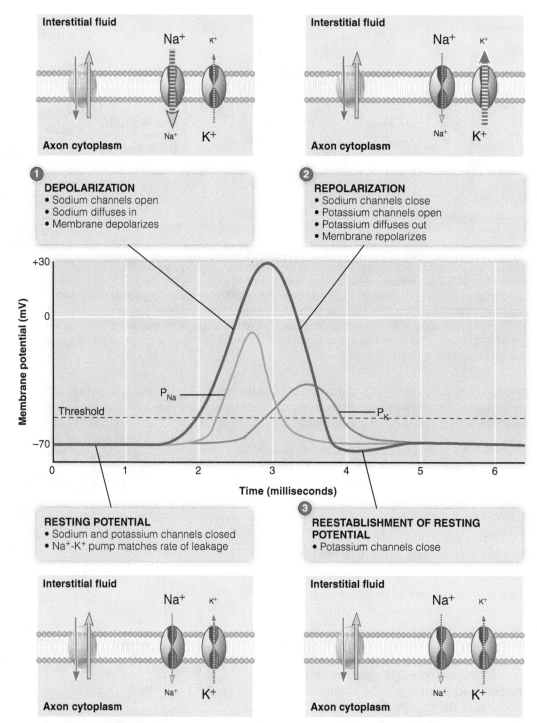

Figure 11.5 Propagation of an action potential. This is a graph of changes in potential over time recorded from a single point on the axon. At rest, the sodium-potassium pump transports sodium and potassium, and the sodium and potassium channels are essentially closed. **(1)** Depolarization: once threshold is exceeded, voltage-sensitive sodium channels open briefly and the membrane permeability to sodium (P_{Na}) increases. Sodium diffuses rapidly into the axon, depolarizing the membrane. **(2)** Repolarization: sodium channels close. Potassium channels open and the membrane permeability to potassium (P_K) increases. Potassium diffuses outward, repolarizing the membrane. **(3)** Reestablishment of resting potential: after a brief hyperpolarization caused by a delay in the full closure of potassium channels, the membrane potential returns to its normal resting value.

☑ *Explain in your own words why the blue line goes down when the green line goes up.*

action potentials always travel in one direction only, because an area of the axon that has just experienced an action potential cannot produce another one right away.

The absolute refractory period is followed by a brief *relative refractory period* during which it is harder than usual to generate the next action potential. In practical terms, this means that by encroaching into the relative refractory period, very strong stimuli can generate more frequent action potentials than relatively weak stimuli can. The absolute and relative refractory periods are shown in Figure 11.6.

Whether or not a neuron is generating action potentials, the sodium-potassium pumps continue to maintain the normal concentrations of Na$^+$ and K$^+$ and the normal resting potential. The actual number of Na$^+$ and K$^+$ ions that diffuse across the membrane during a single action potential is so small compared to the activity of the sodium-potassium pumps that an axon can transmit many action potentials in a short period of time without adversely affecting the subsequent resting membrane potential.

✅**Quick Check** *Suppose a neuron is placed in a solution that has no Na$^+$ ions, but is a normal extracellular solution in other respects (normal concentrations of osmotic particles, normal charge). If the membrane voltage were brought to threshold, would the neuron be able to generate an action potential? Explain your answer.* ⬤

Action potentials are all-or-none and self-propagating

As we have seen, an action potential does not occur unless a certain threshold membrane voltage is reached. Once it is triggered, however, it always looks exactly the same in form and voltage. Even if the graded stimulus that causes it is significantly higher than the threshold level, the form and amplitude of the action potential are always the same. Consequently an action potential is an "all-or-none" phenomenon: either it occurs or it does not. It's like firing a gun. A certain amount of pressure—the threshold level—is required to make the gun fire. Pressing the trigger too lightly will not make it fire, and pressing it harder than necessary will not cause the bullet to leave the gun any faster.

An action potential is also a self-propagating event, meaning that it continues to propagate itself in the next region of the axon. This is because the local spread of electrical current forward from the region of the axon that is currently undergoing an action potential brings the next region of the axon to threshold. Thus the action potential is propagated continuously down the axon like a moving wave, at a constant rate of speed and amplitude.

If all action potentials are alike, how does a neuron transmit information about stimulus intensity? Simple, really: it's encoded by the number of action potentials generated and transmitted per time unit, ranging from near zero to perhaps several hundred per second. Stronger stimuli generate *more* action potentials per time unit, not faster or bigger ones.

Although the speed of travel of an action potential is always constant for a given neuron, the speed in different neurons can vary from about 5 mph up to 250 mph. Action potential speed is greater in larger-diameter axons and in axons covered by an insulating sheath, as we'll see in a minute.

↺ **Recap** A neuron's resting potential of about –70 millivolts is maintained by the constant action of the sodium-potassium pump. Impulses arriving from other neurons can cause small, local changes in the neuron's membrane potential called *graded potentials*. The sum of all graded potentials may initiate a self-propagating, all-or-none action potential in a neuron. An action potential involves three events: depolarization, repolarization, and reestablishment of the resting potential. ⬤

11.4 Neuroglial cells support and protect neurons

Only about 20% of cells in the human nervous system are neurons. The rest are **neuroglial cells**, which provide physical support and protection to neurons and help maintain healthy concentrations of important chemicals in the fluid surrounding them. (Neuroglia derives from the Greek words for "neuron" and "glue.") Neuroglial cells do not generate or transmit impulses.

In the peripheral nervous system, many neuron axons are enclosed and protected by specialized neuroglial cells called *Schwann cells*. Schwann cells produce a fatty insulating material called *myelin*. During development, individual

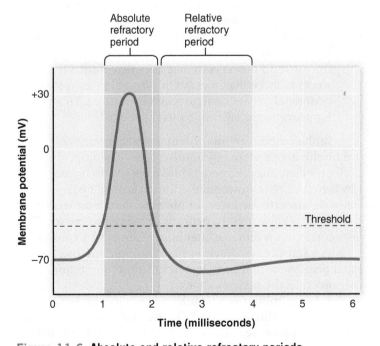

Figure 11.6 Absolute and relative refractory periods.

Schwann cells wrap themselves around a short segment of an axon many times as a sort of insulating blanket, creating a shiny white protective layer around the axon called a **myelin sheath**. Between adjacent Schwann cells are short uninsulated gaps called *nodes of Ranvier*, where the surface of the axon is still exposed (**Figure 11.7**). Neurons that have axons wrapped in a sheath of myelin are called **myelinated neurons**.

In saltatory conduction, the nerve impulse jumps from node to node.

a) A myelinated motor neuron of the peripheral nervous system.

Node of Ranvier

Schwann cell

Myelin sheath

Neuron axon

b) TEM cross section of part of an axon (yellow) and its surrounding myelin sheath (beige).

Figure 11.7 A myelinated motor neuron of the peripheral nervous system. The axon of the motor neuron is wrapped by individual Schwann cells, which produce an insulating substance called *myelin*. Between adjacent Schwann cells are uninsulated sections called *nodes of Ranvier*. In myelinated neurons, electrical impulses appear to jump rapidly from node to node as a result of local current flows both within and outside the neuron (shown by thin, black arrows).

The myelin sheath around the axon serves three important functions:

- *It saves the neuron energy.* The insulating layer of myelin prevents some of the slow inward leak of sodium and outward leak of potassium that would otherwise occur. These leaks normally have to be replaced by active transport processes requiring energy (see section 11.3).
- *It speeds up the transmission of impulses.* The myelin sheath prevents nearly all leakage of charged ions across the axon membrane, except where the axon is bare (at the nodes of Ranvier). When an action potential occurs at a node of Ranvier, the local depolarizing current spreads much farther within the axon—all the way to the next node of Ranvier. The rate of travel of this local current within the axon is even faster than the rate of travel of a continuously propagated action potential along an unmyelinated axon. At the next node of Ranvier, the local depolarizing current brings the axon membrane to threshold, triggering a new action potential. In effect, a succession of action potentials appears to jump from node to node at a very fast rate. This "leaping" pattern of conduction along myelinated neurons is called **saltatory conduction** (from *saltare*, Latin for "dance"). Continuously propagated action potentials in unmyelinated neurons travel at a speed of only about 5 mph (2.3 meters per second). In contrast, saltatory conduction in myelinated neurons can reach speeds of up to 250 mph (about 110 meters per second).
- *It helps damaged or severed axons of the peripheral nervous system regenerate.* If a neuron axon is severed, the portion of the axon distal to the cell body may degenerate. However, the cut end of the axon still attached to the cell body can regrow through the channel formed by the sheath, eventually reconnecting with the cell that it serves. Depending on the length of the axon, the regeneration process can take anywhere from a few weeks to more than a year. On average, an axon in the peripheral nervous system grows by nearly 1/16 inch (approximately 1.5 millimeters) per day.

In the central nervous system, protective sheaths of myelin are produced by another type of neuroglial cell called an *oligodendrocyte*. Unlike the sheath formed by Schwann cells, however, the sheath formed by oligodendrocytes degenerates once the axon it protects is destroyed. Consequently, neurons of the central nervous system do not regenerate after injury. This is why spinal cord injuries and CNS disorders such as multiple sclerosis result in a permanent change or loss of function (see section 11.13, Disorders of the nervous system).

In the autoimmune disorder *multiple sclerosis* (MS), the sheaths of myelinated neurons in the brain and spinal cord become progressively damaged until they form hardened (sclerotic) scar tissue. These sclerotic areas can no longer insulate the neurons effectively, disrupting and slowing the transmission of impulses. People with MS can experience a variety of symptoms depending on which areas of the CNS are damaged. Common symptoms include muscle weakness, visual impairment, and urinary incontinence. The disease usually appears in people between 20 and 40 years of age. Although the disease is generally progressive, people with MS may experience periods of remission.

A similar but rarer disease is *amyotrophic lateral sclerosis* (ALS), also known as Lou Gehrig's disease. In ALS the sclerotic areas typically begin in regions of the spinal cord involved in the motor control of skeletal muscle. The primary symptom of ALS is progressive weakening and wasting of skeletal muscle tissue. People with ALS usually die from respiratory failure, because both the diaphragm and the intercostal muscles are comprised of skeletal muscle.

⟲ Recap Neuroglial cells support and protect neurons. Neuroglial cells called *Schwann cells* (in the PNS) and *oligodendrocytes* (in the CNS) form myelin sheaths that protect axons and speed transmission of impulses. ▪

11.5 Information is transferred from a neuron to its target

Once an action potential reaches the axon terminals of a neuron, the information inherent in it must be converted to another form for transmittal to its target (muscle cell, gland cell, or another neuron). In essence, the action potential causes the release of a chemical that crosses a specialized junction between the two cells called a **synapse**. This chemical substance is called a **neurotransmitter** because it transmits a signal from a neuron to its target. The entire process of transmission from a neuron to its target is called *synaptic transmission*. As you know if you've already studied how muscles are activated by nerves (Chapter 6), synaptic transmission occurs between a neuron and a muscle cell. Now we'll see how it occurs between neurons.

Neurotransmitter is released

Figure 11.8 illustrates the structure of a typical synapse and the events that occur during synaptic transmission. At a synapse, the *presynaptic membrane* is the cell membrane of the neuron that is sending the information. The *postsynaptic membrane* is the membrane of the cell that is about to receive the information. The small fluid-filled gap that separates the presynaptic and postsynaptic membranes is the *synaptic cleft*.

Each axon terminal of the presynaptic neuron ends in an axon bulb that contains neurotransmitter stored in membrane-bound vesicles. The events that occur during synaptic transmission follow a particular pattern.

Axon bulbs form synapses with a postsynaptic neuron

1. An action potential arrives, causing Ca²⁺ to diffuse into the axon bulb.

2. Ca²⁺ causes vesicles containing neurotransmitter to fuse with the cell membrane, releasing neurotransmitter.

Action potential
Axon of presynaptic neuron
Ca²⁺
Axon bulb
Mitochondrion
Vesicles containing neurotransmitter
Presynaptic neuron
Synaptic cleft
Dendrite or cell body of postsynaptic neuron
Close-up of a synapse
Presynaptic membrane
Postsynaptic membrane

Synaptic cleft
Neurotransmitter
Na⁺
Na⁺
Cytoplasm of postsynaptic cell

3. Neurotransmitter binds to receptors on chemically gated sodium channels, causing the channels to open.

4. Diffusion of sodium produces a graded potential in the local region of the synapse.

Figure 11.8 Summary of synaptic transmission.

1. An action potential arrives at the axon bulb, causing calcium (Ca^{2+}) channels in the presynaptic membrane to open. Ca^{2+} diffuses into the axon bulb.
2. The presence of Ca^{2+} causes the vesicles to fuse with the presynaptic membrane and release their contents of neurotransmitter directly into the synaptic cleft. Because the synaptic cleft is so narrow (about 0.02 micrometer, or one-millionth of an inch), the neurotransmitter molecules reach the postsynaptic membrane by diffusion.
3. Molecules of neurotransmitter bind to receptors on the postsynaptic membrane. This causes certain chemically gated channels, such as those for sodium, to open.
4. Sodium ions diffuse inward, producing a graded depolarization of the postsynaptic membrane in the area of the synapse.

Note that graded potentials are caused by the opening of *chemically* sensitive ion channels (the chemical being a neurotransmitter), rather than voltage-sensitive ones.

✅ **Quick Check** *If there were no available Ca^{2+} in the synaptic cleft, would action potentials still travel down the presynaptic neuron's axon in the usual fashion? Would the presynaptic neuron be able to release neurotransmitters into the synaptic cleft? Explain your answer.* ◼

Neurotransmitters exert excitatory or inhibitory effects

The response of the postsynaptic cell to neurotransmitter depends on several factors, including the type of neurotransmitter, its concentration in the synaptic cleft, and the types of receptors and chemically sensitive ion channels in the postsynaptic membrane.

To date, scientists have identified more than 50 chemicals that can function as neurotransmitters. All are stored in vesicles within the axon bulb and released into the synaptic cleft in response to an action potential. All produce a graded potential in the postsynaptic cell, though the effects may be quite different because they can affect different ion channels.

Neurotransmitters are classified as excitatory, inhibitory, or both. Excitatory neurotransmitters depolarize the postsynaptic cell, causing threshold to be approached or exceeded. Therefore, excitatory neurotransmitters encourage the generation of new impulses in the postsynaptic neuron. Inhibitory neurotransmitters cause the postsynaptic cell to hyperpolarize, meaning that the cell's interior becomes even more negative than before. Hyperpolarization makes it harder for threshold to be reached, so inhibitory neurotransmitters tend to prevent the generation of action potentials in the postsynaptic neuron. Some neurotransmitters can be excitatory or inhibitory, depending on the type of receptor to which they bind on the postsynaptic membrane.

Table 11.1 summarizes the actions of several common neurotransmitters.

The effects of neurotransmitters are relatively short-lived because the neurotransmitter remains in the synaptic cleft for only a short time. Prompt removal of neurotransmitter causes neural signals to be terminated almost as rapidly as they are initiated. Only then can the next message be received and recognized. The neurotransmitter may be removed from the synaptic cleft in any or all of three ways: (1) it may be taken back up again by the presynaptic neuron and repackaged into membrane-bound vesicles, to be used again; (2) it may be destroyed by enzymes in the synaptic cleft; or (3) it may diffuse away from the synaptic cleft into the general circulation, where it will ultimately be destroyed.

Table 11.1 Actions of common neurotransmitters

Neurotransmitter	Sites where released	Principal actions
Acetylcholine	Neuromuscular junctions, autonomic nervous systems, brain	Excitatory on skeletal muscles; excitatory or inhibitory at other sites, depending on receptors
Norepinephrine	Areas of brain and spinal cord, autonomic nervous system	Excitatory or inhibitory, depending on receptors; plays a role in emotions
Serotonin	Areas of brain, spinal cord	Usually inhibitory; involved in moods, sleep cycle, appetite
Dopamine	Areas of brain, parts of peripheral nervous system	Excitatory or inhibitory, depending on receptors; plays a role in emotions
Glutamate	Areas of brain, spinal cord	Usually excitatory; major excitatory neurotransmitter in brain
Endorphins	Many areas in brain, spinal cord	Natural opiates that inhibit pain; usually inhibitory
Gamma-aminobutyric acid	Areas of brain, spinal cord	Usually inhibitory; principal inhibitory neurotransmitter in brain
Somatostatin	Areas of brain, pancreas	Usually inhibitory; inhibits pancreatic release of growth hormone

Postsynaptic neurons integrate and process information

The conversion of the signal from electrical (action potential) to chemical (neurotransmitter) allows the postsynaptic cell to do a lot of integration and information processing. This is because a single all-or-none action potential in the presynaptic neuron does not always cause a corresponding all-or-none action potential in the postsynaptic neuron, as it does in a muscle cell. A single action potential produces only a small graded potential in the postsynaptic neuron, and a lot of these graded potentials generally are required for threshold to be reached.

One way for threshold to be reached in a postsynaptic neuron is for the presynaptic neuron (or a few neurons) to increase their frequency of stimulation, sending lots of action potentials in a short time (hundreds per minute). In addition to stimulus intensity, other factors affecting whether threshold is reached in the postsynaptic neuron include (1) how many other neurons form synapses with it, and (2) whether those synaptic connections are stimulatory or inhibitory. Typically, one neuron receives input from many neurons, a phenomenon known as *convergence*. In turn, its action potential goes to many other neurons, a phenomenon known as *divergence* (Figure 11.9).

Figure 11.9 Neural information processing by convergence and divergence. Convergence occurs when several presynaptic cells form synapses with a single postsynaptic cell. Divergence occurs when one nerve cell provides information to a variety of postsynaptic cells.

Though it would be incorrect to say that neurons "interpret" information—that would imply that a neuron has a brain—the effect of convergence is that neurons may integrate and process thousands of simultaneous incoming stimulatory and inhibitory signals before generating and transmitting their own action potentials. They also reroute the information to many different destinations. Individual neurons do not see, smell, or hear, yet their combined actions allow us to experience those complex sensations.

Consider again the example given at the beginning of this chapter, in which you were able to ignore certain incoming signals—the smell of doughnuts, the sound of your shoes on pavement, the sensation of being cold—and focus on others, such as the noises made by the truck and its horn. You tapped your memory banks for the probable meaning of these sounds (danger approaching!), and then coordinated your muscles to turn around, see the truck, and jump out of the way—all in a fraction of a second. This is a complex set of events, and it is all done with neurons, action potentials, and neurotransmitters.

Muscle cells are also target cells of presynaptic neurons. However, skeletal muscle cells do not process and integrate information like postsynaptic neurons do. There are two reasons for this. First, a muscle cell receives input from only one neuron. There are no converging neural inputs to process. Second, the neuromuscular junction is quite large, with many points of contact between neuron and muscle cell. Consequently, threshold is reached in a skeletal muscle cell every time the motor neuron sends even a single action potential. Functionally, this means that the nervous system has absolute and final control over the activity of skeletal muscle cells.

Recap A neuron transmits information to another cell across a synapse. At a synapse, neurotransmitter released from a presynaptic neuron diffuses across the synaptic cleft and binds to receptors on the postsynaptic membrane, opening ion channels and causing a graded potential in the postsynaptic cell. Postsynaptic neurons may integrate incoming signals from many different presynaptic neurons. ▪

11.6 The PNS relays information between tissues and the CNS

Now that we have seen how neurons generate and transmit action potentials, we look at how this information travels throughout the nervous system. As stated earlier, the nervous system has two major subdivisions: the central nervous system (CNS), which includes the spinal cord and brain, and the peripheral nervous system (PNS), which consists of nerves that transmit information between body tissues and the CNS.

Nerves carry signals to and from the CNS

A single nerve axon is like a single fiber-optic fiber in that both transmit specific kinds of information from one location to another. By the same token, a nerve is like a large fiber-optic cable strung between two cities. A **nerve** consists of the axons of many neurons, all wrapped together in a protective sheath of connective tissue and all coming from and going to the same place. The function of each nerve depends on where it originates and the organs or tissues to which it travels.

The peripheral nervous system consists of cranial nerves and spinal nerves. The 12 pairs of **cranial nerves** connect directly with the brain. Cranial nerves carry action potentials between the brain and the muscles, glands, and receptors of the head, neck, and thoracic and abdominal cavities.

The 31 pairs of **spinal nerves** connect with the spinal cord. Each spinal nerve attaches to the spinal cord via two short branches of the spinal cord called the *dorsal root* and the *ventral root*. The dorsal root contains the sensory neurons that transmit incoming action potentials from body tissues to the spinal cord. The ventral root contains motor neurons that carry action potentials away from the spinal cord to the rest of the body. Thus each spinal nerve carries both sensory and motor (incoming and outgoing) information.

activated either by conscious control from the brain or by an involuntary response called a *reflex*.

Spinal reflexes are involuntary responses that are mediated primarily by the spinal cord and spinal nerves, with little or no involvement of the brain. Figure 11.10 illustrates two such spinal reflexes. Stepping on a sharp object, for example, activates pain receptors, producing action potentials in sensory neurons traveling to your spinal cord. The sensory neurons stimulate interneurons within the spinal cord, which in turn transmit signals to motor neurons in your leg, causing you to flex the appropriate muscles to lift your foot. This is called the *flexor (withdrawal) reflex*. Meanwhile, other interneurons that cross over to the opposite side of the spinal cord are also stimulated by the sensory neuron. These interneurons stimulate motor neurons to extend, rather than flex, certain skeletal muscles in your other leg. After all, it wouldn't do to flex both legs and fall on the sharp object! This second reflex is called a

Sensory neurons provide information to the CNS

The nervous system must have good information if it is to take appropriate action. That information arrives at the CNS as action potentials traveling in sensory neurons located throughout the body. Because information provided by sensory neurons to the CNS may affect the motor output of both the somatic and autonomic divisions of the PNS, the sensory (input) component of the PNS cannot be classified as belonging specifically to either the somatic or autonomic motor (output) divisions.

The somatic division controls skeletal muscles

Recall that the motor (or output) neurons of the peripheral nervous system are organized into the somatic division and the autonomic division. The **somatic division** controls voluntary and involuntary skeletal muscle movement. Somatic motor neurons transmit information from the spinal cord to skeletal muscles.

As described in the chapter on muscles (Chapter 6), a single somatic motor neuron controls several skeletal muscle cells (together they form a motor unit), and every time the neuron sends an action potential down its axon, all the muscle cells of that motor unit experience an action potential and contract. Motor neurons are

Figure 11.10 Spinal reflexes. In this example, a painful stimulus on one side of the body initiates different reflex actions on the two sides of the body: a flexor reflex (flexion of the leg) on the stimulated side and an extension reflex (extension of the leg) on the opposite side. Sensory information is also relayed to the brain to make you aware of the painful stimulus.

crossed extensor reflex—crossed because the signal initiating it crossed over from the other side of the body.

Notice that these events did not require conscious thought. A simple spinal reflex is processed primarily at the level of the spinal cord, allowing a rather complex series of actions to occur quickly. Some sensory information does ascend to the brain as well, allowing the brain to integrate the sensory information from your foot with all the other information it is receiving and determine your next course of action (such as sitting down and examining your foot). But most of the spinal reflex itself occurs without any involvement of the brain.

Another type of spinal reflex is a *stretch reflex*. In a stretch reflex, stretch receptors in a skeletal muscle stimulate sensory nerves, which carry the signals to the spinal cord. In the spinal cord, motor neurons to the stretched muscle are activated. At the same time, motor neurons to any antagonistic muscles are inhibited so that contraction will be effective. Stretch reflexes play an important role in maintaining upright posture and movement, as they allow us to stand and move without having to concentrate on our actions.

Stretch reflexes associated with posture and movement are often modified slightly by signals from higher brain centers. Physicians can test such reflexes to determine whether the spinal cord and areas of the brain involved in stretch reflexes are intact and functioning properly. An example is the well-known knee-jerk reflex. When the patellar tendon is tapped lightly below the kneecap, the resulting slight stretch of the thigh muscles initiates a spinal reflex that ultimately results in contraction of the thigh muscles and an upward movement of the foot and lower leg (Figure 11.11). If the neural pathways are not intact or if the brain is not modifying the reflex properly, the reflex may be either less vigorous or more vigorous than normal.

✅**Quick Check** *Compare and contrast the patellar (knee-jerk) reflex and the reflex responses to a painful stimulus applied to the foot. What are the major similarities and differences?* ■

The autonomic division controls automatic body functions

Motor neurons carrying information to smooth or cardiac muscle and to all other tissues and organs except skeletal muscle belong to the **autonomic division** (*autonomic* derives from the Greek words for "self" and "law"). The autonomic division of the peripheral nervous system carries signals from the CNS to the periphery that control "automatic" functions of the body's internal organs. Many of these activities occur without our ever being aware of them.

Unlike the somatic division in which one neuron extends from the CNS to the target cell, the autonomic division requires two neurons to transmit information from the CNS to the target cell. The cell bodies of the first neurons (called *preganglionic neurons*) lie within the central nervous system. The axons of many of these neurons go to structures called *ganglia* (singular: *ganglion*) that lie outside the CNS. Ganglia are clusters of neuron cell bodies of the

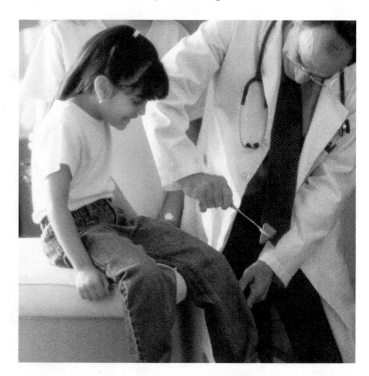

Figure 11.11 The patellar (knee-jerk) reflex. The physician tests the integrity of the patellar reflex to verify that certain sensory and motor nerves, the spinal cord, areas of the brain, and skeletal muscle are all functioning normally.

second neurons (called *postganglionic neurons*). Axons of the postganglionic neurons extend to the far reaches of the body to communicate with internal glands and organs.

The sympathetic and parasympathetic divisions oppose each other

There are two types of motor neurons in the autonomic division: sympathetic and parasympathetic. Both function automatically, usually without our conscious awareness, to regulate body functions. They innervate smooth muscle, cardiac muscle, glands, the epithelial cells of the kidneys, and virtually every internal organ except skeletal muscle, bone, and the nervous system itself.

In most organs, the actions of the sympathetic and parasympathetic divisions have very opposite effects, as shown in Figure 11.12. Which division predominates at any one time determines what happens in your body. And with two opposing systems active at all times, control can be very precise. It is as if you were driving a car with one foot on the gas pedal and one on the brake—you could speed up by hitting the gas pedal, releasing the brake pedal a little, or both.

The sympathetic division arouses the body Preganglionic motor neurons of the **sympathetic division** originate in the thoracic and lumbar regions of the spinal cord.

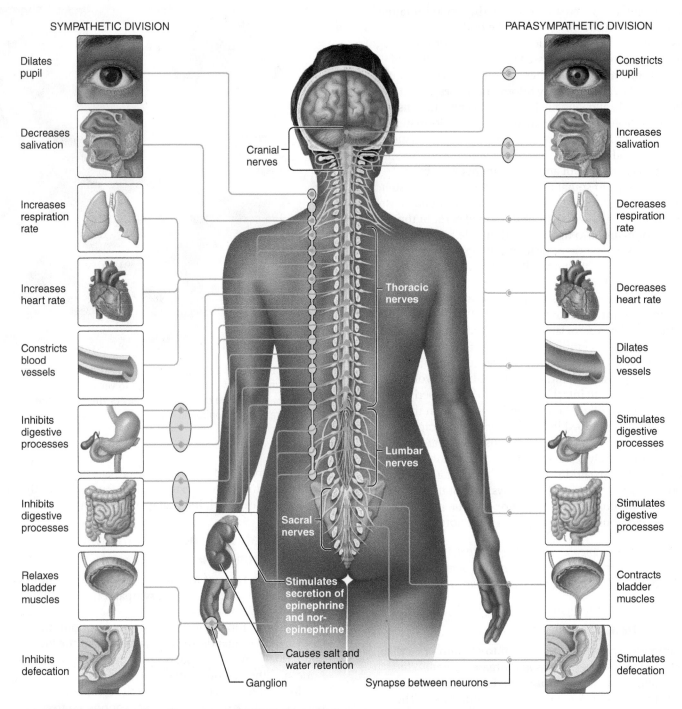

SYMPATHETIC DIVISION

PARASYMPATHETIC DIVISION

Dilates pupil

Decreases salivation

Increases respiration rate

Increases heart rate

Constricts blood vessels

Inhibits digestive processes

Inhibits digestive processes

Relaxes bladder muscles

Inhibits defecation

Cranial nerves

Thoracic nerves

Lumbar nerves

Sacral nerves

Stimulates secretion of epinephrine and nor-epinephrine

Causes salt and water retention

Ganglion

Synapse between neurons

Constricts pupil

Increases salivation

Decreases respiration rate

Decreases heart rate

Dilates blood vessels

Stimulates digestive processes

Stimulates digestive processes

Contracts bladder muscles

Stimulates defecation

Figure 11.12 The sympathetic and parasympathetic divisions of the autonomic nervous system.
The parasympathetic division predominates in the body's relaxed state. The sympathetic division is associated with fight-or-flight responses. The nerves of the parasympathetic division arise from cranial and sacral segments, whereas the nerves of the sympathetic division arise in the thoracic and lumbar segments of the spinal cord. Ganglia (groups of nerve cell bodies) are shown in yellow.

Many of their axons extend to a chain of sympathetic ganglia that lie alongside the spinal cord, where they form synapses with the postganglionic cells. Because these ganglia are connected to each other, the sympathetic division tends to produce a unified response in all organs at once. Axons of the postganglionic neurons branch out to innervate all the organs. The neurotransmitter released by

sympathetic postganglionic neurons in the target organs is *norepinephrine*.

The sympathetic division transmits signals that prepare the body for emergencies and situations requiring high levels of mental alertness or physical activity, such as fighting or running away from danger ("fight or flight"), and even play and sexual activity. It increases heart rate and respiration, raises blood pressure, and dilates the pupils—effects that help you detect and respond quickly to changes in your environment. The sympathetic division also reduces blood flow to organs that do not help you cope with an immediate crisis, such as the intestines and kidneys, and inhibits less important body functions such as digestion and production of saliva (this is why your mouth feels dry when you are anxious).

The effects of the sympathetic division are sometimes called the *fight-or-flight response*, reflecting its association with emergency situations.

The parasympathetic division predominates during relaxation
Preganglionic neurons of the **parasympathetic division** originate either in the brain, becoming part of the outflow of certain cranial nerves, or from the sacral region of the spinal cord. The ganglia where the preganglionic neurons synapse with the postganglionic neurons is generally some distance from the CNS and may even be in the target organ itself. The neurotransmitter released by parasympathetic postganglionic neurons at their target organs is acetylcholine, the same neurotransmitter used at the neuromuscular junction.

In contrast to the sympathetic division, the parasympathetic division predominates in situations in which you are relaxed. It transmits signals that lower heart rate and respiration, increase digestion, and permit defecation and urination, among other actions. The parasympathetic division exerts calming, restorative effects ("rest and repose") that counteract the fight-or-flight stimulation of the sympathetic division. Parasympathetic nerves are also responsible for the vasodilation that causes erection in males and swelling of the labia and erection of the clitoris in females.

✔**Quick Check** *Suppose a person took a drug that blocked the release of norepinephrine from all peripheral nerves. Which division of the peripheral nervous system would be affected, and what would be some of the likely symptoms?* ▪

The sympathetic and parasympathetic divisions work antagonistically to maintain homeostasis As we have seen, the actions of the sympathetic and parasympathetic divisions oppose each other. They work antagonistically to accomplish the automatic, subconscious maintenance of homeostasis.

Both systems are intimately involved in feedback loops that control homeostasis throughout the body.

An example is the control of blood pressure, described in the chapter on the heart and blood vessels (Chapter 8). Certain sensory nerves are activated by stretch receptors (called *baroreceptors*) located in various places in the vascular system. When blood pressure rises, the baroreceptors are activated, and the sensory nerves send more frequent action potentials to the brain. The brain integrates this information with the other information it is receiving. Then it decreases the number of action potentials traveling in sympathetic nerves and increases the number of action potentials traveling in parasympathetic nerves serving the heart and blood vessels. As a result, heart rate slows, blood vessels dilate, and blood pressure falls until it is back to normal.

The sympathetic and parasympathetic divisions can also cause a widespread response, such as arousing the entire body. They can even carry out many localized homeostatic control mechanisms simultaneously and independently. Table 11.2 summarizes the functions of the somatic and autonomic divisions of the PNS.

↩ **Recap** Twelve pairs of cranial nerves transmit action potentials between the brain and the head, neck, and thoracic and abdominal cavities. Thirty-one pairs of spinal nerves transmit action potentials to and from the spinal cord to all regions of the body. Sensory neurons provide information (input) to the CNS. The somatic output division of the PNS controls voluntary (conscious) and involuntary (reflex) skeletal muscle movement. The autonomic division of the PNS includes sympathetic and parasympathetic components that regulate automatic body functions to maintain homeostasis. ▪

11.7 The brain and spinal cord constitute the CNS

A neuron does not think or love, yet humans do. Scientists are still trying to unravel the biology of emotion and thought, but we do know that they originate in the central nervous system, specifically in the brain.

The central nervous system, consisting of the brain and spinal cord, is "central" both in location and action. It is

Table 11.2 The somatic and autonomic divisions of the PNS

Somatic division		Autonomic division	
		Sympathetic	*Parasympathetic*
Functions	Serves skeletal muscles	Fight or flight; arouses body to deal with situations involving physical activity, mental alertness	Relaxes body; promotes digestion and other basic functions
Neurotransmitter	Acetylcholine	Norepinephrine	Acetylcholine
Number of neurons required to reach the target cell	One	Two (preganglionic and postganglionic)	Two (preganglionic and postganglionic)

where integration, or processing, of information occurs. It is where information is received and where complex outputs are initiated. It's where billions of action potentials traveling in millions of neurons all come together as a conscious thought. That is not a very satisfactory explanation for "thinking," but it may be the best we can do.

Bone, meninges, and the blood-brain barrier protect the CNS

The central nervous system is vital to proper functioning of the entire body, so it is no surprise that it is well protected against physical injury and disease.

First, the CNS is protected by bone. The brain is encased in the skull, and the spinal cord is enclosed in a hollow channel within the vertebrae. This shell of bone around the central nervous system helps shield it from physical trauma.

Second, the CNS is enclosed by three membranes of connective tissue, called **meninges**, named (from outermost to innermost layers) the *dura mater*, the *arachnoid*, and the *pia mater*. These three meninges protect the neurons of the CNS and the blood vessels that service them.

Third, the CNS is bathed in its own special liquid, called **cerebrospinal fluid**, which fills the space between the arachnoid and the pia mater. In addition to serving as a liquid shock absorber around the brain and spinal cord, cerebrospinal fluid tends to isolate the central nervous system from infections. Inflammation of the meninges due to a bacterial or viral infection is called *meningitis*. Meningitis can be serious because it may spread to the nervous tissue of the CNS.

Cerebrospinal fluid is somewhat similar to the interstitial fluid that bathes all cells, but it does not exchange substances as freely with blood. It is secreted from specialized capillaries into four hollow cavities (called *ventricles*) in the brain. From the ventricles, it flows through a system of fluid-filled cavities and canals, bathing and surrounding the neurons in the brain and spinal cord (Figure 11.13).

a) **Anterior view.**   b) **Sagittal view.**

Figure 11.13 The ventricles of the brain and circulation of cerebrospinal fluid. Cerebrospinal fluid is secreted into the four brain ventricles (left, right, third, and fourth). From there it flows through a series of cavities, bathing the brain and spinal cord.

Most capillaries in the body are fairly leaky because there are narrow slits between adjacent capillary cells. However, the cells of the capillaries that produce cerebrospinal fluid are fused tightly together. Consequently, substances must pass through rather than between the capillary cells in order to get from blood to cerebrospinal fluid. Lipid-soluble substances such as oxygen and carbon dioxide can diffuse easily through the lipid bilayer of the cell membrane. Certain important molecules such as glucose are actively transported. However, most charged molecules and large objects, such as proteins, viruses, and bacteria, generally are prevented from entering the cerebrospinal fluid.

This functional barrier between blood and brain is called the **blood-brain barrier**. Thanks to this isolation, bacterial and viral infections of the brain and spinal cord are rare, but when these illnesses occur they are generally serious and difficult to treat. Many of our best antibiotics are not lipid soluble, which means they cannot cross the blood-brain barrier and so are ineffective against CNS infections. Lipid-soluble substances that cross the blood-brain barrier rather easily include alcohol, caffeine, nicotine, cocaine, and general anesthetics.

✔️**Quick Check** *What are the major differences in fluid composition between cerebrospinal fluid and interstitial fluid elsewhere in the body? Also, do you think antibiotics would be effective in fighting an infection in the central nervous system? Why or why not?* ▪

The spinal cord relays information

The **spinal cord** serves as the superhighway for action potentials traveling between the brain and the rest of the body. As we have seen, the spinal cord can also process and act on certain information on its own via spinal reflexes, without necessarily involving the brain. However, its power to act independently is limited, and such actions never reach the level of conscious awareness.

Approximately the diameter of your thumb, the spinal cord extends from the base of the skull to the area of about the second lumbar vertebra, or about 17 inches (**Figure 11.14**). It is protected by the vertebral column. The outer portions of the spinal cord consist primarily of bundles of axons, which in the CNS are called *nerve tracts* rather than nerves. Because these axons are generally myelinated, giving them a whitish appearance, the areas of the cord occupied by

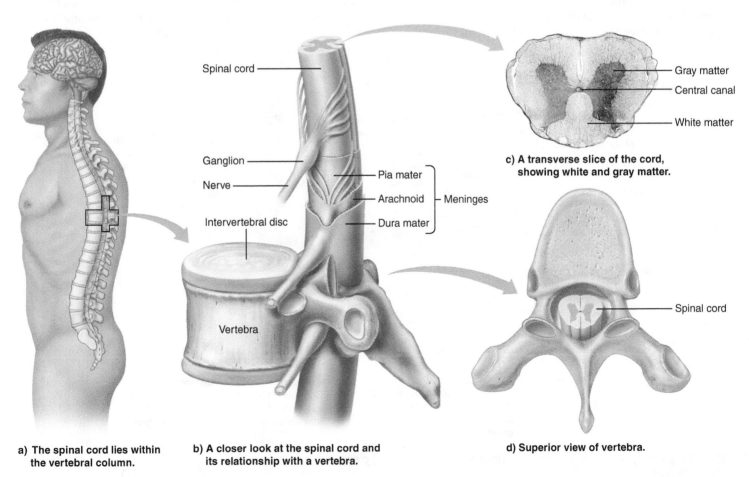

a) **The spinal cord lies within the vertebral column.**

b) **A closer look at the spinal cord and its relationship with a vertebra.**

c) **A transverse slice of the cord, showing white and gray matter.**

d) **Superior view of vertebra.**

Figure 11.14 **The human spinal cord.**

these ascending (sensory) and descending (motor) nerve tracts are called *white matter*. Neurons of the PNS enter and leave the spinal cord at regular intervals via the dorsal (sensory) and ventral (motor) horns that fuse to form spinal nerves.

Near the center of the spinal cord is a region occupied primarily by the cell bodies, dendrites, and axons of neurons of the CNS, and also neuroglial cells. These structures are not myelinated, so the area they occupy is referred to as *gray matter*. Within the gray matter, sensory and motor neurons synapse with neurons of the CNS that transmit signals up the spinal cord to the brain.

Recap The CNS consists of the brain and spinal cord. It is well protected by bone, the meninges, and cerebrospinal fluid. The capillaries that produce cerebrospinal fluid have special properties that result in a functional blood-brain barrier. The spinal cord transmits information between the brain and the rest of the body. It contains white matter (myelinated axons) and gray matter (unmyelinated neural structures). ▪

11.8 The brain processes and acts on information

The **brain** is the command center of the body. The brain receives information in the form of action potentials from various nerves and the spinal cord, integrates it, and generates the appropriate response.

Within the brain, certain areas specialize in integrating different types of information or performing certain motor tasks. Action potentials derived from various receptors, such as light and sound, arrive at the brain in different sensory neurons that specialize in processing those signals. For example, one area of the brain responds to visual stimuli and another area responds to stimuli that help us maintain our balance.

Three major anatomical and functional divisions of the brain have been identified:

- The *hindbrain* coordinates basic, automatic, and vital tasks.
- The *midbrain* helps coordinate muscle groups and responses to sights and sounds.
- The *forebrain* receives and integrates sensory input from the external environment and determines most of our more complex behavior.

Figure 11.15 illustrates these major divisions and their components.

The hindbrain: Movement and automatic functions

The **hindbrain** is connected to the spinal cord. From an evolutionary standpoint the hindbrain is the oldest, most primitive brain division, and the one most similar among animals. Important components of the hindbrain include the medulla oblongata, the cerebellum, and the pons.

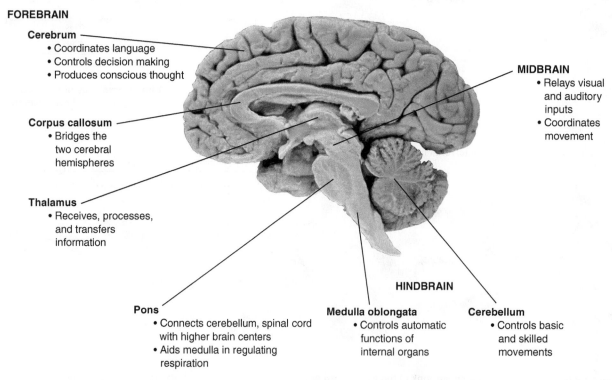

FOREBRAIN

Cerebrum
- Coordinates language
- Controls decision making
- Produces conscious thought

Corpus callosum
- Bridges the two cerebral hemispheres

Thalamus
- Receives, processes, and transfers information

MIDBRAIN
- Relays visual and auditory inputs
- Coordinates movement

HINDBRAIN

Pons
- Connects cerebellum, spinal cord with higher brain centers
- Aids medulla in regulating respiration

Medulla oblongata
- Controls automatic functions of internal organs

Cerebellum
- Controls basic and skilled movements

Figure 11.15 The brain. A sagittal section (front to back on a vertical plane) of a human brain near the midline.

The medulla oblongata controls automatic functions The **medulla oblongata** connects to the spinal cord. It contains areas that control vital automatic functions of internal organs. Within the medulla oblongata, the *cardiovascular center* regulates heart rate and blood pressure, and the *respiratory center* integrates information about blood levels of oxygen and carbon dioxide, and adjusts respiration accordingly. Other areas coordinate reflexes such as coughing, vomiting, sneezing, and swallowing.

All information passing between the higher areas of the brain and the spinal cord must pass through the medulla oblongata. An interesting feature of the way the body is "wired" is that the motor nerves from one side of the forebrain cross over to the other side of the body in the medulla oblongata. As a result, the left side of the brain controls the right side of the body, and vice versa.

The cerebellum coordinates basic movements Located just behind the medulla oblongata, the **cerebellum** coordinates basic body movements that are below the level of conscious control. For example, the cerebellum ensures that antagonistic muscles do not contract at the same time. The cerebellum also stores and replicates (without our conscious thought) whole sequences of skilled movements, such as tying a shoe, shifting a car, or hitting a home run (hitters sometimes say they just "pull the trigger" and the rest happens automatically). To coordinate these skilled activities, the cerebellum receives sensory input from many sources, including joint and muscle receptors, balance and position receptors in the ear, and visual receptors.

Excessive consumption of alcohol acts on the cerebellum and disrupts its normal functions. This is why people who are drunk can't coordinate their movements or walk a straight line.

The pons aids information flow Just above and partially surrounding the medulla oblongata, the pons (from the Latin for "bridge") connects higher brain centers and the spinal cord. The pons contains groups of axons that extend from the cerebellum to the rest of the CNS, and is especially important in coordinating the flow of information between the cerebellum and higher brain centers. In addition, the pons aids the medulla oblongata in regulating respiration.

✅ **Quick Check** *If a person's medulla oblongata were temporarily rendered nonfunctional for just one hour, do you think he could survive? How about if the cerebellum were rendered nonfunctional for an hour? Explain.* ▪

The midbrain: Vision and hearing

Most functions of the **midbrain** relate to vision and hearing. Visual and auditory sensory inputs pass through the midbrain before being relayed to higher brain centers. The midbrain coordinates movements of the head related to vision and hearing, such as turning toward a sudden sound or flash of light, and it controls movement of the eyes and size of the pupils. The midbrain also monitors the unconscious movement of our skeletal muscles so that their actions are smooth and coordinated.

A group of neurons collectively called the *reticular formation* extends through the medulla oblongata, the pons, and the midbrain. The reticular formation works with the cerebellum to coordinate the skeletal muscle activity that maintains posture, balance, and muscle tone. Neurons in the reticular formation are also responsible for maintaining our level of wakefulness, as explained later in this chapter.

The forebrain: Emotions and conscious thought

The **forebrain** determines our most complex behavior, including emotions and conscious thought. Important areas in the forebrain are the hypothalamus and thalamus, limbic system, and cerebrum. It also includes two glands, the pineal and the pituitary, which are described in the chapter on the endocrine system (Chapter 13).

The hypothalamus and thalamus maintain homeostasis and process information The **hypothalamus** is a small region at the base of the forebrain that coordinates some automatic functions of the pituitary gland, such as water and solute balance, temperature control, carbohydrate metabolism, and production of breast milk. It plays an important role in regulating homeostasis because it monitors sensory signals relating to sight, smell, taste, noise, and body temperature. A "hunger center" located in the hypothalamus alerts us when we need to eat, and a "thirst center" signals us to drink something when body fluids become too concentrated.

The larger **thalamus**, located just above the hypothalamus, is primarily a receiving, processing, and transfer center. It integrates and relays some outgoing motor activity as well. The thalamus accepts sensory signals from other parts of the body and brain and channels them to the cerebrum to be interpreted. As sensory information—for example, pain, pressure, and temperature changes—arrives at the thalamus, we are conscious of the sensation but cannot identify where it originates. After the information reaches the cerebrum, we become aware of which part of the body is experiencing the sensation.

The limbic system is involved in emotions and memory The *limbic system* refers to a group of neuronal pathways that connect parts of the thalamus, hypothalamus, and inner portions of the cerebrum. The limbic system is associated with emotions and memory, and we will look at it in more detail later in this chapter when we discuss memory and behavior.

The cerebrum deals with higher functions In humans, the large **cerebrum** is the most highly developed of all brain regions. It deals with many of the functions that we associate with being human: language, decision making, and conscious thought.

The cerebrum (Figure 11.16) consists of left and right cerebral hemispheres joined in the middle by a network of nerve tracts called the *corpus callosum*. The corpus callosum enables the two hemispheres to share sensory and motor information. The outer layer of the cerebrum is called the **cerebral cortex** (Figure 11.16a). The cerebral cortex

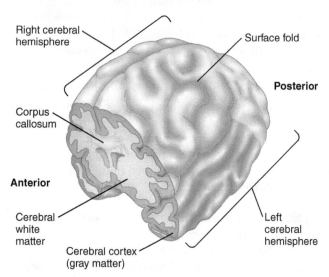

Right cerebral hemisphere

Surface fold

Posterior

Corpus callosum

Anterior

Cerebral white matter

Cerebral cortex (gray matter)

Left cerebral hemisphere

a) The cerebral cortex (gray matter; outer layer, shown in four colors) consists of interneurons that integrate and process information. White matter (inner core) consists of ascending and descending nerve tracts. The two separate hemispheres are joined by the corpus callosum.

Parietal lobe
• Interprets sensory information from skin

Occipital lobe
• Processes visual information

Frontal lobe
• Initiates motor activity
• Responsible for speech
• Conscious thought

Temporal lobe
• Interprets auditory information
• Comprehends language
• Perceptual judgment

b) The functions of the four lobes of the cerebral cortex are location-specific.

Figure 11.16 The cerebrum.

☑ *Explain how a blow to the back of the head can sometimes cause blindness, even if the eyes are undamaged.*

is primarily gray matter, consisting of CNS neurons with unmyelinated axons and their associated neuroglial cells. It has numerous folds on its surface, like a walnut. The inner portion of the cerebrum is mostly white matter containing myelinated nerve axons that connect lower brain areas to the cerebral cortex.

The structure of the cerebrum—an inner section of ascending and descending axons and an outer layer of cells—makes it ideally suited to direct incoming information to the proper region of the brain, integrate the information and process it at the highest level, and then route outgoing motor activity to the appropriate areas of the body.

A closer look at the cerebral cortex Although the cerebral cortex is only about 6 millimeters (about 1/4 inch) thick, it contains roughly 50 to 80 billion neuron cell bodies. It is the center for integrating and interpreting sensory information, but it is much more than that. The cerebral cortex is responsible for memory storage, abstract thought, conscious awareness, and conscious control of skeletal muscle.

All of these functions are location-specific. Functionally, the cortex is divided into four lobes (Figure 11.16b). At the back of the brain, the *occipital lobe* processes visual information. The *temporal lobe* interprets auditory information, comprehends spoken and written language, and is responsible for perceptual judgment. The *parietal lobe* receives and interprets sensory information from the skin, such as temperature, touch, pain, and pressure. Finally, toward the front of the cortex is the *frontal lobe*, perhaps the most highly developed of all brain regions. The frontal lobe initiates motor activity and is also responsible for speech and conscious thought. All four lobes are involved in memory storage.

Notice that the region for speech (frontal lobe) is anatomically separate from the region for understanding spoken language (temporal lobe). The reasons for this separation are not known.

Two areas of the brain that have been studied extensively are the region in the parietal lobe that receives sensory input from the skin (called the *primary somatosensory area*) and the corresponding region of the frontal lobe that initiates motor activity (called the *primary motor area*). Researchers have found very specific regions within each of these areas corresponding to specific parts of the body (Figure 11.17). Body parts that are extremely sensitive, such as the lips and genitals, involve more neurons and consequently larger portions of the primary somatosensory area, whereas less sensitive body parts, such as a thigh, involve fewer neurons and smaller portions. Similarly, body parts that can perform intricate and precise movements, such as the fingers, involve more neurons in the primary motor area than do less dexterous regions, such as an elbow.

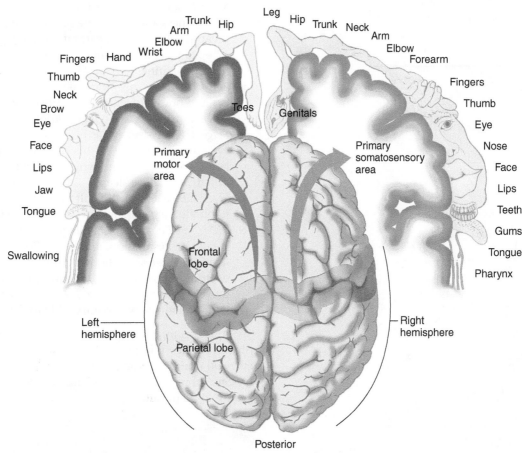

Figure 11.17 Primary somatosensory and motor areas of the cerebral cortex. Note the close similarity of the maps of the two areas. The larger the anatomical representation on the diagram, the more precisely controlled or more sensitive the area. The lips, face, and tongue are particularly well represented.

The location-specific nature of information processing explains why damage to different brain regions can cause such varied, seemingly contradictory, effects. This is often apparent in stroke victims. One stroke patient might be unable to speak yet still be fully capable of understanding speech. Another could have trouble controlling basic skeletal muscle movements but retain the capacity for abstract thought. Physicians use their understanding of these known location-specific functions to diagnose which areas of the brain have been affected.

Recap The brain has three divisions: hindbrain, midbrain, and forebrain. The evolutionarily oldest, more primitive hindbrain controls most automatic activities. The midbrain functions in vision, hearing, and movement. Structures in the forebrain help maintain homeostasis, process information, control emotions and memory, and are responsible for language, decision making, and conscious thought. ▪

11.9 Brain activity continues during sleep

Why do we sleep? This may seem like a simple question, but scientists are still looking for the answer. The obvious hypothesis is that we sleep to get rest. However, brain activity continues even during deep sleep.

Levels of sleep and wakefulness are controlled by the *reticular activating system* (RAS), a group of neurons in the reticular formation. Some neurons of the RAS transmit a steady stream of action potentials to the cerebrum, keeping us awake and alert. A "sleep center" in the RAS releases the neurotransmitter serotonin, which induces sleep by inhibiting the neurons that arouse the brain. Norepinephrine, secreted from another area in the brain, inhibits the effects of serotonin and makes us feel more alert.

We can study what happens to the brain during sleep with *electroencephalograms* (EEGs), recordings of the brain's electrical activity as measured at the body's surface. As Figure 11.18 shows, EEG readings for different states of sleep show characteristic patterns.

a) **EEG recordings in an awake person and during Stages 1–4 and REM sleep.** Note the similarity between REM sleep and wakefulness.

b) **Patterns of sleep during a typical night.**

Figure 11.18 Brain activity patterns during wakefulness and sleep.

- *Stage 1*. Stage 1 is a transitional phase between wakefulness and sleep. The pupils gradually constrict, breathing slows, and heart rate slows. On an EEG, Stage 1 appears as random small waves, only slightly different from wakefulness.
- *Stage 2*. During this phase, skeletal muscles relax, and eye and body movements usually cease. On an EEG, Stage 2 produces sharp waves known as "sleep spindles."
- *Stage 3*. Sleep deepens as heart rate and respiration slow even more. On an EEG, this stage and Stage 4 produce large, slow oscillations, which is why they are sometimes called "slow wave sleep."
- *Stage 4*. Sleepers are difficult to awaken; heart rate and respiration are at their slowest, and body temperature falls.
- *REM (rapid eye movement) sleep*. This is when we dream. Heart rate, respiration, and blood flow to the brain increase. Most of the body's muscles go limp, preventing us from responding to our dreams. Paradoxically, the eyes move rapidly under closed eyelids. EEG patterns show a level of brain activity comparable to that of wakefulness.

A typical night's sleep involves cycling through these phases, as shown in Figure 11.18b. REM sleep returns about every 90 minutes throughout the night and lasts a little longer each time. Toward morning a single REM period may last up to 20 minutes.

Why do the eyes move rapidly during REM sleep? For an interesting view on this subject, visit MJ's blog in the Study Area in MasteringBiology and look under "Rapid Eye Movement (REM) Sleep."

Although it is not clear exactly why we sleep, it is clear that we need a certain amount of sleep. Persons deprived of REM sleep become moody, irritable, and depressed and may even suffer hallucinations if deprived long enough.

↺ **Recap** **The brain remains active even during sleep. Stages of sleep have been correlated with brain wave patterns. The reticular activating system controls levels of sleep and wakefulness.** ▪

11.10 The limbic system is the site of emotions and basic behaviors

Emotions and basic patterns of behavior originate in the **limbic system** (Figure 11.19). Limbic means "border." The name was originally used to describe those structures that bordered the basal regions of the cerebrum. As we learned about the function of these structures, however, The name came to describe all of the neuronal structures that, together, control emotional behavior and motivational drives.

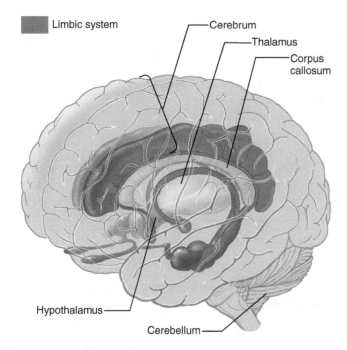

Limbic system
Cerebrum
Thalamus
Corpus callosum
Hypothalamus
Cerebellum

Figure 11.19 The limbic system. The limbic system is a collection of neuronal areas near the base of the cerebrum that are involved in emotions, basic behaviors, and short-term memory.

When different areas of the limbic system are stimulated, we experience strong emotions such as fear, anger, sorrow, or love. These reactions, both pleasant and unpleasant, influence our behavior.

You may have noticed that odors have the power to evoke emotions and vivid recollections. This is because pathways for the sense of smell also pass through the limbic system, creating a strong association between olfactory information and memory.

Recall that the hypothalamus monitors and regulates homeostasis of many basic body functions. The hypothalamus also serves as a gateway to and from the limbic system and thus exerts some control over basic self-gratifying behaviors, such as satisfying hunger, thirst, and sexual desire. The thalamus receives and organizes information regarding these behaviors and transmits it to the cerebrum. The cerebrum integrates this information with the other information it is receiving, and then adjusts behavior accordingly.

Thus, the intensity with which we feel emotions and the extent to which we act on them depends on modification by the cerebrum. To appreciate the importance of cerebral modification, just imagine what would happen if our most basic urges were no longer influenced by social rules or codes of conduct!

Recap A collection of structures bordering the cerebrum called the *limbic system* controls our emotions and behavior. The activities of the limbic system are monitored by the hypothalamus and modified by the cerebrum. ▪

11.11 Memory involves storing and retrieving information

Memory involves storing information and retrieving it later, as needed. Memory has two stages: short-term ("working") memory involves retrieval of information that was stored within the past few hours, and long-term memory is the ability to retrieve information days or years later.

There is a clear difference between how the brain manages the two stages of memory. Short-term memory occurs in the limbic system. When you receive new sensory information (such as reading an unfamiliar telephone number), the stimulus triggers a quick burst of action potentials in the limbic system. You can remember the number for a few seconds or minutes, because neurons that have just fired are easier to fire again in the short term. The pathway becomes entrained, if only for a brief time. If the number is not important, you quickly forget it because the enhancement of the limbic pathway is not long lasting. That particular piece of information does not move into long-term memory.

However, if the number is important to you, as evidenced by the fact that you say it out loud several times, write it down and then read it to yourself, or use it repeatedly over several weeks, the information may be transmitted to your cerebral cortex for storage in long-term memory centers. During this process, neurons undergo a permanent chemical or physical change. Evidence from experimental animals suggests that long-term memory storage creates additional synapses between connecting neurons, enabling those circuits to be activated more easily in the future.

Recap Short-term memory involves quick bursts of action potentials in the limbic system. Long-term memory resides in the cerebral cortex and involves permanent changes in neurons and synapses. ▪

11.12 Psychoactive drugs affect higher brain functions

A drug is any substance introduced into the body for the purpose of causing a physiological change. Psychoactive drugs are those that affect states of consciousness, emotions, or behavior—in other words, the higher brain functions. Some psychoactive drugs are legal, such as alcohol and nicotine. Others are not legal but have found their way into the fabric of our society.

Most drugs, including psychoactive substances, were originally discovered or designed to treat disease. The nonmedical use of drugs is sometimes euphemistically called "recreational" use, but the term *illicit* is certainly a more accurate reflection of the truth.

All psychoactive drugs are able to cross the blood-brain barrier (not all drugs can do so). They work by influencing the concentrations or actions of brain neurotransmitters. Recall that normally the effects of neurotransmitters are short-lived because the neurotransmitter remains in the synaptic cleft for only a brief time. Psychoactive drugs either bind to neurotransmitters or affect their release, action, or reuptake (reabsorption) in some way. This changes normal patterns of electrical activity in the brain.

Depending on which neurotransmitter they influence and where they act, psychoactive drugs can exert a variety of effects. For example, dopamine is one of the most important neurotransmitters in areas of the brain associated with pleasure. Cocaine blocks the reuptake of dopamine back into the presynaptic bulb, leading to too much dopamine in the synaptic cleft and therefore excessive stimulation of postsynaptic neurons. Cocaine initially allows the user to experience pleasurable effects longer than normal.

Psychoactive drugs can lead to *psychological dependence*, meaning that users begin to crave the feelings associated with a drug and alter their behavior to obtain it. Eventually tolerance develops—they need to use more of it, or use it more frequently, to achieve the same effect. Tolerance occurs in part because the liver produces enzymes that detoxify many drugs, and repeated drug use increases circulating levels of these detoxifying enzymes. Soon the original dose is no longer enough to create the desired effect, or sometimes any effect at all. A second reason for tolerance, in the case of cocaine, is that if too much dopamine remains in the synaptic cleft for prolonged periods, the body starts to produce less of it. So with repeated cocaine use, a person needs more and more drug to maintain even a normal amount of dopamine neurotransmitter in the synaptic cleft. Eventually, cocaine addicts become incapable of experiencing pleasure without the drug and cannot even maintain a normal emotional state. At this point, severe anxiety and depression set in.

Tolerance leads to *addiction*, the need to continue obtaining and using a substance despite one's better judgment and good intentions. Essentially, choice is lost. Addiction has serious negative consequences for both emotional and physical health. Eventually, most addicts find it impossible to concentrate and hold a steady job. At the same time, they must spend large amounts of money to support their habit. Personal relationships suffer, and many addicts lose their families, their employment, and their physical health. In addition, they face the probability of *withdrawal*, the symptoms that occur if the drug is removed suddenly.

Cocaine and nicotine are both highly addictive. Alcohol is addictive in some people but not in others, for reasons we do not yet fully understand. One of the most addictive street drugs is crystal methamphetamine (also known as "crank," "ice," "tina," or "glass").

The federal government keeps track of illicit drug use through an annual survey. **Figure 11.20** shows reported illicit drug use during the month prior to the survey by persons aged 12 and older. Illicit drug use peaks in 18- to 20-year-olds and then declines with age. The most commonly used illicit drugs in 18- to 25-year-olds are marijuana and the

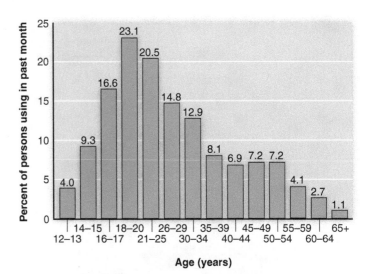

Figure 11.20 Past-month illicit drug use among persons aged 12 and older, 2010.
Source: Substance Abuse and Mental Health Services Administration, *Results from the 2010 National Survey on Drug Use and Health: Summary of National Findings.*

non-medical use of psychotherapeutic drugs (narcotic and opioid pain relievers, sedatives, tranquilizers, stimulants, antidepressants and antianxiety drugs). Less commonly used are cocaine, and hallucinogens (primarily ecstasy, or MDMA).

Drug use in young adults aged 18 to 25 is increasing each year by about 1%, due primarily to an increase in marijuana use. Over half of all 18- to 25-year-olds report having used marijuana at least once in their lives. However, the use of cocaine or methamphetamine by this age group is declining. Only about 15% report ever having used cocaine, and fewer than 4% have used methamphetamine in the past year.

🔄 Recap **Psychoactive drugs work by altering either the concentration or action of brain neurotransmitters. Some lead to psychological dependence, tolerance, and addiction.** ●

11.13 Disorders of the nervous system

Because the nervous system is so complex and controls so many body functions, disorders of the nervous system can be particularly debilitating. We have already discussed stroke in the context of cardiovascular disease. Here we discuss several classes of disorders that affect the nervous system, including trauma, infections, disorders of neural or synaptic transmission, and brain tumors.

Trauma

Trauma (physical injury) to either the brain or spinal cord can be particularly dangerous because the brain controls so many body functions and the spinal cord is the information pathway to virtually all the organs.

Concussion disrupts electrical activity A violent blow to the head or neck can cause *concussion,* a brief period of unconsciousness in which electrical activity of brain neurons is briefly disrupted. After the person "comes to," he or she may experience blurred vision, confusion, and nausea and vomiting. Although most concussions are not associated with permanent injury, one of the biggest dangers is a *subdural hematoma,* or hemorrhage (bleeding) into the space between the meninges.

Because the brain is encased in a rigid skull, any bleeding increases pressure within the skull. Eventually the trapped blood presses against healthy brain tissue and disrupts function. Symptoms can include drowsiness, headache, and growing weakness of one side of the body. Depending on how rapidly bleeding occurs, symptoms may take weeks or even months to appear. Sometimes surgeons drill through the skull to drain the hematoma, relieve the pressure, and repair damaged blood vessels.

Spinal cord injuries impair sensation and function Violent trauma to vertebrae may press against the spinal cord, tear it, or even sever it completely. Damage to the spinal cord usually impairs sensation and body function below the injured area, so the extent of injury depends on the site of damage. Injuries below the neck can cause paraplegia (weakness or paralysis of the legs and sometimes part of the trunk). Injuries to the neck may lead to quadriplegia (weakness or paralysis of the legs, arms, and trunk). The higher the spinal cord injury, the more likely it is to be fatal. Spinal cord injuries may also cause problems with bladder or bowel control because the autonomic division no longer functions properly.

Researchers are investigating many exciting treatments for spinal cord injuries. For more information, see the Health & Wellness feature, *Repairing Spinal Cord Injuries.*

Infections

The brain and spinal cord are spared most of the infections that affect the rest of the body because of the blood-brain barrier. Nevertheless, certain viruses and bacteria do occasionally infect the brain or spinal cord.

Encephalitis: Inflammation of the brain Encephalitis refers to inflammation of the brain, often caused by a viral infection. Frequent sources of encephalitis include the herpes simplex virus (which causes cold sores) and a virus transmitted through mosquito bites. HIV (human immunodeficiency virus) infection is responsible for a growing number of cases.

Symptoms of encephalitis can vary, but often include headache, fever, and fatigue, progressing to hallucinations, confusion, and disturbances in speech, memory, and behavior. Some patients also experience epileptic seizures. Treatment varies depending on the cause, but antiviral drugs may help.

Meningitis: Inflammation of the meninges Meningitis involves inflammation of the meninges, usually due to viral or bacterial infection. Symptoms include headache, fever, nausea and vomiting, sensitivity to light, and a stiff neck. Mild cases may resemble the flu. Viral meningitis tends to be relatively mild and usually improves within a few weeks. Bacterial meningitis can be life-threatening and requires antibiotics.

Rabies: Infectious viral disease Rabies is an infectious viral brain disease of mammals, especially dogs, wolves, raccoons, bats, skunks, foxes, and cats. It is transmitted to humans by direct contact, usually through a bite or a lick over broken skin. The virus makes its way through the sensory neurons in the region of the bite to the spinal cord and then to the brain, where it multiplies and kills cells.

Signs of rabies include swollen lymph glands, painful swallowing, vomiting, choking, spasms of throat and chest muscles, fever, and mental derangement. The symptoms generally appear one to six months after initial infection, followed by coma and death within 2 to 20 days.

If an animal has bitten you, wash the wound thoroughly and consult a physician. If possible, have the animal tested for rabies. If there is any possibility it could be rabid, your doctor will advise you to be immunized, because untreated rabies may be fatal. The rabies vaccine is most effective if administered within a few days after the bite, but it may still work when given weeks or months later.

Brain tumors: Abnormal growths

A brain tumor is an abnormal growth in or on the brain. Brain tumors are not necessarily cancerous, but even noncancerous growths can cause problems if they press against neighboring tissue and increase pressure within the skull. Over time, the rising pressure disrupts normal brain function. Depending on the location and size of the tumor, symptoms include headache, vomiting, visual impairment, and confusion. Some people also experience muscle weakness, difficulty speaking, or epileptic seizures.

Some brain tumors originate from the brain itself, but most are seeded by cancer that spreads from other parts of the body. For more on cancer, see the chapter devoted to that subject (Chapter 18).

BlogInFocus

Why is a cancer drug being used to treat patients with spinal cord injuries? To find out, visit MJ's blog in the Study Area in MasteringBiology and look under "Repairing Spinal Cord Injuries."

Repairing Spinal Cord Injuries

On September 7, 2007, Buffalo Bills football player Kevin Everett suffered a fracture and dislocation of the cervical spine while making a tackle during a game against the Denver Broncos. As he was taken off the field, Kevin moved only his eyes. Two days after the accident Kevin still could barely feel or move his arms and legs. Doctors gave him a "statistically very small" chance of ever walking again.

Injuries like Kevin Everett's generally crush the spinal cord axons rather than actually severing the cord. Although the nerves are initially intact, over the next few weeks many of the damaged neurons die or lose the ability to function.

Until recently it was believed that damaged neurons could not regenerate. However, researchers are investigating a number of exciting possibilities for helping spinal cord patients recover lost function. Current areas of research or treatment include

- *Limiting cell injury and death.* At least three mechanisms of cell injury and death are involved. Researchers are exploring ways to block these injury and death pathways to preserve as many neurons and oligodendrocytes as possible.
- *Controlling inflammation.* Ironically, the inflammatory process, which normally promotes healing, makes matters worse by causing secondary damage to cells that were not injured initially. Anti-inflammatory drugs such as methylprednisolone can help, especially if given within eight hours of the injury.
- *Blocking certain molecules that prevent regeneration.* The CNS of adult mammals contains inhibitory molecules that block neurons from continually

growing and dividing inappropriately in healthy adults. After an injury, however, they become an obstacle to tissue repair. Scientists are working on ways to neutralize these molecules.
- *Stimulating axons to grow.* Some researchers are working with growth factors and guidance molecules to stimulate damaged axons to "sprout" new extensions across the injured area.
- *Replacing lost cells with new tissue.* Stem cells, which have the potential to differentiate into many types of cells, might be stimulated to develop into neurons and neuroglial cells for transplant into a damaged area of the spinal cord.
- *Bridging the injury site or removing barriers to regrowth.* Some researchers are using artificial materials to support and guide neurons as they regenerate across an injured area. Other groups are experimenting with grafts of neural

tissue, or even proteins that can assemble into nanofibers smaller than a human hair. Still others are experimenting with enzymes that dissolve scar tissue and allow neurons to grow through the affected area.
- *Stimulating muscles electronically.* Computer-controlled functional electrical stimulation (FES) systems help patients move by activating their muscles with electrodes.

Some of this research is beginning to pay off. Kevin Everett attended the Super Bowl on January 31, 2008, and was able to walk under his own power during an appearance on the *Oprah* show that same day. Today, 90% of people with spinal cord injuries survive and live a near-normal life span. Unfortunately, fewer than half of spinal cord injury victims are able to return to the workforce. Perhaps with further advances that number will rise. ■

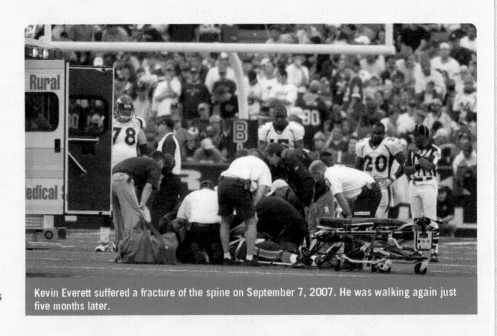

Kevin Everett suffered a fracture of the spine on September 7, 2007. He was walking again just five months later.

Some brain tumors can be surgically removed. If tumors are inaccessible or too large to be removed, radiation and chemotherapy treatments may shrink them or limit their growth.

Disorders of neural and synaptic transmission

The nervous system depends on action potentials traveling in neurons and the chemical transfer of signals from one neuron to another across a synapse. It should come as no surprise, then, that problems involving neural or synaptic transmission can cause disease. The symptoms of these disorders depend on which nerves and/or neurotransmitters are affected.

Epilepsy: Recurring episodes of abnormal electrical activity Epilepsy is a disorder characterized by transient, recurring bouts of abnormal brain cell activity. Fatigue, stress, or patterns of flashing lights may trigger epileptic attacks, known as seizures. Seizures vary widely, because virtually any activity controlled by the brain may be affected. Some epileptic seizures are almost unnoticeable: perhaps a short episode of staring or nonpurposeful movements, a shaking limb, or repeated hand rubbing. Some seizures result in changes in the way things smell, taste, or sound to the patient or cause temporary speech disturbances. These seizures end quickly without causing any loss of consciousness. Other seizures affect larger areas of the brain and thus have more noticeable symptoms, such as sudden collapse, convulsions (stiffening and shaking of the extremities or the entire body), or temporary loss of consciousness, from which the person recovers fully after a short time. Epilepsy usually appears during childhood or adolescence. Some cases result from infections (such as meningitis or encephalitis), head injuries, brain tumors, or stroke, but often the cause is not known.

Alzheimer's disease: A buildup of abnormal proteins Alzheimer's disease is the most common cause of *dementia*, the general term for loss of memory and other intellectual abilities serious enough to interfere with daily living. One in every ten people over age 65 has Alzheimer's disease. There appears to be a genetic component, as a family history of the disease increases the risk. Recent studies suggest that an abnormal gene on chromosome 21 may be involved.

Alzheimer's disease begins with memory lapses and progresses to severe memory loss, particularly of recent events. Long-term memory is affected more slowly. Patients suffering from Alzheimer's disease become progressively more disoriented and confused until they may not even recognize their spouses or relatives. For relatives, the hardest part of caring for an Alzheimer patient is their change in personality. Rapid mood changes—from anger and rage to tears—may occur for no reason and at any time. The disease progresses until eventually the patient can no longer function independently.

The study of affected brains at autopsy reveal structural changes in the brain, including tangles of abnormal neurons and the development of unusually large deposits of an abnormal protein called *beta amyloid* around neurons. As the disease progresses, these abnormal proteins choke off neurons until the number of neurons and their supply of neurotransmitter (acetylcholine) becomes insufficient for normal neurotransmission. Metabolic activity in the frontal and temporal lobes declines (**Figure 11.21**).

a) **A PET scan of a healthy brain.**

b) **A PET scan of a patient with Alzheimer's disease, showing decreased activity and an irregular pattern.**

Figure 11.21 Changes in brain metabolic activity in Alzheimer's disease. A positron emission tomography (PET) scan reveals differences in metabolic activity of tissue. Reds and yellows represent high metabolic activity, blues and greens represent lower activity.

Unfortunately, currently the diagnosis of Alzheimer's disease is made only when symptoms appear, and by that time it is too late to do anything about it. Drugs that enhance the brain's production of acetylcholine can slow the progression of the disease once it is identified, but as yet there is no cure. Nevertheless, there may be hope on the horizon. Researchers are studying the possibility of identifying biomarkers (changes in the concentration of a particular protein, for example) that would identify the very earliest stages of a buildup of beta-amyloid before the damage is sufficient for symptoms to appear. They also hope to identify drugs that could halt the progressive buildup of beta-amyloid in potential Alzheimer's sufferers while they are still asymptomatic, once it is known who is at risk or is on a path to developing the disease.

Parkinson's disease: Loss of dopamine-releasing neurons

Parkinson's disease is a progressive, degenerative disorder that strikes nearly 50,000 people a year in North America, most over age 55. In contrast to Alzheimer's disease, which affects primarily memory and intellectual abilities, Parkinson's disease affects primarily physical activity. Symptoms include stiff muscles and muscle tremors in the hands and feet. Eventually people with Parkinson's lose mobility; they may also become mentally impaired and depressed.

We now know that Parkinson's disease is caused by degeneration of dopamine-releasing neurons in the area of the midbrain that coordinates muscle movement. The shortage of dopamine impairs the ability to perform smooth, coordinated motions. The symptoms can be improved by taking L-dopa, a drug that the body converts into dopamine, but this does not slow the loss of neurons. As the disease progresses, even L-dopa becomes ineffective.

However, there is an experimental and highly controversial treatment for patients with Parkinson's disease that might replace lost cells: receiving transplants of fetal neurons directly into the brain. Experiments with animals have shown that transplanted fetal neurons will survive and grow in the recipient animal. In humans, the fetal cells would come from aborted fetuses, which is why the technique generates such controversy.

Recap **Disorders of the nervous system are often serious because of the central role of the nervous system in regulating other body systems. Common disorders include physical trauma and infections, as well as acquired or genetic diseases that disrupt neural transmission in some way, such as epilepsy, Parkinson's disease, and Alzheimer's disease.**

Chapter Summary

The nervous system has two principal parts *p. 246*

- The central nervous system receives, processes, and stores information, and the peripheral nervous system provides sensory input and motor output.
- The PNS has somatic and autonomic divisions.
- The autonomic division of the PNS has sympathetic and parasympathetic divisions.

Neurons are the communication cells of the nervous system *p. 247*

- Neurons generally consist of a cell body, several short extensions called dendrites, and a long, thin extension called an axon.

Neurons initiate action potentials *p. 248*

- Incoming signals from other neurons produce short-lived graded potentials in a neuron that alter its resting potential slightly.
- If the sum of all graded potentials exceeds threshold, voltage-sensitive sodium channels open briefly and an action potential is initiated.
- The three components of an action potential are (1) depolarization, in which sodium channels open briefly and then close; (2) repolarization, in which potassium channels open briefly and then close; and (3) reestablishment of the resting potential by the continuous action of the sodium-potassium pump.

Neuroglial cells support and protect neurons *p. 251*

- Schwann cells produce myelin, an insulating material that increases conduction velocities in neurons.
- Multiple sclerosis is a disease in which the myelin sheath of neurons becomes damaged.

Information is transferred from a neuron to its target *p. 253*

- An action potential in a presynaptic neuron causes ion channels for Ca^{2+} to open in the membrane of the axon bulb.
- Ca^{2+} diffuses into the axon bulb and causes a chemical neurotransmitter to be released into the synaptic cleft.
- The neurotransmitter binds to receptors on the postsynaptic cell membrane, causing a graded potential in the postsynaptic cell.
- Information processing depends on differences in stimulus intensity and on converging and diverging neural connections.

The PNS relays information between tissues and the CNS *p. 255*

- The peripheral nervous system consists of 12 pairs of cranial nerves and 31 pairs of spinal nerves. Each nerve may contain a mixture of sensory, somatic motor, and autonomic motor nerve axons.
- The somatic motor division of the peripheral nervous system controls skeletal muscle.
- The autonomic motor division of the peripheral nervous system controls automatic functions and helps to maintain homeostasis.

The brain and spinal cord constitute the CNS *p. 259*

- The brain and spinal cord are protected by bone, by three layers of connective tissue called meninges, and by cerebrospinal fluid.
- The spinal cord consists of ascending (going to the brain) and descending (coming from the brain) nerve tracts, plus neurons and neuroglial cells of the CNS.

The brain processes and acts on information *p. 262*

- The brain receives sensory information, integrates and stores it, and generates the appropriate response.
- The medulla oblongata contains areas that control blood pressure and respiration.
- The cerebellum coordinates basic and certain skilled body movements.
- The hypothalamus coordinates certain automatic functions and participates in the maintenance of homeostasis.
- The cerebrum is involved in language, decision making, and conscious thought. It is also the site of long-term memory storage.

Brain activity continues during sleep *p. 265*

- The brain exhibits characteristic cyclic patterns of activity during sleep.
- The functional importance of sleep is unknown.

The limbic system is the site of emotions and basic behaviors *p. 266*

- The limbic system is the center of emotions such as fear, anger, sorrow, and love and basic behaviors such as seeking food or sexual gratification.

Memory involves storing and retrieving information *p. 267*

- Short-term memory resides in the limbic system. Long-term memory involves permanent changes to neurons in the cerebral cortex.

Psychoactive drugs affect higher brain functions *p. 267*

- Psychoactive drugs act either by altering the concentrations of brain neurotransmitters or by altering the responses of postsynaptic neurons to them.
- Addiction to psychoactive drugs is characterized by the compulsion to use the drug, often at increasing doses, despite good intentions not to use and the likelihood of negative consequences.

Disorders of the nervous system *p. 268*

- Head trauma can be dangerous because any bruising or bleeding within the confined space of the skull presses against the brain.
- Spinal cord injury can interrupt neural signals traveling up and down the spinal cord, resulting in a loss of sensation and paralysis of muscle.
- Rabies is an infectious viral disease that is transmitted by the bite of an infected animal. The virus travels to the spinal cord and brain via the axon of a sensory nerve.
- Alzheimer's disease is characterized by a decline in the amount of the neurotransmitter acetylcholine in the limbic system and frontal lobe. Although the cause of Alzheimer's is unknown, the disease is associated with deposits of an abnormal protein in the brain.

Terms You Should Know

action potential, *249*
autonomic division, *257*
axon, *247*
blood-brain barrier, *261*
central nervous system (CNS), *246*
cerebellum, *263*
cerebral cortex, *264*
cerebrospinal fluid, *260*
cerebrum, *263*
dendrites, *247*
forebrain, *263*
graded potential, *249*
hindbrain, *262*
interneurons, *247*
midbrain, *263*
motor neurons, *247*
myelin sheath, *252*
nerve, *256*
neuroglial cells, *251*
neurons, *247*
neurotransmitter, *253*
parasympathetic division, *259*
peripheral nervous system (PNS), *246*
resting (membrane) potential, *248*
sensory neurons, *247*
somatic division, *256*
synapse, *253*
sympathetic division, *257*
threshold, *249*

Concept Review

Answers can be found in the Study Area in MasteringBiology.

1. Distinguish between the central nervous system and the peripheral nervous system.
2. Explain what is meant by summation of graded potentials and explain how summation may lead to an action potential.
3. Describe, in terms of the opening and closing of ion channels and the subsequent diffusion of ions, how the depolarization and repolarization phases of an action potential take place.
4. Describe the functions of neuroglial cells.
5. Describe the role of neurotransmitters in the function of neurons.
6. List the three major divisions of the brain and identify their general functional roles.
7. Explain what is meant by the statement that the functions of the cerebral cortex are "location-specific."
8. Define *REM sleep* and indicate the physiological changes that might be observed during REM sleep.
9. Describe why a subdural hematoma is so much more dangerous than a hematoma in a muscle (known commonly as a bruise).
10. Explain why an injury to the spinal cord may impair sensations and motor movement below, but not above, the point of injury.

Test Yourself

Answers can be found in Appendix A.

1. Which of the following statements correctly characterizes an action potential?
   a. Action potentials are initiated by depolarization of the membrane to threshold.

b. Action potentials reverse the membrane potential so that the interior is negatively charged and the exterior is positively charged.

c. A stronger action potential will travel faster than a weaker action potential.

d. Action potentials are more likely to result when the membrane is hyperpolarized.

2. Which of the following influence(s) the speed of an action potential?
   a. the presence of a myelin sheath
   b. the extent of depolarization that initiates the action potential
   c. the diameter of the axon
   d. both the presence of a myelin sheath and the diameter of the axon

3. Which of the following cell types makes up the majority of cells in the nervous system?
   a. sensory neurons
   b. motor neurons
   c. neuroglial cells
   d. interneurons

4. What do multiple sclerosis and ALS (amyotropic lateral sclerosis) have in common?
   a. They both are more common in young men than in young women.
   b. They both impair the initiation of action potentials.
   c. They both damage the myelin sheath, slowing action potential transmission.
   d. They both impair nerve function in the peripheral nervous system.

5. All of the following are directly involved in synaptic transmission except
   a. voltage-sensitive ion channels on the postsynaptic membrane
   b. chemical-sensitive ion channels on the postsynaptic membrane
   c. Ca^{2+}
   d. neurotransmitters

6. An _____ neurotransmitter causes _____ of the postsynaptic membrane.
   a. inhibitory…depolarization
   b. excitatory…depolarization
   c. inhibitory…hyperpolarization
   d. both (b) and (c) are correct

7. Information coming into the central nervous system arrives via _____ while information going from the central nervous system to the muscles, glands, and organs travels via _____.
   a. motor neurons…sensory neurons
   b. neuroglial cells…motor neurons
   c. sensory neurons…motor neurons
   d. sensory neurons…interneurons

8. The brain and spinal cord make up the:
   a. sensory nervous system
   b. central nervous system
   c. sympathetic nervous system
   d. parasympathetic nervous system

9. A spinal reflex requires the participation of each of the following except:
   a. cerebral cortex
   b. sensory neuron
   c. interneuron
   d. motor neuron

10. Which of the following would cause an acceleration of heart rate, an increase in blood pressure, and a slowing of digestive processes?
    a. motor division of the somatic nervous system
    b. sensory branch of the central nervous system
    c. parasympathetic division of the autonomic nervous system
    d. sympathetic division of the autonomic nervous system

11. Which part of the brain is responsible for regulating the heart and respiratory rates and blood pressure?
    a. cerebral cortex
    b. medulla oblongata
    c. cerebellum
    d. thalamus

12. The coordination necessary for a musician to play the piano depends on control exerted by the:
    a. thalamus
    b. cerebral cortex
    c. cerebellum
    d. medulla oblongata

13. All of the following are associated with storage of long-term memory except:
    a. limbic system
    b. cerebral cortex
    c. permanent changes in neurons
    d. formation of new synapses

14. Which of the following is characteristic of psychoactive drugs?
    a. They do not readily cross the blood-brain barrier.
    b. They alter levels of neurotransmitters.
    c. They can alter the amplitude of action potentials.
    d. They alter the speed with which action potentials travel.

15. Which of the following statements regarding infections of the nervous system is accurate?
    a. Most cases of encephalitis are caused by bacteria.
    b. Rabies can be treated with antibiotics.
    c. Bacterial meningitis is generally more severe than viral meningitis.
    d. The blood-brain barrier is not effective at preventing microorganisms from entering the central nervous system.

Apply What You Know

Answers can be found in the Study Area in MasteringBiology.

1. Explain in terms of brain anatomy and function how it would be possible for people to remember whole events in the distant past yet not be able to recall what they had for breakfast.

2. What do you suppose would happen to a person's behavior and emotional expression if the neural connections between the limbic system and the cerebral cortex were severed?

3. A friend is washing dishes one evening and gets a deep cut from a sharp knife hidden in the soap suds. Several weeks after the visit to the ER, the stitches are removed. Your friend mentions that one part of his finger is numb; he cannot feel anything when he touches one spot. Will this numbness ever go away?

4. You're feeding a semi-wild cat outside the campus cafeteria when it accidentally nips you, drawing blood. Your friends advise you to report to the campus medical center immediately for a rabies vaccination. Should you go for the vaccination?

5. Overnight, your roommate develops a high fever. She says she has a severe headache and complains of neck stiffness. An hour later she seems confused. You take her to the hospital and the physician recommends a spinal tap—a test in which a sample of cerebrospinal fluid is removed and analyzed. What might the physician be looking for?

6. Some states still administer the death penalty by lethal injection. The injection may contain an anesthetic (for pain) combined with a high dose of potassium to stop the heart. Why would a large dose of potassium stop the heart?

7. At a party someone offers you an ecstasy pill. Aside from the legal issues involved, what are the short-term and long-term effects of trying it just one time?

8. Certain bacteria, such as those that cause botulism or tetanus, produce toxins that interfere with neuromuscular transmission. From what you know of neuromuscular transmission, how might such toxins work?

BlogInFocus

Answers can be found in the Study Area in MasteringBiology.

1. According to current learning theory, anxious thoughts compete for short-term memory space in the limbic system. As a result, people with severe test anxieties may perform well below their abilities on exams; the more important the exam the worse they perform. Knowing this, can you think of any strategies that might help people with test anxiety perform better on exams? (For at least one view on this subject, visit MJ's blog in the Study Area in MasteringBiology and look under "Anxiety and Memory.")

MasteringBiology®

Go to MasteringBiology for practice quizzes, activities, eText, videos, current events, and more.

Sensory Mechanisms

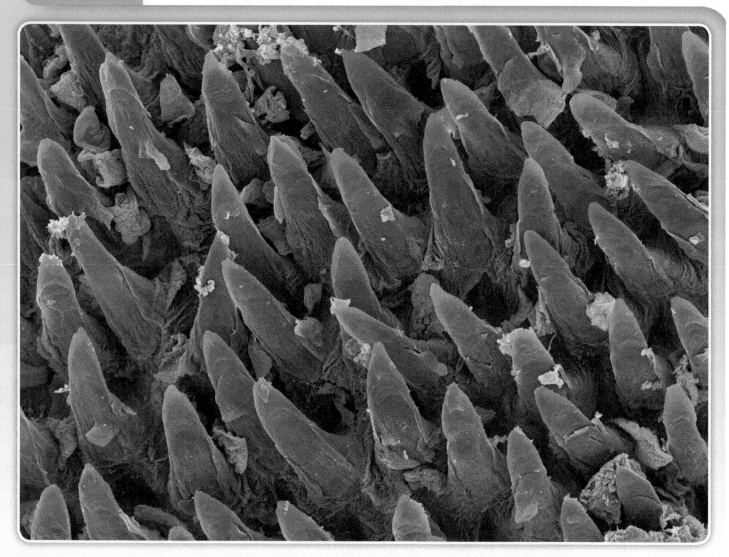

Colorized SEM of the surface of the tongue, showing papillae (pointing toward the back of the tongue).

DWD: Driving While Distracted

On August 5, 2010 a 19-year-old driver slammed into the back of a tractor truck on an interstate highway near Gray Summit, Mo. The next two vehicles on the highway behind the trucks happened to be two school buses carrying high school students to an outing at the Six Flags Missouri amusement park. The buses collided with each other and with the two trucks, smashing the pickup truck into a nearly unrecognizable pile of metal. The driver of the pickup truck and a 15-year-old student on one of the buses were killed and 38 students were injured. The driver of the pickup truck was texting on his cell phone at the time of the accident.

It's not hard to find such examples of the disastrous consequences of driving while distracted, and once you understand how the brain works it's easy to understand why. Your brain is encased in the skull, entirely in the dark. It assesses what is happening in the outside world (and then reacts to it) by processing and organizing a steady stream of sensory input from various sources. It copes with all this sensory input by focusing on the

Driving while distracted.

The driver of the vehicle between the truck cab and the bus was texting while driving.

input it considers most important at the moment, sometimes at the expense of other input. It should be no surprise, then, that anything that distracts you while driving is likely to lower your ability to drive safely. "Every single time someone takes their eyes or their focus off the road—even for just a few seconds—they put their lives and the lives of others in danger," said Transportation Secretary Ray LaHood at a national summit on distracted driving. "Distracted driving is unsafe, irresponsible and in a split second, its consequences can be devastating." Distractions may be visual (taking your eyes off the road), cognitive (thinking about something else), or manual (taking your hands off the wheel). Typical distractions include texting or talking on the phone, putting on makeup, eating, reading, or using a navigation system. Texting while driving is considered especially risky because it involves all three types of

distractions at once (visual, cognitive, *and* manual).

According to the National Highway Traffic Safety Administration (NHTSA), more than half a million injuries and nearly 6,000 deaths a year are due to car crashes involving distracted drivers. The highest proportion of distracted drivers involved in fatal crashes is under 20 years old.

Driving while on the phone and texting while driving are the two most common distractions. Twenty percent of all drivers and half of all drivers between 21 and 24 say that they've text-messaged or e-mailed while driving. NHTSA recommends that drivers not use their cell phones while driving except in an emergency, but it doesn't appear that anyone is listening. According to the NHTSA, at any given moment during daylight hours nearly 800,000 drivers are on their cell phones while driving.

In the United States, driving is a privilege granted by the states, not the federal government. Although the National Transportation Safety Board (NTSB) has issued a strongly worded statement to the states urging them to ban texting while driving, it is up to each state to develop its own laws pertaining to driving and to enforce the penalties for breaking them. Reacting to the statistics and to high-profile deaths like those in Missouri and elsewhere, the states are beginning to take action. Although no states currently ban all cell phone use (including hands-free phones), 35 states now prohibit texting while driving. Many of these states have special restrictions on cell phone use by drivers with learner's permits or drivers under a certain age. Nine states now prohibit all drivers from using handheld cell phones while driving, even for making telephone calls. Other states are likely to follow suit.

Although all this sounds like progress, enforcement is still an issue. Many of the states that currently ban texting while driving also stipulate that texting while driving is not a primary offense, but merely a secondary one. In other words, in some of the 35 states that "ban" texting while driving, a driver cannot be cited merely for texting while driving unless he/she has an accident or violates some other driving law while texting. The penalty for a texting-while-driving offense also varies from state to state.

In Missouri, where the high-profile accident described above took place, only drivers under 21 years old are prohibited from texting while driving. Older drivers are still free to do as they wish.

QUESTIONS TO CONSIDER

1 Is it fair that in some states, a ban on texting while driving only applies to drivers under a certain age?

2 Should the use of all handheld devices, including just talking on the phone, be banned completely while driving?

3 In some states a driver can only be cited for a handheld phone violation if the driver commits another moving violation while on the phone. Is that a reasonable solution?

THE FACTS...

- More than 6,000 deaths and 500,000 injuries per year are attributed to driving while distracted.

- At any given moment during daylight hours, more than 800,000 drivers are talking on their cell phones.

- The highest proportion of distracted drivers is under 20 years old.

- Laws against driving while distracted (texting, talking on a handheld phone) vary from state to state, from complete bans to no ban at all. There is no national standard.

>> **Sensory mechanisms provide information** about the world around us and also about conditions within our own bodies.

>> **Various types of receptors convert different types of sensory stimuli (physical touch, odors, light, etc.) into action potentials.** The brain interprets incoming action potentials correctly by where they go in the brain.

>> **Some receptors adapt quickly,** which is why you stop noticing some stimuli after a while or they may seem less intense.

>> **Receptors are located throughout the body.** They provide us with information about body position, touch, temperature, vibration, pressure, and especially pain.

>> **The five special senses (taste, smell, hearing, balance, and vision) originate from special areas of the body.** Four of them (taste, smell, hearing, and vision) provide us with detailed information about the external world.

Look around you at the complex and colorful world you inhabit. Then, after reading this paragraph, close your eyes and concentrate for a moment on what you can hear. Identify the sources of any sounds you hear and try to judge their direction and distance from you. Describe any odors that you smell, and make a guess at the temperature in the room. Now concentrate on your own body. Move your arms and legs about, and then identify what type of clothing you are wearing. Finally, visualize in your mind the precise position of every part of your body, right down to your fingers and toes.

Your body's sensory mechanisms are constantly providing the brain with detailed information about the world around you, and even about the body itself. In this chapter we learn how different kinds of sensory information are received by the body, how that information is converted to nerve impulses (action potentials), and how the nerve impulses are transmitted to the brain in such a way that the brain can make sense of it all.

12.1 Receptors receive and convert stimuli

Sensory input that causes some change within or outside the body is called a **stimulus** (plural: *stimuli*). The stimulus is often a form of physical energy such as heat, pressure, or sound waves, but it can also be a chemical. A **receptor**—a structure specialized to receive certain stimuli—accepts the stimulus and converts its energy into another form.

Some receptors are evolved from the dendritic structures of a sensory neuron. They convert the stimulus into a graded potential that, if it is powerful enough, initiates an impulse within the sensory neuron. Other receptors are parts of cells that produce graded potentials and release a neurotransmitter, stimulating a nearby sensory neuron. In the end, the effect is the same—generation of an impulse in a sensory neuron.

When the central nervous system receives these impulses, we often experience a **sensation**, meaning that we become consciously aware of the stimulus. A sensation is different from **perception**, which means understanding what the sensation means. As an example, hearing the sound of thunder is a sensation; the belief that a storm is approaching is a perception.

Receptors are classified according to stimulus

Receptors are classified according to the type of stimulus energy they convert, as follows:

- **Mechanoreceptors** respond to forms of mechanical energy, such as waves of sound, changes in fluid pressure, physical touch or pressure, stretching, or forces generated by gravity and acceleration.
- **Thermoreceptors** respond to heat or cold.
- **Pain receptors** respond to tissue damage or excessive pressure or temperature.
- **Chemoreceptors** respond to the presence of chemicals in the nearby area.
- **Photoreceptors** respond to light.

Many of these receptors contribute to sensations, although some (such as joint receptors) contribute no more than a general sense of where our limbs are located. Table 12.1 lists examples of each type of receptor and the sensations they give us.

A few receptors are "silent" in the sense that we are not consciously aware of their actions. These receptors function in negative feedback loops that maintain homeostasis inside the body. They include stretch receptors for monitoring and regulating blood pressure and fluid volumes, and chemoreceptors for regulating the chemical composition of our internal environment. They aren't discussed in detail here, as we discuss most of them in the context of the homeostatic control of various organ systems.

The CNS interprets nerve impulses based on origin and frequency

How can cells in the central nervous system (CNS) interpret some incoming impulses as images and others as sounds? How do they distinguish a loud sound from a soft one and bright lights from dim?

As described in the chapter on the nervous system (Chapter 11), nerve impulses are transmitted from receptors to specific brain areas. For example, impulses generated by visual stimuli travel in sensory neurons whose axons go

Table 12.1 **Types of receptors**

Type of receptor	Examples	Sensation
Mechanoreceptors		
Touch, pressure	Unencapsulated dendritic endings, Meissner's corpuscles, Pacinian corpuscles, Ruffini endings, Merkel disks	Touch and pressure on skin or body hair
Vibration	Pacinian corpuscles	Vibration on skin
Stretch	Muscle spindles	Muscle length
	Tendon receptors	Tendon tension
	Joint position	Joint receptors
Hearing	Hair cells in cochlea of the inner ear	Vibration of fluid originating from sound waves
Balance	Hair cells in semicircular canals of the inner ear. Hair cells in the utricle and saccule of the inner ear	Rotational movement of the head. Static position and linear acceleration and deceleration of the head
Thermoreceptors		
Temperature	Receptors in unencapsulated dendritic endings in skin	Heat or lack of heat (cold)
Pain receptors		
Pain	Receptors in unencapsulated dendritic endings in skin and internal organs	Pain caused by excessive pressure, heat, light, or chemical injury
Chemoreceptors		
Taste	Taste receptors in taste buds	Salty, sweet, sour, and bitter tastes
Smell	Olfactory receptors of nasal passages	Over a thousand different chemical smells
Photoreceptors		
Vision	Rods of the retina	Light (highly sensitive black-and-white vision)
	Cones of the retina	Light (color vision)

directly to brain regions associated with vision. All incoming impulses traveling in these neurons are interpreted as light, regardless of how they were initiated. This is why, when you are hit in the eye, you may "see stars." The blow to your eye triggers impulses in visual sensory neurons. When these signals arrive in the visual area of the brain, they are interpreted as light.

Stronger stimuli activate more receptors and trigger a greater frequency of impulses in sensory neurons. In effect, the central nervous system gets all the information it needs by monitoring where impulses originate and how frequently they arrive.

✔️**Quick Check** *Suppose the axon of a sound-detecting neuron in a person's ear was somehow redirected so that it connected to the visual area of the brain. How will this person likely perceive the action potentials produced in this neuron by an auditory stimulus? Explain.* ■

Answers to ✔️ questions can be found in Appendix A.

Some receptors adapt to continuing stimuli

The central nervous system can ignore one sensation to concentrate on others. For example, you ignore the feel of your clothing when you are more interested in other things. Some sensory inputs are ignored after a while because of **receptor adaptation**, in which the sensory neuron stops sending impulses even though the original stimulus is still present. To demonstrate, try touching a few hairs on your forearm. Notice that the initial feeling of light pressure goes away within a second or so, even though you maintain the same amount of pressure.

Receptors in the skin for light touch and pressure adapt rather quickly. This confers a survival advantage, because they can keep the central nervous system informed of *changes* in these stimuli, without constantly bombarding it with relatively unimportant stimuli. Olfactory (smell) receptors also adapt rapidly. Olfactory adaptation can be hazardous to people if they are continually exposed to low levels of hazardous chemicals that they can no longer smell.

Other receptors—pain receptors, joint and muscle receptors that monitor the position of our limbs, and essentially all of the silent receptors involved in homeostatic feedback control loops—adapt slowly or not at all. Lack of adaptation in these receptors is also important to survival. Persistent sensations such as pain alert us to possible tissue damage from illness or injury and prompt us to take appropriate action. Persistent activity of silent receptors is essential to our ability to maintain homeostasis.

Is texting while driving illegal in your state? To find out, visit MJ's blog in the Study Area in MasteringBiology and look under "Distracted Driving."

Somatic sensations and special senses provide sensory information

The sensations (or senses) provided by receptors are categorized as either somatic or special. The **somatic sensations** originate from receptors present at more than one location in the body (*soma* is the Greek word for "body"). The somatic sensations include temperature, touch, vibration, pressure, pain, and awareness of body movements and position. The five **special senses** (taste, smell, hearing, balance, and vision) originate from receptors that are restricted to particular areas of the body, such as the ears and eyes. The special senses deliver highly specialized information about the external world.

We look at the somatic sensations first and then discuss the five special senses in detail.

🔄 **Recap** Receptors receive a physical or chemical stimulus, causing nerve impulses to be generated in sensory neurons. Receptors are classified according to the type of stimulus they convert. The five classes of receptors are mechanoreceptors, thermoreceptors, pain receptors, chemoreceptors, and photoreceptors. Stronger stimuli activate more receptors and trigger a greater frequency of action potentials in sensory neurons. Some receptors adapt rapidly; others adapt slowly or not at all. ▪

12.2 Somatic sensations arise from receptors throughout the body

The somatic sensations of temperature, touch, pressure, vibration, pain, and awareness of body movements and position are essential to help us coordinate muscle movements, avoid danger, and maintain body temperature. Some somatic sensations contribute to pleasurable feelings as well, such as our response to the gentle touch of a loved one.

Receptors that detect the somatic sensations are located throughout the body in skin, joints, skeletal muscles, tendons, and internal organs. Sensory neurons linked to these receptors send their impulses to the brain, specifically to the primary somatosensory area of the parietal lobe of the cerebral cortex (review Figure 11.17). As you already know, body parts with the greatest sensory sensitivity, such as the mouth and fingers, involve more neurons in the somatosensory area, whereas less sensitive body parts involve fewer neurons.

The somatosensory area processes the information and sends it to the nearby primary motor area in the frontal lobe. If necessary, impulses are then generated in motor (output) neurons of the peripheral nervous system to cause body movement.

Mechanoreceptors detect touch, pressure, and vibration

Receptors for sensing touch, pressure, and vibration are called *mechanoreceptors*. Though they may take several different forms, all mechanoreceptors are the modified dendritic endings of sensory neurons. Any force that deforms the plasma membrane of the dendritic ending produces a typical graded potential. If the graded potential (or the sum of multiple graded potentials) is large enough to exceed threshold, the sensory neuron initiates an impulse.

The various receptors for touch, pressure, and vibration differ in their locations, the intensity of the stimulus that must be applied in order to generate an impulse (pressure is a stronger mechanical force than light touch), and the degree to which they adapt. Vibration-sensitive receptors adapt so quickly that it takes a rapidly changing physical deformation (many on-and-off cycles per second) to keep them stimulated. Vibration-sensitive receptors are particularly useful for providing information about potentially harmful flying insects because those receptors respond to the kinds of vibrations generated by insects' wings.

Figure 12.1 depicts the skin with several types of receptors for detecting somatic sensations. They are

- **Unencapsulated dendritic endings.** Naked dendritic endings of sensory neurons around hairs and near the skin surface signal pain, light pressure, and changes in temperature.
- **Merkel disks.** Merkel disks are modified unencapsulated dendritic endings that detect light touch and pressure.
- **Meissner's corpuscles.** Encapsulated touch receptors located close to the skin surface detect the beginning and the end of light pressure and touch.
- **Ruffini endings.** These encapsulated receptors respond continually to ongoing pressure.
- **Pacinian corpuscles.** Several kinds of dendritic endings are encapsulated (enclosed) in epithelial or connective tissue. The best known, called *Pacinian corpuscles,* are encapsulated receptors located in the dermis that respond to either deep pressure or high-frequency vibration. The encapsulation structure of the Pacinian corpuscle permits the mechanoreceptor to adapt rapidly, even to a continuously applied stimulus (Figure 12.2).

Figure 12.1 Sensory receptors in skin. Thermoreceptors, some of the receptors for light touch, and the receptors for pain are the free endings of sensory neurons. Other receptors for touch, pressure, and vibration are modified or encapsulated endings of sensory neurons.

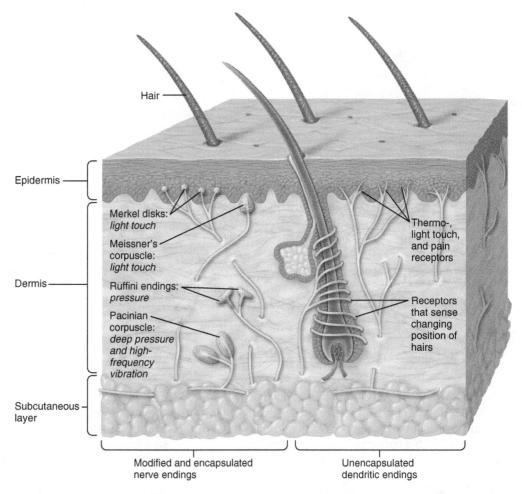

Hair

Epidermis

Merkel disks: *light touch*

Meissner's corpuscle: *light touch*

Dermis

Ruffini endings: *pressure*

Pacinian corpuscle: *deep pressure and high-frequency vibration*

Subcutaneous layer

Thermo-, light touch, and pain receptors

Receptors that sense changing position of hairs

Modified and encapsulated nerve endings

Unencapsulated dendritic endings

Receptor

Stimulus

Nerve axon

Action potentials

a) At rest.

b) The initial application of a stimulus deforms the encapsulation layers and bends the receptor ending of the nerve, producing more action potentials in the nerve axon.

c) With continuous application of the stimulus, the layers of encapsulation slide past each other and come closer together, permitting the receptor ending to return to its initial shape.

Figure 12.2 The Pacinian corpuscle.

Mechanoreceptors indicate limb position, muscle length, and tension

With your eyes closed, try to describe the positions of your arms and legs. You can probably describe their position rather well. You may even be able to tell which muscle groups are contracting. You do this with a variety of mechanoreceptors in joints (for joint position), in skeletal muscles (for muscle length), and in tendons (for tension). Perhaps the best known of these mechanoreceptors are the specialized structures for monitoring muscle length, called **muscle spindles**. For most joints, muscle length determines joint position because of the way the muscle is attached to the bones.

A muscle spindle is a small bundle of modified skeletal muscle cells located within a skeletal muscle (Figure 12.3). Muscle spindles are innervated by sensory nerves whose dendritic endings are mechanoreceptors that respond to stretch (lengthening). One type of dendritic ending wraps around the middle of a muscle spindle cell. Another has several branches that attach nearer the end of the muscle spindle cell. When the whole muscle is stretched, the receptors attached to the muscle spindle cells are stretched as well. Mechanical distortion of the mechanoreceptors produces local graded potentials in the dendritic endings and (if threshold is passed) an action potential.

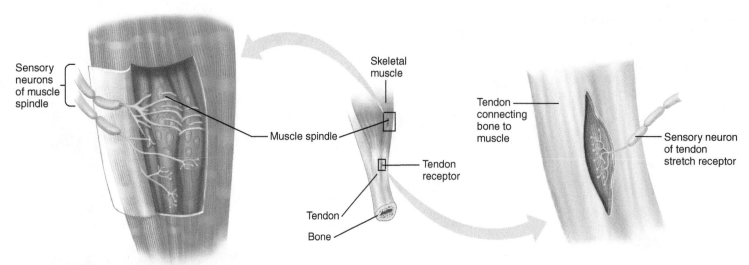

a) **Muscle spindle.** A muscle spindle responds to muscle length. Passive stretch of a muscle stretches the muscle spindle, stimulating mechanoreceptors in the nerve endings of the sensory neurons. Conversely, muscle contraction shortens the muscle spindle, reducing muscle spindle mechanoreceptor stimulation.

b) **Tendon receptor.** A tendon receptor responds to tension in tendons. When a muscle contracts and also when it is stretched passively, tension on the tendon increases, activating tendon receptors.

Figure 12.3 Muscle spindles and tendon receptors.

This is exactly what happens in the classic patellar stretch reflex, described in the chapter on the nervous system. When a physician taps your patellar tendon (at the front of your knee) with a hammer, the patellar tendon and quadriceps (thigh) muscle are stretched, stretching the muscle spindle as well. Stretch of the muscle causes sensory neurons innervating the muscle spindle to transmit action potentials to the spinal cord. Within the cord, motor nerves to the quadriceps are activated, causing the quadriceps to contract. All this occurs in a fraction of a second.

Tendons, which connect muscle to bone, also have mechanoreceptors. Tendon receptors respond to tension, but they cannot distinguish between tension produced by passive stretch and tension produced by active muscle contraction. Tendon receptors may play a protective role in preventing injury by extremely high tensions. For example, if you were to fall out of a tree but land on your feet, the impact when you hit the ground would produce high levels of tension, activating your tendon stretch receptors. The sensory information they provide inhibits muscle contraction, so you would crumple to the ground rather than stay upright. This reflex-induced collapse protects your muscles from tearing and your bones from breaking.

✅ **Quick Check** *A friend is trying to touch his toes (with his legs straight) by bouncing his upper body up and down. This sort of bouncing typically stimulates muscle spindles, but not tendon receptors. Explain whether this is a good method of stretching the hamstring muscles in the back of the legs.* ∎

Thermoreceptors detect temperature

Near the skin's surface, thermoreceptors for heat and cold provide useful information about the external environment.

These receptors adapt quickly, allowing us to monitor changes in temperature accurately and yet adjust sensory input so it becomes more bearable. For example, when you step into a hot shower the water may seem uncomfortably warm at first, but you soon become used to it.

Other thermoreceptors located in abdominal and thoracic organs throughout the body monitor internal temperature (also called *core temperature*). In keeping with their role in maintaining homeostasis, these thermoreceptors do not adapt rapidly.

Pain receptors signal discomfort

As much as we dislike pain, the ability to perceive pain is essential for survival. Pain warns us to avoid certain stimuli and informs us of injuries. Pain receptors are unencapsulated endings that respond to injury from excessive physical pressure, heat, light, or chemicals. Pain is described as either fast or slow, depending on its characteristics.

Fast pain, also called *sharp* or *acute pain*, occurs as soon as a tenth of a second after the stimulus. Receptors for fast pain generally respond to physical pressure or heat and usually are located near the surface of the body. They inform us of stimuli to be avoided—for example, stepping on a nail or touching a hot burner on the stove. The reflex withdrawal response to fast pain is rapid and strong.

In contrast, *slow pain* generally arises from muscles or internal organs. Slow pain, which may not appear until seconds or even minutes after injury, is due to activation of chemically sensitive pain receptors by chemicals released from damaged tissue. Slow pain from internal organs is often perceived as originating from an area of the body completely removed from the actual source. This phenomenon, called **referred pain**, happens because action potentials from internal pain receptors are transmitted to the brain by the same spinal neurons that transmit action potentials from pain receptors in the skin and skeletal muscles. The brain has no way of knowing the exact source of the pain, so it assigns the pain to another location.

Referred pain is so common that physicians use it to diagnose certain disorders of internal organs. For example, a heart attack usually manifests itself as pain in the left shoulder and down the left arm. **Figure 12.4** shows where pain from internal organs may be felt. The close association between areas of referred pain from the heart and esophagus is why it can be difficult, by sensations alone, to distinguish a heart attack from the less serious problem of esophageal spasm.

Pain receptors generally do not adapt. From a survival standpoint this is beneficial, because the continued presence of pain reminds us to avoid doing whatever causes it. However, it also means that people with chronic diseases or disabilities can end up experiencing constant discomfort.

Recap Somatic sensations include temperature, touch, pressure, vibration, pain, and awareness of body movements and position. Mechanoreceptors in skeletal muscle, tendons, and joints provide information about the position of our limbs and the amount of tension on muscles. Thermoreceptors near the skin surface monitor the temperature of the external environment, and thermoreceptors in internal organs maintain homeostasis of body temperature. Fast pain arises from receptors near the body surface, whereas slow pain originates in muscles or internal organs. Pain is important to survival because it warns us of injury. ∎

12.3 Taste and smell depend on chemoreceptors

We turn now to the five special senses: taste, smell, hearing, balance, and vision. As mentioned earlier, these senses originate from receptors located in special areas of the body.

The first senses we consider, taste and smell, are both due to the action of chemoreceptors. The rich fragrance of a rose, the less pleasing odor of a skunk, the tart taste of an orange—all depend on our ability to convert a chemical stimulus into the only language the central nervous system can understand: action potentials.

Taste: Chemoreceptors bind with dissolved substances

The tongue has a rough texture because its surface is composed of numerous small projections, called *papillae*, surrounded by deep folds (**Figure 12.5**). About 10,000 **taste buds** are located

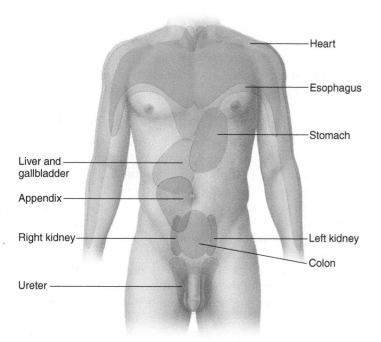

Liver and gallbladder

Appendix

Right kidney

Ureter

Heart

Esophagus

Stomach

Left kidney

Colon

Figure 12.4 Locations of referred pain from various internal organs. Note that the areas of overlap for esophageal and heart pain are so extensive that it is often difficult to tell them apart by location.

a) The tongue. Most of the receptors for taste are located at the edges and at the front and back of the tongue.

Large papilla   Small papilla

b) A view (approximately × 75) of the surface of the tongue showing that it is covered with large and small papillae.

Large papilla Fold   Taste buds

c) A sagittal section (approximately × 200) through several large papillae showing the location of the taste buds along their sides, just beneath the tongue's surface.

Taste hairs   Taste cell   Supporting cell

Sensory nerve cells

d) A taste bud is composed of a group of taste cells and supporting cells. Each taste cell connects to a sensory neuron.

Figure 12.5 The structure of the receptors for taste.

at the surface of many of these folds. A taste bud is a cluster of about 25 taste cells and 25 supporting cells that separate the taste cells from each other.

The exposed tip of a taste cell has hairs that project into the mouth. The hairs contain chemoreceptors that are specific for certain chemicals (called *tastants*). When we eat or drink, tastants dissolve in our saliva and bind to the chemoreceptor. The binding of tastant to chemoreceptor causes the taste cell to release a neurotransmitter, which stimulates a nearby sensory neuron to produce action potentials. Note that the taste cell itself is not a sensory neuron. It takes two cells (the taste cell and a sensory neuron) to convert the chemical stimulus into a nerve impulse, but the ultimate effect is the same as if it were one cell.

The four commonly accepted primary taste qualities are sweet, sour, salty, and bitter. In recent years a fifth primary taste quality for savory foods, called *umami*, has been added to the list. Taste receptors for umami allow us to appreciate foods like parmesan cheese, mushrooms, beef, soy sauce, and Worcestershire sauce. Although an individual taste receptor and its associated sensory neuron seem to be "tuned" to respond most strongly to only one of the taste qualities, they do respond weakly to the other taste qualities as well.

Most of the taste receptors are located around the edges and at the front and back of the tongue. Although all receptor types can be found in each of these regions, there is some evidence that their distribution is not entirely even. The tongue is slightly more sensitive to sweet tastes on the tip, sour on the sides, salty on the tip and sides, and bitter toward the back (the distribution of umami receptors is not yet well documented). Therefore, to gain the maximum taste sensation, we move food around in our mouth before swallowing. The combined

sensitivities of our taste receptors allow us to distinguish hundreds of different flavors, far beyond the basic five qualities. On the other hand, if we don't want to taste something, we pass it over the center of the tongue and swallow quickly.

It is probably no accident that bitter taste receptors are heavily concentrated at the very back of the tongue. Bitterness is often a sign of an inedible or even poisonous substance, and the location of these receptors makes it difficult to bypass them.

BlogInFocus 🔵

Why do some people not perceive bitter-tasting foods (such as Brussels sprouts) as bitter? To find out, visit MJ's blog in the Study Area in MasteringBiology and look under "Tasting Bitter Foods."

✅ **Quick Check** *If you blot your tongue completely dry, you will find that you temporarily lose the ability to taste dry foods such as sugar or salt. Why?* ■

Smell: Chemoreceptors bind with odorants

The sense of smell also relies on a chemoreceptor mechanism. There are two fundamental differences between taste and smell: (1) The receptors for smell are located on true sensory neurons, and (2) there are receptors for over 1,000 different "odorant" chemicals, as opposed to just four tastant classes. With these 1,000 different receptor types and our sense of taste we can distinguish as many as 10,000 taste and smell sensations.

Odors are detected by **olfactory receptor cells** located in the upper part of the nasal passages. The receptor cells are sensory neurons, each with a modified dendritic ending that branches to become several olfactory hairs (**Figure 12.6**). The olfactory hairs extend into a layer of mucus covering the surface of the nasal passages. The mucus, produced by nearby olfactory glands, keeps these hairs from drying out.

Gaseous and airborne odorants enter the nasal passages, become dissolved in the mucus, bind to chemoreceptors located on the olfactory hairs, and cause the olfactory receptor cell to generate impulses. Olfactory receptor cells synapse with olfactory neurons in a nearby area of the brain called the *olfactory bulb*, where information is partially integrated and then passed to higher brain centers.

Our sense of smell complements our sense of taste because when food is chewed it releases chemicals that come into contact with olfactory receptors. The combined sensations

Figure 12.6 Olfactory receptors and the mucus-producing olfactory glands. Odorants become trapped in mucus and then bind to the olfactory hairs of receptor cells.

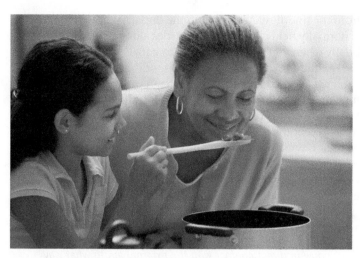

Figure 12.7 Smell. Over 1,000 different olfactory receptors contribute to our sense of smell and taste.

Table 12.2 Common noises and your hearing

Sound	Decibels	How it affects your hearing
Rustling leaves	20	Does not cause hearing loss
Normal conversation	50–60	Does not cause hearing loss
Vacuum cleaner	70	Does not cause hearing loss
Power lawn mower	85–100	Cumulative exposure causes hearing loss; newer mowers may be quieter
Live rock concert	110–130	Definite risk of permanent hearing loss
Jackhammer	120–150	Definite risk of permanent hearing loss
Shotgun	140	Repeated exposure likely to cause permanent hearing loss
Jet engine	150	Exposure likely to cause permanent hearing loss

create an effect that is interpreted at higher brain levels (Figure 12.7). When we have a cold, most foods taste less appetizing. In part this is because increased production of mucus prevents odorant molecules from reaching olfactory receptors, impairing our sense of smell.

↩ **Recap** Taste buds contain chemoreceptor cells that bind dissolved chemicals. The five currently accepted basic taste qualities are sweet, salty, sour, bitter, and umami. Our sense of smell augments and complements our sense of taste, allowing us to experience over 10,000 combinations of taste and smell. ▪

12.4 Hearing: Mechanoreceptors detect sound waves

Sounds are waves of compressed air. Sound intensity is a physical property of sound that refers to the energy of the sound, whereas loudness refers to our subjective interpretation of sound. Both intensity and perceived loudness are related to the amplitude of the sound waves, and both are measured in units called decibels (dB). The threshold of human hearing (barely audible) is set at 0 dB. A 10-dB increase represents a 10-fold increase in sound intensity (sound energy), but only a doubling of perceived loudness. In other words, a sound of 30 dB has 100 times more energy than a 10-dB sound, but humans would perceive it as only four times as loud. Hearing loss can result from exposure to sounds louder than 85 dB. Table 12.2 lists the decibels associated with some common sounds.

The tone (or pitch) of a sound is determined by its frequency, the number of wave cycles that pass a given point per second (cycles/sec). Frequency is expressed in *hertz* (Hz). Higher tones are those of a higher frequency (Figure 12.8). The frequency range for normal human hearing is from 20 to 20,000 Hz.

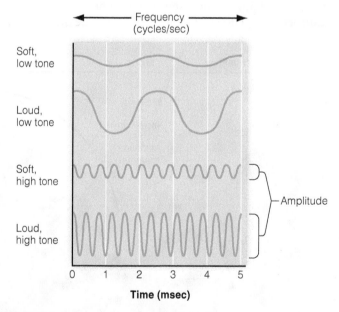

Figure 12.8 Properties of sound waves. Loudness (intensity) is determined by sound wave amplitude. Tone (pitch) is determined by sound wave frequency.

✔ *Draw one more graph, to the same scale, illustrating a sound wave of extremely high tone and intermediate loudness, compared to the sounds illustrated in this figure.*

When waves of sound strike the ear they cause vibration-sensitive mechanoreceptors deep within the ear to vibrate. The vibration causes the production of impulses that travel to the brain for interpretation.

The outer ear channels sound waves

The human ear consists of three functionally different regions: the outer, middle, and inner ear (Figure 12.9).

The **outer ear** consists of the pinna, or visible portion of the ear, and the auditory canal. Sound waves arrive at the pinna and are directed into the auditory canal, which channels them to the **tympanic membrane (eardrum)**. The tympanic membrane serves as a partition between the outer and middle ears.

The middle ear amplifies sound

The **middle ear** consists of an air-filled chamber within the temporal bone of the skull, bridged by three small bones called the *malleus* ("hammer"), *incus* ("anvil"), and *stapes* ("stirrup"). When sound waves strike the tympanic membrane, it moves back and forth slightly (vibrates). Vibration of the tympanic membrane makes the malleus, incus, and stapes vibrate. The stapes touches a smaller membrane, called the **oval window**, causing it to vibrate, too.

All the vibrating force of the much larger tympanic membrane is now concentrated on the smaller oval window. In effect, the middle ear amplifies the sound waves severalfold. Amplification is essential because the oval window must vibrate with sufficient force to produce pressure waves in the watery fluid of the inner ear.

The air-filled middle ear is kept at atmospheric pressure by the **auditory tube** (eustachian tube), a narrow tube that runs from the middle ear chamber to the throat. Although the tube is normally held closed by the muscles along its sides, it opens briefly when you swallow or yawn to equalize air pressure in the middle ear with that of the surrounding atmosphere. When you change altitude quickly, your ears "pop" as the auditory tube opens briefly and air pressures are suddenly equalized. When you have a cold or allergy, inflammation and swelling may prevent the auditory tube from equalizing pressures normally, which is why airplane trips can be painful when you have a cold or allergies. Children tend to get a lot of earaches (middle ear infections) via the auditory tube until the skull elongates, changing the angle of the tube to the ear.

✔ **Quick Check** *Suppose human ears had no outer ear and no middle ear, and just had the inner ear—that is, with the oval window in direct contact with the external air. In what way would our sense of hearing probably be different?* ▪

The inner ear sorts and converts sounds

The **inner ear** sorts sounds by tone and converts them into impulses. It consists of the **cochlea**, where sound is converted, and the *vestibular apparatus* consisting of the vestibule and the three semicircular canals, which does not contribute to hearing at all. We will discuss the vestibular apparatus later in connection with the sense of balance.

The cochlea is a coiled structure shaped a bit like a snail. Figure 12.10a shows what the cochlea would look

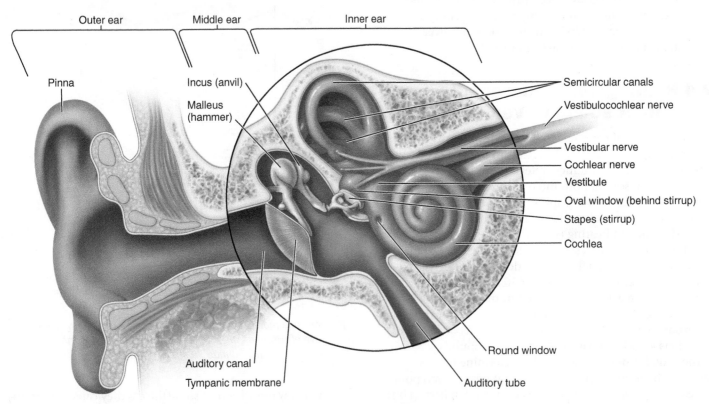

Outer ear · Middle ear · Inner ear

Pinna

Incus (anvil)

Malleus (hammer)

Semicircular canals

Vestibulocochlear nerve

Vestibular nerve

Cochlear nerve

Vestibule

Oval window (behind stirrup)

Stapes (stirrup)

Cochlea

Auditory canal

Tympanic membrane

Round window

Auditory tube

Figure 12.9 Structure of the human ear. The outer ear receives and channels sound, the middle ear amplifies sound, and the cochlea of the inner ear converts the sound to action potentials. The vestibule and the three semicircular canals are responsible for balance.

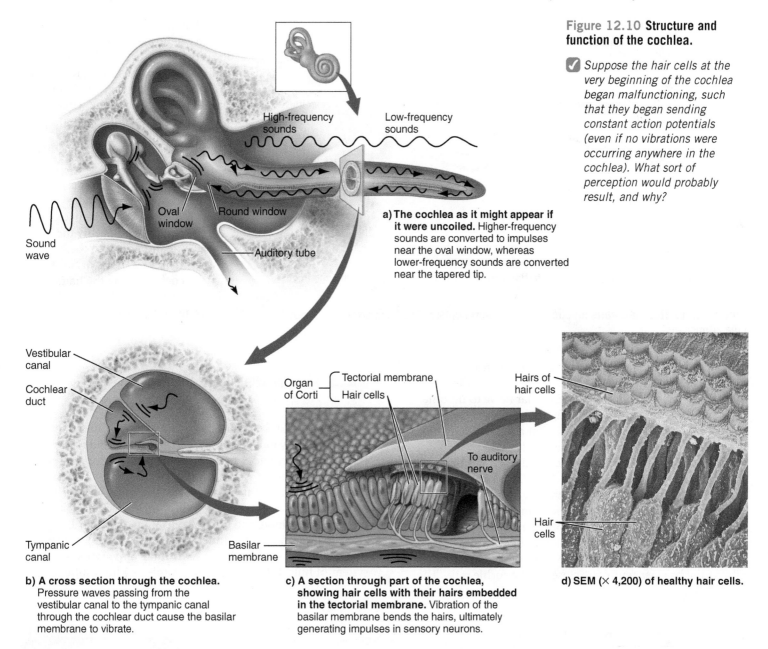

Figure 12.10 Structure and function of the cochlea.

☑ *Suppose the hair cells at the very beginning of the cochlea began malfunctioning, such that they began sending constant action potentials (even if no vibrations were occurring anywhere in the cochlea). What sort of perception would probably result, and why?*

a) The cochlea as it might appear if it were uncoiled. Higher-frequency sounds are converted to impulses near the oval window, whereas lower-frequency sounds are converted near the tapered tip.

b) A cross section through the cochlea. Pressure waves passing from the vestibular canal to the tympanic canal through the cochlear duct cause the basilar membrane to vibrate.

c) A section through part of the cochlea, showing hair cells with their hairs embedded in the tectorial membrane. Vibration of the basilar membrane bends the hairs, ultimately generating impulses in sensory neurons.

d) SEM (× 4,200) of healthy hair cells.

like if it were uncoiled. It is a tapered tube containing two interconnected outer canals called the *vestibular canal* and the *tympanic canal*, surrounding a third, closed fluid-filled space called the *cochlear duct*. The base of the cochlear duct is formed by the **basilar membrane**. The basilar membrane supports a population of about 15,000 **hair cells**, the mechanoreceptor cells of the ear. Hair cells have hairlike projections that are embedded in an overhanging structure called the **tectorial membrane** (the Latin word for "roof" is *tectum*), which is composed of a firm, gelatinous, noncellular material. Together, the hair cells and the tectorial membrane are called the *organ of Corti*, the organ that converts pressure waves to impulses.

When sound waves strike the oval window, it generates pressure waves in the watery fluid in the vestibular canal.

These waves travel around the cochlea to the tympanic canal. Eventually the waves strike another membrane called the *round window*, which bulges inward and outward in synchrony with the oval window, dissipating some of the pressure.

Some of the pressure waves take a shortcut from the vestibular canal to the tympanic canal via the cochlear duct. These pressure waves cause the basilar membrane to vibrate like the strings of a musical instrument. The slight movement of the basilar membrane causes the hair cells above the membrane to vibrate as well. Because the hairs of the hair cells are embedded in the less movable tectorial membrane, vibration of the basilar membrane causes the hairs to bend. This physical movement of the hairs causes the hair cells to release more or less neurotransmitter, depending on which way the hairs are bent. The release of neurotransmitter in

a) **Hair cell at rest.**

b) **Hairs moving in one direction.**

c) **Hairs moving in other direction.**

Figure 12.11 How hair cells function as mechanoreceptors. The hairs are actually modified cilia or microvilli.

identical impulses generated in sensory neurons at these different locations are interpreted by the brain as sounds of specific tones on the basis of where they originated on the basilar membrane. This is yet another example of the location-specific nature of information processing by the brain.

Recap The outer ear receives and directs sound to the middle ear. The three bones of the middle ear amplify the sound and pass it to the cochlea. Vibrations of fluid in the cochlea cause the hairs of receptor hair cells to bend, generating action potentials in nearby neurons. ▪

turn generates impulses in nearby sensory neurons (Figure 12.11). The impulses travel in neurons of the auditory nerve, which joins the vestibular nerve to become the vestibulocochlear nerve leading to the brain.

Vibrations of fluid in the vestibular and tympanic canals are of the same frequency as the original sound waves, which may be of many different tones at once. But because the fibers of the basilar membrane are different lengths at different regions of the cochlea, sound waves are converted to vibrations of the basilar membrane in a location-specific manner according to tone. High-pitched tones vibrate the basilar membrane closer to the base of the cochlea (near the oval and round windows), whereas low-pitched tones vibrate the basilar membrane closer to the cochlear tip. The

12.5 The inner ear plays an essential role in balance

Maintaining your balance against gravity requires integration of multiple sensory inputs. Those sensory inputs include signals from the joint receptors, muscle spindles, and tendon receptors described previously, as well as from special structures associated with the inner ear. Even visual input is involved. The inner ear structures, described next, provide information about rotational movement, position, and linear acceleration of the head.

Looking again at the inner ear (Figure 12.12a), we see that next to the cochlea is the **vestibular apparatus**, a system of fluid-filled canals and chambers. The vestibular

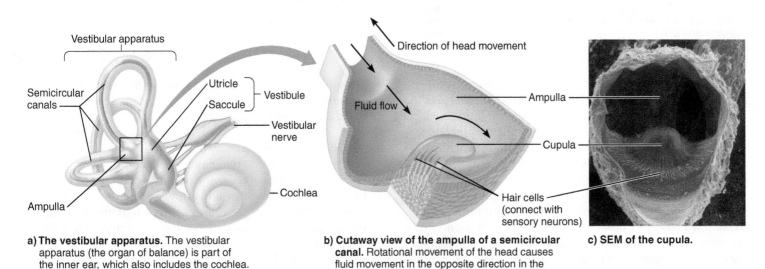

a) **The vestibular apparatus.** The vestibular apparatus (the organ of balance) is part of the inner ear, which also includes the cochlea.

b) **Cutaway view of the ampulla of a semicircular canal.** Rotational movement of the head causes fluid movement in the opposite direction in the semicircular canal. The fluid pushes against the cupula, bending it and activating the mechanoreceptor hairs of the hair cells.

c) **SEM of the cupula.**

Figure 12.12 The vestibular apparatus.

apparatus consists of three *semicircular canals* for sensing rotational movement of the head and body, and an area called the *vestibule,* which senses static (nonmoving) position and linear acceleration and deceleration.

The semicircular canals and the vestibule have mechanoreceptor-type hair cells embedded in a gel-like material. When the head moves or changes position, the gel also moves, although a bit more slowly because of inertia. The movement of the gel bends the hairs, which causes the hair cells to release a neurotransmitter that ultimately generates impulses in sensory neurons of the vestibular nerve.

Sensing rotational movement

The three semicircular canals are fluid-filled tubes of bone. Near the end of each canal is a bulging region called the *ampulla,* containing a soft, gel-like dome called the *cupula* (Figure 12.12b and c). Hairs of mechanoreceptor sensory neurons are embedded in the cupula.

When you turn your head, the fluid in your semicircular canal moves more slowly than your head because of inertia. The shifting position of the fluid bends the soft cupula and the hairs within it, producing impulses. The structure of the hairs enables them to detect the direction of the movement, in addition to movement in general. Because there are three semicircular canals and each is oriented on a different plane, together they can detect any and every possible rotational movement of the head.

✅ **Quick Check** *If you spin in place many times and then suddenly stop spinning, you will experience a sensation as if you are spinning in the other direction (even though you are now standing still). Propose an explanation for this phenomenon.* ▪

Sensing head position and acceleration

To sense the position of the head relative to the Earth, we need a mechanism that is sensitive to gravity. The two fluid-filled chambers of the vestibule, called the **utricle** and the **saccule,** each contain mechanoreceptor hair cells, gel, and hard crystals of bonelike material called **otoliths** (literally, "ear stones") (Figure 12.13).

The otoliths are embedded in the gel near the gel's surface, unattached to the bone wall of the vestibule. The otoliths are indeed like little rocks, and they are considerably heavier than the gel itself. When the head tips forward, for instance, the otoliths slide toward the center of the gravitational pull, causing the gel to slip and bending the hairs of hair cells (Figure 12.13a and b). Again, this produces impulses in nearby sensory neurons that are transmitted to the brain for interpretation.

The utricle and saccule respond to linear acceleration and deceleration as well as static position. When you are in a car that is accelerating rapidly, you feel like you are being pushed backward in your seat. This is the force of acceleration acting against your own inertia. Likewise, your otoliths are being pushed backward, causing the hair cells to bend (Figure 12.13c). The otoliths respond only to acceleration and deceleration (a change in linear velocity), and not to a constant rate of speed in one direction.

a) A cutaway view of the vestibule with the head at rest.

b) Head tilted. A change of head position causes a shift in position of crystals of bonelike material called *otoliths,* which ultimately stimulates hair cells.

c) Linear acceleration. Linear acceleration also causes otoliths to shift position.

d) SEM of otoliths.

Figure 12.13 How the utricle and saccule sense static head position and linear acceleration.

The unpleasant sensation we call "motion sickness" represents a physiological response to abnormal body motion and visual experience. Motion sickness may be due to conflicting sensory inputs from the vestibular apparatus, the eyes, and various receptors in muscles, tendons, and joints throughout the body. The CNS is unable to integrate these conflicting signals into an understandable whole, producing the characteristic symptoms of nausea, cold sweats, hyperventilation, and headache.

Table 12.3 summarizes the structures and functions of the ear.

Table 12.3 **Structures and functions of the ear**

Region of ear	Functions	Structures
Outer ear	Receives and channels sound	Pinna, auditory canal
Middle ear	Amplifies sound	Eardrum, maleus, incus, stapes, oval window, auditory tube
Inner ear	Sorts sounds by tone and converts them into impulses	Cochlea, vestibular canal, tympanic canal, cochlear duct, basilar membrane, hair cells, tectorial membrane, organ of Corti, round window
	Senses rotational movements and converts them into impulses	Semicircular canals, ampulla, cupula, hair cells
	Senses static (non-moving) position and linear acceleration and deceleration; converts them into impulses	Vestibule, utricle, saccule, otoliths, hair cells

↩ **Recap** Rotational movement of the head is sensed as the result of movement of fluid in the three semicircular canals of the inner ear. Head position and linear acceleration are sensed as the result of movement of otoliths (ear stones) in the utricle and saccule of the inner ear. ▪

12.6 Vision: Detecting and interpreting visual stimuli

Light is a form of electromagnetic radiation that travels in waves at a speed of 186,000 miles per second. Our eyes allow us to receive and process light. They enable us to detect light from objects both nearby and distant and from sources either dim or bright, from the candle in your hand to a star light-years away. But first we must collect and focus light onto specialized cells in our eyes called *photoreceptors*.

Structure of the eye

The structure and functional components of the eye are illustrated in Figure 12.14 and summarized in Table 12.4. A tough outer coat known as the sclera, or "white of the eye," covers the outer surface except in the very front, where it is continuous with the clear **cornea**.

Light passes through the cornea and a space filled with fluid called *aqueous humor* that nourishes and cushions the

Figure 12.14 Structure of the eye. Light enters through the transparent cornea and passes through aqueous humor, the pupil, the lens, and vitreous humor before striking the retina at the back of the eye. The macula is the central area of the retina with the highest visual acuity. The nerves and blood vessels exit the eye through the optic disk.

Table 12.4 **Parts of the eye and their functions**

Eye structure	Functions
Sclera	Covers and protects eyeball
Cornea	Bends incoming light (focuses light)
Aqueous humor	Nourishes and cushions cornea and lens
Iris	Adjusts amount of incoming light
Lens	Regulates focus
Ciliary muscle	Adjusts curvature of the lens
Vitreous humor	Transmits light to retina
Retina	Absorbs light and converts it into impulses
Rods	Photoreceptors responsible for black-and-white vision in dim light
Cones	Photoreceptors responsible for color vision and high visual acuity
Macula	Central region of the retina with the highest density of photoreceptors
Optic disk	"Blind spot" where optic nerve exits eye
Optic nerve	Transmits impulses to the brain
Choroid	Nourishes retina and absorbs light not absorbed by retinal photoreceptors

cornea and lens. Light then either strikes the **iris**, a colored, disk-shaped muscle that determines how much light enters the eye, or passes through the **pupil**, the adjustable opening in the center of the iris. Light that passes through the pupil strikes the **lens**, a transparent, flexible structure attached by connective tissue fibers to a ring of circularly arranged smooth muscle called the *ciliary muscle.*

After passing through the main chamber of the eye filled with *vitreous humor*, light encounters the layers at the back and sides of the eye. This is the **retina**, comprising primarily photoreceptor cells, neurons, and a few blood vessels. Between the retina and the sclera at the back of the eye lies the choroid, consisting of pigmented cells and blood vessels. The pigmented cells absorb light not sensed by photoreceptors so that the image does not become distorted by reflected light, and the blood vessels nourish the retina. At the back of the eyeball is the **optic nerve**, which carries information to the thalamus, to be forwarded to the visual cortex for interpretation. Finally, skeletal muscles surround the eye and control its movements, so we can choose exactly where to look.

Several sites on the retina deserve special mention. The **macula** is the central region of the retina, where

photoreceptor density is the highest. When we want high visual acuity we look directly at an object, focusing the image on the macula. At the very center of the macula is a small pit called the *fovea centralis* that is lined with highly packed photoreceptors.

The **optic disk** is the area where the axons of the optic nerve and associated blood vessels exit the eye, so there are no photoreceptors there at all. The optic disk leaves us with a "blind spot" in each eye. To find the blind spots, try the exercise in Figure 12.15.

Regulating the amount of light and focusing the image

The iris adjusts the amount of light entering the eye with two sets of smooth muscle. When bright light strikes the eye, contraction of muscles arranged circularly around the pupil causes the pupil to contract. Otherwise, the intensity of daylight would overwhelm our photoreceptors and temporarily blind us. In dim light, contraction of smooth muscles arranged radially around the pupil causes the pupil to dilate.

Nerves control each set of muscles. When examining an unconscious or injured person, a physician may shine a light in each eye. The pupils should contract in response to light and dilate when the light is removed. Pupils that are "fixed and dilated" (unresponsive to light) are a bad sign, possibly indicating more widespread failure of the nervous system.

Light entering the eye is focused by the cornea and the lens. The cornea, which is curved, is actually responsible for bending most of the incoming light. However, the curvature of the cornea is not adjustable. Our ability to regulate the degree to which incoming light is bent, and therefore our ability to change focus between near and far objects, is accomplished solely by adjusting the curvature of the lens. This is done by the ciliary muscle.

When the ciliary muscle contracts, the inner radius of the muscle shrinks, reducing the tension on the fibers

Figure 12.15 Find your blind spot. To find the blind spot in your right eye, position the figure about four inches directly in front of you. Cover your left eye. While focusing your right eye on the square, slowly move your head away from the figure. Eventually the circle will disappear, because at a certain distance from your right eye, its image will strike the blind spot. You can do the same demonstration with your left eye by covering your right eye and focusing on the circle; the square will disappear.

attached to the lens (**Figure 12.16a**). This allows the lens to bulge, and we focus on a near object. When the ciliary muscle relaxes, the ring of muscle increases the tension on the lens, stretching and flattening it and bringing more distant objects into focus (**Figure 12.16b**). **Accommodation** refers to the adjustment of lens curvature so we can focus on either near or far objects.

The light rays from each point of an object are bent and focused so that the image created on the retina is inverted (upside down). However, the brain interprets the image as right side up.

As we get older, the lens tends to stiffen and cannot resume a bulging shape even when the ciliary muscles are maximally contracted. The result is *presbyopia*, the inability to focus on nearby objects, which generally appears after age 40. People with presbyopia must hold reading material farther away to see the print clearly. Reading glasses can easily correct presbyopia.

✅ **Quick Check** *Suppose a person's lenses were removed entirely. Would the person become entirely blind, able to see some light but no images, able to see blurry images, or able to see sharp images? Explain.* ■

Eyeball shape affects focus

Differences in the shape of the eyeball can affect the ability to focus properly (**Figure 12.17**).

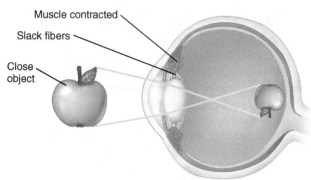

a) For near objects, contraction of ciliary muscles reduces the tension on the fibers and allows the lens to bulge.

b) For focus on distant objects, relaxation of ciliary muscles increases tension on the fibers, which pull on the lens and flatten it.

Figure 12.16 Accommodation. Notice that the images created on the retina are upside down.

Myopia is a common inherited condition in which the eyeball is slightly longer than normal (more rarely, myopia occurs when the ciliary muscle contracts too strongly). Even when the lens is flattened maximally, distant objects focus in front of the retina. People with myopia can see nearby objects, but distant objects are out of focus, which is why it is called *nearsightedness*. Concave lenses, which bend incoming light so it focuses on the retina, can correct nearsightedness.

BlogInFocus 🟦

The prevalence of myopia has increased much too quickly over the past 30 years to be due solely to genetic factors. To view a commentary and a research paper on this subject, visit MJ's blog in the Study Area in MasteringBiology and look under "Myopia."

a) The normal eye.

b) Nearsightedness (myopia). Nearsighted persons can see near objects clearly, but distant objects are out of focus because the focal point is in front of the retina.

c) Farsightedness (hyperopia). Farsighted persons can see distant objects clearly, but near objects are out of focus.

d) Astigmatism. Astigmatism is due to an abnormal curvature of either the cornea or the lens.

Figure 12.17 Examples of abnormal vision. All three types of abnormal vision are correctable.

Less common is the opposite condition, *hyperopia* (farsightedness), which occurs when the eyeball is too short and nearby objects focus behind the retina. Farsighted people can see distant objects clearly, but nearby objects are out of focus. Convex lenses correct farsightedness.

Astigmatism refers to blurred vision caused by irregularities of the shape of the cornea or lens. The result is that light is scattered and may not focus evenly on the retina. Astigmatism can be corrected with specially ground lenses that exactly compensate for the irregularities of the cornea and lens.

Light is converted into action potentials

Like other sensory organs, the eyes convert a stimulus (light) into impulses. In the eye this process occurs in the retina. The unique structure of the retina allows us to see in color, adapt to varying light intensities, and perceive images of the world around us.

Figure 12.18 shows a close-up of the retina, which consists of four layers:

1. The outermost layer consists of pigmented cells that, along with the choroid, absorb light not captured by the photoreceptor cells.

2. Next is a layer of photoreceptor cells called **rods** and **cones** because of their shape.
3. The rods and cones synapse with the third layer, a layer of neurons called *bipolar cells*. Bipolar cells partially process and integrate information and then pass it on to the fourth layer.
4. The innermost layer consists of ganglion cells. Ganglion cells are also neurons. Their long axons become the optic nerve going to the brain.

Notice that light must pass through the third and fourth layers to reach the photoreceptor cells, but this does not significantly hinder the ability of the photoreceptor cells to receive and convert light.

Rods and cones respond to light

Figure 12.19 takes a closer look at the photoreceptor cells, rods, and cones. One end of the cell consists of a series of flattened disks arranged to form either a rod- or cone-shaped structure, as the names imply. The flattened disks contain numerous molecules of a particular light-sensitive protein called a *photopigment*.

A photopigment protein undergoes a change of shape when it is exposed to energy in the form of light. The change in photopigment molecule shape causes the photoreceptor (rod or cone) to close some of its sodium channels and reduce the amount of neurotransmitter it normally releases. Because the neurotransmitter released by rods or cones normally inhibits the bipolar cells, light ultimately increases the activity of the bipolar cells, which in turn activate the ganglion cells (see Figure 12.18).

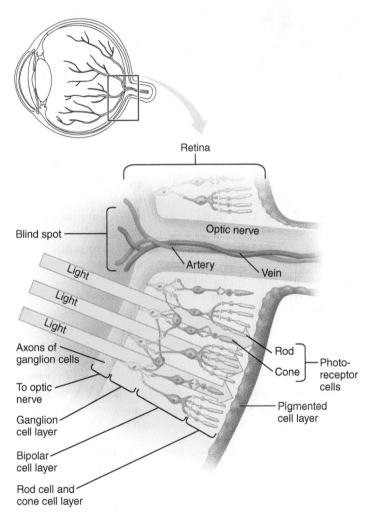

Figure 12.18 Structure of the retina. Light must pass between the axons of the ganglion cells and through the ganglion and bipolar cell layers to reach the photoreceptor cells, the rods and cones.

a) **The structure of cones and rods.**

Figure 12.19 The photoreceptor cells, cones and rods. The photopigments in the flattened disks are sensitive to light.

LASIK to Correct Vision Problems

Nearsightedness, farsightedness, and astigmatism are all visual problems that can be corrected with eyeglasses or contact lenses of one sort or another. But if you want a more permanent solution, you might consider LASIK surgery.

LASIK stands for laser in-situ keratomileusis, a generally safe and effective surgical technique in which lasers are used to permanently change the shape of the cornea. The technique can be done under local anesthesia in the ophthalmologist's office. The surgeon creates a thin flap of corneal tissue, folds it back, and then removes a small amount of corneal tissue from the cornea to reshape the cornea and correct the visual problem. The flap of tissue is returned to its original position and the eye is allowed to heal.

Most patients who undergo LASIK surgery will have vision close to 20/20 (normal) once the eye has healed completely. Normal vision is not assured, but most patients come pretty close to it. Some people experience halos of light around objects or are sensitive to glare after surgery, but these side effects generally are temporary. Every patient is different, of course, but complications from the surgery are rare. Answers to questions about *your* chances of attaining normal vision with LASIK should be addressed to your surgeon.

Not everyone is a good candidate for LASIK. People whose eyesight is still changing are generally advised to wait until their prescription for eyeglasses or contacts has been stable for at least two years. In addition, LASIK does not correct presbyopia, the condition for which one uses reading glasses. Nevertheless, many people who wear glasses or contacts all the time for nearsightedness, farsightedness, and astigmatism experience the freedom of being able to get rid of their corrective lenses entirely. ∎

There are approximately 120 million rods and 6 million cones, but only 1 million ganglion cells with axons going to the brain. Clearly, a great deal of convergence and summation of signals occurs at each level of neuron transfer.

Rods provide vision in dim light

Rods all have the same photopigment, called **rhodopsin**. Rhodopsin is much more sensitive to light than the photopigments in cones, and therefore in dim light our vision is dependent primarily on rods. However, rods do not give us color vision, which is why objects appear less colorful in dim light.

As we have seen, there are about 20 times more rods than cones. If we imagine that all 120 million rods converge on only half of the ganglion cells (one-half million), there would be 240 rods converging on a single ganglion cell. This convergence increases our ability to see in very dim light, but at the expense of acuity (accuracy and detail). As a result, our vision in very dim light is not very colorful and not very detailed, but at least we can see.

Rods and cones are not distributed evenly on the retina. Regions of the retina farthest away from the fovea have the highest ratio of rods to cones. If you want to see a dim star at night, don't look directly at it—look off to the side just a little.

Cones provide color vision and accurate images

Not all animals perceive color, but humans do. We are able to see colors because we have three different kinds of cones: red, green, and blue. Each contains a photopigment that absorbs the energy of red, green, or blue light particularly well.

Our ability to distinguish a variety of colors is due to the way the brain interprets the ratios of impulses coming from the ganglion cells connected to the three types of cones. When all three types are activated by all different wavelengths, we perceive white light. The perception of black is no light at all.

Cones also are responsible for visual acuity. However, cones require stronger light to be activated because the cone photopigments are much less sensitive to light than the rhodopsin in rods. This is why your ability to distinguish between colors declines in dim light and it becomes difficult to tell whether a dark-colored car is green or red. In dim light you are seeing primarily with your rods, which can detect only black and white.

✔ **Quick Check** *Do you think that animals active only at night, such as most owls, can see in color? Explain your answer.* ∎

Visual receptors adapt

From your own experience you know that vision adapts to changing light conditions over several seconds or minutes.

Adaptation seems to take longer when going from bright to dim light than it does in the opposite direction. Adaptation depends on rapid adjustment of the pupil by the iris and on adaptation by the rods.

The absorption of light by rhodopsin "uses up" the photopigment temporarily. Light energy actually breaks the rhodopsin into two molecules. These molecules can be resynthesized into rhodopsin again, but only over a period of minutes.

When you have been out in bright light, most of the rhodopsin in the light-sensitive rods has been broken down. Then, when you enter a dim room and the cones no longer are functioning, there is not enough intact rhodopsin for good vision in dim light. With time (5 to 15 minutes) the rhodopsin is resynthesized and available again.

Conversely, when you go out into sunlight from a dimly lit room, the light seems very bright because you have the maximal amount of photopigment available in both rods and cones. Most of the rhodopsin in the rods is quickly used up, however, and you revert to using primarily cones in bright light.

> **Recap** Light passes through the cornea, the lens, and the aqueous fluid of the eye before striking the photoreceptors in the retina. The iris regulates the amount of light entering the eye, and the cornea and the lens adjust the focus. Light energy alters the structure of photopigments—rhodopsin in rods, and red, blue, or green photopigments in cones. Rods provide vision in dim light. Cones are responsible for color vision and detailed images. ▪

12.7 Disorders of sensory mechanisms

Disorders of the ears

Deafness: loss of hearing Deafness can have many causes. Deafness caused by damage to hair cells (**Figure 12.20**) is called **nerve deafness** because sounds cannot be converted into impulses in sensory nerves. Nerve deafness is generally the result of frequent exposure to loud sounds. Damage to the tympanic membrane or the bones of the middle ear, on the other hand, is called **conduction deafness**. In conduction deafness sound waves simply are not transferred to the inner ear at all. Conduction deafness is frequently due to arthritis of the middle ear bones.

Some types of hearing loss may be partially corrected with a hearing aid, which amplifies incoming sounds, but even amplification won't be very effective if hair cells are missing. Some people with nerve deafness benefit from a cochlear implant, a tiny implanted microprocessor that converts sound waves into electrical signals.

Otitis media: Inflammation of the middle ear A common cause of earache is *otitis media*, or inflammation of the middle ear. Usually this results from an upper respiratory tract infection that extends up the auditory tube. The tube may become blocked and trap fluid in the middle ear. Otitis media usually responds to antibiotics.

Ménière's syndrome: Inner ear condition impairs hearing and balance Ménière's syndrome is a chronic condition of the inner ear. The cause is unknown, but it may be due to excess fluid in the cochlea and semicircular canals. Symptoms include repeated episodes of dizziness and nausea accompanied by progressive hearing loss. Balance is usually affected to the point that patients find it difficult to stay upright. Mild cases can be treated with motion sickness medications. Severe cases may benefit from surgery to drain excess fluid from the inner ear.

Disorders of the eyes

Retinal detachment: Retina separates from choroid If the thin retina is torn, the vitreous humor may leak through the tear and peel the retina away from the choroid, like peeling wallpaper from a wall (**Figure 12.21a**). The most common cause of retinal detachment in healthy persons is a blow to the head. The detached region of the retina loses most of its blood supply and its ability to focus an image properly. Symptoms include flashes of light, blurred vision, or loss of peripheral vision. Retinal detachment is an emergency, but prompt surgery can usually repair the damage.

Cataracts: The lens becomes opaque Cataracts are a decrease in the normal transparency of a lens (Figure 12.21b). Normally, the lens contains a particular kind of protein folded in such a way that it is transparent. If the delivery of nutrients to the lens is not sufficient, these proteins may denature, or clump, making the lens opaque. Some cataracts are congenital, but most are age-related or secondary to diabetes or other diseases.

About 5.5 million people in the United States (1 in 50) have a cataract impairing their vision. The treatment, which is usually successful, involves removing the lens surgically and replacing it with an artificial lens.

a) Normal healthy hair cells of the cochlea of a guinea pig.

b) Hair cells after 24 hours of exposure to loud sounds.

Figure 12.20 Damage to hair cells in the ears.

Glaucoma: Pressure inside the eye rises As mentioned previously, aqueous humor fills the chamber between the cornea and the lens. Capillaries located near the ciliary

a) Retinal detachment. In this ophthalmoscope view of a patient's eye the retina has peeled away from the choroid (upper third of the eye). At lower center is the yellow optic disk, through which the blood vessels travel.

b) Cataracts. The cataract in this person's right eye was caused by a chronic inflammatory disease process.

Figure 12.21 Common eye disorders.

muscles of the eye produce aqueous humor, which brings nutrients and oxygen to the lens and cornea and carries away wastes. Normally, aqueous humor is drained from the eye and returned to the venous blood by a vessel called the *canal of Schlemm* (review Figure 12.14). Glaucoma is a condition in which this drainage vessel becomes blocked. The excess fluid increases pressure inside the eye and compresses blood vessels supplying the retina. Cells of the retina or optic nerve may eventually die, impairing vision and ultimately leading to blindness. The impairment of vision often starts as a loss of peripheral vision (Figure 12.22a and b below).

Glaucoma generally develops slowly and painlessly over several years, without any outward symptoms. About 2 million people in the United States (1 in 136) are visually impaired by glaucoma. Most patients do not realize they have it until they have already lost some vision. Less commonly, glaucoma develops acutely (within hours) with symptoms of blurred vision and red, swollen, sometimes painful eyes. Acute glaucoma is a medical emergency that requires immediate attention by an eye doctor.

Both chronic (slow-onset) and acute glaucoma can be detected with a simple test that measures the pressure in the eye. If it is detected early enough, glaucoma can be controlled with drugs or surgery before any permanent damage is done. However, any vision that has already been lost cannot be restored. This is why a test of pressure in the eye is usually included in any comprehensive eye examination.

Age-related macular degeneration Age-related macular degeneration (AMD) is a disease of visual impairment caused by detachment of the retina and degeneration of photoreceptor cells in the macular region of the retina. The most common cause of AMD is accumulation of cellular debris between the choroid and the retina. Less commonly, it may be caused by abnormal growth of blood vessels in the region. In both cases the result is a loss of visual acuity in the center of the visual field, making it difficult to recognize faces or to read (Figure 12.22c). AMD affects about 1.75 million people in the United States (1 in 155). Because it is the leading cause

a) Normal vision.

b) Glaucoma.

c) Age-related macular degeneration.

Figure 12.22 Visual impairments caused by glaucoma and age-related macular degeneration.

of loss of vision in persons over 60, its prevalence is expected to rise dramatically as the U.S. population continues to age, unless a cure is found. There is no effective cure yet for most cases of AMD, although various vascular growth factors and vitamin treatments show promise at slowing or delaying the progression of the disease.

Color blindness: Inability to distinguish the full range of colors Color blindness is a general term for the inability to distinguish the full range of colors. Most forms of color blindness are caused by deficient numbers of particular types of cones. Less common are conditions in which one of the three cones is completely missing.

People with red-green color blindness, the most common form, are deficient in either red cones or green cones. They have trouble distinguishing between red and green, or they perceive them as the same color. The color they see is red or green, depending on which type of cone is missing.

The inability to perceive any color at all is quite rare in humans because it occurs only when two of the three types of cones are completely missing.

Color blindness is often inherited. Red-green color blindness is an X-linked recessive trait that is more common in men than in women. It affects approximately 8% of Caucasian males but only 1% of Caucasian females, and is less common in other races. Traffic lights always have the red ("stop") light at the top and the green ("go") light at the bottom so that color-blind people can tell them apart by position. Color blindness is easily tested with a series of colored test plates (Figure 12.23).

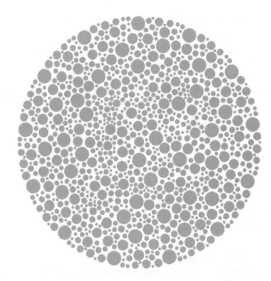

Figure 12.23 Test plate for diagnosing color blindness. A person with red-green color blindness would not be able to see the number 12 in this test plate. The original plate should be used for accurate testing of color blindness.

✓ *Suppose a woman had no blue cones at all in her retinas, but had normal numbers of the other types of rods and cones. Could she see the "12" in this picture? Explain.*

↩ **Recap** A detached retina is a retina that has separated from the underlying choroid. Glaucoma is a condition in which fluid pressure inside the eye rises, constricting the blood vessels that normally supply the living cells. Age-related macular degeneration is the most common cause of loss of vision in older persons. ∎

Chapter Summary

Receptors receive and convert stimuli *p. 278*

- Receptors convert the energy of a stimulus into impulses in sensory neurons.
- The brain interprets incoming impulses on the basis of where the sensory neurons originate.
- Some types of receptors adapt to continuous stimulation, whereas others (most notably pain receptors) do not.
- The somatic senses (temperature, touch, vibration, pressure, pain, and awareness of body position and movements) arise from receptors throughout the body.
- The five special senses (taste, smell, hearing, balance, and vision) arise from only certain specialized areas of the body.

Somatic sensations arise from receptors throughout the body *p. 280*

- The skin contains receptors for heat, cold, vibration, pressure, light touch, and pain. Receptors for temperature and for pain are also located in some internal organs.

- Receptors in joints sense joint position.
- Muscle spindles sense muscle length, and tendon receptors sense tendon (and muscle) tension.

Taste and smell depend on chemoreceptors *p. 283*

- Chemoreceptors for taste are located in structures called *taste buds*, most of which are on the tongue.
- The receptors for smell (called *olfactory receptors*) are located in the nasal passages. Humans have over 1,000 different olfactory receptor types.

Hearing: Mechanoreceptors detect sound waves *p. 285*

- The outer ear channels sound waves to the tympanic membrane, the middle ear amplifies the sound waves, and the cochlea of the inner ear converts sound waves to impulses.
- Sound waves of different tones are converted to impulses at different locations in the cochlea.

The inner ear plays an essential role in balance *p. 288*

- The vestibular apparatus of the inner ear consists of three semicircular canals and the vestibule.

- The semicircular canals are structures that sense rotational movement of the head on three planes.
- Structures of the vestibule sense static (nonmoving) head position and linear acceleration.

Vision: Detecting and interpreting visual stimuli *p. 290*

- The eye is the organ of vision, with structures for moving the eye (muscles), regulating the amount of light entering the eye (iris), focusing the visual image (lens), and converting light to impulses (retina).
- The photoreceptor cells in the retina are called *rods* and *cones*.
- Rods are 20 times more numerous than cones. They give us vision in dim light, but not in color and not with the highest detail.
- The three types of cones have different photopigments, so each type responds best to a different wavelength (color) of light. Cones are most effective in bright light, and they give us color vision and the sharpest image.
- Photoreceptors adapt to conditions of varying light intensities (brightness). It takes about 15 minutes to fully adapt to very dim light.

Disorders of sensory mechanisms *p. 295*

- Inflammation of the middle ear is a common cause of earache.
- Common eye disorders include retinal detachment, cataracts, glaucoma, age-related macular degeneration, and color blindness.

Terms You Should Know

accommodation, *292*	optic disk, *291*
auditory tube, *286*	photoreceptor, *278*
basilar membrane, *287*	receptor adaptation, *279*
chemoreceptors, *278*	retina, *291*
cochlea, *286*	rhodopsin, *294*
cones, *293*	rods, *293*
cornea, *290*	somatic sensations, *280*
hair cells, *287*	special senses, *280*
iris, *291*	taste bud, *283*
lens, *291*	thermoreceptors, *278*
macula, *291*	tympanic membrane
mechanoreceptors, *278*	(eardrum), *286*
muscle spindle, *281*	vestibular apparatus, *288*
olfactory receptor cell, *284*	

Concept Review

Answers can be found in the Study Area in MasteringBiology.

1. List the five classifications of receptors in terms of types of stimulus they convert.
2. Describe how receptor adaptation works.
3. Describe what information the somatic sensations provide.
4. Name the five special senses.
5. Compare and contrast fast pain, slow pain, and referred pain.
6. Describe the overall function of the three bones (the malleus, the incus, and the stapes) of the middle ear.
7. The eye contains both skeletal muscle and smooth muscle. Describe where each is located and indicate their functions.

8. Compare and contrast rods and cones.
9. Explain why it may take up to 15 minutes to become fully adapted to very dim light conditions.
10. Explain what causes glaucoma.

Test Yourself

Answers can be found in Appendix A.

1. What do the receptors in the skin for light touch and the receptors in the nose for smell have in common?
   a. They both respond to pressure.
   b. They both respond to chemicals.
   c. They send action potentials to the same area of the brain.
   d. They both adapt very quickly.

2. Which of the following are NOT found among the somatosensory receptors?
   a. mechanoreceptors
   b. thermoreceptors
   c. chemoreceptors
   d. pain receptors

3. A more powerful stimulus will:
   a. result in action potentials that travel more quickly
   b. result in activation of more receptors
   c. result in more frequent action potentials
   d. both (b) and (c)

4. Receptor adaptation results when:
   a. sensory neurons stop sending action potentials
   b. a stimulus is discontinued
   c. action potentials from different neurons cancel one another out
   d. the action potentials do not reach the brain

5. In what order do the structures of the ear come into play when hearing?
   a. malleus – tympanic membrane – cochlea – stapes – cochlear nerve
   b. auditory tube – malleus – cochlea – incus – cochlear nerve
   c. auditory canal – tympanic membrane – malleus – cochlea – cochlear nerve
   d. auditory canal – cochlea – tympanic membrane – cochlear nerve – malleus

6. Different pitched sounds will result in stimulation of receptors located in different regions of:
   a. hair cells
   b. round and oval windows
   c. the vestibular apparatus
   d. the cochlea

7. Which of the following correctly traces the path of light through the eye?
   a. cornea – aqueous humor – pupil – lens – vitreous humor – retina
   b. aqueous humor – pupil – cornea – lens – vitreous humor – retina
   c. pupil – cornea – vitreous humor – lens – aqueous humor – retina
   d. cornea – vitreous humor – lens – pupil – aqueous humor – retina

8. When we adjust our head and eye position to carefully look at something we are directing the image to focus on:
   a. the optic disk
   b. the macula
   c. the periphery of the retina
   d. the optic nerve

9. Which of the following will regulate the amount of light entering the eye?
   a. the cornea
   b. the lens
   c. the iris
   d. the retina

10. Which of the following is/are involved in focusing light?
    a. lens
    b. pupil
    c. cornea
    d. both (a) and (c)

11. Which of the following correctly describes the distribution of rods and cones in the retina?
    a. Rods and cones are evenly distributed throughout the retina.
    b. There are more cones on the periphery of the retina.
    c. Cones are more highly concentrated in the fovea centralis.
    d. Rods are more highly concentrated in the optic disk.

12. Which of the following statements explains why vision is less sharp in dim light than in bright light?
    a. Cones are more responsive in dim light.
    b. There are more rods than cones in the eye.
    c. Many rods converge on a single ganglion.
    d. The dilated pupil lets in more light than the lens can focus.

13. Conduction deafness would most likely be caused by damage to:
    a. the cochlear nerve
    b. the malleus, incus, and/or stapes
    c. the hair cells in the cochlea
    d. the vestibular apparatus

14. Which of the following would most readily be treated with antibiotics?
    a. cataracts
    b. otitis media
    c. glaucoma
    d. Ménière's syndrome

15. Which of the following can be corrected with corrective lenses?
    a. myopia
    b. color blindness
    c. hyperopia
    d. both (a) and (c)

Apply What You Know

Answers can be found in the Study Area in MasteringBiology.

1. With the eyes closed, would an astronaut in outer space be able to detect lateral movement of the head (would the semicircular canals be functioning normally)? Would the astronaut be able to detect static head position (would the utricle and saccule be functioning normally)? Explain.

2. Why do you suppose that you are not normally aware of the blind spot in each eye?

3. Our sense of smell is closely linked to our feelings and emotions. Bad odors usually evoke negative feelings, whereas pleasant odors give us a general sense of well-being or may be associated with good memories (perfume makers know this). The house of a pet owner can have an odor that a guest finds objectionable but the owner may not even be aware of. With a long enough visit even the guest may not notice the pet odors. Why is this?

4. Walk into any drugstore and you'll find dozens of over-the-counter products for reducing pain. Why is the experience of pain so common and so problematic?

5. An amateur boxer reported on an online forum that he saw lights flash before his eyes after being hit on the top of the head. This was unusual since he's normally hit in the chin or ear and knows what it's like to brownout during a knockout blow. Once the lights faded he was able to continue the fight. What happened when he was hit on the top of the head?

6. Try taking a really, really deep breath. If done correctly, there should be a moment of sharp pain in your chest. What's causing this?

7. What do you think might cause motion sickness, the combination of nausea and dizziness that some people get after a roller-coaster ride or when riding in a boat or a car? And why don't gymnasts get motion sick when they're performing?

BlogInFocus

Answers can be found in the Study Area in MasteringBiology.

1. Humans and other mammals respond to chemicals (called *pheromones*) released into the air by other members of their species, even though they can't consciously smell them. Based on what you have learned in this chapter about sensory mechanisms, where do you think the receptors for pheromones would most likely be located? (For more on pheromones, visit MJ's blog in the Study Area in MasteringBiology and look under "Pheromones.")

MasteringBiology®

Go to MasteringBiology for practice quizzes, activities, eText, videos, current events, and more.

The Endocrine System

A growth hormone–producing cell in the pituitary gland. The hormone is stored in secretory vesicles (brown) within the cytoplasm (gold), awaiting secretion.

Endocrine Disruptors in the Environment

In this chapter you will learn that the endocrine system plays a critical role in the maintenance of homeostasis. It also triggers or supports certain key events such as sexual maturation and puberty, childbirth, lactation, and certain aspects of metabolism. The endocrine system relies on hormones as signalling molecules.

Certain compounds are known to disrupt the function of the endocrine system. Known collectively as *endocrine disruptors*, they are defined by the Environmental Protection Agency (EPA) as "exogenous agents that interfere with the production, release, transport, metabolism, binding, action, or elimination of the natural hormones in the body responsible for the maintenance of homeostasis and the regulation of developmental processes." Endocrine disruptors are found nearly everywhere in trace amounts: in the environment, in the consumer products we use, and even in our bodies. Should we be concerned? The answer to that question is largely unknown and is a hot topic of debate, as the following two examples will show.

Phthalates: The plastic duck scare of 1997

In the fall of 1997 right before the Christmas shopping season, the well-known European environmental group Greenpeace launched a highly visible campaign called "Play Safe" simultaneously in London and New York. Its target was polyvinyl chloride (PVC), a soft plastic used to make many consumer goods, including children's toys and other children's items. A little-known group of chemicals called **phthalates**, added to PVC to make it soft and pliable, was targeted as a dangerous endocrine disruptor that should be banned from children's toys. The public became concerned, certain toys were shunned that Christmas season, and there were calls for a ban on phthalates in children's toys. The public outcry had the desired effect, though it took 10 years before action was taken. In 2008 the Consumer Product Safety Commission banned several of the phthalates from children's toys and childcare articles, even though there was no clear scientific evidence to support a ban.

Children's toys such as this plastic duck once contained phthalates.

Phthalates are still being widely used today. They're found in nail polishes, hair sprays, vinyl floor and wall coverings, and soft plastic consumer products such as shower curtains. They're even found in blood collection bags, medical tubing, and some pharmaceutical pills. People have been exposed to phthalates for nearly 50 years, and there is still no convincing evidence of a human disease having been caused by phthalates. And yet, if you Google "phthalate ban" or "phthalate scare" today, you will find very polarized and firmly entrenched views regarding the safety of phthalates.

Should we be worried? Perhaps yes, perhaps no. The evidence against phthalates comes primarily from toxicology studies in animals, in which animals are deliberately fed ever-larger amounts of phthalates to determine at what point they cause a negative health effect. In toxicology studies, phthalates are endocrine disruptors, interfering with the action of testosterone on the development of the male reproductive system. They can cause low sperm counts, liver failure, and even cancer. No human has ever been subjected to these kinds of doses.

The newest concern: Bisphenol A (BPA)

A newer and potentially more problematic endocrine disruptor is **Bisphenol A (BPA)**. BPA is added to many hard, clear plastic products to make them more pliable. It is present in the plastic lining of food cans, hard plastic food and beverage containers, dental sealants and fillings, and some baby bottles. It is widespread in our environment due to losses at production sites and leaching from landfills. It is used to coat the paper used in heat-sensitive printers, so it is even found in many cash register receipts. According to the 2008–2010 National Health and Nutrition Examination Survey, BPA can be detected in the urine of 92% of all persons over the age of six.

BPA is called an "environmental estrogen" because it interferes with many estrogenic endocrine control mechanisms. There is concern that it may be responsible for a number of trends in human health over the past several decades, including an increase in obesity and Type 2 diabetes, decreases in sperm count in males, increases in hormonally mediated cancers (prostate and breast), and early sexual maturation in females. The potential effects of low-dose exposure to BPA over the human lifespan and on fetal and early childhood development are "great cause for concern," according to an expert panel convened in 2006.[1]

BPA represents a difficult problem for policymakers because it is a high-volume production chemical used in a wide variety of manufacturing processes and consumer products. Over 7 billion pounds of it are produced each year—a pound for every person on earth. Over the past several years, proposals to Congress to restrict or ban the use of BPA have failed due to intense lobbying by the chemical industry. Industry lobbyists argue that BPA is safe, that there

Hard plastic reusable water bottles may contain BPA.

are not good alternatives to BPA, and that jobs are at stake. But that hasn't stopped many states are taking things into their own hands. As of 2012, 12 states have banned the use of BPA in children's bottles and sippy cups, and others are likely to follow suit.

As these two examples show, the issue of endocrine disruptors is likely to remain controversial for a while. We are just beginning to learn how widespread endocrine disruptors already are in our environment and the many ways they might affect body systems. More research is needed, of course. The big question is what to do about them now, if anything.

When something is suspected of causing harm but there is no proof of harm, perhaps it makes sense to err on the side of caution. But where is the proper balance between caution, and jobs? You decide.

QUESTIONS TO CONSIDER

1 Would you be in favor of a federal ban on BPA from baby bottles? Why or why not?

2 Do you think that phthalates and/or BPA should be further restricted from additional consumer products? Why or why not? If you're not sure, what additional information would you like to have before making a decision?

---

[1] vom Saal, Frederick S. Chapel Hill bisphenol A expert panel consensus statement; Integration of mechanisms, effects on animals and potential to impact human health at current levels of exposure. *Reprod. Toxicol.* 24:131–138, 2007.

THE FACTS...

- Our environment contains many chemicals, collectively called "endocrine disruptors," that have been proven (in animal studies) to disrupt the function of endocrine systems.

- The effects of endocrine disruptors on human health and development are largely unknown.

- Regulators face the difficult task of deciding whether to ban or restrict the use of endocrine disruptors, many of which are important chemicals in manufacturing processes.

>> The endocrine system produces chemical messenger molecules called *hormones* and secretes them into the blood.

>> Hormones only act on certain cells, called the hormone's *target cells*, because only a hormone's target cells have specific receptors for the hormone.

>> Steroid and nonsteroid hormones have different mechanisms of action. Steroid hormones enter the target cell before binding to a receptor, whereas nonsteroid hormones bind to receptors at the outer surface of the cell membrane.

>> Some hormones participate in negative feedback loops that maintain homeostasis. Other hormones regulate major life-changing processes such as growth and sexual maturation.

>> The pituitary gland is sometimes called *the master gland*. It secretes eight different hormones that in turn regulate the production of many other hormones.

At about ages 11–13, something strange and wonderful happens to the human body and mind. The body grows rapidly, and secondary sex characteristics develop. Many boys get interested in girls, and many girls get interested in boys with an intensity that sometimes seems to border on obsession, when only months before they couldn't care less.

Welcome to the endocrine system, an internal system of powerful chemicals that controls a host of body functions. The endocrine system triggers sexual maturation, sexual desire, uterine contractions during childhood, and milk letdown. It is involved in responses to stress, digestion, cellular metabolism, and overall organ growth and development. And it is wholly or partly responsible for the maintenance of homeostasis of many of the most important variables in the body, including salt and water balance, blood pressure, the production of red blood cells, and blood calcium concentration. Essentially all body systems are impacted in some way by the endocrine system.

13.1 The endocrine system produces hormones

The **endocrine system** is a collection of specialized cells, tissues, and glands that produce and secrete circulating chemical messenger molecules called **hormones**. Hormones are secreted by **endocrine glands**—ductless organs that secrete their products into interstitial fluid, lymph, and blood (*endocrine* means "secreted internally"). In contrast, **exocrine glands** secrete products such as mucus, sweat, tears, and digestive fluids into ducts that empty into the appropriate sites. Approximately 50 known hormones circulate in the human bloodstream, and new ones are still being discovered.

Hormones are bloodborne units of information, just as nerve impulses are units of information carried in nerves. Some hormones participate in feedback control loops regulating various body functions. We need these hormones to maintain homeostasis. Other hormones produce specific effects, such as contraction of the uterus at birth, growth during childhood, and the development of sexual characteristics at puberty. Figure 13.1 shows the various tissues and organs that make up the endocrine system and the most important hormones they secrete. The many functions of these hormones are discussed in this chapter and in other chapters where appropriate.

The endocrine system has certain characteristics that set it apart from the nervous system as a communications system.

1. *Hormones of the endocrine system reach nearly every living cell.* This attribute gives the endocrine system a distinct advantage over the nervous system. Delivery of hormones to nearly all cells occurs because hormones circulate in the blood, and almost every cell in the body is near a blood vessel. (An exception is the central nervous system, which is effectively isolated from exposure to most systemic hormones by the blood-brain barrier.) With the endocrine system there is no need for the direct connections (the hard wiring, so to speak) required by the nervous system.

2. *Each hormone acts only on certain cells.* As all hormones circulate together in the same well-mixed blood, how can one hormone specifically regulate red blood cell production, whereas another regulates blood calcium concentration? The answer is that each hormone acts only on a certain group of cells, called its **target cells**, because only the hormone's target cells have the appropriate receptor to fit it. When a hormone binds to a receptor on its target cell, a change occurs within the cell. The cell may grow, divide, or change its metabolism in some way. All other cells of the body fail to respond to the hormone because they lack the appropriate receptor. As an analogy, consider that your car is a cell, the car's ignition switch is the receptor, and the car key is the hormone. Your car key fits only your car (the "target" car) and no other. Fitting your key into the ignition and turning it causes the car to start. Gas is consumed, engine parts rotate, and heat is generated.

BlogInFocus (MB)

How easily does the endocrine disruptor bisphenol A (BPA) leach out of the lining of food cans and into the foods we eat? To find out, visit MJ's blog in the Study Area in MasteringBiology and look under "endocrine disruptors."

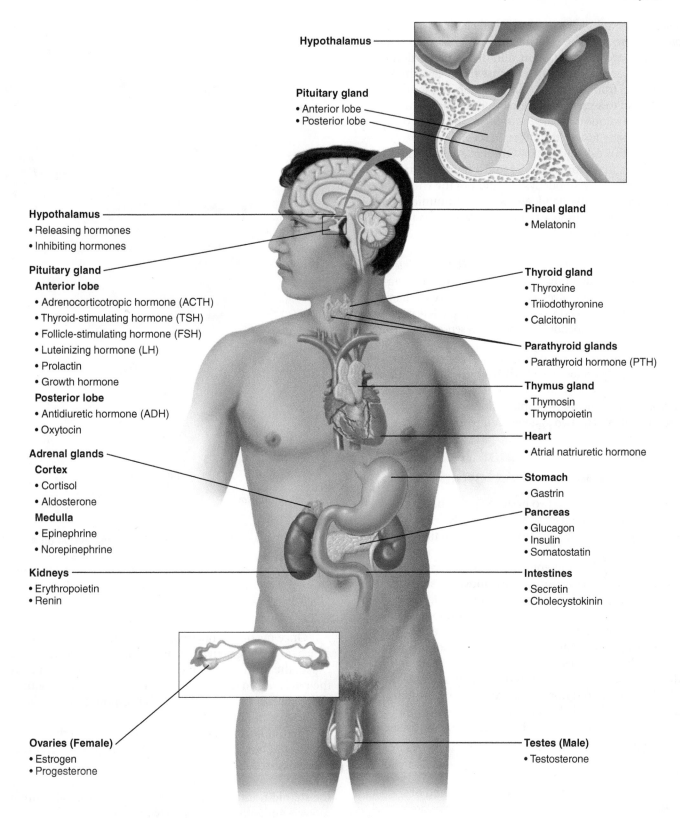

Hypothalamus

Pituitary gland
• Anterior lobe
• Posterior lobe

Hypothalamus
• Releasing hormones
• Inhibiting hormones

Pituitary gland
  Anterior lobe
  • Adrenocorticotropic hormone (ACTH)
  • Thyroid-stimulating hormone (TSH)
  • Follicle-stimulating hormone (FSH)
  • Luteinizing hormone (LH)
  • Prolactin
  • Growth hormone
  Posterior lobe
  • Antidiuretic hormone (ADH)
  • Oxytocin

Adrenal glands
  Cortex
  • Cortisol
  • Aldosterone
  Medulla
  • Epinephrine
  • Norepinephrine

Kidneys
• Erythropoietin
• Renin

Ovaries (Female)
• Estrogen
• Progesterone

Pineal gland
• Melatonin

Thyroid gland
• Thyroxine
• Triiodothyronine
• Calcitonin

Parathyroid glands
• Parathyroid hormone (PTH)

Thymus gland
• Thymosin
• Thymopoietin

Heart
• Atrial natriuretic hormone

Stomach
• Gastrin

Pancreas
• Glucagon
• Insulin
• Somatostatin

Intestines
• Secretin
• Cholecystokinin

Testes (Male)
• Testosterone

Figure 13.1 Components of the human endocrine system. Note that some organs with nonendocrine primary functions (the heart, stomach, intestines, and kidneys) produce and secrete hormones as secondary functions.

3. *Endocrine control tends to be slower than nervous system control.* There is a price for using the cardiovascular system as the message delivery system, and that is a reduction in speed—a lengthening of the response time. Nerve impulses can travel from head to toe in a fraction of a second. It takes longer to secrete a hormone into the bloodstream, have the hormone circulate to its target, and exert its effect. At the very fastest, this takes 20 seconds or so.

Given this difference in speed, it is not surprising that reflexes that prompt us to avoid a hot flame are controlled by the nervous system and not the endocrine system. On the other hand, endocrine communication is highly effective for longer-term controls, such as regulation of blood pressure, production of red blood cells, and onset of puberty.

4. *The endocrine and nervous systems can (and often do) interact with each other.* The timing of growth and sexual maturation, for example, involves a complex sequence of changes in both neural and endocrine signals, and the release of some hormones depends on input from sensory neurons.

Recap Hormones secreted by glands of the endocrine system act only on target cells with appropriate receptors. Hormones reach their targets via the circulatory system, making endocrine system control slower than nervous system control. The two systems frequently interact. ▪

13.2 Hormones are classified as steroid or nonsteroid

Hormones are classified into two basic categories based on their structure and mechanism of action. **Steroid hormones** are structurally related to cholesterol (a lipid), and therefore they are lipid soluble. Steroid hormones act by entering the cell, binding to an intracellular receptor, and activating genes that produce new proteins. **Nonsteroid hormones** are structurally related to proteins; therefore, they are lipid insoluble and cannot cross the cell membrane. Nonsteroid hormones act by binding to receptors on the cell's surface, which initiates a series of events that ultimately alters cellular activity in some way, even though the hormones never entered the cell at all.

Most of the hormones discussed in this chapter are nonsteroid. The only steroid hormones are those produced by the cortex of the adrenal gland (cortisol and aldosterone) and the sex hormones produced by the testes (testosterone) and ovaries (estrogen and progesterone).

Steroid hormones enter target cells

Recall that the cell membrane is primarily composed of a bilayer of phospholipids. Because steroid hormones are related to cholesterol and therefore are lipid soluble, they can easily diffuse right across both the cell membrane and the nuclear membrane. Once inside the cell, steroid hormones bind to specific hormone receptors, forming a hormone-receptor complex either within the nucleus (Figure 13.2) or within the cytoplasm (not shown). If the hormone-receptor complex was formed in the cytoplasm, it too can diffuse into the nucleus.

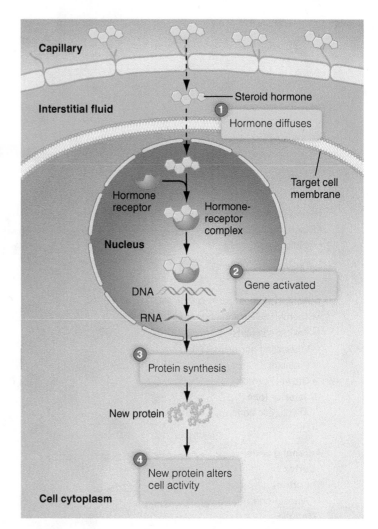

Figure 13.2 Mechanism of steroid hormone action on a target cell. Lipid-soluble steroid hormones diffuse across the cell and nuclear membranes into the nucleus, where they bind to hormone receptors that activate genes. Gene activation results in the production of a specific protein.

Once inside the nucleus, the hormone-receptor complex attaches to DNA, activating specific genes. Gene activation causes the formation of messenger RNA, which then leaves the nucleus and directs the synthesis of certain proteins. The proteins then carry out the cellular response to the hormone, whatever it might be.

Steroid hormones tend to be slower acting than nonsteroid hormones because the entire protein production process (starting with gene activation) begins only after arrival of the hormone within the cell. Starting from the time the steroid hormone first enters the cell, it can take minutes or even hours to produce a new protein.

Nonsteroid hormones bind to receptors on target cell membranes

Nonsteroid hormones cannot enter the target cell because they are not lipid soluble. Instead they bind to receptors located on the outer surface of the cell membrane. The receptors are generally associated with, or are part of, protein molecules floating in the phospholipid bilayer of the cell membrane (Chapter 3). The binding of hormone to receptor causes a change in the shape of the membrane protein, which in turn initiates a change within the cell. It's like turning the lights on in a room by flipping a switch located in the hall outside, without ever having to enter the room.

Some nonsteroid hormones cause ion channels in the cell membrane to open or close, similar to the action of a neurotransmitter. More commonly, hormone-receptor binding converts an inactive molecule within the cell into an active molecule. The activated molecule generated within the cell is called a **second messenger** because it carries the message provided by the hormone (the "first messenger") without the hormone ever entering the cell. A common second messenger is cyclic AMP, produced from ATP. Cyclic AMP then activates an enzyme already present within the cell, which activates another, which in turn activates another, and so on (Figure 13.3). The last enzyme produces the cellular product from a precursor molecule. At each successive activation

step the effect is amplified, so that even a small amount of hormone can produce a large amount of final product.

In fact, amplification is the norm for both steroid and nonsteroid hormones. If a hormone were a lighted match, the effect of the hormone would be the equivalent of a bonfire. Hormones start something small (a change in protein synthesis or activation of an enzyme), but the final effect can be as dramatic as the development of secondary sexual characteristics.

Most nonsteroid hormones tend to be faster-acting than steroid hormones because they activate enzymes that already exist within the cell in inactive form. An entire cascade of existing enzymes can be activated within seconds or minutes.

✅ **Quick Check** *Would you expect a steroid hormone to result in production of a second messenger? Why or why not?* ▪

Hormones participate in negative feedback loops

As messenger molecules, some hormones participate in internal homeostatic control mechanisms and control vital physiological processes. It is essential to regulate carefully the rate at which each hormone is secreted, so that its concentration in blood is just right to carry out its function.

As described previously (Chapter 4), homeostasis is generally maintained by a negative feedback control loop. In a negative feedback loop involving a hormone, the endocrine gland is the control center, the hormone represents the pathway between the control center and the effectors, and the effectors are the hormone's target cells, tissues, or organs (Figure 13.4). A negative feedback loop

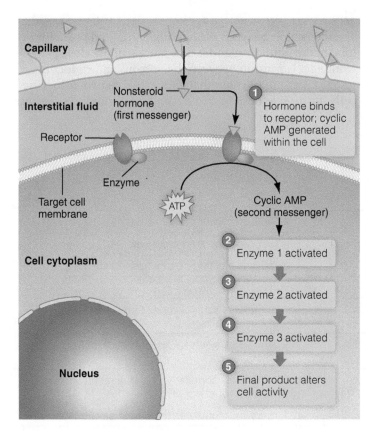

Figure 13.3 Mechanism of nonsteroid hormone action on a target cell. Nonsteroid hormones bind to receptors in the cell membrane, leading to the conversion of ATP to cyclic AMP (the second messenger) within the cell. Cyclic AMP initiates a cascade of enzyme activations, amplifying the original hormonal signal and generating a cellular response.

✅ *If the binding of one hormone molecule to its receptor on the cell's surface results in production of 10 cyclic AMPs and then there is an additional 10-fold amplification at each subsequent enzyme step, how many molecules of final product will be produced?*

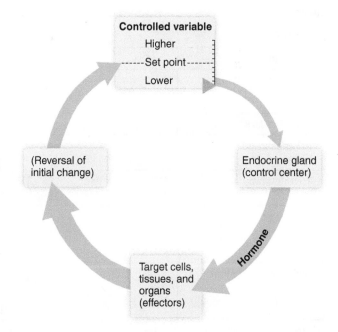

Figure 13.4 A negative feedback loop involving a hormone. In response to a change in the controlled variable, the endocrine gland releases a hormone that acts on target cells to return the controlled variable to its normal state.

Answers to ✅ **questions can be found in Appendix A.**

involving an endocrine gland and a hormone is a stable, self-adjusting mechanism for maintaining homeostasis of the controlled variable, because any change in the controlled variable sets in motion a response that reverses that change.

Not all negative feedback loops involving hormones are quite as simple as the one depicted in Figure 13.4. In some cases the real control center is the brain, which activates an endocrine gland via nerves. Nevertheless the effect is the same—reversal of the initial change in the controlled variable.

A few hormones are secreted in response to specific environmental cues or for specific purposes, such as to avoid danger or to initiate puberty. This type of hormone secretion is not part of a negative feedback loop.

We turn now to some key endocrine glands and their hormones. Some of the hormones mentioned here are covered in more depth in other chapters, when the function of specific organ systems is discussed.

↩ **Recap** Many hormones participate in negative feedback loops that maintain homeostasis. Steroid hormones enter the target cell, activate specific genes, and cause the production of new proteins. Nonsteroid hormones bind to a cell membrane receptor that either opens or closes ion channels or activates a second messenger within the cell. ▪

13.3 The hypothalamus and the pituitary gland

The **hypothalamus** is a small region in the brain that serves as a homeostatic control center. It is an important link between the nervous system and the endocrine system. The hypothalamus receives neural input about certain internal environmental conditions such as water and solute balance, temperature, and carbohydrate metabolism. It produces two hormones of its own, and it monitors and controls the hormone secretions of the pituitary gland. The pituitary gland is located directly beneath the hypothalamus and connected to it by a thin stalk of tissue.

The **pituitary gland** is sometimes called the "master gland" because it secretes eight different hormones that in turn regulate many of the other endocrine glands (Table 13.1). It consists of two lobes: a posterior lobe that appears to be a bulging extension of the connecting stalk, and a larger, more distinct anterior lobe (Figure 13.5).

The posterior pituitary stores ADH and oxytocin

The interaction between the hypothalamus and posterior lobe of the pituitary gland is an example of the close working relationship between the nervous and endocrine systems. Cells in the hypothalamus called **neuroendocrine cells** function as both nerve cells and endocrine cells, because

Table 13.1 **Hormones of the pituitary gland**

Hormone	Abbreviation	Main targets	Primary actions
Posterior Pituitary			
Antidiuretic hormone	ADH	Kidneys	Reduces amount of water lost in urine
Oxytocin	—	Uterus	Induces uterine contractions
		Mammary glands	Induces ejection of milk from mammary glands
Anterior Pituitary			
Adrenocorticotropic hormone	ACTH	Adrenal cortex	Stimulates adrenal cortex to release glucocorticoids
Thyroid-stimulating hormone	TSH	Thyroid gland	Stimulates synthesis and secretion of thyroid hormones
Follicle-stimulating hormone	FSH	Ovaries	In females, stimulates egg maturation and the secretion of estrogen
		Testes	In males, stimulates the formation of sperm
Luteinizing hormone	LH	Ovaries	In females, stimulates ovulation (egg release) and the secretion of progesterone
		Testes	In males, stimulates testosterone secretion
Prolactin	PRL	Mammary glands	Stimulates the development of mammary gland cells and production of milk
Growth hormone	GH	Most cells	Stimulates growth in young individuals; plays multiple roles in cell division, protein synthesis, and metabolism in adults

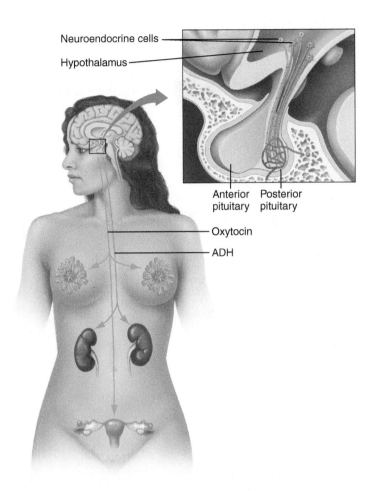

Figure 13.5 **Posterior pituitary lobe and hypothalamus.**
Individual neuroendocrine cells of the hypothalamus and the
posterior pituitary secrete either ADH or oxytocin. The hormones
enter the blood supply of the posterior pituitary and make their
way to the general circulation. ADH acts on the kidneys to regulate
water balance in the body. Oxytocin primarily acts on the mammary
glands and uterus muscles of lactating and pregnant women,
respectively.

the same cells generate nerve impulses and secrete hormones
into blood vessels.

Figure 13.5 illustrates the posterior pituitary lobe and
its connections to the hypothalamus. The cell bodies of the
neuroendocrine cells are located in the hypothalamus. Their
axons that extend down the stalk between the hypothalamus
to the posterior pituitary and into the posterior pituitary
itself. Neurons make either antidiuretic hormone (ADH)
or oxytocin in the hypothalamus and then transport the
hormones down the axon to the posterior pituitary, where
they are stored prior to release.

When the hypothalamus is stimulated to release the
hormones, the neuroendocrine cells send impulses down the
axon, causing hormone to be secreted into nearby capillaries.
The hormones are carried to their target cells by the blood.

ADH regulates water balance You may think of ADH as the
"water-conserving hormone." ADH reduces the amount of

water lost in urine, helping to maintain the body's overall
water balance. The primary target cells for ADH are in the
kidneys, where it causes changes in cell permeability to water
in the kidney's tubules. The action of ADH is discussed in more
detail in the chapter on the urinary system (Chapter 15).

The control of ADH secretion is an example of a
negative feedback loop, in this case one that maintains
homeostasis of water volume and concentration. When
the hypothalamus detects low concentrations of water
(equivalent to a high concentration of solute particles)
in the blood, neuroendocrine cells release ADH from the
posterior pituitary. ADH circulates in blood to the kidneys,
where it stimulates the reabsorption of water. When water
concentrations rise to normal levels, the hypothalamus is
no longer stimulated to release ADH, and ADH secretion
declines.

☑ **Quick Check** *What would happen to your ADH levels if you
drank a large amount of water, and what effect would this have
on the kidneys?* ▪

Oxytocin causes uterine contractions and milk ejection The
primary target cells for oxytocin are in the uterus and the
mammary glands (breasts) of pregnant and lactating females,
respectively. Oxytocin is secreted at high concentrations during
childbirth and also when an infant nurses at its mother's breast
(Figure 13.6). It stimulates contractions of the uterus during
childbirth and ejection of milk into the ducts of the mammary
glands during suckling.

The stimulation of oxytocin secretion by nursing is an
example of a *neuroendocrine reflex*, in which a nervous system
stimulus (activation of sensory mechanoreceptors in the
mother's breast) is responsible for secretion of a hormone.
When a baby suckles, sensory receptors in the nipple are
stimulated. Impulses are transmitted to neuroendocrine
cells in the hypothalamus, which release oxytocin from the
posterior pituitary. The hormone circulates to breast tissue,
binds with receptors, and causes contractions of smooth
muscle that eject milk.

Oxytocin is also present in males. In both sexes it is
thought to play a role in sexual arousal and the feeling of
sexual satisfaction after orgasm.

The anterior pituitary produces
six key hormones

The anterior lobe of the pituitary gland produces the
following six key anterior pituitary hormones:

- Adrenocorticotropic hormone (ACTH), also called
  corticotropin
- Thyroid-stimulating hormone (TSH), also called
  thyrotropin
- Follicle-stimulating hormone (FSH)
- Luteinizing hormone (LH)
- Prolactin (PRL)
- Growth hormone (GH)

3 Neuroendocrine cells release oxytocin when stimulated.

Neuroendocrine cell

Hypothalamus

Spinal cord

Anterior pituitary

4 Oxytocin is transported by blood to mammary glands.

2 Sensory and spinal nerves carry impulses to the neuroendocrine cells of hypothalamus.

Milk ejected

Posterior pituitary

Oxytocin

1 Nursing stimulates nerve receptors in nipple.

Figure 13.6 The control of oxytocin secretion by nursing. The act of suckling triggers a series of events that ultimately eject milk from the nipple.

Each anterior pituitary hormone is produced and secreted by a separate cell type, and each hormone is regulated by separate mechanisms. The first four hormones (ACTH, TSH, FSH, and LH) act by stimulating the release of yet other hormones from other endocrine glands.

The secretion of anterior pituitary hormones depends partly on the hypothalamus, but the mechanism differs from that of the posterior pituitary. The connection between the hypothalamus and anterior pituitary is endocrine, not neural; it relies on specific releasing and inhibiting hormones secreted by neuroendocrine cells in the hypothalamus (Figure 13.7). These releasing and inhibiting hormones, in turn, alter the secretion of the six anterior pituitary hormones. Releasing and inhibiting hormones are produced in miniscule quantities. However, they are secreted directly into a special blood supply that runs directly between the hypothalamus and anterior pituitary (called the *pituitary portal system*), so their concentrations are sufficient to regulate anterior pituitary hormone secretions.

ACTH stimulates the adrenal cortex The names of hormones generally offer a clue to their function or site of action. The target cells for ACTH are located in the outer layer, or cortex, of the adrenal gland (in *adrenocorticotropic* the suffix –*tropic* means "acting upon").

ACTH stimulates the adrenal cortex to release another group of hormones called *glucocorticoids*, which are steroid hormones involved in stress-related conditions and the control of glucose metabolism (see section 13.5). ACTH secretion is regulated by a negative feedback loop involving a releasing hormone from the hypothalamus and the concentration of glucocorticoids in blood.

TSH acts on the thyroid gland TSH stimulates the thyroid gland to synthesize and release thyroid hormones. There is a TSH-releasing hormone from the hypothalamus, mentioned earlier.

FSH and LH stimulate the reproductive organs FSH and LH are called *gonadotropins* because they stimulate the growth, development, and function of the reproductive organs (gonads) in both males and females. In females, FSH induces egg development, LH promotes ovulation (egg release), and both hormones stimulate the secretion of the ovarian hormone estrogen. In addition, LH stimulates the secretion of the ovarian hormone progesterone after ovulation. In males, FSH induces sperm development and LH stimulates the production of the hormone testosterone by the testes.

FSH and LH are essentially absent until about age 10–13. A major increase in the production of these two hormones is what initiates sexual maturation and the development of secondary sex characteristics (puberty).

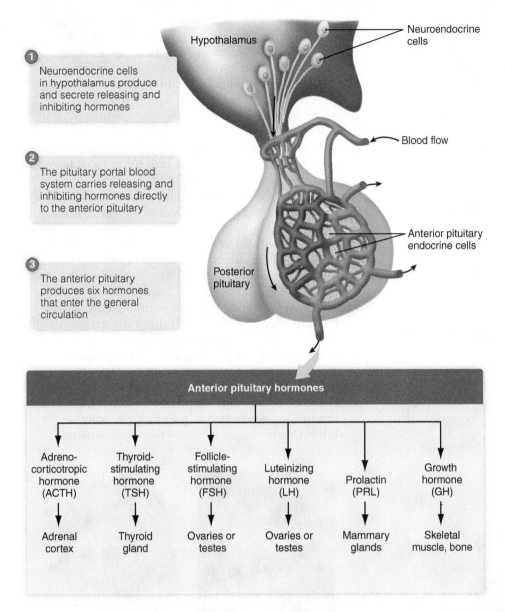

① Neuroendocrine cells in hypothalamus produce and secrete releasing and inhibiting hormones

② The pituitary portal blood system carries releasing and inhibiting hormones directly to the anterior pituitary

③ The anterior pituitary produces six hormones that enter the general circulation

Hypothalamus

Neuroendocrine cells

Blood flow

Anterior pituitary endocrine cells

Posterior pituitary

Anterior pituitary hormones

Adreno-corticotropic hormone (ACTH)	Thyroid-stimulating hormone (TSH)	Follicle-stimulating hormone (FSH)	Luteinizing hormone (LH)	Prolactin (PRL)	Growth hormone (GH)
Adrenal cortex	Thyroid gland	Ovaries or testes	Ovaries or testes	Mammary glands	Skeletal muscle, bone

Figure 13.7 The relationship between the hypothalamus and the anterior pituitary gland. Neuroendocrine cells in the hypothalamus secrete releasing hormones and inhibiting hormones into a system of capillaries that goes directly to the anterior pituitary. Specific hypothalamic hormones inhibit or stimulate each anterior pituitary hormone.

Prolactin (PRL): Mammary glands and milk production

Prolactin's primary function is to stimulate the development of mammary gland cells and the production of milk. Prolactin is present in males but its function is unknown. In females, the prolactin concentration in blood rises toward the end of pregnancy because estrogen stimulates the hypothalamus to step up production of *prolactin-releasing hormone,* one of the releasing hormones mentioned earlier. When estrogen levels decline after birth, prolactin-releasing hormone and prolactin levels are kept high by a sensory neural reflex associated with nursing.

When a woman is not in late pregnancy or breast-feeding, prolactin secretion is suppressed by *prolactin-inhibiting*

hormone, another releasing/inhibiting hormone from the hypothalamus. It is now thought that a prolactin-inhibiting hormone is actually identical to the neurotransmitter, dopamine.

✅ **Quick Check** *Suppose a pregnant woman has a mutant version of oxytocin that cannot bind to oxytocin receptors, but she produces normal prolactin. Will she still be able to give birth, produce milk, and nurse her baby?* ▪

Growth hormone (GH): Widespread effects on growth

The effects of growth hormone are so widespread that it is difficult to define a specific target cell or action. The effects of GH are most obvious in bone and muscle. In general, GH influences cells in ways that promote growth. Specific actions include stimulating protein synthesis and cell division, and using body fat as a source of energy.

GH is present throughout life, but most of its growth-promoting effects occur during childhood and adolescence. At these times it causes a dramatic increase in the mass and length of muscles and bones. Abnormal GH concentrations during development can lead to permanent changes in the final height of an adult. In adults it continues to help regulate metabolism by promoting the utilization of fats and amino acids as cellular fuel and by helping to maintain blood glucose levels.

Pituitary disorders: Hypersecretion or hyposecretion

As you might guess, maintaining just the right quantities of hormones in the blood is a delicate balance that can sometimes go awry. Many diseases and disorders are chronic conditions of too much hormone (hypersecretion) or too little hormone (hyposecretion). Some are inherited. To illustrate the types of things that can go wrong, we focus on hyposecretion of one posterior pituitary hormone (ADH) and both hyposecretion and hypersecretion of an anterior pituitary hormone (GH).

ADH affects maintenance of water balance by the kidneys. Hyposecretion of ADH causes the kidneys to lose too much water, leading to a disorder called *diabetes insipidus.* Symptoms include excessive urination, dehydration, thirst, headache, and dry mouth. Some cases of diabetes insipidus are caused by head trauma or brain surgery that disrupts the normal production of ADH.

Even when ADH hormone levels are normal, diabetes insipidus can still occur if the kidney cells that normally respond to ADH are lacking the specific ADH receptors. As a general rule, then, an endocrine control loop can be disrupted either by lack of a hormone or by lack of target cell receptors for that hormone. Either way, the system does not function effectively. Endocrine disorders due to defects in target cell receptors are quite common and are often inherited.

Growth hormone has much longer-acting effects than ADH. Recall that in children, growth hormone stimulates the bone-lengthening activity of the growth plate, so that bones grow longer along with the child's overall growth. It is not surprising, therefore, that abnormalities of growth hormone secretion are most damaging when they occur before puberty. Hyposecretion of growth hormone during childhood can result in *pituitary dwarfism*. Conversely, hypersecretion of growth hormone during childhood and adolescence produces *gigantism* (Figure 13.8).

Dwarfism can be prevented if children are diagnosed early and treated with a growth hormone throughout childhood. However, once adulthood is reached, dwarfism cannot be overcome by administering a growth hormone. The sex steroid hormones cause the cartilaginous growth plates at the ends of long bones to be replaced by bone during puberty, and after that time, bones cannot grow longer.

Excessive production of a growth hormone in adults over long periods produces a condition called *acromegaly*. The features of acromegaly are quite different from gigantism, because bones can no longer lengthen in adults. Instead, under the influence of growth hormone there is gradual thickening of the bones in the face, hands, and feet. The most notable visible effect is a change in facial features (Figure 13.9). Excessive production of a growth hormone in adults usually results from a tumor of either the pituitary or the hypothalamus. Acromegaly is no longer common because growth hormone–secreting tumors are now usually diagnosed and treated early enough to prevent the development of the condition. Excessive growth hormone secretion is diagnosed by measuring growth hormone levels.

🔄 **Recap** ADH acts on the kidneys to regulate water balance. Oxytocin stimulates uterine contractions and milk ejection in pregnant and lactating females, respectively. In both sexes, oxytocin contributes to feelings of sexual satisfaction. The six hormones produced by the anterior pituitary are ACTH, TSH, FSH, LH, prolactin (PRL), and GH. The release of each hormone is controlled in part by a releasing or inhibiting hormone from the hypothalamus. ▪

Figure 13.8 Effect of growth hormone on body growth. The tall person exhibits the traits of gigantism caused by excessive secretion of growth hormone during childhood. The short person has pituitary dwarfism, the result of too little growth hormone during childhood.

Figure 13.9 Effect of excessive growth hormone as an adult. This woman developed acromegaly as a result of too much growth hormone as an adult. She was symptom-free at 16.

13.4 The pancreas secretes glucagon, insulin, and somatostatin

The **pancreas** is both an endocrine gland (secreting hormones into the blood) and an exocrine gland (secreting enzymes, fluids, and ions into the digestive tract to aid in digestion). In this chapter we deal with its endocrine function.

The endocrine cells of the pancreas are located in small clusters scattered throughout the pancreas called the *islets of Langerhans* (an islet is a little island), or just the pancreatic islets. The pancreatic islets contain three types of cells and produce three hormones, all having to do with the regulation of blood sugar (glucose). One hormone raises blood sugar, the second lowers it, and the third inhibits the secretion of the other two hormones.

1. Alpha cells secrete **glucagon**, which raises blood sugar. As blood glucose levels decline between meals, glucagon is secreted into the bloodstream. In the liver, glucagon causes the breakdown of glycogen (a stored form of sugar) to glucose, raising blood glucose levels. Glucagon is particularly important between meals for increasing the supply of glucose to cells that need it.

2. Beta cells secrete **insulin**, which lowers blood sugar. After a meal, blood glucose levels rise as sugars are absorbed from the digestive tract. The high glucose concentration stimulates the beta cells to secrete insulin into the blood, where it does the opposite of glucagon. Insulin promotes the uptake of glucose by cells of the liver, muscle, and fat tissue. It also promotes the conversion of glucose into glycogen in the liver, both glycogen and proteins in muscle, and fats in adipose tissue.

3. Delta cells secrete somatostatin. The physiological significance of pancreatic somatostatin is not well understood, though it appears to inhibit the secretion of both glucagon and insulin. Somatostatin is also secreted by the hypothalamus, where it is the inhibitory hormone for growth hormone secretion, and the digestive tract, where it helps regulate several digestive secretions. The example of somatostatin reinforces the principle that the function of a hormone in any particular tissue or organ depends on the types of target cells present in those locations.

Figure 13.10 illustrates how the pancreas might respond to a meal. In actual fact, insulin and glucagon are both secreted in modest amounts all of the time. Adjusting the blood sugar is just a matter of altering the relative secretion rates of these two hormones—more insulin and less glucagon when blood sugar is high, and the inverse when blood sugar is low.

↺ Recap Hormones secreted by the pancreas include glucagon, insulin, and somatostatin. Glucagon raises blood glucose levels by increasing production of glucose from glycogen. Insulin lowers glucose levels by facilitating glucose uptake and storage. Somatostatin inhibits the secretion of both glucagon and insulin. ▪

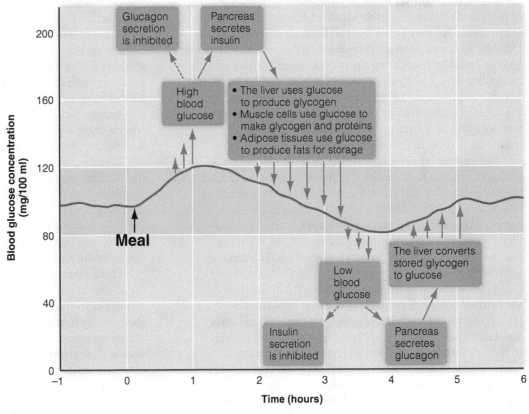

Figure 13.10 How the pancreas responds to a meal. The normal range for blood glucose concentration is 80–120 mg/100 ml. As blood glucose concentration rises, the secretion of insulin increases and the secretion of glucagon decreases, promoting the uptake and storage of glucose. If glucose concentration falls to near its normal lower limit, the secretion of glucagon increases and the secretion of insulin is inhibited. In the steady state, both hormones are secreted in modest amounts.

13.5 The adrenal glands comprise the cortex and medulla

The **adrenal glands** are two small endocrine organs located just above the kidneys. Each gland has an outer layer called the **adrenal cortex**, and an inner core called the *adrenal medulla*. The cortex and medulla function as two separate endocrine glands. (**Cortex** and **medulla** are general terms for outer and inner regions; you'll hear the terms again in the context of the kidneys, and you're already aware of the cerebral cortex of the brain.)

The adrenal cortex: Glucocorticoids and mineralocorticoids

The adrenal cortex produces small amounts of the sex hormones estrogen and testosterone (most of the sex hormones are produced by the ovaries and testes, discussed later) and two classes of steroid hormones called *glucocorticoids* and *mineralocorticoids*. Their names give a clue to their functions: glucocorticoids help regulate blood glucose levels, and mineralocorticoids help regulate the minerals sodium and potassium.

Glucocorticoids: Cortisol The adrenal cortex produces a group of glucocorticoids with nearly identical structures. **Cortisol** accounts for approximately 95% of these glucocorticoids. During prolonged fasting, cortisol assists in maintaining blood glucose levels by promoting the utilization of fats and by increasing the breakdown of protein to amino acids in muscle. The free amino acids are then converted to new glucose by the liver. In addition to its role in controlling blood glucose, cortisol is also important in suppressing inflammatory responses that occur following infection or injury.

Cortisol secretion is controlled by a typical feedback loop. A releasing factor from the hypothalamus stimulates the secretion of ACTH from the anterior pituitary gland, which in turn stimulates the adrenal cortex to secrete cortisol. When cortisol reaches its upper limit of normal blood level, it inhibits further secretion of the releasing hormone from the hypothalamus and of ACTH from the anterior pituitary.

A fall in blood glucose concentration can override the normal feedback control mechanism and increase cortisol secretion significantly. So, too, can physical injury and emotional stress. All of these stimuli act at the level of the hypothalamus, which secretes more releasing hormone, ultimately raising both ACTH and cortisol. The elevated cortisol concentration helps to restore the blood glucose concentration to normal and makes more amino acids available to repair damaged tissues. It also reduces inflammation by decreasing fluid loss from capillaries.

Cortisol and cortisol-like drugs can be administered topically to treat inflammation or injury. When used for prolonged periods, however, these drugs suppress the immune system.

✅ **Quick Check** *How does an increase in cortisol in response to stressful experiences such as physical injury and emotional stress help your body adjust to the stressful situation?* ▪

Mineralocorticoids: Aldosterone The other hormones produced by the adrenal cortex are the mineralocorticoids, the most abundant of which is **aldosterone**. Aldosterone is the hormone primarily responsible for regulating the amounts of sodium and potassium in the body. With ADH, it helps maintain body water balance.

Adrenal secretion of aldosterone increases whenever the total amount of sodium and water in the body is too low or when too much potassium is present (see Chapter 15 for details). In turn, aldosterone acts on cells in the kidneys to promote sodium reabsorption and potassium excretion, precisely what you would expect it to do if it were part of a homeostatic control loop for these ions.

The adrenal medulla: Epinephrine and norepinephrine

The **adrenal medulla** produces the nonsteroid hormones **epinephrine** (adrenaline) and **norepinephrine** (noradrenaline). These hormones affect cellular metabolism as well as blood pressure, respiration, and heart activity.

Epinephrine and norepinephrine are considered both hormones and neurotransmitters, depending on the situation. When they are released into the blood from the adrenal medulla and act on distant target cells, they are functioning as hormones. When they are released by a presynaptic neuron into a synaptic cleft and then bind to receptors on a postsynaptic neuron (Chapter 11), they are functioning as neurotransmitters.

Like the hypothalamus and the posterior pituitary, the adrenal medulla is really a neuroendocrine organ. Epinephrine and norepinephrine are synthesized and stored in specialized cells called *chromaffin cells* in the adrenal medulla that are innervated by sympathetic nerves. When sympathetic nerves are activated, the chromaffin cells secrete epinephrine and norepinephrine (Figure 13.11).

Once released, the two hormones participate in a wide range of actions that are essentially like the fight-or-flight responses of the sympathetic division. They raise blood glucose levels, increase heart rate and force of contraction, increase respiration rate, and constrict or dilate blood vessels in many organs, all actions that prepare the body for emergency activity.

You may have noticed that approximately 30 seconds to a minute after you are frightened by a dangerous situation such as avoiding an auto accident, your heart starts to pound, you breathe faster, and you feel "pumped up," alert, and a little shaky. These changes may occur even though the danger has already passed. You are experiencing an "adrenal rush" due to intense stimulation of your adrenal glands by the sympathetic nervous system.

Figure 13.11 **Secretion of norepinephrine and epinephrine by the adrenal medulla.** The secretion of these two hormones is closely linked with the activity of the sympathetic division of the autonomic nervous system (ANS). Neural pathways are noted in dark brown; hormonal pathways, in light brown.

The adrenal hormonal response occurs about half a minute after the event because it takes that long for the two hormones to be released, circulate to all tissues, bind to receptors on their target cells, and initiate the appropriate intracellular cascade of events. The response is also short-lived, lasting only a couple of minutes at most. Norepinephrine and epinephrine from the adrenal glands enhance the neural action of the sympathetic nervous system because the hormones reach more cells and are released in large amounts.

↻ **Recap** The main secretory products of the adrenal cortex are cortisol and aldosterone. Cortisol raises blood glucose levels and suppresses inflammatory responses, and aldosterone regulates water balance by promoting sodium reabsorption. The hormones secreted by the adrenal medulla (epinephrine and norepinephrine) contribute to the fight-or-flight response initiated by the sympathetic nervous system. ▪

13.6 Thyroid and parathyroid glands

The thyroid and parathyroid glands are anatomically linked. The **thyroid gland** is situated just below the larynx at the front of the trachea, and the two lobes of the thyroid gland wrap part of the way around the trachea (Figure 13.12). The four small **parathyroid glands** are embedded in the back of the thyroid.

The thyroid and parathyroid glands are also functionally linked; both help to regulate calcium balance. In addition, the thyroid has a separate and important role in controlling metabolism.

The two main hormones produced by the thyroid gland are thyroxine and calcitonin. The parathyroid glands produce parathyroid hormone.

The thyroid gland: Thyroxine speeds cellular metabolism

The thyroid gland produces two very similar hormones called **thyroxine** (T_4) and *triiodothyronine* (T_3). Thyroxine and triiodothyronine are identical except that thyroxine contains four molecules of iodine (hence the abbreviation T_4), whereas triiodothyronine contains only three. Because they are so similar we consider them together as thyroxine.

Structurally, thyroxine is not a steroid hormone. Nevertheless, it acts like a steroid because it is lipid soluble. It crosses the cell and nuclear membranes, binds to nuclear receptors, and activates genes as its mode of action. Those genes carry the code for the various enzymes that regulate our metabolic rate.

Thyroxine increases the production and use of ATP from glucose in nearly all body cells. When thyroxine concentration increases, the basal metabolic rate (BMR) also increases (see section 14.11). Conversely, decreasing the blood concentration of thyroxine reduces energy utilization and BMR.

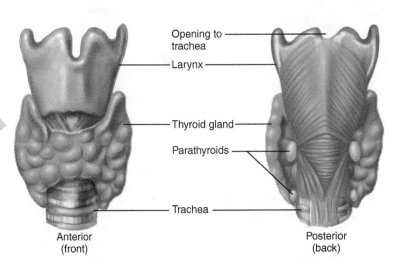

Figure 13.12 **The thyroid and parathyroid glands.**

The basal rate of thyroxine secretion is regulated by a typical negative feedback loop (Figure 13.13). Any fall in thyroxine concentration would increase the secretion of the hypothalamic releasing hormone for TSH, which would increase pituitary TSH concentration, ultimately increasing thyroxine secretion and driving thyroxine concentration back toward normal. Superimposed on this normal feedback loop, conditions that increase the body's energy requirements (such as exposure to cold temperatures) can stimulate the hypothalamus and raise the steady-state concentrations of *all* hormones in the loop.

✅ **Quick Check** *Do you think thyroxine levels would rise or fall in people who are starving (or who are dieting)? Why?* ▪

Iodine deficiency can cause goiter Production of active thyroid hormones requires iodine. In fact, the main reason we need iodine in our diet is to ensure adequate production of thyroxine. Iodine deficiency can result in a thyroid-deficiency disease. When thyroxine is absent or abnormally low, the normal feedback inhibitory controls on the hypothalamus and pituitary are missing, so the hypothalamus and pituitary continue to secrete large quantities of the releasing hormone and TSH unchecked.

Figure 13.14 **A goiter caused by dietary iodine deficiency.**

The high TSH levels stimulate the thyroid gland to grow to enormous size in an effort to get the thyroid to make more hormone, which it cannot do because it lacks iodine. An enlarged thyroid, as a result of iodine deficiency or other factors, is called a *goiter* (Figure 13.14). Goiter is less common today in industrialized nations because iodine is added to table salt. However, it is still a public health problem in certain areas of the world, most notably in Africa, China, and mountainous regions where rain has leached iodine from the soil.

Calcitonin promotes bone growth Calcitonin, the other main hormone of the thyroid gland, is produced by a separate group of thyroid cells. Calcitonin decreases the rate of bone resorption by inhibiting the activity of osteoclasts. It also stimulates the uptake of calcium by bone. These two actions tip the normal balance of bone deposition/resorption toward deposition, which over time increases bone mass. Calcitonin is part of a negative feedback control mechanism for calcium, in which high blood calcium levels stimulate calcitonin release and low blood calcium levels inhibit its release.

Calcitonin is particularly important for the growth and development of bones in children. Once adulthood is reached, bone responsiveness to calcitonin declines. In adults, calcitonin is not essential for the normal regulation of blood calcium concentration. However, calcitonin may play

Figure 13.13 **Negative feedback control of thyroxine secretion.** A fall in plasma thyroxine concentration causes the hypothalamus and anterior pituitary to increase their secretion of the releasing hormone and TSH. The increase in TSH stimulates thyroid gland production and secretion of thyroxine, returning the plasma concentration to normal. Conversely, a rise in thyroxine causes a fall in the releasing hormone and TSH. Cold temperatures alter the feedback loop (raise plasma thyroxine concentration) by increasing hypothalamic secretion of the releasing hormone.

a role in protecting the skeleton when calcium demand is high, such as during pregnancy.

Parathyroid hormone (PTH) controls blood calcium levels

The parathyroid glands produce only one hormone, **parathyroid hormone (PTH)**, which

1. Removes calcium and phosphate from bone,
2. Increases absorption of calcium by the digestive tract, and
3. Causes the kidneys to retain calcium and excrete phosphate.

Together these actions tend to raise the blood calcium concentration (and coincidentally lower blood phosphate concentration). As you might expect for a negative feedback control system, the secretion of PTH is stimulated by low blood calcium levels and inhibited by high blood calcium levels. Figure 13.15 shows the overall regulation of blood calcium concentration.

The effect of PTH on calcium absorption by the digestive tract is actually indirect, through vitamin D. Vitamin D is required for calcium absorption by the intestines. However, vitamin D circulates in an inactive form until it is activated by a biochemical alteration that occurs in the kidneys. PTH is required for the renal activation step. An increase in PTH concentration increases the renal activation of vitamin D, which in turn enhances calcium absorption from the digestive tract.

As mentioned previously, calcitonin plays little or no role in the normal maintenance of blood calcium concentration once adulthood is reached. In adults, the primary regulator of blood calcium concentration is PTH.

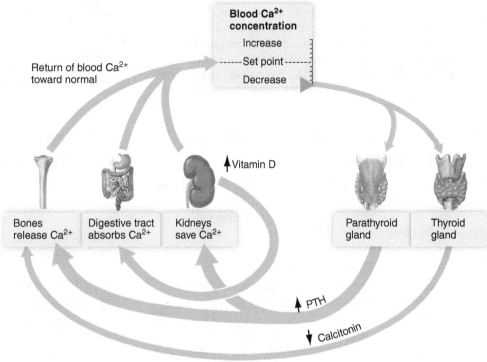

a) **Responses to a fall in blood calcium.**

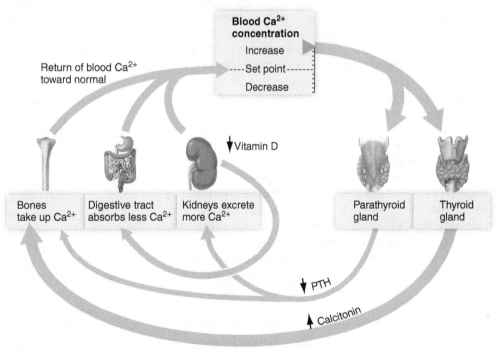

b) **Responses to a rise in blood calcium.** The importance of calcitonin is greatest in children, declining once adulthood is reached.

Figure 13.15 The homeostatic regulation of blood calcium concentration.

✓ *Draw a diagram similar to part b illustrating how blood glucose is brought back to normal after it rises following a meal. (Refer to Figure 13.10 for a reminder of the principles involved.)*

↩ **Recap** Production of the thyroid gland hormones (T_4 and T_3) requires iodine. T_3 and T_4 speed cellular metabolism and have widespread effects on growth in children and basal metabolic rate (BMR) in adults. Calcitonin (from the thyroid) lowers blood calcium levels and PTH (from the parathyroids) raises blood calcium. ▪

13.7 Testes and ovaries produce sex hormones

The human gonads are the testes of males and the ovaries of females. These organs are responsible for the production of sperm and eggs, respectively. Both organs are also endocrine glands in that they produce the steroid sex hormones.

Testes produce testosterone

The testes, located in the scrotum, produce androgens, the male sex hormones. The primary androgen produced by males is testosterone.

Before birth, testosterone production by the fetal testes is responsible for the development of the external male genitalia. Testosterone production declines essentially to zero between birth and puberty. During puberty the anterior pituitary gland begins to release luteinizing hormone (LH), which stimulates the testes to resume testosterone production.

In males, testosterone regulates the development and normal functioning of sperm, the male reproductive organs, and male sex drive. It is also responsible for the spurt of bone and muscle growth at puberty and the development of male secondary sex characteristics such as body hair and a deepening voice. LH, FSH, and testosterone continue to maintain the male reproductive system after puberty.

The adrenal glands in both sexes produce a small amount of a testosterone-like androgen called *dihydroepiandrosterone* (DHEA). DHEA has no demonstrable effect in males because they have an abundance of the more powerful testosterone. In females, DHEA from the adrenal glands is responsible for many of the same actions as testosterone in males, including enhancement of female pubertal growth, the development of axillary (armpit) and pubic hair, and the development and maintenance of the female sex drive.

Ovaries produce estrogen and progesterone

The ovaries, located in the abdomen, produce the female sex hormones known collectively as *estrogens* (17b-estradiol, estrone, and estriol), and also progesterone. The estrogens are often commonly referred to just as estrogen.

During puberty, the anterior pituitary starts to release luteinizing hormone (LH) and follicle-stimulating hormone (FSH). These hormones stimulate the ovaries to begin secreting estrogen and progesterone.

Estrogen initiates the development of female secondary sex characteristics such as breast development, widening pelvis, and distribution of body fat. Both estrogen and progesterone

regulate the menstrual cycle, the monthly changes in the tissue of the uterus that prepare the female body for pregnancy. Release of LH, FSH, estrogen, and progesterone continues throughout a woman's reproductive years.

We discuss male and female hormones and reproductive systems in greater detail in the chapter on reproductive systems (Chapter 16).

13.8 Other glands and organs also secrete hormones

Two lesser known glands (the thymus and pineal glands) and several organs (the heart, the digestive system, and the kidneys) also produce hormones. The hormones of the heart, digestive system, and kidneys are described briefly here and then discussed in more detail in later chapters.

Thymus gland hormones aid the immune system

The **thymus gland** is located between the lungs, behind the breastbone and near the heart. Sometimes it is considered part of the lymphatic system. For years the function of the thymus gland went unrecognized because its removal in an adult has little effect.

We now know that the thymus gland secretes peptide hormones called *thymosin* and *thymopoietin*, which help lymphocytes develop into mature T cells. The thymus is relatively important in children, but it shrinks and reduces its secretion in adults, especially after age 30.

The pineal gland secretes melatonin

The **pineal gland** is a pea-sized gland located deep within the brain, in the roof of the third ventricle. Its name derives from the fact that it is shaped like a small pine cone (*pineas* in Latin). More than 200 million years ago the pineal gland of our ancestors was a photosensitive area, or "third eye," located near the skin's surface. Although it is now shielded from light by the skull, it still retains its photosensitivity because it receives input indirectly from the eyes via the optic nerve and nerve pathways in the brain.

The pineal secretes the hormone **melatonin** (not to be confused with the skin pigment, melanin) in a cyclic manner, coupled to the daily cycle of light and dark. Melatonin is sometimes called the "hormone of darkness" because its rate of secretion rises nearly 10-fold at night and then falls again during daylight. Its secretion appears to be regulated by the absence or presence of visual cues. During the day when a person is exposed to strong light, nerve impulses from the retina inhibit its release.

We are just beginning to understand what melatonin does. Researchers believe that it may be important in synchronizing the body's rhythms to the daily light/dark cycle (the *circadian cycle*). Some scientists suggest that declining sensitivity to melatonin may contribute to the onset of puberty; evidence in favor of this hypothesis is that destruction of the pineal gland by disease is associated with early puberty.

Table 13.2 **Hormones of endocrine glands other than the hypothalamus and pituitary**

Gland	Hormone(s)	Main targets	Primary actions
Pancreas	Glucagon	Liver	Raises blood sugar levels
	Insulin	Liver, muscle, adipose tissue	Lowers blood sugar levels
	Somatostatin	Pancreas, hypothalamus, digestive tract	Inhibits release of glucagon, insulin, growth hormone, and digestive secretions
Adrenal cortex	Glucocorticoids (including cortisol)	Most cells	Raise blood glucose levels and promote breakdown of fats and proteins; suppress inflammation
	Mineralocorticoids (including aldosterone)	Kidneys	Regulate body water balance by promoting sodium reabsorption, potassium excretion
Adrenal medulla	Epinephrine and norepinephrine	Liver, muscle, adipose tissue	Raise blood sugar; increase heart rate and force of contraction; dilate or constrict blood vessels, increase respiration
Thyroid	Thyroxine (T_4) and triiodothyronine (T_3)	Most cells	Regulate the rate of cellular metabolism; affect growth and development
	Calcitonin	Bone	Lowers blood calcium levels
Parathyroid glands	Parathyroid hormone (PTH)	Bone, digestive tract, kidneys	Raises blood calcium levels
Testes	Testosterone	Most cells	Development of sperm, male secondary sex characteristics, and reproductive structures
Ovaries	Estrogen, progesterone	Most cells	Development of female secondary sex characteristics and reproductive structure; regulation of menstrual cycle
Thymus	Thymosin, thymopoietin	Lymphocytes	Help lymphocytes mature, especially in children
Pineal	Melatonin	Many cells	Synchronizes body rhythms; may be involved in onset of puberty

Melatonin is readily available over the counter as a pill. Some people take it as a natural sleep aid, although its effectiveness is controversial.

Table 13.2 lists all of the primary endocrine organs other than the hypothalamus and the pituitary, and summarizes their targets and hormonal actions.

✔ **Quick Check** *During winter when days are short, many office workers never see the sun at all because they spend their days indoors working under relatively dim office lights. How might this affect their melatonin levels over a 24-hour period and what effect, if any, might that have on their mood or behavior?* ▪

Endocrine functions of the heart, the digestive system, and the kidneys

The heart, the digestive system, and the kidneys all have functions unrelated to the endocrine system. Nevertheless, all three of these organs secrete at least one hormone. The hormones they secrete and the functions of the hormones are listed on the next page and summarized in Table 13.3.

Table 13.3 **Hormones of the digestive tract, kidneys, and heart**

System or organ	Hormone(s)	Main targets	Primary actions
Digestive tract	Gastrin, secretin, cholecystokinin	Stomach, pancreas, gallbladder	Stimulate activities of the stomach, pancreas, and gallbladder
Kidneys	Erythropoietin	Bone marrow	Stimulates red blood cell production
Kidneys and liver	Renin-angiotensin system	Adrenal cortex, blood vessels	Stimulates aldosterone secretion, constricts blood vessels
Heart	Atrial natriuretic hormone (ANH)	Kidney, blood vessels	Increases sodium excretion, dilates blood vessels

- *Atrial natriuretic hormone (ANH)* is a peptide (nonsteroid) hormone secreted by the atria of the heart that helps regulate blood pressure. When blood pressure rises, ANH increases the rate at which sodium and water are excreted in urine. This decreases blood volume and lowers blood pressure. We discuss how ANH acts on the kidneys in the chapter on the urinary system (Chapter 15).

- *Gastrin, secretin,* and *cholecystokinin* are all hormones secreted by the digestive system. They have effects on the stomach, pancreas, and gallbladder (Chapter 14).

- *Erythropoietin* and *renin* are secreted by the kidneys. Erythropoietin is a hormone that stimulates the production of red blood cells in bone marrow (Chapter 7). Renin is actually an enzyme, but it is generally included in any discussion of hormones because it is a critical component of the *renin-angiotensin system*, which functions overall as a hormonal negative feedback control system. The other critical component of the renin-angiotensin system comes from the liver. The renin-angiotensin system is discussed in the chapter on the urinary system (Chapter 15).

13.9 Other chemical messengers

Some chemical messengers can function in ways similar to hormones but are not considered hormones because they are not secreted into the blood. Their actions are primarily local (near their site of release). You already know about neurotransmitters, one group of chemical messengers that act on nearby cells. Other non-hormonal chemical messengers include histamine, prostaglandins, nitric oxide, and various growth factors and growth-limiting factors, plus dozens of other molecules about which we still know very little (Table 13.4). Most of these substances are short-lived

because they are either quickly destroyed or taken back up by the cells that produced them.

Histamine is important in inflammation

Histamine was mentioned in the chapter on the immune system (Chapter 9). Mast cells release histamine into the local interstitial fluid in response to tissue injury or the presence of an allergen. In turn, the histamine increases local secretion of mucus by mucus-secreting cells, dilates blood vessels, and increases the leakiness of capillaries, all part of a constellation of symptoms called *inflammation*.

Histamine is largely responsible for the runny nose of a cold and the nasal congestion of allergies. This is why over-the-counter drugs for colds and allergies generally contain compounds that block the action of histamine.

Prostaglandins: Local control of blood flow

Prostaglandins are a group of chemicals derived from a fatty acid precursor. Their name comes from the fact that they were first discovered in semen and were thought to originate from the prostate gland, but they have since been found in nearly every tissue in the body.

Prostaglandins have a variety of functions, including local control of blood flow. Some prostaglandins constrict blood vessels; others dilate blood vessels. They also contribute to the inflammatory response and are involved in blood clotting at the site of an injury.

Nitric oxide has multiple functions

Nitric oxide (NO) is a gas that has only recently received attention as a chemical messenger. NO was originally called "endothelial-derived relaxing factor" because an extract of the endothelial cells lining blood vessels caused blood vessels to relax, or dilate. We now know that NO is produced in many other tissues as well.

Nitric oxide functions include regulating local blood flow in many tissues of the body, controlling penile erection, and regulating smooth muscle contraction in the digestive tract. Macrophages use it as a "chemical warfare" agent against bacteria, and it also interferes with clotting mechanisms. It even functions as a neurotransmitter in the brain.

Growth factors regulate tissue growth

Chemical messenger molecules called *growth factors* modulate development of specific tissues at the local level. The list includes nerve growth factor, epidermal growth factor, fibroblast growth factor, platelet-derived growth factor, tumor angiogenesis growth factors, insulin-like growth factor, and many more. Growth factors influence when a cell will divide and even in what direction it will grow. For example, nerve growth factors help to determine the direction of neuron axon growth so that nerves develop properly.

Table 13.4 Other chemical messengers

Messenger(s)	Primary actions
Histamine	Important in inflammatory response; increases secretion of mucus, dilates blood vessels, increases leakiness of capillaries
Prostaglandins	Control local blood flow; constrict blood vessels, dilate blood vessels, contribute to inflammatory response and blood clotting
Nitric oxide (NO)	Regulates local blood flow, controls penile erection, regulates smooth muscle contraction in digestive tract, acts as a "chemical warfare" agent against bacteria, interferes with clotting mechanisms, acts as a neurotransmitter in brain
Growth factors	Modulate growth of tissues at local level

Recap Various chemical messengers (histamine, prostaglandins, nitric oxide, and growth factors) act primarily locally. Among their actions are regulating local blood flows, participating in local defense responses, and regulating growth of specific types of tissue. ▪

13.10 Disorders of the endocrine system

Because the endocrine system is one of the two primary systems for controlling body functions, any disruption to it can have dramatic and widespread effects on the body. We have already discussed several endocrine disorders earlier in this chapter. Here we look at several more.

Diabetes mellitus: Inadequate control of blood sugar

Diabetes mellitus means "a high flow of urine with a sweet taste." Called diabetes for short, it is a disease of sugar regulation. The common feature of the several types of diabetes is an inability to get glucose into cells where it can be used. The result is an abnormally high glucose concentration in the blood—so high that it overwhelms the kidney's ability to reabsorb all that is filtered. Glucose and excessive water appear in the urine (hence the name of the disease), causing dehydration and thirst. In addition to these symptoms, many diabetics experience fatigue, frequent infections, blurred vision, cuts that are slow to heal, and tingling in the feet or hands.

Without the ability to metabolize glucose properly, the body turns to the metabolism of fat and proteins. The abnormal metabolism of glucose, fats, and proteins causes most of the other medical problems associated with diabetes, including cardiovascular and neural diseases, renal failure, blindness, and damage to small blood vessels that may lead to the need for amputations. There are two types of diabetes.

- *Type 1 diabetes* (5–10% of all cases) is caused by the failure of the pancreas to produce enough insulin. It is called *insulin-dependent diabetes* because the person depends on daily injections of insulin to allow glucose to enter the cells. Typically it is not governed by lifestyle; rather, it is an autoimmune disorder in which the person's own immune system attacks the insulin-producing cells in the pancreas. It is thought to have a strong genetic component (close relatives of a person with Type 1 diabetes are at increased risk), but it may also require an environmental trigger, such as a viral infection. Typically it appears in childhood or adolescence.

BlogInFocus (MB)

How accurate are glucose monitoring devices? Visit MJ's blog in the Study Area in MasteringBiology and look under "Glucose Monitoring Devices."

- *Type 2 diabetes (non-insulin-dependent diabetes)* represents 90–95% of all cases. Its hallmark is *insulin resistance*—cells fail to respond adequately to insulin even when it is present. Type 2 diabetes usually occurs in adults beyond the age of 40; however, in recent years it has been occurring more frequently and at younger ages. Type 2 diabetes may have a genetic component, but lifestyle factors are thought to be the major determinants.

How does lifestyle affect the development of Type 2 diabetes? Apparently, persistent exposure of a cell to too much glucose causes cells to become resistant to the effects of insulin. As a result, blood glucose rises even higher. That, in turn, may cause the pancreas to secrete even more insulin in an attempt to overcome the resistance, which leads to a vicious cycle of further increases in insulin resistance, blood glucose, and insulin. Eventually the pancreas may wear out and insulin secretion may decline. Type 2 diabetics may or may not have enough insulin, but what they all have in common is resistance to insulin and blood sugar concentrations out of control.

Some Type 2 diabetics and "prediabetics" whose blood sugars are just approaching the diabetic range can sometimes control the disease entirely through lifestyle changes—maintaining a healthy weight, eating a nutritious diet, and exercising regularly. Some need to take insulin, especially to supplement their lifestyle changes when necessary. Other treatments include oral drugs that stimulate the pancreas to secrete more insulin, drugs that improve the action of the body's natural insulin, and drugs that increase the uptake of glucose by liver and muscle cells. More permanent solutions, such as implanting an artificial pancreas or transplanting human pancreatic cells, are under investigation.

✔️ **Quick Check** *In general, do you think it would be easier to treat disorders that result from failure to produce a hormone (such as Type 1 diabetes) or disorders that result from failure to respond to a hormone (such as Type 2 diabetes)? Why?* ▪

Hypothyroidism: Underactive thyroid gland

Hypothyroidism refers to underactivity of the thyroid gland (hyposecretion of thyroid hormones). Mild cases of hypothyroidism may not have any signs, but more severe deficiencies can cause a variety of symptoms.

In children, insufficient thyroxine production for any reason can slow body growth, alter brain development, and delay the onset of puberty. Left untreated, this deficiency can result in cretinism, a condition of mental retardation and stunted growth.

In adults, insufficient thyroxine can lead to myxedema, a condition characterized by edema (swelling) under the skin, lethargy, weight gain, low BMR, and low body temperature. Hyposecretion of the hormone can be treated with thyroxine pills.

Dealing with Diabetes: Prevention or Treatment?

According to the World Health Organization (WHO), 30 million people worldwide had diabetes in 1985. By 2010 the number was up to 285 million, and by 2030 it is estimated to be a whopping 438 million. In the United States the number of people with diabetes has nearly quadrupled in just under 30 years. What are the health-care costs associated with diabetes, and how are we going to deal with them?

The true cost of diabetes includes the many medical problems associated with the disease if it is left untreated. For example, in the United States approximately 40,000 diabetics develop kidney disease each year. Many of them progress to kidney failure, at which point they require treatment at a cost of over $50,000 per year (assuming the treatment, called *dialysis*, is available to them). Their lives and the lives of their families begin to revolve around managing their disease as they spend several half-days a week in a hospital or dialysis unit. Eventually they may need a kidney transplant, which can cost $100,000 or more. Currently, the total cost of treating the long-term complications of diabetes in the United States is estimated to be $174 billion/year—the equivalent of $1,300 for every U.S. taxpayer.

A concerted effort by health professionals and governments aimed at promoting healthy lifestyles so that fewer people develop diabetes in the first place, combined with early detection and effective management of those who do develop diabetes, would reduce the total cost of diabetes in the long run. Unfortunately the U.S. health care reimbursement system does not focus on maintaining wellness; it focuses on treating disease once it occurs. Hospitals, doctors, and health care centers make their money through payments from government sources (such as Medicare and Medicaid) and private insurers. At current reimbursement rates, they generally lose money on preventive care and early disease management, but make money every time a diabetic is hospitalized for a major complication such as a kidney transplant or an amputation. One recent study estimated that New York health care centers lost $40–$55 every time a diabetic patient met with a diabetes educator to learn how to monitor blood sugar properly or administer insulin or other treatment,

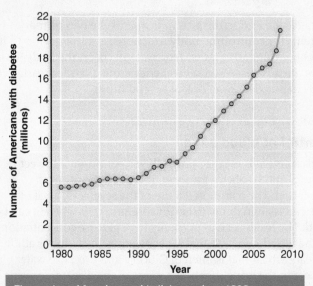

The number of Americans with diabetes since 1980.

and another $40–$55 when the patient met with a nutritionist to discuss controlling blood sugar through weight loss and a proper diet. In contrast, hospitals earned $1,500 to over $10,000 for every amputation, depending on the type of amputation and its complications.

Is it any wonder that hospitals are more likely to hire a surgeon than to add nutritionists or health educators to their staff? Until something changes, the health-care costs related to diabetes will continue to rise. ■

Hyperthyroidism: Overactive thyroid gland

Hyperthyroidism involves an overactive thyroid gland and hypersecretion of thyroid hormones. Too much thyroxine increases BMR and causes hyperactivity, nervousness, agitation, and weight loss.

The most common form of hyperthyroidism is Graves' disease, an autoimmune disorder in which a person's antibodies stimulate the thyroid to produce too much thyroxine. Graves' disease is often accompanied by protruding eyes caused by fluid accumulation behind the eyes.

Addison's disease: Too little cortisol and aldosterone

Addison's disease is caused by failure of the adrenal cortex to secrete sufficient cortisol and aldosterone. Lack of cortisol lowers blood glucose levels, and lack of aldosterone lowers blood sodium. Addison's disease tends to develop slowly, with chronic symptoms of fatigue, weakness, abdominal pain, weight loss, and a characteristic "bronzed" skin color. It can be successfully treated with medications that replace the missing hormones.

Cushing's syndrome: Too much cortisol

The symptoms of Cushing's syndrome are due to the exaggerated effects of too much cortisol, including (1) excessive production of glucose from glycogen and protein, and (2) retention of too much salt and water. Blood glucose concentration rises, and muscle mass decreases because of the utilization of protein to make glucose. Some of the extra glucose is converted to body fat, but only in certain areas of the body, including the face, abdomen, and the back of the neck (Figure 13.16). Symptoms of Cushing's syndrome include muscle weakness and fatigue, edema (swelling due to too much fluid), and high blood pressure. The disease can be caused by tumors of the adrenal gland or the ACTH-secreting cells of the pituitary. It can also be due to excessive use of cortisol and cortisol-like drugs (cortisone, prednisone, dexamethasone, and others) to control chronic inflammatory conditions such as allergies and arthritis.

a) Before the disease.

b) During the disease a characteristic hump of fat develops at the back of the neck.

Figure 13.16 Cushing's syndrome.

Chapter Summary

The endocrine system produces hormones *p. 302*

- The endocrine system is a collection of glands that secrete hormones into the blood.
- Hormones are chemical messengers secreted by the endocrine system that circulate in the blood and act on specific target cells.

Hormones are classified as steroid or nonsteroid *p. 304*

- Steroid hormones are lipid soluble; they enter the target cell in order to function.
- Nonsteroid hormones generally are not lipid soluble. They bind to receptors on the outer surface of the cell membrane of the target cell.

The hypothalamus and the pituitary gland *p. 306*

- The hypothalamus of the brain and the pituitary gland of the endocrine system link the nervous and endocrine systems.
- The posterior lobe secretes two hormones (ADH and oxytocin) that are produced by the hypothalamus.
- The anterior lobe of the pituitary produces and secretes six hormones (ACTH, TSH, FSH, LH, PRL, and GH). The first four stimulate the release of other hormones from other endocrine glands.
- Abnormalities of ADH secretion lead to disorders of water balance.
- Hypersecretion of growth hormone in a child leads to gigantism; hyposecretion causes dwarfism. In an adult, hypersecretion of growth hormone causes acromegaly.

The pancreas secretes glucagon, insulin, and somatostatin *p. 311*

- Within the pancreas, clusters of cells called the *pancreatic islets* produce and secrete three hormones (glucagon, insulin, and somatostatin).

- Glucagon raises blood glucose levels, insulin lowers blood glucose levels, and somatostatin appears to inhibit the secretion of glucagon and insulin.

The adrenal glands comprise the cortex and medulla *p. 312*

- The outer zone of the adrenal gland, called the *cortex*, secretes steroid hormones that affect glucose metabolism (glucocorticoids) and salt balance (mineralocorticoids).
- The inner zone of the adrenal gland, called the *medulla*, is actually a neuroendocrine organ. The adrenal medulla secretes epinephrine and norepinephrine into the blood.

Thyroid and parathyroid glands *p. 313*

- The thyroid gland produces thyroxine (T_4), triiodothyronine (T_3), and calcitonin.
- The four small parathyroid glands produce PTH, which, along with calcitonin, is responsible for the regulation of blood calcium concentration.

Testes and ovaries produce sex hormones *p. 316*

- The primary male sex hormone is testosterone, produced by the testes.
- The ovaries produce the two female sex hormones, estrogen and progesterone.

Other glands and organs also secrete hormones *p. 316*

- The thymus gland produces two hormones (thymosin and thymopoietin) that help lymphocytes mature into T cells.
- Melatonin from the pineal gland synchronizes the body's daily rhythms to the daily light/dark cycle.
- The heart secretes atrial natriuretic hormone, the kidneys secrete renin and erythropoietin, and the digestive tract secretes gastrin, secretin, and cholecystokinin.

Other chemical messengers *p. 318*

- Some substances not defined as hormones (because they are not specifically secreted into the bloodstream) nevertheless serve as chemical messengers.
- Most of these chemical messengers tend to act locally, near their site of secretion. They include histamine, prostaglandins, nitric oxide, and growth factors.

Disorders of the endocrine system *p. 319*

- Because the endocrine system controls so many body functions, disruptions can have widespread effects.
- Hypothyroidism can lead to cretinism (stunted growth and mental retardation) in children and myxedema in adults. Graves' disease is the most common form of hyperthyroidism.
- Insufficient cortisol and aldosterone can cause Addison's disease, and hypersecretion of cortisol results in Cushing's syndrome.

Terms You Should Know

adrenal cortex, *312*
adrenal medulla, *312*
aldosterone, *312*
calcitonin, *314*
cortisol, *312*
endocrine glands, *302*
epinephrine, *312*
glucagon, *311*
hormones, *302*
hypothalamus, *306*
insulin, *311*
neuroendocrine cells, *306*

nonsteroid hormone, *304*
norepinephrine, *312*
parathyroid gland, *313*
parathyroid hormone (PTH), *315*
pineal gland, *316*
pituitary gland, *306*
second messenger, *305*
steroid hormones, *304*
target cells, *302*
thymus gland, *316*
thyroid gland, *313*
thyroxine, *313*

Concept Review

Answers can be found in the Study Area in MasteringBiology.

1. List the functions of the six hormones secreted by the anterior lobe of the pituitary gland.
2. Explain the characteristics of the endocrine system that make its reactions different from those of the nervous system.
3. Compare and contrast the mechanisms by which steroid and nonsteroid hormones act.
4. Define when you would call a norepinephrine a neurotransmitter and when you would call it a hormone.
5. Explain why a 30-year-old short person cannot be made taller by taking a growth hormone.
6. Describe the function of the two hormones from the thymus gland. Why is this function likely to be more important in children than in adults?
7. Explain how the pineal gland can be sensitive to light, even though it is located deep within the brain.
8. Describe why substances such as histamine and nitric oxide, although they are chemical messengers, are not considered true hormones.
9. Name the hormone that is released from the posterior pituitary of lactating females when the infant nurses.
10. Describe the role of the pineal gland in the circadian cycle.

Test Yourself

Answers can be found in Appendix A.

1. _____ hormones enter target cells and bind to intracellular receptors, whereas _____ hormones bind to cell membrane receptors and never enter the target cells.
   a. Nonsteroid. . .steroid
   b. Protein. . .peptide
   c. Steroid. . .nonsteroid
   d. Steroid. . .carbohydrate

2. Which of the following statements comparing steroid and nonsteroid hormones is true?
   a. Steroid hormones typically act through second messengers such as cAMP.
   b. Nonsteroid hormones usually are faster acting than steroid hormones.
   c. Steroid hormones are secreted by the anterior pituitary gland, and nonsteroid hormones are secreted by the posterior pituitary gland.
   d. Steroid hormones are produced only after puberty, whereas nonsteroid hormones are produced throughout the lifespan.

3. Secretion of hormones by the anterior pituitary gland is closely regulated by the:
   a. hypothalamus
   b. posterior pituitary gland
   c. cerebellum
   d. adrenal cortex

4. Which two hormones most directly regulate lactation?
   a. estrogen and progesterone
   b. estrogen and prolactin
   c. progesterone and oxytocin
   d. oxytocin and prolactin

5. All of the following represent hormone pairs with antagonistic activities except:
   a. estrogen. . .progesterone
   b. insulin. . .glucagon
   c. parathyroid hormone. . .calcitonin
   d. aldosterone. . .ANH

6. Which of the following hormones/chemical messengers is produced exclusively in males?
   a. prostaglandins
   b. melatonin
   c. testosterone
   d. none of these choices

7. Hormones secreted by the anterior pituitary gland control the activity of all of the following glands except:
   a. adrenal medulla
   b. thyroid gland
   c. testes
   d. ovaries

8. Which of the following hormones is/are involved in normal functioning of the male reproductive system?
   a. testosterone
   b. LH
   c. FSH
   d. all of these choices

9. Which of these endocrine disorders is associated with the inability of the pancreas to produce insulin?
   a. diabetes insipidus
   b. Addison's disease
   c. Type 1 diabetes mellitus
   d. Type 2 diabetes mellitus

10. Which of these statements comparing the nervous system and the endocrine system is true?
   a. The endocrine system exclusively controls development, whereas the nervous system controls homeostasis.
   b. The nervous system can access and communicate with all cells in the body, whereas the access of the endocrine system to different cells and tissues is more limited.
   c. The nervous system enables more rapid communication and signaling than does the endocrine system.
   d. The nervous system is fully functioning at birth, whereas the endocrine system doesn't begin to function until puberty.

11. Which of the following statements about the adrenal cortex or its hormones is true?
   a. The adrenal cortex secretes a mixture of steroid and nonsteroid hormones.
   b. The adrenal cortex secretes hormones that may decrease the inflammatory response and suppress immune responses.
   c. The secretion of hormones by the adrenal cortex is controlled by the sympathetic division of the nervous system.
   d. Hypersecretion of cortisol and aldosterone is seen in Addison's disease.

12. Which of the following statements about glucagon is true?
   a. Glucagon causes glycogen to break down to form glucose.
   b. Glucagon secretion is highest following a heavy meal.
   c. Glucagon promotes the uptake of glucose by liver and muscle cells.
   d. Glucagon works with cortisol to lower blood glucose levels.

13. Which of the following would be least likely to be affected by a tumor of the pituitary gland?
   a. cortisol secretion
   b. thyroid hormone secretion
   c. lactation
   d. secretion of epinephrine by the adrenal medulla

14. Which of the following is incorrectly paired?
   a. insulin. . .diabetes insipidus
   b. growth hormone. . .acromegaly
   c. thyroid. . .Grave's disease
   d. cortisol. . .Cushing's syndrome

15. Which of the following would be triggered by a drop in blood Ca^{2+} levels?
   a. increase in PTH secretion
   b. decrease in calcitonin secretion
   c. increase in ADH secretion
   d. both (a) and (b)

Apply What You Know

Answers can be found in the Study Area in MasteringBiology.

1. If the biological effectiveness of a hormone were greatly reduced because its target cells lacked the appropriate receptors, would you expect the hormone concentration to be high, normal, or low? Explain. (*Hint:* It may help to draw the components of a negative feedback loop.)

2. Explain why an injection of epinephrine to combat an acute immune reaction (such as an allergic response to a bee sting) has an almost immediate effect, whereas an injection of a steroid hormone can take hours to have an effect.

3. From what you read in section 13.5, draw the negative feedback control loop for cortisol secretion. Then indicate on your diagram how stress or injury would affect the feedback loop. Check your diagram with a classmate or your teacher—if you can draw it and explain it, you understand it!

4. When a pregnant woman goes into labor, a series of strong muscle contractions force the baby from the uterus through the birth canal. Labor can be painful. Normally, such pain would initiate a negative feedback loop that would inhibit muscle contractions to prevent such pain, but that doesn't happen during labor. Why not?

5. Diabetics have to be particularly careful about sugar intake. Some are able to control the condition through careful diet. What sorts of foods should diabetics avoid, what foods should they try to get more of, and what can they do if they make a mistake?

6. A student finishes up the fall semester with several term papers and a number of big exams. After the semester she goes home for the holidays and comes down with a bad cold. The following year the same thing happens; she's sick for the holidays. During her senior year the fall semester isn't too bad, but applications to graduate school are due and she spends most of her semester break filling out forms and nervously worrying about what she will do next year. She's again sick for the beginning of the next term. Is this student just unlucky, or is something else at work?

BlogInFocus

Answers can be found in the Study Area in MasteringBiology.

1. Scientists managed to develop an inhalable insulin product, so that Type 1 diabetics would not have to inject their insulin. They expected it to be a blockbuster drug, but it was soon dropped by the drug company that developed it because of weak sales. What do you think would cause sales of such a product to be so weak? (Visit MJ's blog in the Study Area in MasteringBiology and look under "Inhalable Insulin.")

MasteringBiology®

Go to MasteringBiology for practice quizzes, activities, eText, videos, current events, and more.

The Digestive System and Nutrition

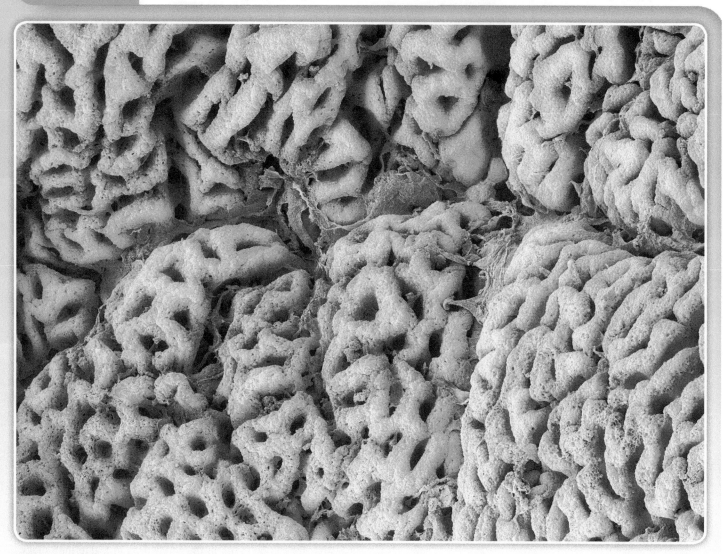

Colored SEM (× 20) of the lining of the stomach. The large folds flatten out when the stomach is full. The small indents are gastric pits.

Is "Overweight" Overstated?

If you have a body mass index (BMI) of greater than 25 but under 30, then you're officially considered overweight by the federal government. The government believes that your health may be at risk, and it's out to save you. You're likely to feel like you're being targeted by a concerted campaign to get you to eat better, exercise more, and above all, slim down! It's all very well meaning, of course, but there's a problem: Some of the statements made about the dangers of being overweight are based on poor science and weak statistics.

Several recent books have challenged the conventional wisdom that too much body fat is bad for your health. But they also have very little data to back up their claims—they're just telling us what we want to hear. It's time for a little scientific skepticism.

The hard fact is that nearly every scientific study conducted on the relationship between body fat and health risk has found a positive association between BMIs above the normal range and the risk of certain diseases. Those diseases include hypertension, Type 2 diabetes, coronary heart disease, stroke, gallbladder disease, osteoarthritis, and several types of cancers. Being slightly overweight is *sometimes* a risk factor, but being obese generally *always* is.

The question becomes, then, "How much body fat is too much for *me*?" That's where the truth is unknown and misinformation begins. The answer depends on the specific disease you're concerned about and your lifestyle and genetic risk factors, not just on your BMI. To understand this, we need to understand the BMI scale; when it's useful and when it's not.

BMI and the Definition of "Overweight"

You and I tend to judge our fatness by getting on a bathroom scale. BMI is a bit more precise because it takes height

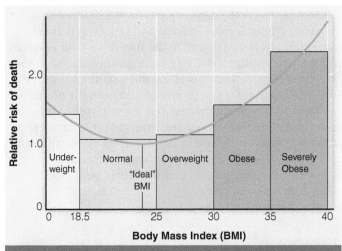

A representation of the typical J-shaped relationship between BMI and relative risk of death in a large population. The lowest risk of death is at a BMI of 24.

into account (see Figure 14.18). It is the simplest comparative measure of fatness. Its value is that it is easy to obtain, even as a self-report over the phone or on a questionnaire.

Before 1980 the BMI scale primarily was used by life insurance companies to predict mortality risk (risk of death). By then it was known that there's a normal, predictable U- or J-shaped relationship between risk of death and BMI (see graph), with people at the low and high ends of the scale at greater risk of dying in a given year.

It wasn't long before medical researchers began to use the BMI scale to look for the health risks associated with high BMIs within large populations. Literally hundreds of studies came to the same conclusion—that especially at very high BMIs in the obese range, there is a positive relationship between BMI and certain chronic diseases.

But if that was true, shouldn't we be doing something about it? If everyone were at that ideal BMI of 24, imagine all the lives that would be saved! It wasn't long before the government declared that women with a BMI over 27 and men with a BMI over 28 were officially "overweight," and overweight began to be lumped with

obesity as a health risk. A concerted educational campaign was begun to get us to eat better, exercise more often, and above all, lose that weight. The overzealous authors of one study even declared that "adults should try to maintain a BMI between 18.5 and 21.9 to minimize their risk of disease."

But the weight of the average U.S. adult kept rising, and government concern rose with it. In 1998 the federal government lowered its definition of overweight to include everyone over a BMI of 25. Overnight, another 29 million Americans were labeled as overweight. And that's why by 2008, over two-thirds of the U.S. population is considered to be either overweight or obese.

Overweight versus Obese— Different Levels of Risk

The first problem with any population-based definition of overweight is that it is not a good predictor of an individual's level of fitness or health. People who have a high muscle mass or who are just genetically built with larger body frames are likely to be labeled overweight or even obese by the BMI scale. The BMI may be a useful research tool for epidemiologists and public policymakers as they study whole populations, but it should not be used to make a recommendation about your personal lifestyle.

The second problem with the current definition of overweight is that it may have been oversold as a risk factor. Look again at the graph depicting mortality versus BMI. As a group, the overweight category

has essentially no greater risk of dying than the normal group. To be fair, a population with a BMI in the overweight range *is* at increased risk for some of those specific diseases listed previously, such as diabetes, hypertension, and heart disease. But as you might expect, the risks are not as great as the risks associated with obesity or severe obesity. It's a matter of degree.

Is the government right to worry about obesity and to try to do something about it through public education? The answer is a resounding "yes." If every U.S. adult could somehow magically lose 10 pounds, would the incidence of hypertension, diabetes, and mortality go down? The answer again is "yes," but probably because it would reduce the number of obese or severely obese individuals, not because it would improve the health of people just barely overweight. If you've been labeled as overweight but you exercise regularly and eat properly, then lose 10 pounds if you want to, but don't do it because you think you'll live longer.

Regardless of her BMI, tennis champion Serena Williams would best be described as "fit."

QUESTIONS TO CONSIDER

1 Do you agree with the government's definition of overweight as BMIs above 25? Why or why not?

2 What do you think is government's proper role (if any) when it comes to noncommunicable health risks such as obesity?

>> **The digestive system and its accessory organs digest and absorb nearly everything we eat and drink,** regardless of how much we eat or drink. The leftover non-absorbed waste products and bacteria are stored until they are eliminated as feces.

>> **The stomach stores ingested food and water until it can be delivered to the small intestine.** It also secretes a strong acid—hydrochloric acid (HCl)—that breaks down proteins and also kills most bacteria.

>> **Nutrients and water are absorbed in the small intestine** and to a lesser extent, the large intestine. Enzymes from the pancreas and the small intestine break down carbohydrates and fats so that they can be absorbed. The inner surface of the small intestine has many *villi* and *microvilli*, which markedly increase the surface area for absorption.

>> **Our nutritional requirements for good health include certain vitamins and minerals.** Some of these are not stored within the body for long periods, so we need a consistent supply.

>> **To maintain a constant body weight, energy intake must equal energy expenditure.** Any consistent imbalance in energy intake versus energy expenditure over time leads to weight gain or loss. Exercise can dramatically change how many calories we expend. To lose weight we must eat less, exercise more, or do a little of both.

>> **A healthy diet contains a variety of grains, fruits, vegetables, and low-fat milk products.** Saturated fats, foods containing cholesterol, and refined sugars should be consumed in moderation.

Stop for a moment and make a list of what you ate for lunch—a hamburger, fries, and a soft drink? Pizza and bottled water? A salad, apple, and milk?

All cells need **nutrients**—substances in food that are required for growth, reproduction, and the maintenance of health. Quite simply, the cells of your body must live on whatever you choose to eat. Right now the nutrients in your last meal (as well as nutrients stored in your body from previous meals) are being used to fuel cellular activities, build cell components, and serve other vital functions. Your cells draw these nutrients from your blood, and your blood obtains them from your digestive system or from nutrient storage pools.

In many ways the digestive system is a highly efficient disassembly line. It takes in food and processes it, breaking it into small pieces and digesting the fragments with enzymes and strong chemicals. Then it passes the mixture down the line, absorbing its nutrients along the way, and stores the leftover waste until it can be eliminated from the body.

Does what you eat matter? Yes! Poor nutrition is associated with diseases ranging from cancer to cavities. Good nutrition, on the other hand, improves overall health and lowers the risk of health problems. In this chapter we follow the digestive process and the fate of your food. Then we discuss how you can apply this information to promote a healthy diet and body weight.

BlogInFocus (MB)

People with eating disorders communicate on the Internet, using specific code words to find each other. To learn what one social networking Web site is doing about it, visit MJ's blog in the Study Area in MasteringBiology and look under "Self-harm Blogs."

14.1 The digestive system brings nutrients into the body

The **digestive system** consists of all the organs that share the common function of getting nutrients into the body. It includes a series of hollow organs extending from the mouth to the anus: the mouth, pharynx, esophagus, stomach, small intestine, large intestine, rectum, and anus. These organs form a hollow tube called the **gastrointestinal (GI) tract** ("gastric" is the adjective for stomach). The space within this hollow tube—the area through which food and liquids travel—is called the *lumen*.

The digestive system also includes four accessory organs—the salivary glands, liver, gallbladder, and pancreas. Figure 14.1 summarizes the functions of the organs and accessory organs of the digestive system.

The walls of the GI tract are composed of four layers

From the esophagus to the anus, the walls of the GI tract share common structural features (Figure 14.2). The walls of the GI tract consist of four layers of tissue.

1. **Mucosa.** The innermost tissue layer (the mucous membrane in contact with the lumen) is the mucosa. All nutrients must cross the mucosa to enter the blood.

2. **Submucosa.** Next to the mucosa is a layer of connective tissue containing blood vessels, lymph vessels, and nerves, called the *submucosa*. Components of food that are absorbed across the mucosa enter the blood and lymph vessels of the submucosa.

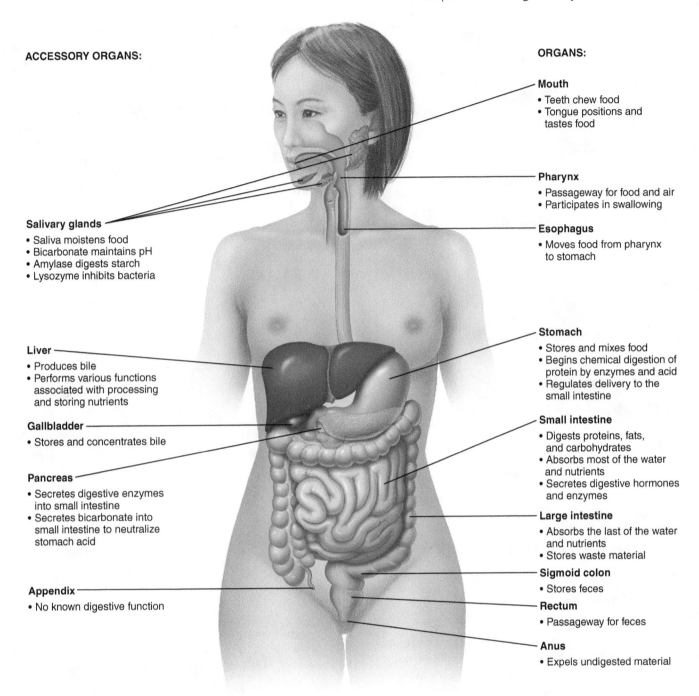

ACCESSORY ORGANS:

Salivary glands
- Saliva moistens food
- Bicarbonate maintains pH
- Amylase digests starch
- Lysozyme inhibits bacteria

Liver
- Produces bile
- Performs various functions associated with processing and storing nutrients

Gallbladder
- Stores and concentrates bile

Pancreas
- Secretes digestive enzymes into small intestine
- Secretes bicarbonate into small intestine to neutralize stomach acid

Appendix
- No known digestive function

ORGANS:

Mouth
- Teeth chew food
- Tongue positions and tastes food

Pharynx
- Passageway for food and air
- Participates in swallowing

Esophagus
- Moves food from pharynx to stomach

Stomach
- Stores and mixes food
- Begins chemical digestion of protein by enzymes and acid
- Regulates delivery to the small intestine

Small intestine
- Digests proteins, fats, and carbohydrates
- Absorbs most of the water and nutrients
- Secretes digestive hormones and enzymes

Large intestine
- Absorbs the last of the water and nutrients
- Stores waste material

Sigmoid colon
- Stores feces

Rectum
- Passageway for feces

Anus
- Expels undigested material

Figure 14.1 **Organs and accessory organs of the digestive system and their functions.**

3. **Muscularis.** The third layer of GI tract tissue, called the *muscularis*, is responsible for motility or movement. The muscularis consists of two or three sublayers of smooth muscle. In general, the fibers of the inner sublayer are oriented in a circular fashion around the lumen, whereas those in the outer sublayer are arranged lengthwise, parallel to the long axis of the digestive tube. The exception is the stomach, which has a diagonal (oblique) sublayer of muscle inside the other two.

4. **Serosa.** The outermost layer of the GI tract wall, or serosa, is a thin connective tissue sheath that surrounds and protects the other three layers and attaches the digestive system to the walls of the body cavities.

Some of the organs of the GI tract are separated from each other by thick rings of circular smooth muscle called *sphincters*. When these sphincters contract they can close off the passageway between organs.

Serosa
• Connective tissue outer covering
• Protects and anchors the digestive tract

Longitudinal layer

Circular layer

Lumen

Muscularis
• Two layers of smooth muscle
• Responsible for motility of the digestive tract

Submucosa
• Connective tissue layer
• Contains blood vessels, lymph vessels, and nerves

Mucosa
• Mucous membrane layer
• Lines the digestive tract

Vein — Lymph vessel
Artery
Nerve

Figure 14.2 The four tissue layers of the GI tract wall.

Five basic processes accomplish digestive system function

In practical terms, the digestive system is a long disassembly line that starts with huge chunks of raw material (we call it food) and takes them apart so that the nutrients in the food can be absorbed into the body. The digestive system accomplishes this task with five basic processes.

1. *Mechanical processing and movement.* Chewing breaks food into smaller pieces, and two types of movement (motility) mix the contents of the lumen and propel it forward.
2. *Secretion.* Fluid, digestive enzymes, acid, alkali, bile, and mucus are all secreted into the GI tract at various places. In addition, several hormones that regulate digestion are secreted into the bloodstream.
3. *Digestion.* The contents of the lumen are broken down both mechanically and chemically into smaller and smaller particles, culminating in nutrient molecules.

4. *Absorption.* Nutrient molecules pass across the mucosal layer of the GI tract and into the blood or lymph.
5. *Elimination.* Undigested material is eliminated from the body via the anus.

Two types of motility aid digestive processes

The smooth muscle of the GI tract produces two kinds of motility, called *peristalsis* and *segmentation*. The functions of peristalsis and segmentation are quite different.

Peristalsis propels food forward (Figure 14.3a). Peristalsis begins when a lump of food (called a *bolus*) stretches a portion

Esophagus
Bolus of food
Stomach

a) Peristalsis.

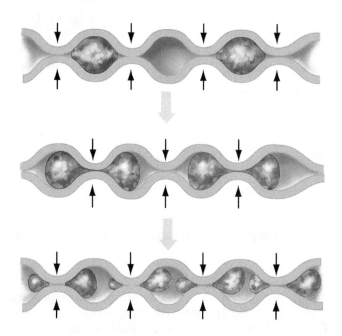

b) Segmentation.

Figure 14.3 Motility of the gastrointestinal tract. a) Peristalsis in the esophagus. The three sequential diagrams show how peristalsis moves the contents of the lumen onward. b) Segmentation in the small intestine. Segmentation mixes the contents of the lumen.

of the GI tract, causing the smooth muscle in front of the bolus to relax and the muscle behind it to contract. The contractions push the food forward, stretching the next part of the tube and causing muscle relaxation in front and contraction behind. The peristaltic wave of contraction ripples through the organs of the GI tract, mixing the contents of the stomach and pushing the contents of the esophagus and intestines forward. Peristalsis occurs in all parts of the GI tract, but is especially prevalent in the esophagus, where it transports food rapidly to the stomach.

Segmentation mixes food (Figure 14.3b). In segmentation, short sections of smooth muscle contract and relax in seemingly random fashion. The result is a back-and-forth mixing of the contents of the lumen. Food particles are pressed against the mucosa, enabling the body to absorb their nutrients. Segmentation occurs primarily in the small intestine as food is digested and absorbed.

Recap The digestive system consists of organs and accessory organs that share the function of bringing nutrients into the body. The wall of the GI tract consists of four tissue layers: the mucosa, the submucosa, the muscularis, and the serosa. The five basic processes of digestion are (1) mechanical processing and movement, (2) secretion, (3) digestion, (4) absorption, and (5) elimination.

14.2 The mouth processes food for swallowing

The mouth, or oral cavity, is the entrance to the GI tract. Digestion begins in the mouth with the process of chewing, which breaks food into smaller and smaller chunks. Essentially, the mouth functions as an effective food processor.

Teeth bite and chew food

The teeth chew food into pieces small enough to swallow. There are four types of teeth, each specialized for a different purpose (Figure 14.4a). The sharp-edged incisors cut food and the pointed canines tear it. The flat surfaces of the premolars and molars are well adapted to grinding and crushing food.

Children have only 20 teeth. They develop by about age 2 and are gradually replaced by permanent teeth. Permanent teeth usually develop by late adolescence, except for the wisdom teeth (third molars), which generally appear by age 25. Most adults have 32 permanent teeth.

Each tooth (Figure 14.4b) consists of a visible region called the *crown* and a region below the gum line called the *root*. The crown is covered by a layer of enamel, an extremely hard nonliving compound of calcium and phosphate. Beneath the enamel is a bonelike living layer called *dentin*. The soft innermost pulp cavity contains the blood vessels that supply the dentin, as well as the nerves that cause so much pain when a tooth is infected or injured. The entire tooth sits in a socket in the jawbone that is lined with periodontal membrane.

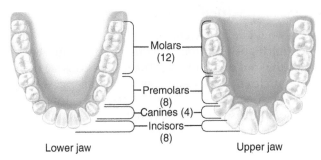

a) Locations and types of adult human teeth.

b) Anatomy of a tooth.

c) Bacteria on a tooth's surface (approx. × 8,000).

Figure 14.4 **Teeth.**

Our mouths contain large numbers of bacteria that flourish on the food that remains between the teeth (Figure 14.4c). During their metabolism these bacteria release acids that can dissolve enamel, creating cavities or *dental caries*. If not treated, cavities deepen, eroding the dentin and pulp cavity and causing a toothache. Tooth decay may inflame the soft gum tissue (gingiva) around the tooth, causing *gingivitis*. Decay that inflames the periodontal membrane leads to *periodontitis*. However, good dental hygiene—including regular exams and teeth cleaning—can prevent most dental problems from becoming serious.

The tongue positions and tastes food

Chewing would be inefficient without the muscular tongue, which positions food over the teeth and mashes it against the roof of the mouth. The tongue consists of skeletal muscle enclosed in mucous membrane, so we have voluntary control over its movements. The tongue contributes to the sense of taste (Chapter 12) and also is important for speech.

Saliva begins the process of digestion

Three pairs of **salivary glands** produce a watery fluid called *saliva*. The parotid gland lies near the back of the jaw, and the smaller sublingual and submandibular glands are located just below the lower jaw and below the tongue, respectively (**Figure 14.5**). All three glands connect to the oral cavity via ducts.

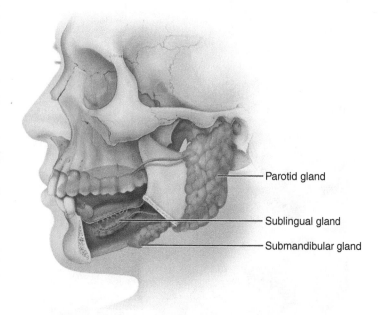

Parotid gland

Sublingual gland

Submandibular gland

Figure 14.5 The salivary glands. The three pairs of glands deliver saliva to the mouth via salivary ducts.

Saliva moistens food, making it easier to chew and swallow. Saliva contains four main ingredients, each with important functions. One is *mucin,* a mucus-like protein that holds food particles together so they can be swallowed more easily. An enzyme called *salivary amylase* begins the process of digesting carbohydrates. *Bicarbonate* (HCO_3^-) in saliva maintains the pH of the mouth between 6.5 and 7.5, the range over which salivary amylase is most effective. Salivary bicarbonate may also help protect your teeth against those acid-producing bacteria. Saliva also contains small amounts of an enzyme called *lysozyme,* which inhibits bacterial growth.

Recap The four kinds of teeth (molars, premolars, canines, and incisors) mechanically digest chunks of food. Salivary glands secrete saliva, which moistens food, begins the chemical digestion of carbohydrates, maintains the pH of the mouth, and protects the teeth against bacteria. ▪

14.3 The pharynx and esophagus deliver food to the stomach

After we have chewed our food and mixed it with saliva, the tongue pushes it into the **pharynx**, or throat, for swallowing. The act of swallowing involves a sequence of events that is coordinated with a temporary halt in breathing.

First, voluntary movements of the tongue and jaws push a bolus of food into the pharynx (**Figure 14.6a**). The presence of the food in the pharynx stimulates receptors that initiate the "swallowing reflex," an involuntary act that cannot be stopped once it is started. The purpose of the swallowing reflex is to close off the passageways for air to and from the pharynx while the bolus of food passes through the pharynx. Breathing is halted temporarily during the swallowing reflex. The soft palate rises to close off the passageway into the nasal cavity, and the epiglottis bends down to close the airway to the trachea. At the same time the tongue pushes the food back even farther, sliding it past the epiglottis and into the esophagus (Figure 14.6b).

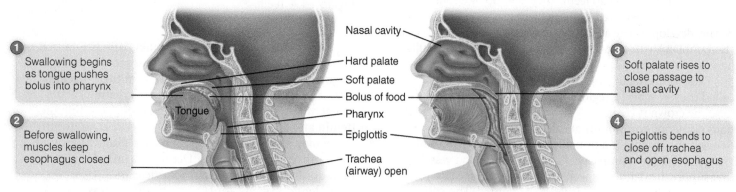

1 Swallowing begins as tongue pushes bolus into pharynx

2 Before swallowing, muscles keep esophagus closed

Tongue

Nasal cavity

Hard palate

Soft palate

Bolus of food

Pharynx

Epiglottis

Trachea (airway) open

3 Soft palate rises to close passage to nasal cavity

4 Epiglottis bends to close off trachea and open esophagus

a) Voluntary phase.

b) Involuntary phase.

Figure 14.6 **Swallowing.**

Just beyond the pharynx is the **esophagus**, a muscular tube consisting of both skeletal and smooth muscle that connects the pharynx to the stomach. The lining of the esophagus produces lubricating mucus that helps food slide easily. Occasionally thick foods such as mashed potatoes or peanut butter stick briefly to the mucosa of the esophagus, causing a painfully strong reflex contraction behind the food. If the contraction does not dislodge the food, drinking liquid may help.

Gravity assists peristalsis in propelling food. However, peristaltic contractions enable the esophagus to transport food even against gravity, such as when we are lying down.

The lower esophageal sphincter, located at the base of the esophagus, opens briefly as food arrives and closes after it passes into the stomach. The sphincter prevents reflux of the stomach's contents back into the esophagus. Occasionally this sphincter malfunctions, resulting in the backflow of acidic stomach fluid into the esophagus. This condition, known as *acid reflux*, is responsible for the burning sensation known as "heartburn." Acid reflux becomes more common with weight gain, pregnancy, and age. Occasionally it indicates a *hiatal hernia*, a condition in which part of the stomach protrudes upward into the chest through an opening (hiatus) in the diaphragm muscle. Mild or temporary acid reflux is usually not serious and often improves with weight loss. However, prolonged acid reflux may cause esophageal ulcers because stomach acid can erode the mucosa of the esophagus.

Recap Swallowing begins with voluntary movements of the tongue; the presence of food initiates an involuntary swallowing reflex. Peristalsis and gravity transfer food through the esophagus to the stomach.

14.4 The stomach stores food, digests protein, and regulates delivery

The **stomach** is a muscular, expandable sac that performs the following three important functions:

- *Food storage.* Humans tend to eat meals several times a day. The stomach stores the food until it can be digested and absorbed. The stomach shrinks when empty, and then expands to 1–3 liters of capacity when we eat.
- *Digestion.* The stomach is more than a storage bag, however. It also digests proteins, using strong acid and protein-digesting enzymes. The strong acid also kills most bacteria. Muscle contractions mix these secretions with food, assist in mechanically breaking apart food particles, and push the mixture into the small intestine.
- *Regulation of delivery.* The stomach regulates the rate at which food is delivered to the small intestine.

Gastric juice breaks down proteins

The walls of the stomach consist of the usual four layers: mucosa, submucosa, muscularis, and serosa (Figure 14.7a).

a) Stomach wall.

b) Gastric glands.

c) Gastric pits.

Figure 14.7 The stomach.

A closer look at the mucosal layer reveals millions of small openings called *gastric pits* that lead to gastric glands below the surface (Figure 14.7b, c). Some of the cells lining the glands secrete either hydrochloric acid (HCl) or mucus, but most secrete pepsinogen, a large precursor molecule that becomes a protein-digesting enzyme called **pepsin** once it is exposed to acid in the stomach. Collectively, the HCl, pepsinogen, and fluid that are secreted into the glands are known as *gastric juice*.

The stomach typically produces 1–2 liters of gastric juice per day, most of it immediately after meals. The acid in gastric juice gives the stomach an acidic pH of approximately 2. The pepsin and acid in gastric juice dissolve the connective tissue in food and digest proteins and peptides into amino acids so they can be absorbed in the small intestine. The watery mixture of partially digested food and gastric juice that is delivered to the small intestine is called **chyme**. The pyloric sphincter, between the stomach and the small intestine, regulates the rate of transport of chyme into the small intestine.

If gastric juice is powerful enough to digest proteins, why doesn't it digest the stomach, too? The reason is that some of the cells lining the stomach and the gastric glands continuously produce a protective barrier of mucus. Normally the stomach contents are in contact with mucus, not living cells. If the mucous layer becomes damaged, however, this leaves the underlying tissue vulnerable. An open (sometimes bleeding) sore called a **peptic ulcer** (from the Greek word *peptein*, meaning "digest") may form. Peptic ulcers occasionally occur in the esophagus and upper part of the small intestine as well.

In addition to pepsinogen, HCl, and mucus, some mucosal cells secrete *intrinsic factor*, a protein that binds to vitamin B12 so that it can be absorbed in the small intestine. Finally, certain cells in the gastric glands secrete a hormone called *gastrin* into the bloodstream. We will talk about gastrin when we discuss the regulation of the digestive process.

✓ Quick Check *Suppose the acid-secreting cells were not working properly and did not secrete any HCl. Would the stomach still contain pepsin? Which of the stomach's functions would be affected?* ■

Stomach contractions mix food and push it forward

While your stomach is empty, muscle contractions keep it small. When you eat a meal, contractions cease and the stomach relaxes and stretches to accommodate the food. Stretching signals peristalsis to increase.

Each wave of peristalsis starts at the lower esophageal sphincter and moves toward the pyloric sphincter, becoming stronger as it proceeds. The peristaltic wave pushes the chyme forward and then, when there is nowhere else for it to go, backward again in a squeezing, mixing motion (Figure 14.8). Each contraction propels about a tablespoon of chyme into the small intestine before the pyloric sphincter closes momentarily. A peristaltic contraction occurs every 15–25 seconds. Have you ever noticed your stomach gurgling at this rate after a meal? You're hearing peristalsis in action.

It takes two to six hours for the stomach to empty completely after a meal. Most forceful when the stomach is full, peristalsis declines as the stomach empties. Chyme with a high acid or fat content stimulates the release of hormones that slow stomach peristalsis, giving the small intestine more time to absorb the nutrients.

The stomach does not absorb nutrients because it lacks the required cellular transporting mechanisms and because its inner lining is coated with mucus. Exceptions to this rule are alcohol and aspirin, both of which are small lipid-soluble substances that can cross the mucus barrier and be absorbed into the bloodstream directly from the stomach. Nevertheless, this is not the primary absorptive pathway for alcohol; most alcohol is absorbed in the intestine along with the nutrients.

Answers to ✓ questions can be found in Appendix A.

Lower esophageal sphincter — Stomach

— Pyloric sphincter

Key: ——▶ = Location and direction of peristalsis

—— = Movement of stomach contents

Figure 14.8 Peristalsis of the stomach. A peristaltic wave of contraction occurs in the stomach approximately every 15–25 seconds. Peristalsis mixes the contents of the stomach and forces a small amount of chyme into the small intestine with each contraction.

Recap The stomach stores food, digests it, and regulates its delivery to the small intestine. Gastric juice dissolves connective tissue, large proteins, and peptides in food. The presence of food stretches the stomach and increases peristalsis. Peristaltic contractions mix the chyme and push it gradually into the small intestine. ▪

14.5 The small intestine digests food and absorbs nutrients and water

The process of digestion continues in the small intestine, so-named because it is smaller in diameter than the final segment of the digestive tract, the large intestine. The small intestine has two major functions.

1. *Digestion.* The stomach partially digests proteins to smaller peptides, under the influence of strong acids and pepsin. Protein digestion continues in the small intestine, but here we also digest carbohydrates and lipids. Digestion of proteins, carbohydrates, and lipids in the small intestine involves neutralizing the highly acidic gastric juice and adding additional digestive enzymes from the intestine and pancreas.
2. *Absorption.* Eventually the proteins, carbohydrates, and lipids in food are broken down to single amino acids, monosaccharides, fatty acids, and glycerol, which are small enough to be transported across mucosal cells into the blood. Nearly 90% of the absorbable nutrients and water is absorbed in the small intestine.

The small intestine consists of three different regions. The first region, the **duodenum**, is only about 10 inches long, but it is here that most of the digestion takes place. The products of digestion are absorbed primarily in the other two segments, the *jejunum* and the *ileum*, which together are about 10 feet long.

The structure of the small intestine wall makes it well suited for absorption (Figure 14.9). The mucosa contains large folds covered with microscopic projections called **villi** (singular: **villus**). Each epithelial cell of the villi has dozens of even smaller, cytoplasmic projections called *microvilli*. The microvilli give the mucosal surface a velvety appearance, which is why they are sometimes called the "brush border." Combined, the folds, villi, and microvilli enlarge the surface area of the small intestine by more than 500 times, increasing its ability to absorb nutrients. At the center of each villus are blood capillaries and a small blind-ended lymphatic capillary called a *lacteal*. Lacteals transport nutrients, some of which are too large to enter the blood capillaries, to larger lymph vessels and eventually back to the blood.

Recap The small intestine has two major functions: 1) digesting proteins, carbohydrates, and lipids, and 2) absorbing approximately 90% of the nutrients and water we consume. Projections called *villi* in the mucosa increase the small intestine's surface area for absorption. ▪

a) The wall of the small intestine contains numerous folds that increase its surface area.

b) Each fold is covered with smaller folds called villi.

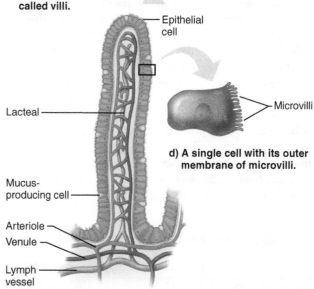

d) A single cell with its outer membrane of microvilli.

c) A close-up view of a villus showing the single layer of mucosal cells covering the surface and the centrally located lymph vessel (lacteal) and blood vessels.

e) Human intestinal villi (×270).

Figure 14.9 **The small intestine.**

14.6 Accessory organs aid digestion and absorption

As mentioned earlier, the digestive system has four accessory organs: salivary glands, pancreas, gallbladder, and liver. We have already discussed the salivary glands. Before discussing absorption in more detail, let's look at the roles of the other three accessory organs.

The pancreas secretes enzymes and NaHCO$_3$

The **pancreas** is an elongated organ that lies just behind the stomach (Figure 14.10). In the chapter on endocrine systems (Chapter 13) we learned that the pancreas is an endocrine gland that secretes several hormones (most importantly insulin and glucagon) into the blood. But in addition, the pancreas is an exocrine gland that produces and secretes several products directly into ducts leading to the digestive tract. The exocrine products of the pancreas are:

- *Sodium bicarbonate* (NaHCO3). Except for pepsin, most digestive enzymes work best at a fairly neutral pH. Sodium bicarbonate from the pancreas neutralizes the stomach acid in the small intestine so that further digestion can proceed.
- *Digestive enzymes.* Most of the enzymes involved in digestion come from the pancreas. (The small intestine contributes only a limited amount of protein- and carbohydrate-digesting enzymes.) Digestive enzymes secreted by the pancreas include:
  - *proteases* (enzymes that digest proteins), such as trypsin, chymotrypsin, and carboxypeptidase,
  - *pancreatic amylase*, which continues the digestion of carbohydrates only partially accomplished by salivary amylase, and
  - *lipase*, a lipid-digesting enzyme. The small intestine does not have lipase, so this product of the pancreas is particularly important.

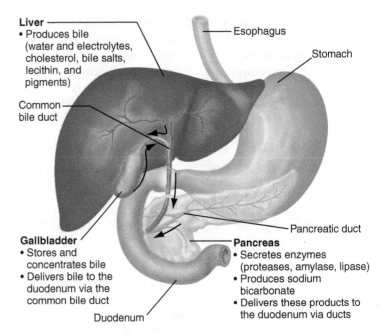

Liver
- Produces bile (water and electrolytes, cholesterol, bile salts, lecithin, and pigments)

Common bile duct

Gallbladder
- Stores and concentrates bile
- Delivers bile to the duodenum via the common bile duct

Duodenum

Esophagus

Stomach

Pancreatic duct

Pancreas
- Secretes enzymes (proteases, amylase, lipase)
- Produces sodium bicarbonate
- Delivers these products to the duodenum via ducts

Figure 14.10 Locations and digestive functions of the liver, gallbladder, and pancreas. These three accessory organs are connected to the small intestine via ducts. The common bile duct joins one of the two pancreatic ducts just before it enters the duodenum. Arrows indicate direction of movement of secretory products.

Table 14.1 lists major digestive enzymes in the gastrointestinal tract.

The liver produces bile and performs many other functions

The liver is a large organ located in the upper-right abdominal cavity. The liver performs many significant functions, some of which are associated with digestion.

Table 14.1 Major enzymes of digestion

Enzyme	Source	Where active	Substance digested	Breakdown products
Carbohydrate Digestion				
Salivary amylase	Salivary glands	Mouth	Polysaccharides	Disaccharides
Pancreatic amylase	Pancreas	Small intestine	Polysaccharides	Disaccharides
Intestinal enzymes	Small intestine	Small intestine	Disaccharides	Monosaccharides (e.g., glucose)
Protein Digestion				
Pepsin	Stomach	Stomach	Proteins	Peptides
Trypsin	Pancreas	Small intestine	Proteins	Peptides
Chymotrypsin	Pancreas	Small intestine	Proteins	Peptides
Carboxypeptidase	Pancreas	Small intestine	Peptides	Amino acids
Intestinal enzymes	Small intestine	Small intestine	Peptides	Amino acids
Lipid Digestion				
Lipase	Pancreas	Small intestine	Triglycerides	Free fatty acids, monoglyceride

The liver's primary digestive function is to facilitate the digestion and absorption of lipids by producing **bile**. Bile is a watery mixture containing electrolytes, cholesterol, bile salts derived from cholesterol, a phospholipid called *lecithin*, and pigments (primarily bilirubin) derived from the breakdown of hemoglobin. The bile salts emulsify lipids in the small intestine; that is, they break them into smaller and smaller droplets. Eventually the droplets are small enough to be digested by lipases (lipid-digesting enzymes) from the pancreas.

An important feature of the vascular anatomy of the GI tract is the **hepatic portal system** (Figure 14.11). In general terms, a *portal system* carries blood from one capillary bed to another: we have seen a portal system before, in the vascular connection between the hypothalamus and the anterior pituitary gland. In the digestive system the hepatic portal system carries nutrient-rich blood directly from the digestive organs to the liver (*hepatos* is the Greek word for "liver") via the hepatic portal vein. Therefore, the liver is ideally located to

begin processing and storing nutrients for the body just as soon as digestion and absorption have begun. After passing through the liver the blood is returned to the general circulation.

The liver serves a number of other functions that maintain homeostasis.

- Storing fat-soluble vitamins (A, D, E, and K) and iron
- Storing glucose as glycogen after a meal, and converting glycogen to glucose between meals
- Manufacturing plasma proteins, such as albumin and fibrinogen, from amino acids
- Synthesizing and storing some lipids
- Inactivating many chemicals, including alcohol, hormones, drugs, and poisons
- Converting ammonia (NH_3), a toxic waste product of metabolism, into less toxic urea
- Destroying worn-out red blood cells

Because of its central role in so many functions, liver injury can be particularly dangerous. Overexposure to toxic chemicals, medications, or alcohol can damage the liver because it takes up these substances to "detoxify" them, killing some liver cells in the process. Long-term exposure, such as prolonged alcohol abuse, can destroy enough cells to permanently impair liver function, a condition known as *cirrhosis*.

✅**Quick Check** *Many people eat the livers of domestic animals such as cows and chickens. Considering the contents of the liver (see above), do you think liver is generally a nutritious food choice? Can you think of any situations in which it might be dangerous?* ▪

The gallbladder stores bile until needed

The bile produced by the liver flows through ducts to the **gallbladder**. The gallbladder concentrates bile by removing most of the water, and then stores the concentrated bile until it is needed. After a meal, bile is secreted into the small intestine via the common bile duct, which joins the pancreatic duct.

↩ **Recap** The pancreas secretes digestive enzymes and sodium bicarbonate. The sodium bicarbonate neutralizes stomach acid, making the digestive enzymes more effective. The liver produces bile, which is stored in the gallbladder until after a meal. The liver also produces plasma proteins; inactivates toxic chemicals; destroys old red blood cells; stores vitamins, iron, and certain products of metabolism; and performs other functions important for homeostasis. ▪

14.7 The large intestine absorbs nutrients and eliminates wastes

By the time the contents of the digestive tract reach the large intestine, most of the nutrients and water have been absorbed. The **large intestine** absorbs most of the remaining nutrients and water and stores the now nearly solid waste material until it can be eliminated.

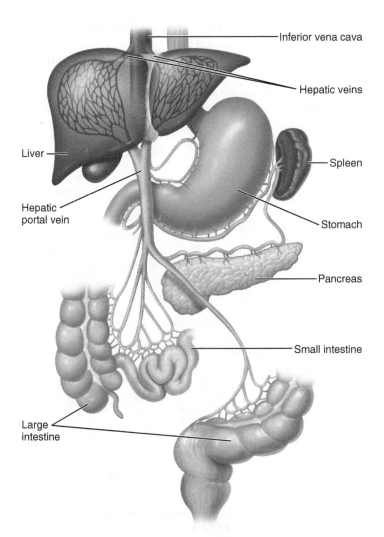

Figure 14.11 The hepatic portal system. The hepatic portal system carries nutrient-rich venous blood from the stomach, intestines, pancreas, and spleen directly to the liver before the blood is returned to the general circulation. Only the first part of the large intestine is shown.

Labels: Inferior vena cava, Hepatic veins, Liver, Spleen, Hepatic portal vein, Stomach, Pancreas, Small intestine, Large intestine

Although the large intestine is larger in diameter than the small intestine, it is only about half as long. It begins at a pouch called the *cecum*, which receives the chyme from the small intestine (Figure 14.12). A small fingerlike pouch, the **appendix**, extends from the cecum. The appendix has no known digestive function, but we become acutely aware of its presence if it becomes inflamed or infected, a condition called *appendicitis*.

Most of the large intestine consists of four regions collectively called the **colon**. The ascending colon rises along the right side of the body (the left side of Figure 14.12, viewed from the front), the transverse colon crosses over to the left side, and the descending colon passes down the left side to the short final segment, the sigmoid colon. Feces are stored in the sigmoid colon until defecation, when they pass through the rectum to the anus.

In addition to indigestible material, the feces contain about 5% bacteria by weight. Many strains of bacteria thrive on the leftover material in the colon that we cannot digest. Some of these bacteria release by-products that are useful to us, such as vitamin K, which is important for blood clotting. They also produce less helpful substances such as intestinal gas, a by-product of their metabolism as they break down food.

Defecation is controlled by a neural reflex. Normally the anus is kept closed by contraction of a ring of smooth muscle called the *internal anal sphincter*. But when feces enter the rectum and the rectum is stretched, a neural reflex causes the internal anal sphincter to relax and the rectum to contract, expelling the feces.

We can prevent defecation by voluntarily contracting the *external anal sphincter*, a ring of skeletal muscle under our conscious control. "Potty training" of children involves learning to control the external anal sphincter. Until they learn how to control it consciously, children defecate whenever the defecation reflex occurs.

⮌ Recap **The large intestine absorbs the last of the water, ions, and some nutrients and stores feces until defecation occurs.** ∎

14.8 How nutrients are absorbed

Once food has been digested, how does your body absorb the nutrients? The mechanism depends on the type of nutrient.

Proteins and carbohydrates are absorbed by active transport

In the small intestine, enzymes from the pancreas and enzymes secreted by the mucosal layer of the stomach and from the small intestine break down proteins into amino acids, completing the digestion of proteins that began in the stomach. The amino acids are then actively transported into the mucosal cells. Eventually they move by facilitated diffusion out of the mucosal cells and make their way into the capillaries (Figure 14.13).

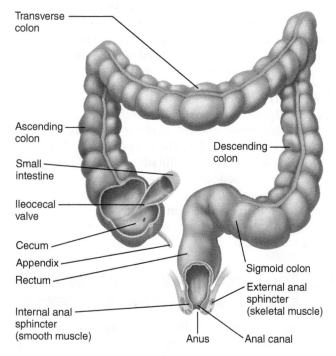

Figure 14.12 The large intestine. The large intestine begins at the cecum and ends at the anus.

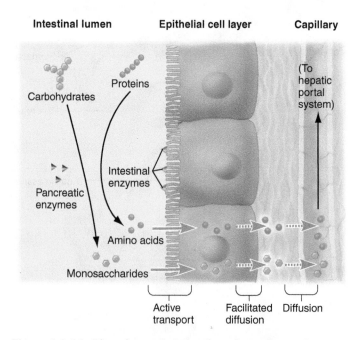

Figure 14.13 Digestion and absorption of proteins and carbohydrates in the small intestine. Digestion depends on enzymes from the pancreas and enzymes attached to the surface of the epithelial cells of the intestine. The amino acid and carbohydrate products of digestion cross the epithelial cell layer of the mucosa and enter a capillary for transport to the liver.

Carbohydrate digestion begins in the mouth, where salivary amylase breaks down polysaccharides into disaccharides (review Table 14.1). It is completed in the small intestine with the addition of pancreatic amylase and enzymes from the small intestine. Together these enzymes break down the remaining carbohydrates into monosaccharides (simple sugars such as glucose). Monosaccharides follow transport pathways that are similar to those for amino acids. However, they use different active transport proteins.

Lipids are broken down, then reassembled

Recall that bile salts emulsify lipids into small fat droplets, which are then digested by pancreatic and intestinal lipases. The products of lipid digestion are fatty acids and monoglycerides. Because they are nonpolar, the fatty acids and monoglycerides quickly dissolve in *micelles*—small droplets composed of bile salts and lecithin that have a polar outer surface and a nonpolar inner core. The function of micelles is to transport fatty acids and monoglycerides to the outer surface of the mucosal cells so that they can be absorbed into the cells (Figure 14.14).

Once inside the cells, the fatty acids and monoglycerides recombine into triglycerides. Clusters of triglycerides are then coated with proteins to form water-soluble droplets called *chylomicrons*. Chylomicrons are released from the cell by exocytosis. However, they are too large to enter the capillaries directly. Instead, they enter the more permeable lacteals and travel in the lymph vessels until the lymph is returned to the venous blood vessels near the heart.

Water is absorbed by osmosis

As nutrients are absorbed in the small intestine (or when you drink pure water), the concentration of the water in the intestinal lumen becomes higher than in the intestinal cells or in the blood. A higher concentration of water in the lumen represents a strong driving force for the diffusion of water through the epithelial layer of cells of the small intestine and into the blood. The capacity for water absorption by the small intestine is nearly limitless, which explains why you do not experience diarrhea every time you drink a lot of fluid.

Water absorption continues in the large intestine, but here the capacity is limited. Conditions that cause the small intestine to deliver too much food residue to the large intestine or that speed up the rate of movement through the large intestine can lead to diarrhea (watery feces). A common cause of diarrhea is a bacterial infection in the small intestine.

The opposite problem is constipation, in which the food residue, now called *feces*, remains in the large intestine and colon so long that too much water is absorbed. The feces become dry and hard, making defecation difficult. Constipation can result from stress, lack of exercise, or insufficient fiber (indigestible material) in the diet.

Vitamins and minerals follow a variety of paths

How vitamins are absorbed depends on whether they are fat soluble or water soluble. Fat-soluble vitamins dissolve in the micelles and are absorbed by diffusion across the lipid membrane of the mucosal cell layer, just like the components of lipids. Water-soluble vitamins are absorbed either by active

Figure 14.14 Digestion and absorption of fats in the small intestine. Bile salts emulsify large fat droplets into smaller droplets so that lipases can digest the fats into fatty acids and monoglycerides. The fatty acids and monoglycerides dissolve in micelles composed of bile salts and lecithin. Micelles near the cell's surface release their fatty acids and monoglycerides, which then diffuse across the cell membrane. In the cell the fatty acids and monoglycerides are resynthesized to triglycerides and coated with protein. The protein-coated triglycerides are called *chylomicrons*. Chylomicrons exit the cell by exocytosis and enter a lacteal for transport to the circulation.

☑ *Blood capillaries and lacteals are both present in the area directly beneath a small intestinal cell (review Figure 14.9c). Why do chylomicrons enter a lacteal, rather than a blood capillary?*

transport or diffusion through channels or pores. Minerals (ions) such as sodium, potassium, calcium, phosphate, sulfate, and magnesium are electrically charged and hence not lipid soluble. These are either actively transported or are absorbed by diffusion via specific transport proteins, pores, or channels.

In addition to the nutrients we ingest in our food, the body digests and reabsorbs the components of the digestive secretions themselves. Nearly 9 liters of gastric juice, pancreatic juice, digestive enzymes, and bile are produced every day. The water and minerals in the digestive secretions are reabsorbed by the normal mechanisms for these nutrients. Enzymes are digested to their component amino acids, and the amino acids are then reabsorbed. Bile salts are reabsorbed, returned to the liver, and used again.

🔄 **Recap** Proteins and carbohydrates are transported into the cells lining the small intestine by active transport processes, and then diffuse into capillaries. The products of lipid digestion are transported to the mucosa in micelles, diffuse into the cell, and recombine into lipids within the cell. Then they are coated with protein to become chylomicrons that enter the lymph. The intestines also absorb water, vitamins, minerals, and digestive secretions. ▪

14.9 Endocrine and nervous systems regulate digestion

The digestive system is most active when food or chyme is present and fairly inactive when it is not. Regulation involves altering the motility and secretions of various organs so that each operates as efficiently as possible.

Most regulatory mechanisms operate to maintain a constant internal environment. Regulation of the digestive system, on the other hand, promotes rapid, efficient digestion and absorption of whatever is delivered to the system, regardless of homeostasis. The digestive process actually alters the internal environment temporarily because all those absorbed nutrients enter the blood in a relatively short time—a few hours.

Regulation depends on volume and content of food

The endocrine system and nervous system regulate digestion according to both the volume and content of food. Because most digestion and absorption occurs in the stomach and small intestine, most regulatory processes involve those organs.

When the stomach stretches to accommodate food, neural reflexes increase stomach peristalsis and secretion of gastric juice. Stretching and the presence of protein stimulate the stomach to release the hormone **gastrin**, which triggers the release of more gastric juice.

When chyme arrives at the small intestine, stretching the duodenum increases segmentation to mix the chyme. The duodenum also secretes two hormones into the bloodstream: secretin and cholecystokinin. Acid in chyme triggers release of **secretin**, which stimulates the pancreas to secrete water and bicarbonate to neutralize acid. Fat and protein stimulate release of **cholecystokinin (CCK)**, which signals the pancreas to secrete more digestive enzymes. CCK and stretching the duodenum also stimulate the gallbladder to contract and release bile (Table 14.2).

✔️**Quick Check** *Do carbohydrates result in the release of any hormones from the duodenum? Where in the digestive system are carbohydrates first broken down?* ▪

Secretin, CCK, and stretching of the small intestine inhibit stomach motility and stomach secretions. In other words, if chyme flows too quickly from the stomach, the small intestine will slow stomach activity accordingly.

Gastrin and a neural reflex involving stretching of the stomach increase motility of the large intestine after eating. This is why people often feel the urge to defecate after their first meal of the day.

Nutrients are used or stored until needed

Once all those nutrients have been absorbed, the body must use them. Will they be consumed for immediate energy, stored until later, or combined with more nutrients to create other molecules? Regulation of organic metabolism involves

Table 14.2 Nervous and endocrine systems' regulation of the digestive processes

Organ	Nervous system	Endocrine system
Stomach	Stretching increases peristalsis and secretion of gastric juice.	Stretching and protein trigger release of gastrin, which stimulates gastric glands.
Small intestine	Stretching increases segmentation. Stretching inhibits stomach motility and stomach secretions.	Acid stimulates release of secretin, which stimulates pancreas to secrete bicarbonate, neutralizing acid. Fat and protein stimulate release of cholecystokinin (CCK), which stimulates the pancreas to secrete enzymes and the gallbladder to release bile. CCK and secretin inhibit stomach motility and stomach secretions.
Large intestine	Stomach stretching increases motility.	Gastrin increases motility.

Figure 14.15 The pathways of organic metabolism.

interactions between virtually all organs in the body. Key organs are the pancreas with its two main endocrine secretions (insulin and glucagon) and the liver with its multiple roles in overall metabolism.

Figure 14.15 summarizes how the body utilizes organic molecules. Three concepts are evident from this figure.

1. Depending on which molecules are in short supply and which are in excess at the moment, there can be a great deal of interconversion of one to another. We first introduced this concept in connection with cellular metabolism in Chapter 3. Lipids, carbohydrates, and proteins can all be converted to storage forms of lipid or carbohydrate, and then recycled according to the body's needs.

2. When we consume more energy-containing nutrients than we use, our bodies store the excess for future use. Over time, these mounting reserves can increase body weight.

3. When we consume fewer energy-containing nutrients than we use, the body draws on these storage forms of energy to make up the difference. If we do this on a regular basis, we lose weight.

In the rest of this chapter we discuss nutrition, energy balance, and healthy body weight.

Recap The endocrine and nervous systems regulate digestion based on content and volume of food. Regulatory mechanisms include neural reflexes involving organ stretching and release of the hormones gastrin, secretin, and cholecystokinin. Amino acids and the products of lipid and carbohydrate digestion can all be converted to storage forms of lipid or carbohydrate, to be retrieved and used when needed. ▪

14.10 Nutrition: You are what you eat

Nutrition is the interaction between an organism and its food. Because nearly all nutrients enter the body through the digestive system, it is fair to say that "you are what you eat." What nutrients do we actually need, and why?

ChooseMyPlate.gov offers a personalized approach

Figure 14.16 presents one answer to these questions. Developed by the Center for Nutrition Policy and Promotion at the U.S. Department of Agriculture (USDA), *MyPlate* is a comprehensive, personalized approach that includes physical activity as well as healthy nutrition. It replaces the old food pyramid, which was thought to be too confusing for most consumers. MyPlate divides foods into five groups and gives you recommendations on what to eat from each group.

MyPlate provides many options to help you prepare a personalized nutrition plan. The system includes food plans appropriate to different calorie levels of food intake, based on the latest *Dietary Guidelines for Americans* issued by the USDA and the Department of Health and Human Services. If you enter your age, gender, height, weight, and physical activity level on the MyPlate Web site, the system will match you with the best plan for your needs. It will suggest how many calories you need per day and recommend specific amounts of each food group, as well as the upper limit of empty calories (extra fats and sugars) you should consume per day. You can print worksheets to help you set nutrition goals and monitor your progress. MyPlate even offers advice

Fruits
Focus on fruits.

Vegetables
Vary your veggies.

Grains
Make at least half your grains whole.

Protein Foods
Go lean with protein.

Dairy
Get your calcium-rich foods.

Figure 14.16 MyPlate. MyPlate is a visual representation of the recommended dietary guidelines of the U.S. Department of Agriculture (USDA). The pyramid indicates the recommended consumption of foods from five different groups, taking into account both nutritional needs and concerns about the effects of diet on nutrition-related disease. MyPlate is designed to be highly interactive.

on foods to substitute if you choose not to eat specific foods; what to do if you are a vegetarian, for example.

Most nutritionists would agree with the general components of a healthy diet listed in MyPlate. However, some of the specific recommendations of MyPlate have been challenged by critics, who charge that the dietary guidelines on which it is based are influenced by intense pressure from lobbying groups such as the National Dairy Council and the National Cattleman's Beef Association. For example, current dietary guidelines are that for "improved bone health" (and presumably to prevent osteoporosis), adults should drink three cups of low-fat milk per day. That's over 300 calories just in milk. There are other ways to get the required calcium, of course, and not everyone is at risk of osteoporosis. MyPlate also lumps meat (beef, poultry, and fish) and beans together in the protein category, ignoring the mounting evidence that replacing red meat with a combination of fish, poultry, and beans is a healthier choice. Nevertheless, MyPlate is still a good place to start if you want basic information about a healthy diet overall.

General recommendations for a healthy diet include the following:

- Eat a variety of foods.
- Maintain a healthy weight.
- Eat plenty of fruits, vegetables, and whole-grain products.
- Choose a diet low in cholesterol and saturated fat.
- Use sugar only in moderation.
- Consume salt and sodium in moderation (less than 2,300 milligrams, or about 1 teaspoon of salt per day).

- If you drink alcoholic beverages, do so in moderation. How much is "moderate"? The equivalent of up to one drink per day for women and up to two drinks per day for men.

We consider the three basic nutrient groups first—carbohydrates, lipids, and proteins—before discussing vitamins, minerals, and the importance of fiber.

Carbohydrates: A major energy source

Carbohydrates are one of the body's main sources of energy, and many nutritionists recommend that approximately 45–65% of our calorie intake come from carbohydrates.

Carbohydrates may be either simple or complex (Table 14.3). Simple carbohydrates (sugars) are found in many natural foods such as fruit and honey. Refined sugars, such as granulated sugar and corn syrup, have had most other nutrients removed, so they are less nutritious than their natural counterparts. Complex carbohydrates, such as starch or glycogen, consist of many sugar units linked together. Whole foods containing complex carbohydrates are better for us than refined sugars because they release sugars more slowly and also contribute fiber, vitamins, and minerals. In the body, stored starch and glycogen are broken down to glucose, one of the premier sources of energy.

It is difficult to tell exactly how much refined sugar we eat because so much is disguised on food labels as "corn sweeteners," "dextrose," or "fructose" (levulose). The USDA estimates the average North American consumes more than 142 pounds of sweeteners and refined sugar annually— almost 3 pounds each week.

Table 14.3 Good sources of natural carbohydrates

Simple carbohydrates	Complex carbohydrates
Fruit	**Starchy vegetables**
Citrus	Potatoes
Berries	Corn
Melons	Peas
	Beans
Unsweetened fruit juice	**Grains**
Honey	Whole-grain breads and cereals
	Whole-grain pasta
	Rice
	Oatmeal
	Wheat bran

Lipids: Essential cell components and energy sources

Lipids (including fats) are essential components of every living cell. Phospholipids and cholesterol make up most of the cell membrane. Cholesterol also forms the backbone of steroid hormones and is used to synthesize bile. Fat stores energy, cushions organs, insulates the body under the skin, and stores several vitamins. Most of the fats in food are triglycerides, which consist of three fatty acids attached to a glycerol molecule. Recall from Chapter 2 that fats are classified according to the ratio of hydrogen to carbon atoms in their fatty acids.

- *Saturated fats.* Saturated fats have two hydrogen atoms for every carbon atom in their fatty acid tails. They tend to be solids at room temperature. Red meats and dairy products are higher in saturated fats than poultry and fish. Saturated fats are also found in a few plant sources such as coconut and palm kernel oil. They tend to raise blood levels of LDL cholesterol, the "bad" cholesterol that is associated with atherosclerosis and heart disease (Chapter 8).

- *Unsaturated fats.* Unsaturated fats are missing one or more pairs of hydrogen atoms in their fatty acid tails. Every missing pair of hydrogen atoms leads to a double bond between adjacent carbons and a kink, or bend, in the tail, making it more difficult for adjacent molecules to form bonds with each other. Consequently, unsaturated fats are liquids (oils) at room temperature. In general, unsaturated fats are considered healthier than saturated fats because they tend to lower LDL cholesterol levels. Olive, canola, safflower, and corn oils are all unsaturated fats derived from plants. Certain cold-water fish (salmon, trout, and sardines) are rich in omega-3 fatty acids, polyunsaturated fatty acids that have been linked to a reduced risk of heart disease.

Vegetable oils can be turned back into solids at room temperature by partial hydrogenation of the fatty acid tails. However, the process of partial hydrogenation reconfigures the positions of some of the remaining unpaired hydrogen atoms, producing *trans fats*. Trans fats were once very popular with fast-food restaurants as a deep-frying oil because they increase the shelf life and flavor stability of foods. Trans fats are used in commercial baked goods (cookies, crackers, and snacks) and are also found in vegetable shortening and margarine. However, like saturated fats, trans fats tend to raise LDL cholesterol and thus may increase the risk of cardiovascular disease. Food manufacturers now list the percentage of trans fats in the Nutrition Facts panel on product labels, and many fast-food restaurants no longer use trans fats in their deep fryers.

BlogInFocus (MB)

California is the only state (so far) to ban the use of trans fats in restaurant foods and retail baked goods. Should other states do the same? Visit MJ's blog in the Study Area in MasteringBiology and look under "Trans Fats."

The liver can synthesize cholesterol and most of the lipids the body needs, but it cannot produce every last one of them. The few fatty acids that our bodies cannot make, called *essential fatty acids*, must be consumed as food. Two examples are linoleic and linolenic acids, present in corn and olives, both of which contribute to proper cell membrane structure. A teaspoon of corn or olive oil, or its equivalent in food, is enough to satisfy our daily requirements.

Although lipids are essential to human health, most of us consume far more than we need. Nutritionists recommend that lipids account for no more than 20–35% of calories consumed per day. In addition to watching the amount of fat we eat, though, it's important to pay attention to the type. Diets high in saturated fat, cholesterol, and trans fats place us at risk for cardiovascular disease and certain cancers. Less than 10% of calories consumed daily should come from saturated fats, with less than 300 milligrams per day of cholesterol and as little trans fat as possible.

✓ **Quick Check** *Why are fish living in cold waters particularly likely to have stores of unsaturated fats in their bodies, rather than saturated fats? (Hint: With few exceptions, fish are "cold-blooded," meaning their body temperature is the same as the temperature of the surrounding water.)* ■

Complete proteins contain every amino acid

Like lipids, **proteins** are vital components of every cell. They make up the enzymes that direct metabolism, they serve as receptor and transport molecules, and they build our muscle fibers. A few are hormones.

Despite their variety, all proteins are composed of just 20 different amino acids. The body can make 12 of these amino acids. The 8 that the body cannot produce (isoleucine, leucine, lysine, methionine, phenylalanine, threonine, tryptophan, and valine) are called **essential amino acids** because they must be ingested in food. Two more that the body can make, histidine and arginine, are sometimes considered essential in children because their rapidly growing bodies cannot synthesize these amino acids fast enough.

A **complete protein** contains all 20 of the amino acids in proportions that meet our nutritional needs. Most animal proteins are complete, but nearly all plant proteins (with the exception of soybeans) lack one or more of the essential amino acids. Vegetarians must be careful to choose the right combinations of plant-based foods to obtain all amino acids. A combination of foods from any two of the three rightmost columns of Figure 14.17 will provide the necessary balance of all essential amino acids. Foods such as trail mix (roasted soybeans and nuts), hummus (chick peas and sesame seeds), a bean burrito in a corn tortilla, and red beans and rice do just that.

Approximately 15% of our calories should come from protein. In many parts of the world protein deficiency is a

Complete proteins	Incomplete proteins: low in lysine	Incomplete proteins: low in methionine	Incomplete proteins: low in tryptophan
Legumes: Soybean Tofu Soy milk	**Legumes:** Peanuts	**Legumes:** Beans (dried) Black-eyed peas Chickpeas Lentils Lima beans Mung beans Peanuts	**Legumes:** Beans (dried) Garbanzos Lima beans Mung beans Peanuts
Cereal grains: Wheat germ	**Cereal grains:** Barley Corn Oats Rice Rye Wheat	**Fresh vegetables:** Asparagus Broccoli Green peas Mushrooms Potatoes	**Fresh vegetables:** Green peas Mushrooms Swiss chard
Dairy products: Milk Cheeses Yogurt Eggs	**Nuts, seeds:** Almonds Cashews Coconut English walnuts Hazelnuts Pecans Sunflower seeds Sesame seeds	**Nuts, seeds:** Hazelnuts	**Nuts, seeds:** Almonds English walnuts
Animal products: Meats Fish			

Figure 14.17 Getting the essential amino acids. Most plants are low in one or more of the essential amino acids. A vegetarian should choose a combination of foods from any two of the three rightmost columns to ensure an adequate intake of all essential amino acids.

serious health problem. Every enzyme has a unique amino acid sequence, so if even one amino acid is missing in the diet, the body may be unable to produce crucial enzymes at the proper time in development. Protein deficiencies during pregnancy and childhood can retard growth and alter physical and mental performance. Unfortunately, foods with complete proteins such as meat and milk are often expensive in poor societies, and many people remain uninformed about ways to achieve a balanced diet of plant proteins.

✅ **Quick Check** *Do you think eggs and milk contain complete proteins? Why or why not? (Hint: What are eggs and milk used for in nature?)* ▪

Vitamins are essential for normal function

In addition to carbohydrates, lipids, and proteins, humans need **vitamins**, a group of at least 13 chemicals that are essential for normal functioning. The body can produce only a few vitamins; our skin synthesizes vitamin D when exposed to sunlight, and bacteria living in the colon manufacture vitamins K, B6, and biotin. We must obtain all others from our food and absorb them in the digestive tract. Table 14.4 (next page) lists the 13 vitamins along with their sources, functions, and signs of deficiency or excess.

Vitamins fall into two groups: fat soluble and water soluble. The distinction reflects how a vitamin is absorbed and stored and how steady a supply of it is needed. Fat-soluble vitamins are absorbed more readily if there is fat in the diet. They tend to be absorbed along with the components

of fat, and they are stored in fat tissue and released as needed. Body stores of some fat-soluble vitamins may last for years, so it is rarely necessary to take supplements.

Water-soluble vitamins are absorbed more readily than fat-soluble vitamins, but they are stored only briefly and rapidly excreted in urine. Thus we need to consume foods containing water-soluble vitamins on a regular basis.

✅ **Quick Check** *Vegans—people who do not eat meat, dairy products, or eggs—are particularly vulnerable to a deficiency of a particular vitamin. Looking at Table 14.4, can you tell which one? Explain.* ▪

Minerals: Elements essential for body processes

Minerals are the atoms of certain chemical elements that are also essential for body processes. They are the ions in blood plasma and cell cytoplasm (sodium, potassium, chloride, and many others). They represent most of the chemical structure of bone (calcium, phosphorus, and oxygen). They also contribute to the activity of nerves and muscles (sodium, potassium, and calcium), among many other functions. Twenty-one minerals are considered essential for animals. Nine of the 21 (arsenic, chromium, cobalt, manganese, molybdenum, nickel, selenium, silicon, and vanadium) are called *trace minerals* because they represent less than 0.01% of your body weight. Table 14.5 (on page 344) lists the 12 most important minerals.

How much do we need of each vitamin and mineral? The National Research Council publishes the current best estimate, the **Recommended Dietary Allowance (RDA)**. Most healthy people can achieve the RDA without taking supplements if they eat a balanced diet of whole foods. That's a big "if" for some of us, considering our diets. Scientific studies suggest that supplements may also benefit certain groups, such as newborns, the elderly, or people taking medications that interfere with nutrient absorption. Calcium is advised for postmenopausal women to prevent the bone loss of osteoporosis.

Never take massive doses of any vitamin or mineral unless prescribed by your doctor. As the "excess" columns show, more is not always better.

Fiber benefits the colon

Fiber—found in many vegetables, fruit, and grains—is indigestible material. Even though our bodies cannot digest it, we need a certain amount in our diet. Fiber is beneficial because it makes feces bulky and helps them pass more efficiently through the colon.

Table 14.4 **Vitamins**

Vitamin	Common sources	Primary functions	Signs of severe, prolonged deficiency	Signs of extreme excess
Fat-Soluble Vitamins				
A	Fortified dairy products, egg yolk, liver, yellow fruits, yellow and dark green leafy vegetables	Synthesis of visual pigments and the development of bones and teeth	Night blindness, dry scaly skin, increased susceptibility to infections	Damage to bone and liver, blurred vision
D	Fish oil, fortified milk, egg yolk; also produced by skin	Promotes absorption of calcium, required for healthy bones and teeth	Bone deformities in children, bone weakening in adults	Calcium deposits in tissues, leading to cardiovascular and kidney damage
E	Vegetable oils, nuts, whole grains	Thought to be an antioxidant that prevents cell membrane damage	Damage to red blood cells and nerves	Generally nontoxic
K	Green vegetables, also produced by bacteria in colon	Formation of certain proteins involved in blood clotting	Defective blood clotting, abnormal bleeding	Liver damage and anemia
Water-Soluble Vitamins				
B$_1$ (thiamine)	Whole grains, legumes, eggs, lean meats	Coenzyme in carbohydrate metabolism	Damage to heart and nerves, pain	None reported
B$_2$ (riboflavin)	Dairy products, eggs, meat, whole grains, green leafy vegetables	Coenzyme in carbohydrate metabolism	Skin lesions	Generally nontoxic
Niacin	Nuts, meats, grains, green leafy vegetables	Coenzyme in carbohydrate metabolism	Causes a disease called *pellagra* (damage to skin, digestive tract, and nervous system)	Skin flushing, potential liver damage
B$_6$	High-protein foods in general; also made by colonic bacteria	Coenzyme in amino acid metabolism	Muscle, skin, and nerve damage, anemia	Poor coordination, numbness in feet
Folic acid (B$_9$)	Green vegetables, nuts, grains, legumes, orange juice	Coenzyme in nucleic acid and amino acid metabolism	Anemia, digestive disturbances	Masks vitamin B$_{12}$ deficiency
B$_{12}$	Animal products	Coenzyme in nucleic acid metabolism	Anemia, nervous system damage	Thought to be nontoxic
Pantothenic acid	Widely distributed in foods, especially animal products	Coenzyme in glucose metabolism, fatty acid and steroid synthesis	Fatigue, tingling in hands and feet, intestinal disturbances	Generally nontoxic except occasional diarrhea
Biotin	Widely distributed in foods; also made by colonic bacteria	Coenzyme in amino acid metabolism, fat and glycogen formation	Scaly skin (dermatitis)	Thought to be nontoxic
C (ascorbic acid)	Fruits and vegetables, especially citrus fruits, cantaloupe, broccoli, and cabbage	Antioxidant; needed for collagen formation; important for bone and teeth formation; improves iron absorption	A disease called *scurvy*, poor wound healing, impaired immune responses	Digestive upsets

A low-fiber diet can lead to chronic constipation, *hemorrhoids* (swollen veins in the lining of the anus, often caused by straining during defecation), and a disorder called *diverticulosis* (see section 14.12). A low-fiber diet has also been associated with a higher risk of colon cancer, perhaps because cancer-causing substances remain in the colon longer (see Chapter 18). Doctors recommend eating 20–35 grams of fiber every day—considerably more than the average 12–17 grams that most North Americans consume.

Table 14.5 Major minerals in the human body

Mineral	Common sources	Primary functions	Signs of severe, prolonged deficiency	Signs of extreme excess
Calcium (Ca)	Dairy products, dark green vegetables, legumes	Bone and teeth formation, nerve and muscle action, blood clotting	Decreased bone mass, stunted growth	Kidney damage, impaired absorption of other minerals
Chloride (Cl)	Table salt	Role in acid-base balance, acid formation in stomach, body water balance	Poor appetite and growth, muscle cramps	Contributes to high blood pressure in susceptible people
Copper (Cu)	Seafood, nuts, legumes	Synthesis of hemoglobin, melanin	Anemia, bone and blood vessel changes	Nausea, liver damage
Fluoride (F)	Fluoridated water, tea, seafood	Maintenance of teeth and perhaps bone	Tooth decay	Digestive upset, mottling of teeth
Iodine (I)	Iodized salt, marine fish and shellfish	Required for thyroid hormone	Enlarged thyroid (goiter), metabolic disorders	Goiter
Iron (Fe)	Green leafy vegetables, whole grains, legumes, meats, eggs	Required for hemoglobin, myoglobin, and certain enzymes	Iron-deficiency anemia, impaired immune function	*Acute:* shock and death. *Chronic:* liver and heart failure
Magnesium (Mg)	Whole grains, green leafy vegetables	Coenzyme in several enzymes	Nerve and muscle disturbances	Impaired nerve function
Phosphorus (P)	Meat, poultry, whole grains	Component of bones, teeth, phospholipids, ATP, nucleic acids	Loss of minerals from bone, muscle weakness	Depressed absorption of some minerals, abnormal bone deposition
Potassium (K)	Widespread in the diet, especially meats, grains	Muscle and nerve function; a major component of intracellular fluid	Muscle weakness	*Acute:* cardiac arrhythmias and death. *Chronic:* muscle weakness
Sodium (Na)	Table salt; widespread in the diet	Muscle and nerve function; major component of body water	Muscle cramps	High blood pressure in susceptible people
Sulfur (S)	Meat, dairy products	Component of many proteins	None reported	None reported
Zinc (Zn)	Whole grains, meats, seafood	Component of many enzymes	Impaired growth, reproductive failure, impaired immune function	*Acute:* nausea, vomiting, diarrhea. *Chronic:* anemia and impaired immune function

Recap A healthy diet includes plenty of fruits, vegetables, and whole grains and adequate fiber. Saturated fat, sugar, salt, and alcohol should be ingested only in modest amounts. Some essential fatty acids and eight essential amino acids must be ingested to meet the body's nutritional requirements because the body cannot synthesize them. Complete proteins contain all 20 amino acids. Most animal proteins are complete, but most plant proteins are incomplete. All minerals and nearly all vitamins must be obtained from food. ▪

14.11 Food Labels

By law, packaged foods must have a food label on their packaging that lists certain key pieces of nutritional information. Food labels can help you make nutritional choices if you take the time to read and understand them.

A typical food label is shown in **Figure 14.18**. This particular one is from a box of whole-grain wheat crackers. At the top is information on serving size and serving per container. You may find that the serving size is quite small compared to the amount you might choose to eat and that it will vary between products, so keep that (and the calories per serving) in mind when comparing products.

Below the serving size and calories data is a breakdown of the percent of the recommended daily value of certain nutrients provided by just one serving. For some nutrients (fats, cholesterol, sodium), the goal should be to keep your daily intake *under* 100% of the percent daily value; for others (fiber, protein, and certain vitamins), the goal is to get *at least* 100% of the percent daily value each day.

At the bottom of the food label is a listing of the actual amounts of certain nutrients you should eat each day. Note that the amounts will depend on the total number of calories you aim to consume each day. Again, for some nutrients the

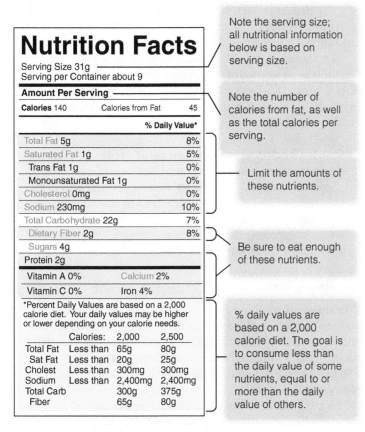

Figure 14.18 A food label.

goal is to stay under the listed amount; for others, it should be to get at least that amount.

Beneath the food label itself is another good source of information: the list of ingredients. These are always listed in order, top to bottom, by weight. If you are trying to reduce your sugar intake, for example, you might be startled to see that sugar is among the first three ingredients in a product you regularly buy. You may also be surprised to see how many different ingredients there are, including flavorings, colorings, and preservatives. If you are allergic to any one potential food ingredient, here is where to look.

Reading and understanding the food labels on all the different products we buy is probably more work than most of us are willing to do. However, if you are trying to choose between two fairly similar products, it gets a lot easier; just compare the labels side by side. Which one has more calories in the serving size you would eat? Which one contains cholesterol, and which one doesn't? Used this way, food labels can provide you with information that will help you make healthier choices.

14.12 Weight control: Energy consumed versus energy spent

The body requires energy to fuel metabolic processes and other activities. When we digest nutrients, we can put the energy they contain to use.

Energy is measured in units called **calories**. Technically, a calorie is the amount of energy needed to raise the temperature of 1 gram of water by 1° Celsius. Because this is not much energy in biological terms, nutritionists generally measure the energy content of food and the energy used to perform biological activities in terms of kilocalories (1,000 calories). However, in subsequent usage the "kilo" is usually dropped, and consequently a kilocalorie of energy is referred to as just one nutritional calorie. We will follow that convention here as well.

BMR: Determining how many calories we need

If we want to maintain a stable body weight, the number of calories we consume must equal the number we use. Your daily caloric energy needs are determined by your **basal metabolic rate (BMR)**, the energy your body needs to perform essential activities such as breathing and maintaining organ function. BMR can be influenced by the following factors:

- *Gender and body composition.* BMR is higher in males. Muscle tissue consumes more energy than fat tissue; because men generally have more muscle than women, they have a higher BMR. Also, highly muscular men and women have a faster BMR than their less muscular counterparts.
- *Age.* BMR declines over time.
- *Health.* Some health conditions (such as fever, infections, and hyperthyroidism) increase BMR. Other conditions (such as hypothyroidism) lower it.
- *Stress.* Norepinephrine and epinephrine raise BMR.
- *Food intake.* Eating increases the metabolic rate, whereas fasting and extreme dieting decrease it. This is why crash diets often fail to lower body weight permanently. Although weight may fall temporarily, a slower BMR makes it difficult to keep the pounds from returning.
- *Genetics.* Rates of metabolism vary between individuals, independent of the factors listed above. Genetics plays a strong role in determining your BMR, although precisely how has not been fully determined.

How can we get a rough estimate of our own BMR? The formula is roughly one calorie per kg body wt/hr for males, 0.9 calorie per kg body wt/hr for females. So if you're male, divide your weight in pounds by 2.2 (lb/kg) to get your weight in kg; then multiply by 24 (hrs/day) to get calories per day. Females would divide their weight in pounds by 2.2, and then multiply by 0.9 before multiplying by 24 hrs/day. Try it yourself and you'll see that a 200-lb man has an estimated BMR of 2,182 calories per day. A 130-lb woman would have an estimated BMR of 1,276 calories/day.

By definition, your BMR only indicates your *basal* metabolic energy needs. Most people's energy expenditure is 50–100% higher than their BMR unless they spend all day in bed. The additional energy is expended to do work (physical activity).

Energy balance and body weight

Healthy weight control involves balancing energy intake against energy expenditure. Notice that the three classes of nutrients have quite different caloric contents. Fat contains about 9 calories per gram, but carbohydrates and proteins contain only 4. Thus, although fat is a good energy source, a high-fat diet can easily contain more calories than we need. This is one reason why controlling fat intake is so important.

When we eat more calories than we use, the excess energy is stored in specialized cells as fat. The number of fat cells a person has is largely determined by the time he or she is an adult. This may be why some people find losing weight so difficult and others do not. Research suggests that overweight people have two to three times more fat cells than normal-weight individuals, so when they diet and shrink their fat reserves in each cell, their bodies respond as if they are starving. Dieting is difficult for chronically overweight persons because they are constantly fighting the body's own weight-control system, which responds as if their excess weight were normal.

Physical activity: An efficient way to use calories

Although the BMR stays fairly constant, the amount of exercise we get can dramatically change the total number of calories we burn each day. Table 14.6 compares the number of calories spent per hour by a 130-, 155-, or 190-pound person performing various types of exercise. Note that heavier people do more work per hour for the same level of activity. To lose one pound of fat, we must use up about 3,500 calories.

BlogInFocus

A controversial diet called the Simeons therapy includes daily injections of human chorionic gonadotropin (hCG). Does it work? Visit MJ's blog in the Study Area in MasteringBiology and look under "Simeons Diet Therapy."

The best approach to weight loss is a gradual one. Nutritionists recommend reducing caloric intake by a small amount each day while gradually increasing physical activity.

Of course, exercise has many benefits in addition to weight loss. It improves cardiovascular health, strengthens bones, tones muscles, and promotes a general sense of well-being. Your best strategy is a healthful diet combined with moderate exercise.

☑ **Quick Check** *Suppose two women start an exercise program. They are the same weight, they eat the same diet, and they both choose to do exactly 200 calories' worth of physical activity per day. However, they choose different forms of exercise: One woman lifts weights to build stronger muscles, whereas the other person walks, which does not result in muscle growth. Which person is likely to lose more body fat? Why?* ∎

Healthy weight improves overall health

Why do we worry about caloric intake and body weight, anyway? A primary reason is that there is a link between obesity and health status. According to the federal Economic Research Service, nutrition-related health conditions cost the United States $80 billion annually in medical expenses and lost productivity. Numerous studies reveal a direct correlation between obesity and the incidence of heart disease, diabetes (see the Current Issue at the beginning of the chapter), cancer, arthritis, and other health problems. The connection is strong enough that government groups and insurance companies regularly publish charts that use a person's height and weight to define **body mass index (BMI)**. Read your own BMI from the chart in Figure 14.19.

According to the government, a BMI of between 18.5 and 25 is considered healthy, 25 to 30 is considered overweight, and 30 or higher represents obesity. These numbers should be considered a general guide only because they are based on population statistics and do not take into

Table 14.6 Approximate number of calories burned per hour by various activities

Activity	130-lb Person	155-lb Person	190-lb Person
Swimming, freestyle, fast	590	704	863
Swimming, freestyle, moderate	472	563	690
Bicycling, 16-19 mph, racing	708	844	1,035
Bicycling, 12-15.9 mph, mod. effort	472	563	690
Bicycling, 10-11.9 mph, light effort	354	422	518
Bicycling, <10 mph, leisure	236	281	345
Running, 10.9 mph (5.5-min mile)	1,062	1,267	1,553
Running, 8.6 mph (7-min mile)	826	985	1,208
Running, 6.7 mph (9-min mile)	649	744	949
Running, 5 mph (12-min mile)	472	563	690
Walking, 4 mph, very brisk	236	281	345
Walking, 2 mph, slow pace	148	176	216

Source: Adapted from Wisconsin Department of Health and Family Services publication PPH 40109.

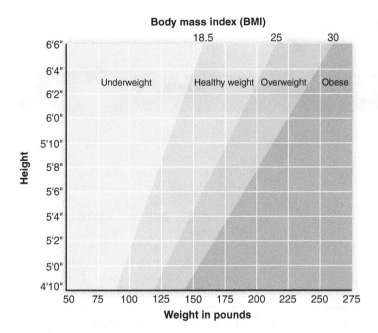

Body mass index (BMI)

Figure 14.19 **Find your BMI.** Find your height in the left column of the chart and read right to find your weight, shown at the bottom. The government's weight categories (Underweight, Healthy weight, Overweight, or Obese) are indicated by colors. Their corresponding BMI ranges are shown at the top of the chart. The weight categories are government definitions based on large population groups. They are not a good measure of an individual's health or fitness.

account such factors as bone structure, fitness, or gender. BMI may overestimate the amount of body fat in individuals who are very muscular or have a heavy bone structure. It may also underestimate the amount of body fat in people who have lost muscle mass. Thus, BMI charts do not provide definitive information about the appropriate weight status for any one individual. Within each range, the higher weights generally apply to men and the lower weights to women.

Recap Weight control involves balancing energy consumed in food against energy spent. Calculating your BMR helps you estimate how many calories you need each day. Increasing physical activity is an efficient way to increase calorie expenditure. The best strategy for losing weight combines a healthy diet with moderate regular exercise.

14.13 Eating disorders

Eating disorders are a group of conditions characterized by abnormal eating habits, to the point of damaging a person's physical or mental health. They are most common in women living in industrialized Western countries, especially young women with a history of extreme dieting. The three most common eating disorders are anorexia nervosa, bulimia nervosa, and binge eating disorder.

Anorexia nervosa (anorexia) is a condition in which a person diets excessively or stops eating altogether, even to the point of starvation and death (Figure 14.20). Untreated anorexia has the highest mortality rate of any mental illness. One of the most famous anorexics was singer Karen Carpenter, who died in 1983 at the age of 32.

Symptoms include the following:

- Refusal to maintain healthy body weight; people with anorexia often weigh less than 85% of their ideal weight.
- Intense fear of gaining weight, even though underweight.
- Distorted perception or preoccupation with body weight or shape.
- In premenopausal women, the absence of at least three consecutive menstrual cycles. Severe undernutrition interferes with the hormonal cycles of menstruation. Male anorexics also experience hormonal abnormalities.

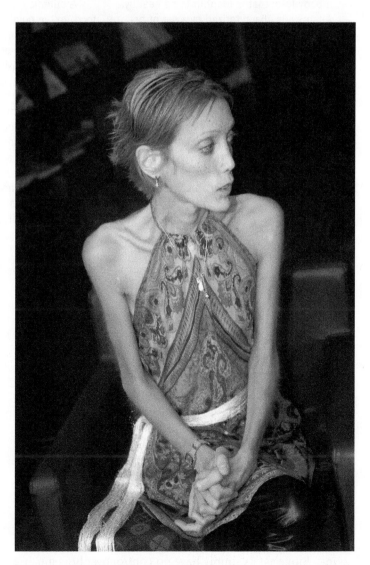

Figure 14.20 **Anorexia nervosa.** French model Isabelle Caro posed for a controversial "No Anorexia" campaign in 2007. She died in 2010 at the age of 28.

Health & Wellness

Do You Know Someone with an Eating Disorder?

Eating disorders such as anorexia, bulimia, and binge eating often go undiagnosed because the signs and symptoms are not necessarily unique to eating disorders. Do you know someone who you think has an eating disorder but you're just not sure? How can you tell, and is there anything you can do to help them?

Anorexia is not defined by just having a body form that is too thin to be healthy. Anorexia is characterized by a set of behaviours that favor weight loss rather than weight gain even when the person is already too thin for good health. Anorexics sometimes cut food into very small bites and then spend more time playing with it than actually eating it. They may carefully measure food, obsessively count calories, or cook for others but then not eat. Anorexics may exercise excessively or dress in layered clothes to try to hide their weight loss. They seem to have an obsession about losing weight, even though you perceive them as already too thin. They

may begin to withdraw from family and friends (including you), and spend a lot of time on Web sites frequented by other anorexics. They may become moody or depressed. Most of these symptoms are not unique to anorexia, but they take on extra significance in the context of someone who has lost a lot of weight recently or is severely underweight.

A bulimic may seem obsessed with food, to the point that food is a frequent focal point of conversation. He/she may seem to have an enormous capacity for food, but paradoxically does not gain weight. You may notice frequent trips to the bathroom (to vomit) after or during an eating binge. A bulimic who is aware of his/her disorder but is unwilling to admit it may become secretive about food or hoard food in strange places.

Binge eating is like bulimia without the purge. A bulimic may eat enormous amounts at one sitting, to the point of discomfort. Predictably, binge eaters are

likely to gain weight or be grossly overweight already. But binge eaters are not just normal people with a serious weight problem; they are people with no effective control over how much they eat.

Most people who have an eating disorder either don't think they have one or are unwilling to admit it to others. The first step to recovery for persons with an eating disorder is for them to recognize the problem and become willing to do something about it. You and their other close friends might be able to get through to them in ways that an outsider could not. You could start by honestly sharing with them your concern for their health, while assuring them of your unconditional love and support. If they agree that they have a problem, they'll need to find a qualified counsellor or medical professional (or treatment center) that can provide them with the help they need. That may be the best you can do, but if it works then you have been a good friend indeed! ∎

Bulimia nervosa (bulimia) is a binge-and-purge condition in which someone eats and deliberately vomits or takes other steps to minimize the calories ingested. Symptoms of bulimia include the following:

- Recurrent episodes of binge eating. An episode of binge eating involves both (1) eating large amounts of food and (2) feeling a lack of control over eating.
- Taking recurrent inappropriate steps to prevent weight gain, such as self-induced vomiting; misusing laxatives, diuretics, enemas, or other medications; fasting; or exercising excessively.
- Binge eating and compensatory behaviors that occur, on average, at least twice a week for three months.
- Preoccupation with body shape and weight. However, unlike anorexics, some bulimics maintain a normal weight.

Binge Eating Disorder is like bulimia but without the purge. Binge eaters simply have no control over how much they eat on certain occasions. They are compulsive eaters, likely to eat even when they are not hungry.

All three forms of eating disorders play havoc with the body and mind. Anorexics become malnourished and suffer insomnia, hair loss, fatigue, and moodiness. Over time, they lose bone mass and develop osteoporosis. Bulemics are likely to suffer ulcers, chronic heartburn, and rectal bleeding due to repeated trauma to the digestive system. Recurrent vomiting also damages gums, erodes tooth enamel, and makes salivary glands swell, giving the bulimic a chipmunk-like appearance. Binge eaters have a tendency to become obese (but that does *not* mean that all obese persons are binge eaters).

The underlying causes of (or triggers for) eating disorders are not well known but seem to vary widely. They may include low self-esteem, fear, or anxiety; a dysfunctional home life; a feeling of helplessness and a desire for control where there is none; difficulty managing emotions and a tendency toward depression; or unhappiness with one's physical appearance. These are complex emotional issues rather than dietary or nutritional ones. Effective treatment of eating disorders generally requires a team of professionals who can address the patient's medical, psychiatric, dental, psychological, and nutritional needs.

14.14 Disorders of the digestive system

Although common, many digestive problems are not necessarily life threatening. One of the most common conditions worldwide is *food poisoning*, caused by food and beverages contaminated with bacteria or their toxic products. Diarrhea and vomiting often accompany food poisoning. *Food allergies* can also cause diarrhea, vomiting, and generalized allergic responses throughout the body. Common food allergens include shellfish, wheat, peanuts, and eggs.

Disorders of the GI tract

Lactose intolerance: Difficulty digesting milk Human infants are born with the enzyme lactase in their small intestines for digesting lactose, the primary sugar in milk. However, many adults gradually lose the enzyme, and with it their ability to digest lactose. The result is lactose intolerance. Symptoms of lactose intolerance include diarrhea, gas, bloating, and abdominal cramps after ingesting milk products. Diarrhea occurs because the undigested lactose causes fluid to be retained in the digestive tract. The gas, bloating, and abdominal cramps are due to bacterial fermentation of the lactose, which produces gases.

Lactose-intolerant people can eat cheese or yogurt because the lactose in these milk products has already been digested. Lactose-free milk is also available.

Peptic ulcers: sores in the stomach Peptic ulcers are painful erosions of the mucosal lining of the stomach or duodenum. Most peptic ulcers are associated with infection by one of the few bacteria that can live in the acidic environment of the stomach, called *Helicobacter pylori*. The bacterial infection leads to chronic inflammation, an increase in gastric acid secretion, and damage to the mucosal lining. Peptic ulcers can also be caused by excessive use of aspirin or non-steroidal anti-inflammatory drugs (NSAIDs). NSAIDs block the production of the mucus that protects the gastric mucosa from gastric acid.

After treatment to eliminate any *H. pylori* infection, most peptic ulcers heal on their own. Antacids may also be prescribed as needed. The use of aspirin and NSAIDs should be discontinued if possible.

✅ **Quick Check** *Why do peptic ulcers typically occur in the stomach or duodenum, but not in the rest of the small intestine or the large intestine?* ▪

Celiac disease (gluten intolerance) When people with celiac disease (also known as sprue) eat gluten, a protein found primarily in wheat, rye, and barley, their immune systems respond by damaging or destroying the villi that line the small intestine. The result is malabsorption of nutrients of all kinds, not just gluten. Celiac disease is an inherited disorder with a prevalence of about 1 in 130 persons. Symptoms vary widely, from acute abdominal pain and vomiting to chronic fatigue, depression, and eventually malnutrition, depending on a person's age, how much gluten they eat, and how sensitive they are to it.

Celiac disease often goes undiagnosed at first because its symptoms are so varied and so similar to other diseases and conditions. A definitive diagnosis is made by a blood test for a certain autoantibody in the patient's blood. The only effective treatment is a gluten-free diet.

Diverticulosis: Weakness in the wall of the large intestine Diverticulosis gets its name from its characteristic diverticula (small sacs produced when the mucosal lining of the large intestine protrudes through the other layers of the intestinal wall). Most people with diverticulosis do not experience discomfort, but sometimes the diverticula become infected or inflamed, in which case it is called *diverticulitis*. Antibiotics usually resolve the problem.

Inadequate dietary fiber is thought to contribute to the development of diverticulosis. A low-fiber diet produces smaller feces, narrowing the colon and making its contractions more powerful. This increases the pressure on colon walls, forcing weak areas outward and forming diverticula. The disease is more prevalent with advancing age. Although it is rare in someone under 40, it may be present in up to two-thirds of all 85-year-olds.

Colon polyps: Noncancerous growths A polyp is a noncancerous growth that projects from a mucous membrane. Polyps can develop in many areas of the body, including the colon. The majority of colon polyps do not become cancerous, but because most colon cancers start as polyps, doctors recommend removing them. Polyps can be detected and removed in a *colonoscopy*, an outpatient procedure in which a flexible fiber-optic scope is inserted into the colon through the anus.

Disorders of the accessory organs

Hepatitis: Inflammation of the liver **Hepatitis** refers to inflammation of the liver, generally caused by viruses or toxic substances. Researchers have identified at least five viruses that cause hepatitis. The most common are hepatitis A, B, and C.

Hepatitis A is transmitted by contaminated food or water and causes a brief illness from which most people recover completely. A vaccine is available for hepatitis A. Although the vaccine is not considered necessary for most residents of industrialized nations, it may be a good idea for travelers to underdeveloped countries.

Hepatitis B travels in blood or body fluids, so it is usually passed via contaminated needles, blood transfusions, or sexual contact with infected individuals. Approximately 300,000 new cases are diagnosed each year. If not treated, hepatitis B can lead to liver failure. Symptoms include jaundice (the skin takes on a yellowish color due to accumulated bile pigments in the blood), nausea, fatigue, abdominal pain, and arthritis. A vaccine is available for hepatitis B. Federal law requires all healthcare workers to be vaccinated.

Hepatitis C is also transmitted in infected blood, usually through contaminated needles or blood transfusions. By 1992 U.S. blood banks began routine testing for hepatitis C, so the risk of contracting it from transfusions has fallen. However, researchers estimate that as many as 4 million Americans may already be infected, and many of them have no symptoms. Hepatitis C may remain dormant for years but still damage the liver. Severe cases can lead to chronic hepatitis, cirrhosis, or liver cancer. Doctors recommend testing for anyone who has had kidney dialysis (Chapter 15) or an organ transplant before 1992. Also at risk are those who have injected drugs or had sexual contact with a hepatitis C carrier.

Gallstones can obstruct bile flow The gallbladder normally concentrates bile about 10-fold by removing about 90% of the water. Excessive cholesterol in the bile may precipitate out of solution with calcium and bile salts, forming hard crystals called *gallstones* (Figure 14.21). Only about 20% of gallstones ever cause problems, but if the crystals grow large enough they can obstruct bile flow and cause intense pain, especially after a meal. Treatments include drugs to dissolve the crystals, ultrasound vibrations or laser treatments to break the stones apart, or surgery to remove the gallbladder.

Malnutrition: Too many or too few nutrients

Malnutrition refers to conditions in which human development and function are compromised by an unbalanced or insufficient diet. Malnutrition can be caused either by overnutrition or undernutrition. Overnutrition can lead to obesity. Worldwide, however, undernourishment is far more common. The United Nations estimates that 800 million people, or about 13% of the world's population, are undernourished.

Figure 14.21 Gallstones.

Deficiencies of one or more nutrients can produce specific effects. For example, years of vitamin A deficiency lead to eye damage and night blindness. In children, undernutrition stunts growth and increases susceptibility to infection. Severe undernutrition, or starvation, is still the leading cause of malnutrition worldwide. Nearly 20 million people, most of them children, die every year of starvation or related diseases.

Obesity: A worldwide epidemic?

Estimates of the prevalence of obesity vary depending on how it's defined and how the data are collected. Nevertheless, the World Health Organization calls obesity a global epidemic. In the United States, obesity has increased from 13% of the population in 1990 to 36% in 2010. Figure 14.22 compares

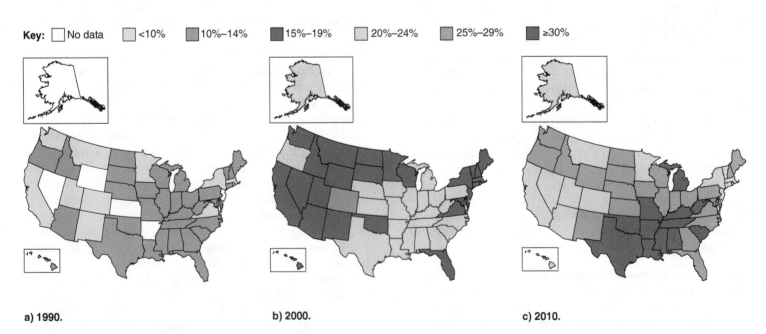

Key: ☐ No data ☐ <10% ☐ 10%–14% ☐ 15%–19% ☐ 20%–24% ☐ 25%–29% ☐ ≥30%

a) 1990. b) 2000. c) 2010.

Figure 14.22 Obesity trends among U.S. adults, 1990, 2000, and 2010. These maps show the percentage of the population classified as obese in each state. Obesity is defined as a body mass index greater than 30.

Source: Behavioral Risk Factor Surveillance System, Centers for Disease Control.

☑ *Why do you think there are regional differences in the prevalence of obesity? Can you think of any local dietary or activity patterns that might be contributing factors?*

the figures state by state. Obesity is rising even in some less industrialized countries: Five percent of women in Papua New Guinea are obese today, though obesity was virtually unseen in 1980.

Body weight is determined by both internal factors (such as genetic makeup) and environmental factors (such as activity level and availability of food). There's a lot of interest in genetic factors these days, such as "fat genes" that might make it harder to maintain a healthy weight. But genetics cannot account for an entire population's weight gain, because genes don't evolve that quickly. It took us millions of years to become what we are, and our collective gene pool cannot change in just 20 years.

We must look to the environment to explain this global rise in obesity. We now live in an environment that favors an imbalance between caloric intake and caloric expenditure. Computers, television, cars, desk jobs—all combine to produce a more sedentary lifestyle. Physical exercise has become, for many of us, a leisure time activity. At the same time, food is relatively cheap and readily available. We eat out (away from home) more often, we eat calorie-rich foods, and we eat more total calories per day—nearly 25% more than in 1970, according to government statistics. The obesity epidemic is all too easy to understand; the question is what to do about it.

↩ **Recap** Disorders of the GI tract and accessory organs include lactose intolerance, diverticulosis, colon polyps, gallstones, and hepatitis. Malnutrition can be caused by over- or undernutrition. Whereas starvation is the leading cause of malnutrition in underdeveloped countries, obesity is increasing in industrialized nations. ▪

Chapter Summary

The digestive system brings nutrients into the body *p. 326*

- The digestive system consists of the gastrointestinal (GI) tract and four accessory organs: the salivary glands, liver, gallbladder, and pancreas.
- The five basic processes of the digestive system are motility, secretion, digestion, absorption, and excretion.
- Two types of motility in the GI tract are peristalsis, which propels food forward, and segmentation, which mixes the contents.

The mouth processes food for swallowing *p. 329*

- The 32 teeth of adults include incisors, canines, premolars, and molars. Teeth cut, tear, grind, and crush food.
- Saliva moistens food, begins the digestion of starch, and helps to protect against bacteria.

The pharynx and esophagus deliver food to the stomach *p. 330*

- Swallowing is a reflex that is initiated by voluntary movements of the tongue. Once started, swallowing is involuntary.
- The sole function of the esophagus is to get food from the mouth to the stomach.
- The lower esophageal sphincter prevents reflux of stomach contents.

The stomach stores food, digests protein, and regulates delivery *p. 331*

- The stomach stores ingested food until it can be delivered to the small intestine.
- Glands in the mucosa of the stomach secrete gastric juice into the lumen, beginning the process of protein digestion.
- Peristalsis of the stomach mixes the food and pushes it toward the small intestine.

The small intestine digests food and absorbs nutrients and water *p. 333*

- Digestion occurs primarily in the first part of the small intestine, called the *duodenum*.
- The jejunum and ileum of the small intestine absorb most of the products of digestion.
- The small intestine has a very large surface area because of its many folds, villi, and microvilli.

Accessory organs aid digestion and absorption *p. 334*

- The pancreas secretes fluid containing bicarbonate and digestive enzymes into the small intestine.
- The liver produces bile and participates in homeostasis in a variety of ways.
- All of the venous blood from the GI tract is routed directly to the liver.
- The gallbladder stores bile from the liver and concentrates it by removal of most of the water.

The large intestine absorbs nutrients and eliminates wastes *p. 335*

- The large intestine absorbs most remaining nutrients and water, and vitamin K produced by bacteria. It also stores wastes.
- Defecation is generally controlled by a neural reflex, but it can be overridden by conscious control.

How nutrients are absorbed *p. 336*

- Amino acids and simple sugars are actively transported into the mucosal cells that line the small and large intestines.
- The products of fat digestion enter the mucosal cells by diffusion, and then reform into triglycerides. Triglycerides are coated with protein and move into lymph vessels for transport to the blood.
- Water is absorbed by osmosis.
- Vitamins and minerals follow a variety of specific pathways.

Endocrine and nervous systems regulate digestion *p. 338*

- The volume and content of food play a large part in regulating digestive processes.
- Stretching of the stomach increases stomach peristalsis and the secretion of gastric juice.
- Stretching of the small intestine inhibits gastric motility, increases intestinal segmentation, and causes the secretion of two digestive enzymes, secretin and cholecystokinin.
- Acid in the small intestine triggers the secretion of pancreatic juice containing bicarbonate.

Nutrition: You are what you eat *p. 339*

- Good nutrition requires a variety of foods weighted toward fruits, vegetables, and whole-grain products.
- The human body needs certain nutritional components that it cannot make, including a few fatty acids, 8 amino acids, 13 vitamins, and all essential minerals.

Food labels *p. 344*

- Packaged foods are required to have food labels listing certain nutritional information.
- Food labels permit easy comparison of the nutritional value of similar packaged foods.

Weight control: Energy consumed versus energy spent *p. 345*

- The basal metabolic rate (BMR) represents the daily energy needs of the body for all essential activities except physical activity.
- Fat contains over twice as many calories per gram as carbohydrate or protein.
- A person must use 3,500 calories more than he or she ingests to lose a pound of body fat.

Eating disorders *p. 347*

- Two serious eating disorders are anorexia nervosa, in which the person diets excessively or stops eating entirely, and bulimia, a binge-and-purge condition in which the person eats and deliberately vomits or takes other steps to minimize caloric intake.
- The most effective treatments are multidisciplinary, addressing medical, psychiatric, dental, psychological, and nutritional needs.

Disorders of the digestive system *p. 349*

- Lactose intolerance is caused by the lack of the enzyme (lactase) that normally digests lactose.
- Hepatitis, or inflammation of the liver, can be caused by several different viruses.
- Starvation is the most common form of malnutrition in the world. However, the incidence of obesity is rising in the United States and other industrialized nations.

Terms You Should Know

anorexia nervosa, *347*
basal metabolic rate (BMR), *345*
bile, *335*
bulimia nervosa, *348*
calories, *345*
cholecystokinin (CCK), *338*
chyme, *332*
colon, *336*
complete protein, *341*
esophagus, *331*
essential amino acids, *341*
gallbladder, *335*
gastrin, *338*
gastrointestinal (GI) tract, *326*
hepatic portal system, *335*
hepatitis, *349*
large intestine, *335*
mucosa, *326*
muscularis, *327*
nutrients, *326*
pancreas, *334*
pepsin, *332*
peptic ulcer, *332*
peristalsis, *328*
Recommended Dietary Allowance (RDA), *342*
salivary glands, *330*
secretin, *338*
segmentation, *329*
serosa, *327*
submucosa, *326*
villus, *333*
vitamin, *342*

Concept Review

Answers can be found in the Study Area in MasteringBiology.

1. Describe the organs of the GI tract including the four accessory organs.
2. Name the five basic processes associated with carrying out the function of the GI tract.
3. Describe the role saliva plays in initiating the digestive process.
4. Compare and contrast *peristalsis* and *segmentation*.
5. Indicate how many teeth adult humans have.
6. Describe the events that occur in the stomach that contribute to the digestive process.
7. Indicate where in the GI tract most of the absorption of nutrients occurs.
8. Rank the major nutrient groups (carbohydrates, lipids, or proteins) according to calories per gram.
9. Indicate what fraction of our daily caloric expenditure is accounted for by our basal metabolic rate (BMR).
10. Explain why it is harder to get an adequate supply of all amino acids from a vegetarian diet than from meat.

Test Yourself

Answers can be found in Appendix A.

1. Which of the GI tract tissue layers is most responsible for peristalsis and segmentation?
   a. serosa
   b. muscularis
   c. submucosa
   d. mucosa

2. All of the following are secreted into the lumen of the digestive tract during the process of digestion except:
   a. acid
   b. digestive enzymes
   c. hormones
   d. bile

3. All of the following are found in saliva except:
   a. mucin
   b. salivary amylase
   c. pepsin
   d. bicarbonate

4. Which of the following might be true of an individual unable to synthesize and secrete intrinsic factor?
   a. They would be unable to absorb adequate amounts of vitamin B12.
   b. They would be unable to digest lactose found in dairy products.
   c. They would be unable to absorb amino acids in the small intestine.
   d. They would be unable to digest and absorb triglycerides.

5. Which of the following nutrients are digested within the small intestine?
   a. proteins
   b. lipids
   c. carbohydrates
   d. all of these choices

6. The region of the digestive tract most responsible for absorption of nutrients is:
   a. the stomach
   b. the small intestine
   c. the large intestine
   d. the liver

7. Which of the following lists structures in order from smallest to largest?
   a. small intestine, folds, microvilli, villi
   b. villi, microvilli, folds, small intestine
   c. microvilli, folds, villi, small intestine
   d. microvilli, villi, folds, small intestine

8. What do the enzymes pepsin, chymotrypsin, trypsin, and carboxypeptidase have in common?
   a. They are secreted and active within the stomach.
   b. They are pancreatic enzymes.
   c. They are secreted and active within the small intestine.
   d. They are enzymes that participate in protein digestion.

9. Once nutrients are absorbed into the circulatory system, the next major organ they pass through is the:
   a. heart
   b. liver
   c. kidneys
   d. brain

10. Which of the following terms does not belong with the others?
    a. monoglycerides
    b. micelle
    c. peptide
    d. bile

11. Each of the following is absorbed into capillaries except:
    a. triglycerides
    b. amino acids
    c. monosaccharides
    d. water

12. Which of the following foods would be the best source of complex carbohydrates?
    a. strawberries
    b. honey
    c. orange
    d. oatmeal

13. Which of the following statements about trans fats is correct?
    a. Trans fats are found in animal products such as meat and dairy.
    b. Trans fats will lower LDL cholesterol levels.
    c. Trans fats are produced by the hydrogenation of unsaturated fats in vegetable oils.
    d. Salmon, trout, and sardines are rich in healthy trans fats.

14. Each of the following is a source of complete protein except:
    a. milk
    b. soy products
    c. peanuts
    d. eggs

15. Which of the following is associated with celiac disease?
    a. inability to digest and absorb proteins in dairy products
    b. damage to the villi resulting from the consumption of wheat products
    c. erosion of the wall of the stomach and duodenum due to hyperacidity
    d. chronic constipation due to low intestinal motility

Apply What You Know

Answers can be found in the Study Area in MasteringBiology.

1. A meal containing a lot of fat takes longer to be emptied out of the stomach than a low-fat meal. Why?

2. Procter & Gamble produces a calorie-free fat substitute called Olean (olestra) that is used to deep-fry foods such as potato chips. Olestra is a fat-soluble molecule that is neither digested nor absorbed. There is a concern that eating too much olestra might lead to certain vitamin deficiencies. What types of vitamins do you think would be affected by the use of olestra, and how might they be affected?

3. Other side effects of the consumption of too much olestra include gas, diarrhea, and a sudden need to defecate. What could be a cause of these?

4. Many prescription medications are supposed to be taken with a meal. Others are only to be taken on an empty stomach. Why would there be such differences?

5. Sometimes the cure for gallstones is to surgically remove the gallbladder. What effect would removal of the gallbladder have on digestion?

6. People with lactose intolerance cannot digest the common dairy sugar lactose. Besides being careful not to eat dairy foods, is there anything else a lactose-intolerant person can do?

7. Cholera is a dangerous infectious disease that is common in places that do not have a steady supply of clean drinking water. Severe untreated cholera can be fatal within a matter of days. Cholera is caused by a bacterial toxin that causes severe diarrhea. What do you think might cause death from cholera, if the only symptom is diarrhea?

BlogInFocus

Answers can be found in the Study Area in MasteringBiology.

1. Why is it so hard for most people to lose weight when they want to? What factors (biological, social, economic, behavioral, etc.) are working against them? (For a look at current thinking on the subject, visit MJ's blog in the Study Area in MasteringBiology and look under "Tackling Obesity.")

MasteringBiology®

Go to MasteringBiology for practice quizzes, activities, eText, videos, current events, and more.

Reproductive Systems

A sperm cell penetrating the surface of an egg cell.

Would You Like a Boy or a Girl?

Your parents probably did not know whether you were a boy or a girl until the very moment you were born, unless ultrasound was performed sometime around 18–26 weeks of pregnancy. They certainly had no way of selecting a child for its gender. But with the advent of DNA technology and advanced fertility methods, all that is changing.

Early Gender Detection—Good Idea or Not?

Back in 2005 a biotech company called Acu-Gen Biolab, Inc., started offering a gender testing service and kit called Baby Gender Mentor™. According to the company, Baby Gender Mentor could determine the gender of an unborn child with 99.9% accuracy as early as five weeks after fertilization. For $275, the company would analyze a small blood sample from the mother and provide confidential results via e-mail, generally within 48 hours. Baby Gender Mentor was based on the principle that a small amount of fetal DNA is generally present in the mother's blood plasma. The presence of Y-chromosomal material in the mother's blood plasma indicates the presence of a boy fetus; the presence of only X-chromosomal material indicates a girl. You'll learn more about the X and Y chromosomes in the chapter on genetics and inheritance (Chapter 19).

Baby Gender Mentor was a big news story when it first came out. But within a year parents who had used the service were suing the company, claiming that it was not nearly as accurate as claimed. The company filed for Chapter 11 bankruptcy in 2009 and the product was taken off the market.

Then and even now, some ethicists question whether knowing a fetus's gender as early as five weeks serves any useful purpose. The one obvious purpose is that it would provide couples with an opportunity to have an elective abortion if the fetus is not of the desired gender. In India, where there is a strong preference for male children, prenatal testing and

The Nash family. Linda and Jack Nash used genetic selection to choose an embryo that could donate umbilical cord blood to their daughter upon birth.

selective abortions are thought to be responsible for a deficit of girls every year. There is no evidence of a similar gender imbalance in the United States, however.

Gender Selection Is Now Possible

If you would prefer to have a child of a specific gender without resorting to an elective abortion, there's a relatively easy way to at least increase the odds. A procedure called *sperm sorting* is based on the fact that the X (female) chromosome is larger and carries more DNA than the Y (male) chromosome. First, the sperm in a semen sample from the would-be father are labeled with a fluorescent dye that attaches to DNA. Because sperm with the female (X) chromosome have more DNA, they fluoresce more brightly than sperm with the male (Y) chromosome. The sperm are then sorted on the basis of light intensity by a machine called a *flow cytometer*. After sorting, either the "female-enriched" or the "male-enriched" sperm sample is used to artificially inseminate the mother. For couples who want a girl, sperm sorting produces girls 91% of the time; for boys the odds are a

bit lower (only 76%), but that's still a lot better than random chance.

Could a couple choose their next child's gender with absolute 100% certainty? Yes, they could, but the techniques involved are expensive. According to the standard procedure at most fertility clinics, eggs and sperm would be collected from the prospective couple and mixed together. Once the early-stage embryos had begun to develop, each one would be tested for the presence or absence of the Y-chromosome by a technique called *preimplantation genetic diagnosis (PGD)*. The presence of a Y-chromosome would indicate a male embryo, whereas the absence of a Y-chromosome would indicate a female embryo. A couple wanting only a boy, then, could choose to have only a boy-embryo implanted into the prospective mother.

The American Society of Reproductive Medicine does not endorse PGD for gender selection. Nevertheless, a number of fertility clinics will perform PGD for this purpose. To avoid controversy over the ethics of gender selection, the clinics may describe gender selection as a way to select against certain diseases (females don't get prostate cancer for example, and males are at very low risk for breast cancer).

Beyond Gender Selection

In addition to gender selection, PDG can be used to test for genetic disorders. It can also be used to select embryos for certain specific genotypes, including being a compatible tissue match for a sibling.

Molly Nash was born with Fanconi's anemia, a rare, incurable disease in which the bone marrow does not produce blood cells normally. Typically people with this condition die in their early 20s. Fanconi's anemia is a genetic disorder. Although neither of Molly's parents have the disease, they both carry the gene that causes it. In a desperate attempt to save their daughter, Molly's parents turned to a fertility clinic that performed PGD. Eggs were harvested from the mother's ovaries, fertilized, and

then tested for the abnormal Fanconi gene, among other genetic disorders. Embryos that lacked the fatal gene were screened further to determine whether they would be a safe tissue donor match for Molly. Only embryos that lacked the fatal gene and that were a good tissue donor match for Molly were implanted into the mother's uterus. After four attempts Molly's mother gave birth to a healthy boy, whom the couple named Adam. Shortly after Adam's birth, blood-forming stem cells harvested from Adam's umbilical cord blood were infused into Molly (see the Current Issue on banking cord blood in Chapter 6). Apparently, enough of these cells became blood-forming stem cells in Molly that she was cured. Today both children are healthy, and Molly has started school.

When the Nash story first hit the press it caused a firestorm of controversy. The media labeled Adam the "savior sibling" and predicted dire effects on his future mental health from knowing that he had been brought into being to save his sister. Molly's parents insisted that they wanted more children anyway, so this procedure enabled them to have a healthy child and also save their daughter's life. However, many people questioned whether it is ethical to have a child for the purpose of being a tissue donor. And of course when multiple eggs are fertilized *in vitro* but only one or two are implanted, there is always the issue of what happens to the embryos not selected for implantation.

There's no doubt that as reproductive technologies improve, our ability to screen for genetic abnormalities will also improve. But beyond just avoiding genetic diseases, what about using PGD to influence physical characteristics such as hair, skin, and eye color, intelligence, even musical ability? If we could pick and choose from a menu of specific traits for our offspring, would we want to?

QUESTIONS TO CONSIDER

1 If you and your partner decided to have a child together, would you want to know its gender before it is born?

2 Would you try to select the gender of your next child by one of the methods described here? Explain why or why not.

3 Would you be willing to select a second child specifically to help an earlier child, as the Nashes did?

THE FACTS...

- Sperm sorting can improve the odds of having a child of the desired gender.
- *In vitro* fertilization and preimplantation testing could guarantee having a child of the desired gender.
- As our ability to specify gender and other genetic traits develops, so does the possibility of being able to "customize" children genetically.

>> **The male reproductive system** can deliver over 100 million sperm at once. **The female reproductive system** usually releases and nurtures just one egg each month.

>> **In females, a cyclic pattern of changes controlled by hormones prepares one egg for release each month.** Another parallel cycle prepares the uterus to receive and nurture the egg if fertilization occurs.

>> **In both males and females, sexual excitement leads to arousal and orgasm.** In males, orgasm leads to ejaculation, the expulsion of sperm.

>> **Birth control (contraceptive) methods and devices include** 1) altering female hormones to disrupt maturation or fertilization of the egg, 2) condoms or diaphragms that prevent sperm and egg from making contact, 3) spermicides that kill sperm, 4) intrauterine devices that prevent implantation of the egg, and 5) surgical sterilization.

>> **Sexually transmitted diseases (STDs) range from mildly irritating to deadly.** Some are difficult or even impossible to cure. For a sexually active person the best defenses against the damaging effects of STDs are know your partner, use physical barriers (condoms) during risky behavior, and get tested if you think you are at risk.

BlogInFocus [MB]

Just how accurate are DNA-based tests of maternal blood for determining fetal gender? Where did Baby Gender Mentor go wrong? To find out, visit MJ's blog in the Study Area in MasteringBiology and look under "Fetal Gender Test."

Most of the organ systems we have considered so far in this book are not exactly topics of daily interest to most people. How many songs have you heard praising the urinary system or digestive processes? How many movies show close-ups of people just breathing? Certainly some of the subjects in this chapter, such as differences in male and female anatomy and in patterns of sexual arousal, get more than their share of attention. The beauty and mystery of sex are a source of endless fascination to us.

On a practical level, sexual attractiveness and sexual arousal are normal events in the human reproductive process—a process that requires the **reproductive systems**. The male and female reproductive systems consist of the tissues and organs that participate in creating a new human being. At first glance, it may seem that the male and female reproductive systems are completely dissimilar. After all, the external and internal structures look different from each other. Even secondary sexual characteristics, such as body form, muscle mass, hair patterns, and distribution of body fat, aren't the same. From an evolutionary standpoint, there must have been a tremendous advantage to having the male and female reproductive systems evolve in this manner.

However, there are many similarities between male and female reproductive systems. Both systems consist of primary reproductive organs, accessory glands, and ducts. Both men and women experience similar phases of sexual desire. Each system has highly specific functions that allow it to complement the other perfectly. And ultimately, both systems share the same goal: to join a sperm and an egg in an environment (the woman's body) that enables the fertilized egg to become an individual.

16.1 The male reproductive system delivers sperm

Figure 16.1 illustrates the organs of the male reproductive system. The male reproductive system evolved to deliver the male reproductive cells, called **sperm**, to the female. As we will see, the chance of any one sperm fertilizing a female reproductive cell (an **egg**) is extremely low. The reproductive strategy of the male, then, is to deliver huge numbers of sperm at a time to improve the odds that one will reach the egg.

Testes produce sperm

The sites of sperm production in the male are the paired **testes** (singular: *testis*). Shortly before birth the testes descend into the **scrotum**, an outpouching of skin and smooth muscle. The scrotum regulates the temperature of the developing sperm within the testes, because sperm develop best at temperatures a few degrees cooler than body temperature. When the temperature within the scrotum falls below about 95° F, the smooth muscle of the scrotum contracts, bringing the testes closer to the warmth of the body. When the temperature warms to above 95° F, the smooth muscle relaxes and the scrotum and testes hang away from the body.

Each testis is only about 2 inches long, but it contains over 100 yards of tightly packed **seminiferous tubules**, where the sperm are produced. The seminiferous tubules join to become the **epididymis**, a single coiled duct just outside the testis. The epididymis joins the long **ductus (vas) deferens**, which eventually joins the duct from the seminal vesicle to become the **ejaculatory duct**. The newly formed sperm are not fully mature (they cannot yet swim) when they leave the seminiferous tubules. Their ability to swim develops in both the epididymis and the ductus deferens. The epididymis and the ductus deferens also store the sperm until ejaculation.

a) A sagittal cutaway view.

b) A posterior view of the reproductive organs and bladder.

Figure 16.1 **The male reproductive system.**

When the male reaches sexual climax and ejaculates, rhythmic contractions of smooth muscle propel the sperm through the short ejaculatory duct and finally through the urethra, which passes through the penis.

The **penis** is the male organ of sexual intercourse. Its function is to deliver sperm internally to the female, safely away from the harsh external environment. The penis contains erectile tissues that permit **erection**—an increase in length, diameter, and stiffness of the penis that facilitates its entry into the vagina.

Accessory glands help sperm survive

Sperm must endure the rapid journey from epididymis to vagina and then continue to live within the woman for many hours. To improve their chances of survival, the male delivers sperm in a thick, whitish mixture of fluids called **semen**. In addition to sperm, semen contains secretions from the seminal vesicles, the prostate gland, and the bulbourethral gland.

The **seminal vesicles** produce seminal fluid, a watery mixture containing fructose and prostaglandins that represents about 60% of the volume of semen. Fructose, a carbohydrate, provides the sperm with a source of energy. The prostaglandins are thought to induce muscle contractions in the female reproductive system that help sperm travel more effectively. The **prostate gland** contributes an alkaline fluid. The vagina is generally fairly acid (pH 3.5–4.0), which helps prevent infections but is too acidic for sperm. The prostate secretions temporarily raise the vaginal pH to about 6, optimal for sperm. Finally, the **bulbourethral glands** secrete mucus into the urethra during sexual arousal. The mucus washes away traces of

acidic urine in the urethra before the sperm arrive and also provides lubrication for sexual intercourse. The sperm are not mixed with seminal and prostate fluids until the moment of ejaculation.

Table 16.1 summarizes the organs and glands of the male reproductive system.

Table 16.1 **Summary of the male reproductive organs and glands**

Organ	Function
Testis (2)	Produces sperm, testosterone, and inhibin
Scrotum	Keeps the testes at the proper temperature
Epididymis (2)	Site of sperm maturation and storage
Ductus deferens (2)	Duct for sperm maturation, storage, and transport
Ejaculatory duct (2)	Duct for transporting sperm and glandular secretions
Penis	Erectile organ of sexual intercourse
Accessory Glands	
Seminal vesicle (2)	Secretes fructose and most of the seminal fluid
Prostate gland	Secretes watery alkaline fluid to raise vaginal pH
Bulbourethral gland (2)	Secretes lubricating mucus

Sperm production requires several cell divisions

Let's take a closer look at the process of sperm production. As mentioned, it takes place in the seminiferous tubules within each testis (Figure 16.2). Toward the outer surface of each tubule are undifferentiated cells (cells that have not yet become any kind of specialized cell) called *spermatogonia* (singular: *spermatogonium*). Spermatogonia are *diploid* cells, meaning they have 46 chromosomes, the normal human number.

The formation of the gametes (sperm and eggs) involves a series of cell divisions called *mitosis* and *meiosis*, discussed in more detail when we describe cell reproduction and differentiation (Chapter 17). The important point to remember here is that during the two successive cell divisions of meiosis (meiosis I and II), the number of chromosomes in the developing gametes is reduced by half. **Gametes** are called *haploid* cells (from the Greek *haploos*, meaning "single") because they contain only 23 chromosomes, rather than the usual diploid number, 46. This ensures that when a sperm and egg unite, the embryo will again have the proper (diploid) number of chromosomes.

Spermatogonia divide several times during the course of sperm development (Figure 16.2b). The first division, by mitosis, ensures a constant supply of *primary spermatocytes*, each with the diploid number of chromosomes. Primary spermatocytes then undergo two successive cell divisions

a) **Partial cross section of a testis showing the coiled seminiferous tubules.**

b) **Sperm originate from undifferentiated spermatogonia located near the outer surface of a seminiferous tubule.** The production of sperm is supported by Sertoli cells.

c) **A cross section through a seminiferous tubule (×100) showing the location of the testosterone-producing interstitial cells between the tubules.** Mature sperm are visible within the lumen of tubule.

d) **Illustration of a sperm, showing the head, midpiece, and tail.**

Figure 16.2 **Sperm formation in a seminiferous tubule.**

☑ *Which gives rise to more sperm, a spermatogonium or a primary spermatocyte? Explain.*

during meiosis to become *secondary spermatocytes* and finally *spermatids*. Spermatids, which are haploid cells, mature slowly to become the male gametes, or sperm. The entire process of sperm formation and maturation takes about 9–10 weeks. During this time the cells are surrounded and nourished by the large **Sertoli cells** that make up most of the bulk of the seminiferous tubules (Figure 16.2c).

A mature sperm has a head, midpiece, and tail (Figure 16.2d). The head contains the DNA, organized into chromosomes. The head is covered by an *acrosome*, a cap containing enzymes that help the sperm penetrate the egg. The sperm's whiplike tail moves it forward, powered by energy produced by mitochondria in the midpiece.

Tens of millions of sperm are produced every day after puberty in young men. A typical ejaculation may contain 100–300 million sperm, but only one sperm will fertilize an egg.

Testosterone affects male reproductive capacity

Male reproductive capacity depends on **testosterone**, a steroid hormone produced by **interstitial cells** located between the seminiferous tubules within the testes (see Figure 16.2c). Testosterone controls the growth and function of the male reproductive tissues, stimulates aggressive and sexual behavior, and causes the development of secondary sexual characteristics at puberty, such as facial hair and deepening voice. Within the testes, testosterone stimulates the undifferentiated spermatogonia to begin dividing and the Sertoli cells to support the developing sperm. Thus, it determines the rate of sperm formation.

The production and secretion of testosterone depends on three hormones: **gonadotropin-releasing hormone (GnRH)** from the hypothalamus, and luteinizing hormone (LH) and follicle-stimulating hormone (FSH) from the anterior pituitary gland. As described in the chapter on the endocrine system (Chapter 13), LH and FSH are called *gonadotropins* because they stimulate the reproductive organs—the gonads. Historically, the names for LH and FSH came from their functions in the female, but they are active hormones in the male as well.

Negative feedback loops involving the hypothalamus, the pituitary, and the testes maintain a fairly constant blood concentration of testosterone, and thus a consistent rate of sperm production (Figure 16.3). When blood concentrations of testosterone fall, the hypothalamus secretes GnRH, which stimulates the anterior pituitary gland to release LH and FSH. LH stimulates the secretion of testosterone by the interstitial cells. The role of FSH is less clear, but it seems to enhance sperm formation indirectly by stimulating the Sertoli cells.

Excessively high concentrations of testosterone inhibit the secretion of GnRH and also LH and FSH. In addition, when Sertoli cells are highly active they secrete a hormone called **inhibin** that directly inhibits the secretion of FSH.

Figure 16.3 Feedback control of blood testosterone concentration and sperm production. Negative feedback control loops effectively maintain testosterone concentration (and hence sperm production) relatively constant over time. Negative feedback (dashed arrows) occurs at both the hypothalamus and the anterior pituitary.

🔄 **Recap** The male reproductive system comprises the testes, the penis, and associated ducts and glands. Semen consists of sperm and three glandular secretions that provide energy and the proper pH environment for the sperm and also lubrication for sexual intercourse. Millions of sperm form every day throughout a man's life; a typical ejaculate contains up to 300 million. Testosterone stimulates the growth and function of the male reproductive system, and encourages aggressive and sexual behavior. Blood levels of testosterone are regulated by a negative feedback loop involving GnRH from the hypothalamus and LH and FSH from the anterior pituitary. ∎

16.2 The female reproductive system produces eggs and supports pregnancy

The female reproductive system evolved to perform more functions than that of the male. Eggs are precious, so the system releases only one or two every month. In addition, because it can never be known for certain if an egg will be fertilized, the female reproductive system must go through cyclic changes every month just to prepare for the possibility of fertilization. If fertilization does occur, the female system adjusts to pregnancy and supports the developing fetus.

Ovaries release oocytes and secrete hormones

Figure 16.4a illustrates the organs of the female reproductive system. The primary female reproductive organs are the two **ovaries**, which release the female gametes, immature eggs called *oocytes*, at regular intervals during the reproductive years. The ovaries also secrete the female sex steroid hormones **estrogen** and **progesterone**. (The term *estrogen* is commonly used to refer to three hormones known collectively as *estrogens*: 17β-estradiol, estrone, and estriol.)

Once released, the oocyte is swept into the open end of an **oviduct** (also called a *Fallopian tube*), which leads from the ovary to the uterus. The open end of the oviduct has fingerlike projections called fimbriae that help move the oocyte into the oviduct. If fertilization by a sperm occurs, it usually takes place in the upper third of the oviduct. The unfertilized oocyte or fertilized egg moves down the oviduct over the course of about 3–4 days to the uterus.

✅ **Quick Check** *Embryos sometimes implant somewhere other than the uterus, most often in the oviduct before it reaches the uterus, and sometimes in the abdominal cavity. How could an embryo end up in the abdominal cavity?* ▪

The uterus nurtures the developing embryo

The **uterus** is a hollow, pear-shaped organ where the embryo grows and develops. The walls of the uterus comprise two layers of tissue (Figure 16.4b).

The inner layer of the uterus, the **endometrium**, is a lining of epithelial tissue, glands, connective tissue, and blood vessels. A fertilized egg attaches to the endometrium in a process called *implantation*. After implantation the

Answers to ✅ questions can be found in Appendix A.

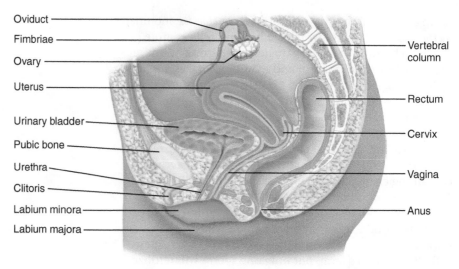

a) Sagittal section showing the components of the system in relation to other structures.

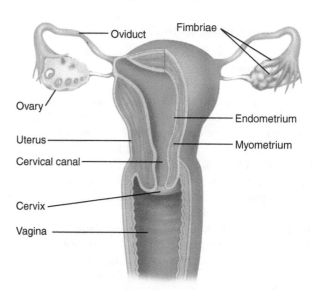

b) Anterior view of internal organs.

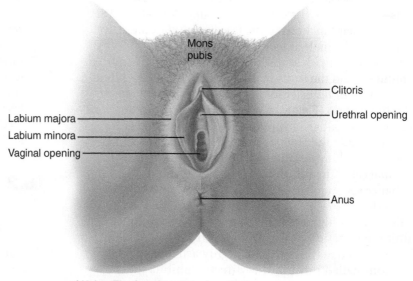

c) Vulva: The female external genitalia.

Figure 16.4 **The female reproductive system.** The labia have been pulled to the sides to expose the vaginal and urethral openings.

endometrium helps to form the *placenta*. The placenta provides nourishment to the developing fetus and also provides for waste removal and gas exchange.

The outer layer of the uterus, or **myometrium**, consists of thick layers of smooth muscle. The myometrium stretches during pregnancy to accommodate the growing fetus. It also provides the muscular force to expel the mature fetus during labor.

The narrow part of the uterus that extends slightly into the vagina is the **cervix**. An opening in the cervix permits sperm to enter the uterus and allows the fetus to exit during birth.

The vagina: Organ of sexual intercourse and birth canal

The cervix joins the **vagina**, a hollow muscular organ of sexual intercourse and also the birth canal. Glands within the vagina produce lubricating secretions during sexual arousal. A thin ring of tissue called the *hymen* may partially cover the opening to the vagina. The hymen is ruptured by the first sexual intercourse, or sometimes by the insertion of tampons or vigorous physical activity.

The vagina is continuous at the body surface with the female external genitalia, collectively called the **vulva** (Figure 16.4c). An outer, larger pair of fat-padded skin folds called the **labia majora** (in Latin, "major lips") surround and enclose the **labia minora** (singular: *labium*), a highly vascular but smaller pair of folds. The **clitoris**, a small organ partly enclosed by the labia minora, is important in the female sexual response. The clitoris and the penis originate from the same tissue during early fetal development, and like the penis, the clitoris contains erectile tissue that is highly sensitive to stimulation. Between the clitoris and the vaginal opening lies the urethral opening. Table 16.2 summarizes the main components of the female reproductive system.

Mammary glands nourish the infant

Human breasts contain **mammary glands**, modified sweat glands that technically are part of the skin, or integumentary system. Though breasts are not required to produce a viable fetus, they undergo developmental changes during puberty in women and they support the infant's development, so we consider them here.

A *nipple* at the center of each breast contains smooth muscles that can contract, causing the nipple to become erect in response to sexual stimulation, cold temperatures, or a nursing infant. Surrounding the

Table 16.2 Summary of the components of the female reproductive system

Component	Function
Ovary (2)	Site of storage and development of oocytes
Oviduct (2)	Duct for transporting oocyte from ovary to uterus; also site of fertilization if it occurs
Uterus	Hollow chamber in which embryo develops
Cervix	Lower part of the uterus that opens into the vagina
Vagina	Organ of sexual intercourse; produces lubricating fluids; also the birth canal
Clitoris	Organ of sexual arousal

nipple is the pigmented *areola*. Internally, the breasts contain the mammary glands, which are specialized to produce milk (Figure 16.5). The mammary glands consist of hundreds of small milk-producing lobules. Contractile cells around each lobule allow the milk to be released, and ducts deliver it to the nipple. Most of the breast consists of adipose tissue, so breast size does not indicate the potential for milk production. A network of fibrous connective tissue supports the glands and adipose tissue.

At puberty, female mammary glands enlarge under the control of the hormone estrogen. Both estrogen and progesterone prepare the glands for **lactation**, or the production of milk, late in pregnancy. At birth, prolactin stimulates lactation and oxytocin stimulates the contractions that release milk during nursing. In males the mammary glands are *vestigial*, meaning that they have no function.

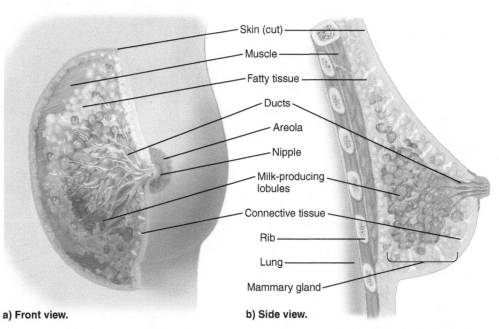

a) Front view. b) Side view.

Figure 16.5 **The female breast.** Anatomical relationships between the milk-producing mammary glands, adipose tissue, and muscle.

Recap The ovaries secrete estrogen and progesterone, store immature oocytes, and (usually) release one oocyte at a time at intervals of about 28 days. The oocyte travels through the oviduct to the uterus, where implantation occurs if the egg has been fertilized. The vagina is the female organ of sexual intercourse and the birth canal; around its opening are the structures of the vulva. Mammary glands are accessory organs that produce and store milk. ◾

16.3 Menstrual cycle consists of ovarian and uterine cycles

Every month, the ovaries and uterus go through a pattern of changes called the **menstrual cycle**. The menstrual cycle lasts about 28 days and is controlled by hormones. Menstrual cycles begin at puberty and generally continue throughout the reproductive years, except during pregnancy.

A complete menstrual cycle consists of two linked cycles, the *ovarian cycle* and the *uterine cycle*. Together, they periodically release oocytes and prepare the uterus to receive a fertilized egg.

The ovarian cycle: Oocytes mature and are released

The **ovarian cycle** is a regular pattern of growth, maturation, and release of oocytes from the ovary. At birth, a female has approximately one million *primary oocytes* already formed and stored in each ovary, and no more are ever produced. Each primary oocyte has already developed partway through meiosis at birth, but at birth all further development halts until after puberty. By puberty 85% of them have been resorbed, leaving only about 300,000 in both ovaries.

Each month perhaps a dozen primary oocytes start the development process, but typically only one completes it. Only about 400 to 500 oocytes are released during a woman's lifetime, a number that contrasts sharply with the 100–300 million sperm released in a single ejaculation.

Figure 16.6 illustrates the events of the ovarian cycle:

1. A primary oocyte is surrounded by a layer of *granulosa cells* that nourish it. Together, a primary oocyte and its granulosa cells constitute an immature **follicle**. At the beginning of the ovarian cycle, an increase in GnRH from the hypothalamus slowly increases the secretion of FSH

Figure 16.6 The ovarian cycle. Approximately a dozen primary follicles start this process each month, but generally only one completes it. For any particular primary follicle the events take place in one location, but for clarity the events are shown as if they migrate around the ovary in a clockwise fashion.

and LH by the anterior pituitary. These two hormones stimulate the follicle to grow, enlarge, and change form. FSH and LH also stimulate the follicle (and surrounding ovarian cells) to secrete estrogen.

2. The granulosa cells begin to divide and to secrete a sugary material (glycoproteins) that becomes the *zona pellucida*, a noncellular coating around the oocyte.

3. A fluid-filled space called the *antrum* develops within the follicle, and some of the granulosa cells begin to secrete estrogen and progesterone.

4. The primary oocyte completes stage I of meiosis to yield a *secondary oocyte* and a nonfunctional *polar body*. The mature follicle, sometimes called a Graafian follicle, consists of a secondary oocyte, a polar body, and numerous granulosa cells, all surrounded by ovarian connective tissue cells.

5. Several days before the midpoint of the ovarian cycle, rising levels of estrogen produced by the follicle and surrounding ovarian cells stimulate the pituitary to release a surge of LH. The LH surge triggers **ovulation** at the midpoint of the cycle—the follicle wall balloons outward and ruptures, releasing the secondary oocyte with its polar body, zona pellucida, and surrounding granulosa cells into the extracellular fluid.

At this point the secondary oocyte enters the oviduct and is swept toward the uterus (and toward any sperm that may be swimming toward it) by peristaltic contractions of the oviduct. If a sperm makes contact with the secondary oocyte and penetrates its outer membrane, the secondary oocyte quickly completes meiosis to produce a mature egg, or *ovum*, which unites with the sperm. The developmental events that follow the union of sperm and egg will be described in more detail when we discuss human development and aging (Chapter 21).

6. But the ovarian cycle is not over yet. A **corpus luteum** forms from what is left of the ruptured follicle (the name "luteinizing hormone" comes from the fact that LH causes the corpus luteum to form). The corpus luteum has an important function: It secretes large amounts of progesterone and estrogen. These hormones prepare the endometrium of the uterus for the possible arrival of a fertilized egg that would need the proper environment for further development. The high levels of progesterone and estrogen also signal the hypothalamus to inhibit FSH secretion, temporarily preventing other follicles from developing.

7. If fertilization does not occur, the corpus luteum degenerates in about 12 days. At this point estrogen and progesterone levels fall rapidly, and the ovarian cycle starts again.

If pregnancy does occur, a layer of tissue derived from the embryo, called the *chorion*, begins to secrete a hormone called *human chorionic gonadotropin (hCG)*. Home-use pregnancy test kits work by detecting hCG in urine. The presence of hCG signals the corpus luteum to produce progesterone and estrogen for another 9–10 weeks. By 10 weeks the developing placenta secretes enough progesterone and estrogen to support the pregnancy, and the corpus luteum degenerates. The high levels of estrogen and progesterone that are maintained throughout pregnancy ensure that ovulation does not occur during pregnancy.

✅ **Quick Check** *A woman has a pituitary tumor removed, and afterward she is unable to produce LH. Will she still have primary oocytes and can she still ovulate? Explain.* ∎

The uterine cycle prepares the uterus for pregnancy

The **uterine cycle** is a series of structural and functional changes that occur in the endometrium of the uterus as it prepares each month for the possibility that a fertilized egg may arrive. The uterine cycle is linked to the ovarian cycle. Because the beginning of the cycle is defined as the first day of menstruation, we begin there. Note that although a complete cycle generally lasts about 28 days, many women have cycles that are shorter or longer. Figure 16.7 summarizes the ovarian, uterine, and hormonal events of a single menstrual cycle of 28 days:

- *Days 1–5: Menstrual phase.* If no fertilized egg from the previous cycle has arrived, body levels of estrogen and progesterone decline precipitously. Without these hormones the uterus cannot maintain its endometrial lining, which has thickened to prepare for a potential pregnancy. **Menstruation** is the process by which the endometrial lining disintegrates and its small blood vessels rupture. The shed tissue and blood pass through the vagina and are excreted. The period of visible menstrual flow, which lasts about 3–5 days, is called the *menstrual period*.

- *Days 6–14: Proliferative phase.* Triggered primarily by rising levels of estrogen from the next developing follicle, the endometrial lining begins to proliferate. It becomes thicker, more vascular, and more glandular. In addition, the lining of the cervix produces a thin, watery mucus that facilitates the passage of sperm, if present, into the uterus from the vagina.

- *Ovulation.* Ovulation occurs midway through the cycle, around the 14th day.

- *Days 15–28: Secretory phase.* Production of estrogen and especially progesterone by the corpus luteum causes the endometrium to continue proliferating, until it becomes almost three times thicker than it was after menstruation. Uterine glands mature and begin producing glycogen as a potential energy source for the embryo. The cervical mucus becomes thick and viscous, forming a "cervical plug" that prevents sperm and bacteria from entering the uterus. These structural changes in the endometrium prepare the uterus for a developing embryo.

If fertilization does not occur, degeneration of the corpus luteum at about 12 days after ovulation results in declining estrogen and progesterone levels, and another menstrual cycle begins.

The menstrual cycle is not a pleasant experience for some women, to put it mildly. It involves rapid hormonal and physical changes that can sometimes cause pain or mood changes.

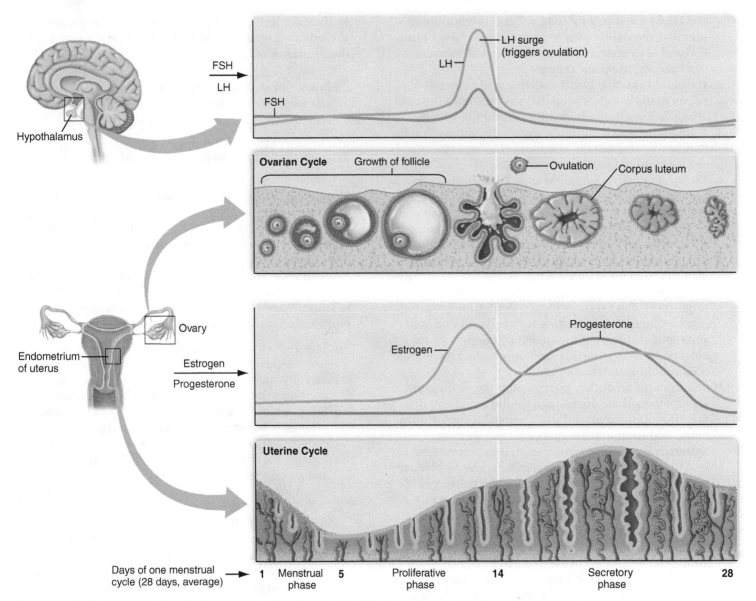

Figure 16.7 The menstrual cycle. The menstrual cycle consists of linked ovarian and uterine cycles. The ovarian cycle is a series of changes associated with oocyte maturation, which depends on the blood levels of FSH and LH. The uterine cycle involves changes in the endometrial lining of the uterus, which depend on the blood levels of estrogen and progesterone.

☑ *What makes progesterone (purple line) rise during the second half of the menstrual cycle, and what makes it fall at the end of the cycle? (Hint: Where is this progesterone coming from?)*

Premenstrual syndrome (PMS) is a group of symptoms often associated with the premenstrual period, including food cravings, mood swings, anxiety, back and joint pain, water retention, and headaches. It generally develops in the second half of the cycle, after ovulation, and lasts until menstruation begins. Exercise and medications that reduce pain and water retention can help.

Painful menstruation is known as *dysmenorrhea*. The endometrium of the uterus produces prostaglandins, which can trigger contractions and cramping of the uterine smooth muscle. Aspirin and ibuprofen may offer some relief from dysmenorrhea because these drugs inhibit prostaglandin formation. Although ovulation itself is usually not

uncomfortable, some women experience a brief sharp pain when the follicle ruptures.

Cyclic changes in hormone levels produce the menstrual cycle

The ovarian and uterine cycles are regulated by cyclic changes in hormone levels. Normally a typical negative feedback control loop controls the hormonal cycles most of the time. But there is a single *positive feedback* event just before the midpoint of the cycle that ultimately triggers ovulation and causes the cycle to repeat itself each month. Positive feedback regulatory events are rare in biology, but when they do occur they have important consequences. Another positive feedback mechanism that you have seen before is the firing of an action potential in a nerve—once the membrane potential is depolarized to threshold, the membrane potential rapidly depolarizes further and an action potential is generated. The cyclic nature of the menstrual cycle is somewhat analogous to an action potential except that it occurs over a month rather than a fraction of a second.

The key regulatory events of the cycle are shown in Figure 16.8. At the beginning of the cycle, LH rises slowly,

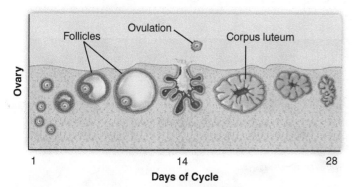

Days of Cycle

Figure 16.8 Regulation of the menstrual cycle. During the first half of the cycle LH and FSH stimulate follicular growth and development. The growing follicle secretes estrogen, which partially inhibits LH secretion. Shortly before the midpoint of the cycle, estrogen from the mature follicle triggers the LH surge, which in turn triggers ovulation. In the second half of the cycle, estrogen and progesterone from the corpus luteum again inhibit LH and FSH secretion, preventing maturation of another follicle until it is determined (by regression of the corpus luteum and a decline in estrogen and progesterone concentrations) that pregnancy has not occurred. Then the cycle can begin again.

☑ *Are there any similarities between hormonal control of the menstrual cycle in women, and hormonal control of reproduction in men? (Hint: Review Figure 16.3.)*

stimulating an immature follicle to develop and secrete estrogen. During this time estrogen from the developing follicle partially inhibits LH secretion, but LH nevertheless continues to rise slowly and the follicle continues to grow and secrete more estrogen.

When the follicle nears maturity and its estrogen secretion is sufficiently high, a threshold concentration of estrogen is reached at which it now *stimulates* LH release (the positive feedback event). This results in the LH surge that ultimately triggers ovulation at about day 14.

During the latter half of the menstrual cycle, the system returns to typical negative feedback control. The LH surge is short-lived because high but steady levels of estrogen and progesterone from the corpus luteum inhibit LH and FSH secretion. Without LH and FSH, the next follicle does not develop. This prevents a second ovulation until the cycle is complete and estrogen and progesterone return to low levels again.

From a functional standpoint, hormonal regulation of the menstrual cycle makes perfect sense. Because only a mature follicle produces enough estrogen to trigger the LH surge, ovulation is triggered at the precise moment that the follicle is ready. And once ovulation occurs, the start of another cycle is delayed until the body determines whether or not pregnancy has taken place. If there is no pregnancy, then estrogen and progesterone return to low levels within about two weeks and the cycle begins again with a slowly rising LH concentration.

↩ **Recap** During the ovarian cycle, a primary oocyte within a developing follicle divides once to form a secondary oocyte. The follicle ruptures, releases the oocyte, and forms the corpus luteum that secretes progesterone and estrogen. Rising levels of estrogen cause the endometrium to proliferate. If pregnancy does not occur, hormone levels fall and the endometrial layer disintegrates and is shed, a process known as *menstruation*. Ovulation is triggered by a surge of LH, which in turn is caused by the positive feedback effect of a high concentration of estrogen from the maturing follicle. During the second half of the menstrual cycle, sustained high levels of estrogen and progesterone from the corpus luteum inhibit further ovulation. ●

16.4 Human sexual response, intercourse, and fertilization

The human sexual response is a series of events that coordinate sexual function to accomplish intercourse and fertilization. The response can have up to four phases in both men and women:

1. *Excitement.* Increased sexual awareness and arousal
2. *Plateau.* Intense and continuing arousal
3. *Orgasm.* The peak of sexual sensations
4. *Resolution.* The abatement of arousal

The male sexual response

In men, excitement is accompanied by pleasurable sensations from the penis and by an erection. Erection occurs when neural activity relaxes (dilates) arterioles leading into vascular compartments within the penis. The compartments fill with blood, and as they fill they press on the veins draining the penis and reduce the rate of venous outflow. As more blood enters the penis and less blood leaves it, the penis swells, lengthens, and stiffens. Heart rate and breathing increase, as does the tone of skeletal muscle. Sights, sounds, memories, and other psychological stimuli; kissing or other physical contact; and especially physical contact with the penis all contribute to excitement. Arousal continues during the plateau phase, which can last for a few seconds or many minutes.

At some point sexual arousal becomes so great that **orgasm** occurs. An orgasm is a brief, intensely pleasurable reflex event that accomplishes **ejaculation**, or the expulsion of semen. During ejaculation, sympathetic nerve activity contracts smooth muscle in the seminal vesicles, epididymis, bulbourethral glands, and prostate to move glandular secretions into the urethra. The internal urethral sphincter closes tightly to prevent urine from leaking into the urethra, and the skeletal muscles at the base of the penis contract rhythmically, forcing semen out of the urethra in several spurts. In a typical ejaculation, the male expels about 3–4 ml (a teaspoon or more) of semen.

During the resolution phase, the erection subsides and breathing and heart rate return to normal. Generally a refractory period follows, during which another erection and orgasm cannot be achieved. The refractory period may last from several minutes up to several hours.

The female sexual response

Women experience the same four phases of the sexual response. As in men, the excitement phase is triggered by sights, sounds, psychological stimuli, and physical stimulation, especially of the clitoris and breasts. Stimulation initiates neural reflexes that dilate blood vessels in the labia, clitoris, and nipples. During arousal the vagina and the area around the labia secrete lubricating fluids. Without these lubricating fluids intercourse can be difficult and sometimes painful for both partners.

The female orgasm, like that of the male, consists of rhythmic and involuntary muscular contractions. Contractions of the uterus and vagina are accompanied by intense feelings of pleasure and sensations of warmth and relaxation. The rate of orgasm is more variable in females than in males. Some women do not experience orgasms frequently, whereas others experience multiple orgasms within one period of sexual contact. Female orgasm is not required for fertilization or pregnancy, nor is arousal, for that matter.

Fertilization: One sperm penetrates the egg

During ejaculation, the male may deposit several hundred million sperm inside the vagina, near the cervix. The sperm have a long way to go, however, before one of them encounters an egg. Random swimming takes some sperm through the cervical opening, through the uterus, and up the two oviducts. The journey can take hours or even a day or more. Fertilization occurs when a sperm encounters an oocyte in an oviduct and penetrates the zona pellucida (**Figure 16.9**). Some sperm may be viable for up to five days in the female reproductive tract, although most do not last more than two days.

Now that we know how fertilization normally takes place, we turn to how to control fertility (avoid pregnancy) should you wish to, and how to improve fertility (increase the chances of becoming pregnant) if infertility becomes a problem. The details of human development from a single fertilized egg into a fully formed baby in just nine months is the subject of another chapter (Chapter 21).

↩ **Recap** Women and men experience the same four phases of sexual responsiveness. Sexual arousal in the male results in penile erection that leads to orgasm and ejaculation. Females experience sexual arousal and pleasurable orgasms marked by rhythmic muscular contractions. During ejaculation, the male deposits several hundred million sperm in the vagina. Fertilization of the egg by a single sperm occurs within five days, if it occurs at all. ▪

Figure 16.9 Colored SEM (× 900) of sperm in contact with an egg. Only one sperm will fertilize the egg.

16.5 Birth control methods: Controlling fertility

Couples or individuals might choose to control fertility for many reasons, and there are many ways to do it. Birth control (contraceptive) methods vary widely in effectiveness (Table 16.3). Some methods reduce the chance of pregnancy from just a single intercourse; others virtually eliminate the chances of pregnancy for a lifetime. An understanding of the advantages and the limitations of each method will help you make an informed choice, should you choose to control your own fertility for any period of time.

Abstinence: Not having intercourse

The only completely effective method of birth control is to not have sexual intercourse at all. *Abstinence*, as it is called, works for many people for short periods of time, and throughout life for others. Abstinence is natural in that no intervention or artificial method is employed. However, the idea of abstinence doesn't resonate with most teens. When abstinence is not the option of choice, there are still many ways to reduce the probability of pregnancy.

Surgical sterilization: Vasectomy and tubal ligation

Both men and women may opt for surgical sterilization (Figure 16.10). Male surgical sterilization is called *vasectomy*. It can generally be performed in a doctor's office under local anesthesia. The doctor makes small incisions in the scrotum, locates each ductus deferens, and ties them in two

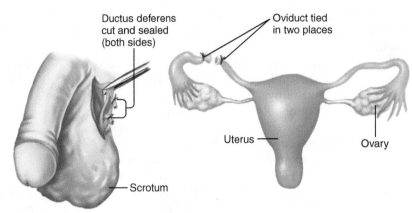

a) **Vasectomy.** Small incisions are made in the scrotum, and each ductus deferens is tied in two places.

b) **Tubal ligation.** An incision is made in a woman's abdominal wall, the two oviducts are located, and each is tied in two places and cut.

Figure 16.10 **Surgical sterilization.**

places. The segments between the two ties are then removed, preventing sperm from reaching the urethra.

After a vasectomy the testes continue to produce testosterone and sperm, and sexual interest and all secondary sexual characteristics remain unchanged. With no access to the urethra, however, the sperm eventually are resorbed, just as they are if ejaculation never takes place. Generally it is impossible to detect a change in semen volume per ejaculation. If done properly, surgical male sterilization is close to foolproof. However, to be on the safe side, the surgeon will probably recommend doing a sperm count several months after the operation.

Female sterilization involves a *tubal ligation*. The doctor makes a small incision in the woman's abdominal wall, locates each oviduct, and ties (ligates) each at two sites. The sections between the ties are cut away, leaving the oocyte no way to reach the uterus or sperm to reach the oocyte. In a newer version of a tubal ligation, called a *hysteroscopy*, a flexible tube is inserted through the vagina and uterus and into the oviduct. The tube emits electrical current that seals shut the oviduct. Both tubal ligation and hysteroscopy are highly effective but require surgery that is slightly more difficult than in the male. In addition, tubal ligation may leave two small but possibly visible scars.

A drawback to surgical sterilization in both men and women is that although it *may* be possible to reverse, sterilization generally is permanent. Sterilization should be carefully considered before it is chosen as a method of birth control.

✅ **Quick Check** *Would a man be sterile the day after a vasectomy, and would a woman be sterile the day after a tubal ligation? Explain.* ∎

Hormonal methods: Pills, injections, patches, and rings

Manipulation of hormone levels provides reasonably effective and safe methods of birth control. The most common method is oral contraceptives, or *birth control pills*.

Table 16.3 **Approximate failure rates of various contraceptive methods**

Contraceptive method	Annual number of pregnancies expected per 100 women
Spermicide alone	30
Female condom	20
Diaphragm with spermicide	15
"Morning after" pills	15
Male condom	11–16
Hormonal contraceptives	
Oral contraceptives	5
Skin patch	5
Vaginal contraceptive ring	5
Injected hormonal contraceptives	1
Intrauterine devices	1
Sterilization surgery—men	1
Sterilization surgery—women	1

Source: Adapted from Birth Control Guide, FDA Office of Women's Health, 2011.

Although the exact mix of hormones in the pills varies, they all administer synthetic progesterone and estrogen in amounts that inhibit the release of FSH and LH. That way, follicles do not mature and ovulation does not take place. It is important to take a pill at the same time every day; if pills are not taken regularly, ovulation (and pregnancy) may occur.

Most birth control pills are taken for three weeks and then replaced with placebo pills for a week so that normal menstrual periods occur each month. However, many physicians have questioned the need for regular monthly periods. In 2003 the FDA approved the first *continuous birth control pill (Seasonale)* that reduces the number of menstrual periods to only four per year. In 2007 the FDA approved a pill that eliminates all periods for a full year (*Lybrel*). Continuous birth control pills are particularly attractive to women who routinely suffer from PMS.

Roughly a third of all women in the United States use birth control pills for at least some period of their lives. Oral contraceptives have several side effects, some beneficial and others harmful. Some women report that oral contraceptives reduce cramps and menstrual flow, and they may offer some protection against cancers of the ovaries and uterus. On the negative side, oral contraceptives can cause acne, headaches, fluid retention, high blood pressure, or blood clots. Women who smoke have a greater risk of blood clots and vascular problems from birth control pills.

To avoid the drawbacks of taking—or forgetting to take—a daily pill, some women opt for hormone injections, skin patches, vaginal rings, or implants. *Depo-Provera* is a progesterone injection that lasts three months; *Lunelle* is a monthly injection of progesterone and estrogen. *Ortho Evra* is a patch that slowly releases hormones through the skin into the bloodstream. The user applies a fresh patch every week for three weeks straight, followed by one week with no patch, during which she menstruates. *NuvaRing*, a flexible ring about 2 inches in diameter, is inserted into the vagina, where it slowly releases hormones. The ring remains in place for three weeks, and then is removed for one week to allow menstruation. Injections, patches, and rings can all have side effects similar to those of hormone pills, including weight gain, headaches, and irregular menstrual periods. The latest in contraception is *Implanon*, a matchstick-size rod containing synthetic progesterone that is implanted under the skin. Implanon provides effective contraception for up to three years.

Hormonal methods of contraception have the advantage of not interfering with sexual activity or foreplay in any way. However, none of them protect against sexually transmitted diseases.

A variety of contraceptive methods are shown in Figure 16.11.

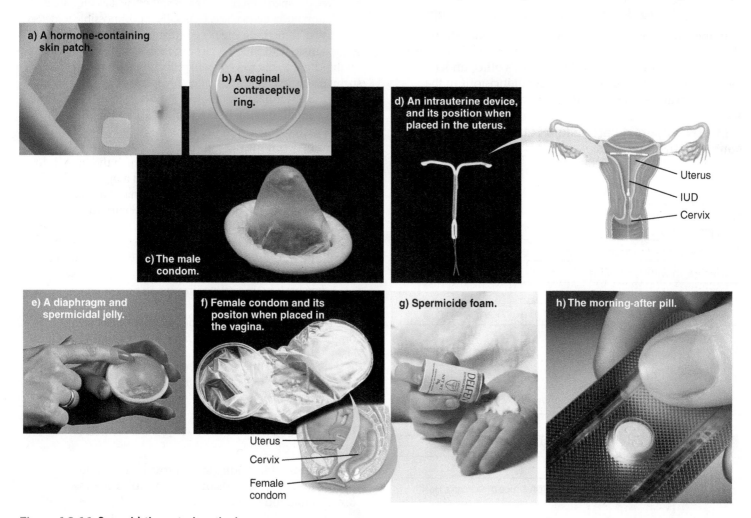

a) A hormone-containing skin patch.

b) A vaginal contraceptive ring.

c) The male condom.

d) An intrauterine device, and its position when placed in the uterus.

Uterus

IUD

Cervix

e) A diaphragm and spermicidal jelly.

f) Female condom and its positon when placed in the vagina.

Uterus

Cervix

Female condom

g) Spermicide foam.

h) The morning-after pill.

Figure 16.11 Some birth control methods.

✅ **Quick Check** *What natural physiological state are these hormonal birth control methods most similar to? Explain.* ◾

IUDs are inserted into the uterus

Intrauterine devices, or *IUDs*, are small pieces of plastic or metal that are inserted into the uterus by a health care provider. They should be removed only by a health care provider.

IUDs create a mild chronic inflammation that prevents either fertilization or implantation of the fertilized egg in the uterine wall. On the positive side, they are relatively effective and, like hormonal methods, do not interfere with sexual activity. However, risks include uterine cramping and bleeding, infection, and possible damage to the uterus. IUDs offer no protection from sexually transmitted diseases.

An IUD called *Mirena* contains small amounts of a progesterone-like steroid. The steroid decreases the possibility of conception and also reduces menstrual flow, a significant benefit to women who normally experience heavy bleeding during their periods. Mirena is effective for up to five years.

Diaphragms and cervical caps block the cervix

Diaphragms and *cervical caps* are latex devices that a woman inserts into her vagina. They cover the cervical opening and prevent sperm from entering the uterus.

Both types of devices must be fitted initially to the user's cervix. A disadvantage is that they must be inserted shortly before intercourse and then removed sometime later, making sexual activity less spontaneous. However, they are fairly effective, especially if inserted correctly and used with chemical spermicides. Diaphragms and cervical caps do not protect against sexually transmitted diseases.

Chemical spermicides kill sperm

Chemical *spermicides*, which destroy sperm, are available in a wide variety of forms—foams, creams, jellies, and douches. Their effectiveness varies. All reduce the risk of pregnancy, but none is 100% effective. Most are inserted into the vagina shortly before intercourse, except douches, which are used after intercourse (and are less effective). Some kill organisms that cause sexually transmitted diseases; others do not.

Condoms trap ejaculated sperm

Despite their decidedly low-tech approach (a condom is just a balloon, really), *condoms* remain one of the most popular forms of birth control. They are fairly effective if used properly. Combining them with a chemical spermicide makes them even more effective. They also offer some protection against sexually transmitted diseases.

The male condom is a soft sheath, made of latex or animal membrane, that encloses the penis and traps ejaculated sperm. There is also a female condom that is essentially a polyurethane liner that fits inside the vagina. Condoms made of latex (but not animal membrane) have the tremendous advantage of offering some protection against diseases, including AIDS.

Withdrawal and periodic abstinence

Two other methods, withdrawal and periodic abstinence, are not very effective in preventing pregnancy. In fact, for a sexually active couple they are so ineffective in the long run that some people believe they should not be classified as birth control at all. Couples who are serious about preventing pregnancy should consider more effective techniques.

In principle, the *withdrawal* method means that the man withdraws his penis from the vagina at just the right moment before ejaculation, so that ejaculation occurs outside the vagina. In practice, it takes skill and commitment on the part of the male and a lot of trust on the part of the female. In addition, some sperm can be flushed into the ejaculatory duct even before ejaculation, so there is a possibility of fertilization even if the man does not ejaculate.

People who practice *periodic abstinence* (sometimes called the *rhythm method*) rely on the fact that fertilization is possible for only a limited time in each menstrual cycle, defined by the life span of sperm and the time during which an oocyte can be fertilized after ovulation. As its name suggests, periodic abstinence requires the woman to avoid intercourse for about an eight-day span every month in the middle of her cycle, from approximately five days before ovulation to three days after ovulation. It is possible to determine the day of ovulation by carefully monitoring body temperature, because the temperature rises slightly—several tenths of a degree—at ovulation and stays elevated for about three days. However, it is difficult to determine which five days *precede* ovulation, because obviously it has not yet occurred.

Pills that can be used after intercourse

When intercourse has occurred in the absence of any birth control method, couples have several options that may either prevent pregnancy or terminate it early on. A product called *Preven* is a series of four pills that, if started within 72 hours *after* intercourse, may prevent a pregnancy entirely. Available only by prescription, Preven contains high doses of progesterone and estrogen. It is thought to work by preventing ovulation if it has not already occurred. It may also prevent fertilization even after ovulation, but this is not well documented. Another after-intercourse pill, called *Plan B*, contains progesterone only. Both Plan B and Preven are commonly called "emergency contraception" or "morning after" pills. Plan B is now available without a prescription to persons aged 17 and older.

The morning-after pill is not yet available to women under the age of 17. To find out why, visit MJ's blog in the Study Area in MasteringBiology and look under "The Morning-After Pill."

More controversial is *Mifeprex* (mifepristone, formerly called RU-486), a drug that *blocks* the action of progesterone. By blocking the action of progesterone, Mifeprex can prevent the endometrial lining from proliferating. If taken in the first few days after intercourse, it can prevent pregnancy by preventing implantation of the pre-embryo in the uterine lining. However, Mifeprex is more commonly prescribed *after* a pregnancy has been identified, because its main advantage is that it is effective up to seven weeks after pregnancy. By causing the endometrial lining to regress to the point that it can no longer nourish the fetus, Mifeprex essentially causes a very early-stage chemical abortion. For this reason, Mifeprex has generally been labeled an "abortion pill" rather than an emergency contraception. Mefeprex first became available in France in 1988, but concern over its mode of action caused so much controversy that it was not approved for sale in the United States until 2000.

Elective abortion

An *elective abortion* is an elective termination of a pregnancy. In common usage the term *elective* is generally understood without being stated. Aside from the very early-stage use of Mifeprex, an abortion can be performed in several ways, including vacuum suctioning of the uterus, surgical scraping of the uterine lining, or infusion of a strong saline solution that causes the fetus to be rejected. Sometimes abortions are performed in cases of incest or rape, or when continuing the pregnancy would endanger the mother's health. Some women choose to have an abortion if medical tests reveal a nonviable fetus.

Abortions are highly controversial. Some people support a woman's right to choose her own reproductive destiny, whereas others support an embryo's right to life. The beliefs on both sides are often based on strongly held moral and religious convictions.

The future in birth control

Several new forms of birth control are still in the research and development stage. Possibilities include a male birth control pill that reduces sperm production, and several vaccines for women. For instance, a vaccine is being developed to immunize women against human chorionic gonadotropin, the hormone that maintains the corpus luteum so implantation can occur. Also under development is a vaccine against sperm.

As it stands today, women have most of the choices. It's worth knowing what the options are so that one's choices can be well informed.

Recap Surgical sterilization should be considered a permanent method of birth control. Hormonal methods—pills, injections, patches, and rings—are also relatively effective but can have side effects. Physical barriers (diaphragms, cervical caps, and condoms) and chemical spermicides are moderately effective; a few afford some protection against diseases. IUDs are fairly effective against pregnancy but do not protect against diseases. Withdrawal and periodic abstinence are not effective forms of birth control in the long term. Abortion is an elective but controversial procedure that terminates a pregnancy.

16.6 Infertility: Inability to conceive

If both partners are healthy, pregnancy is usually not difficult to achieve: The annual pregnancy rate without any birth control averages 85–90%. Timing can improve the odds. For example, if a couple wants to increase their chance of having a child, they might have intercourse near the middle of the menstrual cycle, around the time of ovulation.

Some couples find it difficult to become pregnant. Next, we describe conditions that can impair fertility and solutions that are available.

Infertility can have many causes

A couple is considered infertile if they fail to achieve pregnancy after a year of trying. By this definition, about 15% of all couples in the United States are infertile. Infertility is about equally attributable to men and women.

Male infertility is the insufficiency or lack of normal, healthy sperm. The chance of any one sperm achieving reproductive success is so low that men whose sperm count is below 60 million per ejaculation are, for all practical purposes, infertile. Reasons for a low sperm count include low testosterone levels, immune disorders that attack the sperm, radiation, certain drugs such as anabolic steroids, and diseases such as mumps and gonorrhea.

Sperm function best at temperatures slightly cooler than body temperature. One simple measure that may raise the viable sperm count is to switch from tight-fitting underwear, which hold the testes close to the body, to looser-fitting boxer shorts.

Causes of female infertility are more variable. One of the most common reasons is *pelvic inflammatory disease (PID)*, a general term for any extensive bacterial infection of the internal female reproductive organs. PID that involves the oviducts can result in scar tissue that seals the oviducts shut, preventing passage of either eggs or sperm (Figure 16.12). Abnormal production of LH or FSH may limit the development of oocytes into follicles. Irregular menstrual cycles can make it difficult to time the period of ovulation. Some women produce strongly acidic vaginal secretions or thick cervical mucus that damage sperm or make it difficult for sperm to move toward the egg. Uterine tumors may interfere with implantation.

Figure 16.12 **Pelvic inflammatory disease can make women sterile.** Bacteria that migrate from the vagina into the oviducts can inflame the oviducts, leading to scarring and either partial or complete closure of the oviduct.

Some women (1–3%) develop *endometriosis*, a condition in which endometrial tissue migrates up the oviduct during a menstrual period and implants on other organs such as the ovaries, the walls of the bladder, or the colon. There it grows, stimulated each month by the normal hormonal cycle. Endometriosis can cause pain and infertility, but can sometimes be corrected by surgery, drugs, or hormone therapy.

Female reproductive capacity is more affected by age than male reproductive capacity. By the mid-40s, women begin to run out of oocytes. In addition, the ovaries become less responsive to LH and FSH, leading eventually to menopause and the end of menstrual cycles. Oocytes ovulated later in life are also more likely to have been damaged by years of exposure to radiation, chemicals, and disease.

A common cause of failure to achieve reproductive success even when the couple is fertile is spontaneous abortion, or *miscarriage*, defined as the loss of a fetus before it can survive outside the uterus. Perhaps as many as one-third of all pregnancies end in miscarriages, some of them so quickly that a woman has no idea she ever conceived.

✅ **Quick Check** *A woman who has had several previous miscarriages will sometimes be given a prescription for progesterone pills if she becomes pregnant again. Why?* ▪

Enhancing fertility

Several options are available for infertile couples who wish to have a child. None guarantee success and most are expensive. It is not unusual for couples to spend tens of thousands of dollars, even $200,000 or more, to conceive a child by some of these methods. Some couples choose to hire a surrogate mother.

Artificial insemination By far the easiest, most common, and least expensive technique is *artificial insemination*. Sperm are placed, with a syringe, into the vagina or uterus, as close to the time of ovulation as possible. Artificial insemination is the method of choice when the man's sperm count is low, because his sperm can be collected over a period of time and all delivered at once. It is also a good option for men who produce no sperm, in which case the woman may receive sperm from an anonymous donor who has sold his semen to a "sperm bank," and for single women who make the personal choice to become a parent. However it is not an option when the problem is a woman's failure to conceive. Over 20,000 babies are born in the United States each year as a result of artificial insemination.

Artificial reproductive technologies Artificial reproductive technologies (ART) refers to all techniques in which both sperm and eggs are handled outside the body. ART techniques are the method of choice for couples who are unable to conceive because the woman's oviducts are damaged in such a way that sperm cannot reach the egg. The most usual cause is scarring of the oviduct due to a prior pelvic inflammatory disease.

In all of the various ART techniques, a physician first harvests immature eggs from the woman using a needle guided by ultrasound. Generally the woman is stimulated with fertility-enhancing drugs in advance to ensure that a sufficient number of eggs are ready for harvesting. Sperm is collected from the man. From this point on the methods vary slightly.

The simplest and least expensive ART technique is *in vitro fertilization (IVF)*. In IVF the eggs are allowed to mature in laboratory glassware under sterile conditions and then sperm are added. The method is called *in vitro* fertilization because the eggs are fertilized outside the body, that is, under glass (*vitreus* is Latin for "glass"). Two to four days later, when it is clear that fertilization has occurred because cells are dividing (Figure 16.13), the embryo is inserted into the woman's uterus via the vagina. IVF with vaginal insertion results in a live birth only about 20% of the time, so some couples try it several times before achieving pregnancy.

Two variations on the IVF method that improve success rates are *gamete intrafallopian transfer (GIFT)* and *zygote intrafallopian transfer (ZIFT)*. In GIFT, unfertilized eggs and sperm are placed directly into an oviduct (Fallopian tube) through a small incision in the woman's abdomen, without waiting for an embryo to develop. In ZIFT the egg is first fertilized outside the body and then placed into the oviduct (below any point of scarring, of course).

There are now over 440 ART clinics in the United States that can help infertile couples achieve their dream of having

Figure 16.13 A human embryo at the eight-cell stage, approximately 2-1/2 days after *in vitro* fertilization.

a child. The overall success rate at achieving a live birth from an ART cycle (a cycle of fertility drugs, egg collection, and insertion) is now about 30%. Because the chances of pregnancy in any one cycle are low, some women elect to have several embryos transferred at once. Consequently, among women undergoing ART techniques about a third of all live births are multiple births. Over 60,000 babies are born each year in the United States as a result of ART techniques.

If the woman cannot produce healthy eggs because of an ovarian problem, ART techniques can be performed with eggs donated by another woman. It's also possible to freeze unused embryos from a cycle so they can be used later if the first GIFT or ZIFT attempt isn't successful.

Fertility-enhancing drugs Medications are available to boost the production of developing eggs. Sometimes these drugs are tried before IVF, or given to women who are preparing for IVF so that several eggs may be harvested at once. Occasionally multiple pregnancies can occur as a result of the medications themselves. When you hear news reports of multiple births of four or more babies, the mother was almost certainly taking fertility-enhancing drugs.

Surrogate motherhood Some couples choose to pay another woman, called a *surrogate mother*, to become pregnant and bear a baby for them. The prospective parents may contribute sperm, eggs, or both.

Surrogate motherhood raises a number of difficult legal issues that the couple and surrogate mother should explore before entering into an agreement. The surrogate must confirm legally that she will give up the baby for adoption to the parents. However, there have not yet been enough court cases to define legal precedents should conflicts arise between the surrogate mother and the prospective parents at a later date.

Recap Male infertility is an insufficiency or lack of sperm. Causes of female infertility are variable and include failure to ovulate, damage to oviducts, pelvic inflammatory disease, secretions that impair sperm function, uterine tumors, endometriosis, age-related changes, and miscarriages. The choice of options to improve fertility depends on the cause of the infertility. Options include artificial insemination, *in vitro* fertilization, gamete intrafallopian transfer, zygote intrafallopian transfer, fertility-enhancing drugs, and surrogate motherhood. ▪

16.7 Sexually transmitted diseases

Disorders of the reproductive systems fall into four classes: (1) infertility, (2) complications of pregnancy, (3) cancers and tumors of the reproductive organs, and (4) sexually transmitted diseases. We have already considered infertility and approaches to overcoming it. We discuss potential complications of pregnancy in the chapter on human development (Chapter 21), and we cover cancer in a separate chapter (Chapter 18). In the rest of this chapter, we focus on sexually transmitted diseases.

Sexually transmitted diseases (STDs) are transmitted by sexual contact, whether genital, oral-genital, or anal-genital. STDs are on the rise worldwide, apparently because young people are becoming sexually active earlier, and birth control reduces the fear of pregnancy. In the United States alone, over 12 million people contract an STD each year. A quarter of them are teenagers.

STDs are not just a social embarrassment. Some cause serious organ damage, and a few are deadly. Many don't actually affect the reproductive organs, even though they are transmitted sexually. Some STDs are difficult if not impossible to cure, so an ounce of prevention is definitely worth a pound of (attempted) cure.

Now that we have studied the human reproductive systems, you can see why STDs are so common. Most disease organisms cannot live long outside a warm, moist environment. That's why their most common sites of entry are those that are warm and moist, such as the digestive tract, respiratory tract, and, of course, the reproductive organs. Some organisms, such as the virus that causes AIDS, travel in body fluids. Others, like the pubic lice known as "crabs," simply take the opportunity afforded by intimate contact to hop from one human to another.

STD-causing organisms include viruses, bacteria, fungi, protozoa, and even arthropods. Table 16.4 summarizes common STDs, including causes, symptoms, potential complications, and treatments.

Bacterial STDs: Gonorrhea, syphilis, and chlamydia

Gonorrhea Caused by the bacterium *Neisseria gonorrhoeae*, gonorrhea is easily transmitted—roughly 50% of women and 20% of men contract it after a single exposure. It can be

Table 16.4 **Sexually transmitted diseases**

Disease	Organism	Symptoms	Complications	Comments
Gonorrhea	*Neisseria gonorrhoeae* bacterium	Men: Pus from penis, painful urination Women: Painful urination, vaginal discharge	Men: Inflamed testes and sterility Women: Pelvic inflammatory disease, scarring, sterility	May be asymptomatic, or symptoms may disappear even though disease remains; can be treated with antibiotics
Syphilis	*Treponema pallidum* bacterium	Primary: Chancre at infection site	Secondary: Non-itchy rash, hair loss, gray areas of infection on mucous membranes Tertiary: Widespread damage to cardiovascular and nervous systems, blindness, skin ulcers	Symptoms may disappear spontaneously between phases; can be treated with antibiotics
Chlamydia	*Chlamydia trachomatis* bacterium	Men: Discharge from penis, burning during urination Women: Vaginal discharge, burning, and itching	Pelvic inflammatory disease, urethral infections, sterility, complications of pregnancy	Can be treated with antibiotics
AIDS (also see Chapter 9)	Human immunodeficiency virus (HIV)	Fatigue, fever, chills, night sweats, swollen lymph nodes or spleen, diarrhea, loss of appetite, weight loss	Infections, pneumonia, meningitis, tuberculosis, encephalitis, cancer	Asymptomatic phase can last for years, even though disease is still contagious; no cure
Hepatitis B (also see Chapter 14)	Hepatitis B virus	Nausea, fatigue, jaundice, abdominal pain, arthritis	Cirrhosis, liver failure	Preventable with a vaccine
Genital herpes	Herpes simplex virus types 1 and 2	Genital blisters, painful urination, fever, swollen lymph nodes in groin	Symptoms disappear during remission, then reappear; contagious during active phases	Drugs available to control active phase
Genital warts	Human papillomavirus (HPV)	Warts on penis, labia, anus, or in vagina or cervix	Risk factor for cancers of cervix or penis	Warts can be removed by surgery, freezing, or drugs. Preventable with a vaccine
Yeast infections	*Candida albicans*	Men: Discharge from penis, painful urination Women: Vaginal pain, inflammation, cheesy discharge	Can develop in women without sexual contact, but is transmitted sexually to men	Can be treated with antifungal drugs
Trichomoniasis	*Trichomonas vaginalis* protozoan	Men: Discharge from inflamed penis Women: Frothy, foul-smelling vaginal discharge	Recurrent urethral infections	Can be treated with drugs
Pubic lice	*Phthirus pubis*	Intense itching, skin irritation in pubic area; lice are small but visible	Can also be transmitted through infected sheets, clothing	Can be treated with drugs

transmitted to the mouth and throat by oral-genital contact, or to the mouth or eyes through hand contact. An infected mother can pass gonorrhea to her child during birth, causing a potentially blinding eye infection.

In men, early symptoms include discharge of pus from the penis and painful urination, but the symptoms may disappear even though the disease remains. Women may experience a burning sensation during urination and vaginal discharge that may not appear particularly abnormal. However, nearly 20% of infected men and up to 80% of infected women show no symptoms, at least for periods of time, and so do not seek medical advice. Left untreated, gonorrhea can lead to inflammation, scarring, and sterility.

Gonorrhea is far less common than it was just 20 years ago (Figure 16.14). Although gonorrhea generally responds to antibiotics, in recent years antibiotic-resistant strains have emerged.

Syphilis The bacterium *Treponema pallidum* causes syphilis, one of the most dangerous STDs if left untreated. Fortunately it is no longer very common. Syphilis develops in three phases, often separated by periods in which the disease seems to disappear. One to eight weeks after infection, the disease enters its *primary phase*. A hard, dry, bacteria-filled sore, called a *chancre*, appears at the infection site. The chancre is not painful and disappears spontaneously after several weeks; infected women may not even notice it.

During the *secondary phase*, which can last several years, the bacteria invade lymph nodes, blood vessels, mucous membranes, bones, and the nervous system. Symptoms include a widespread but non-itchy rash, hair loss, and gray patches representing areas of infection on mucous membranes. Again the symptoms may disappear, and

sometimes the symptoms end there. However, some people progress to the *tertiary phase*, characterized by widespread damage to the cardiovascular and nervous systems, blindness, skin ulcers, and eventual death. A child of a syphilis-infected woman can be born blind, malformed, or dead because the bacteria cross the placenta into the developing fetus. Syphilis can be treated with penicillin.

Chlamydia Chlamydia is a bacterial infection caused by *Chlamydia trachomatis*. Although it is easily cured with antibiotics, it often goes undiagnosed and untreated because the symptoms are so mild. Men may experience a discharge from the penis and a burning sensation during urination, and women may have a vaginal discharge and a burning and itching sensation.

Women are diagnosed with chlamydia three times as often as men. Women between 15 and 24 years old are especially at risk, with reported rates of infection nearly 10 times that of the general population (Figure 16.15).

The eventual health consequences for women can be severe despite the apparent mildness of the symptoms. If left untreated, chlamydia can cause pelvic inflammatory disease, permanent scarring of the Fallopian tubes, complications of pregnancy, and sterility. It can also infect a newborn's eyes and lungs at birth, leading to pneumonia. Health officials recommend that all sexually active women under the age of 26 be tested for chlamydia every year.

Viral STDs: HIV, hepatitis B, genital herpes, and HPV

The government does not keep accurate statistics on most of the viral STDs. Some of them are very dangerous; others are just very common.

HIV Human immunodeficiency virus (HIV), the virus that causes *acquired immune deficiency syndrome (AIDS)*, is one of the

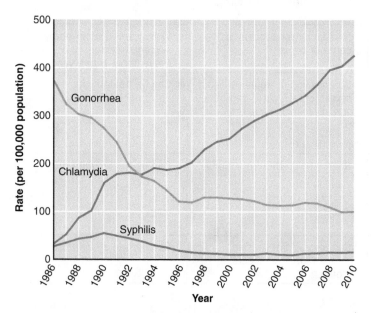

Figure 16.14 Relative rates of infection for the three most common bacterial STDs. Data are expressed in terms of numbers of infection per 100,000 population per year in the United States, since 1986. Syphilis rates refer to primary and secondary syphilis.

✓ *What could explain the fact that the rate of chlamydia infection is increasing, whereas the rates of the other two STDs are declining?*

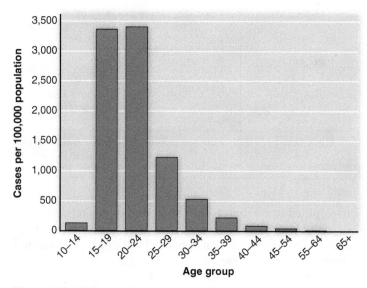

Figure 16.15 Rates of chlamydia infection in women, by age. Young women ages 15–24 are particularly likely to contract chlamydia.

most dangerous STDs of our time. One of the most dangerous features of AIDS is that it can be transmitted from person to person long before symptoms of the disease appear.

HIV slowly destroys the immune system over a period of years. Early symptoms include fatigue, fever and chills, night sweats, swollen lymph nodes or spleen, diarrhea, loss of appetite, and weight loss. As the immune system grows weaker, patients experience numerous infections and complications that lead eventually to death. As you learned previously in the chapter on the immune system (Chapter 9), there are drugs that can keep HIV in remission, but it cannot be cured.

Hepatitis B Several viruses can cause *hepatitis* (inflammation of the liver). The hepatitis B virus is transmitted in blood or body fluids during unprotected sex. It is more contagious than HIV but not as deadly. A vaccine for hepatitis B became widely available in 1991, and since that time the incidence of hepatitis B has declined. The government requires all health care workers to be vaccinated against hepatitis B because of their risk of being stuck with a needle on the job.

Genital herpes Genital herpes is caused by *herpes simplex* viruses. Generally it is caused by herpes simplex virus type 2 (HSV-2) as a result of sexual contact or skin-to-skin contact. Less commonly, the type 1 virus (HSV-1) that causes cold sores or blisters around the mouth may be spread to the genital area during oral sex.

Although the government does not keep accurate statistics on genital herpes, it is thought that over 8% of the population is infected. Most infected people have no or minimal symptoms. The primary symptoms are blisters around the genitals or rectum which eventually break, leaving painful sores that are slow to heal (Figure 16.16). The blisters may recur from time to time, but usually their number and frequency decrease over a period of years. The virus can stay in the body indefinitely.

There is no cure for genital herpes, but drug treatments are available that can suppress the active (and contagious) phase. Like so many STDs, genital herpes can infect infants' eyes during birth and cause blindness if not treated.

Human papillomavirus (HPV) Infection with any one of about 40 HPV viruses can cause **warts** in the genital area, including the penis, the vulva (the area outside the vagina), around the anus, and in the vagina or cervix. Genital warts can be removed by several methods including laser surgery, freezing with liquid nitrogen, or certain drugs, but they have a tendency to reappear.

HPV is the most common sexually transmitted disease worldwide. More than 80% of U.S. women will have been infected with at least one HPV virus by the time they are 50. HPV infections generally go away on their own in less than two years. Most people who are infected will have no symptoms at all (fewer than 5% will get warts), so they don't worry about it much.

The real danger of HPV infections is not the warts they may cause. We now know that at least two of the strains (types 16 and 18) are responsible for nearly all cases of cancers of the cervix, as well as many of the cancers of the penis, vulva, labia, and anus; together, these cancers are responsible for about 5,000 deaths per year in the United States.

These deaths are now largely preventable. In 2006 the FDA approved Gardasil, a vaccine against the two strains of HPV that cause cervical cancer. Three years later the FDA approved a second vaccine called Cervarix. If everyone in the United States were vaccinated with one of these two vaccines before the age of sexual activity, over 4,000 lives could be saved every year (the drugs are not 100% effective). However, to be effective, Gardasil or Cervarix must be given *before* HPV infection; neither drug is effective against an existing infection. For that reason, doctors and the CDC (Centers for Disease Control and Prevention) strongly recommend that all girls be vaccinated with either Gardasil or Cervarix at about age 11 or 12, before their first sexual contact.

BlogInFocus (MB)

For more on HPV vaccines and the controversy surrounding them, visit MJ's blog in the Study Area in MasteringBiology and look under "Vaccines Against HPV."

a) Genital herpes on the external genitalia of the female. Genital herpes is generally caused by HSV-2.

b) Genital herpes on the penis of the male.

c) Oral herpes. Cold sores on the lips (also called fever blisters) generally are caused by HSV-1.

Figure 16.16 Herpes simplex virus.

Have You Had Your Gardasil?

Most women will be sexually active at some point in their lives. Nearly all will contract at least one HPV infection, whether they know it or not. A very few of those infections will lead to cancer. Fortunately, two vaccines are now available to protect against the cancer-causing strains of HPV; Gardasil was approved in 2006, and Cervarix was approved in 2009.

From the time it was first introduced, Gardasil (and now Cervarix) generated controversy. Some parents are concerned that immunizing young girls before they were sexually active, and perhaps even before sex had been discussed with them, might encourage sexual activity at too young an age. Gardasil was quickly labeled the "promiscuity vaccine" by some people. There is also a public outcry against government intervention whenever states try to make the vaccine mandatory for school attendance. Currently, Virginia requires immunization against HPV for all sixth grade girls, and other states are considering it.

As a result of the controversy and perhaps because vaccination requires three shots over six months at a cost of about $400, not as many girls and young women have been vaccinated so far as health authorities might have liked. By 2010 fewer than half of all girls aged 13–17 had received at least one of the three required shots, according to the Centers for Disease Control and Prevention (CDC). The problem is that these vaccines should be given before girls become sexually active, because neither vaccine will protect against an existing infection. And according to the CDC, over a third of all young women aged 14–19 are already infected with a high-risk strain of HPV.

For maximum effectiveness, the HPV vaccine should be given to girls before they become sexually active.

The CDC is now recommending that women up to the age of 26 be vaccinated if they haven't already, because there's still a good chance that they have not yet been exposed to both of the two highest-risk strains of HPV. Studies are under way to see if the vaccines might even be partially effective for older women as well, up to the age of 45.

Gardasil was approved in 2009 for boys as well, because of increasing evidence that they can protect against cancers of the penis and anus that are caused by HPV. However, from a public health standpoint, vaccinating all boys may not be cost-effective because cancers of the penis and anus are more rare than cervical cancer. Vaccinating boys would most likely provide an indirect benefit for girls by reducing HPV transmission rates, according to the American Academy of Pediatrics.

Have you had your Gardasil yet? Are you planning to? ∎

Other STDs: Yeast infections, trichomoniasis, and pubic lice

Yeast infections *Candida albicans* is a yeast (a type of fungus) that is always present in the mouth, colon, and vagina. Normally it is kept in check by competition from other organisms. Sometimes, however, the *Candida* population may grow out of control in the vagina, leading to pain, inflammation, and a thick, cheesy vaginal discharge. A woman with an active yeast infection can pass it to her partner. Infected men sometimes develop a discharge from the penis accompanied by painful urination. It is easily treated by antifungal drugs.

Trichomoniasis Another condition that can cause *vaginitis* (inflammation of the vagina) is *trichomoniasis*, caused by the protozoan *Trichomonas vaginalis*. In women it causes a frothy, foul-smelling vaginal discharge; in men it inflames the penis and causes a discharge. Trichomoniasis can be transmitted even when there are no symptoms, and reinfection is common if partners are not treated simultaneously. It is treatable with drugs.

Pubic lice Pubic lice are tiny arthropods related to spiders and crabs (Figure 16.17). Commonly called "crabs," pubic lice live in hair but especially prefer pubic hair, jumping from one host to the next during sexual contact. They can also be transmitted by infected bed sheets or clothes. The adult lice lay eggs near the base of the hair, and the eggs hatch in a few days. Pubic lice nourish themselves by sucking blood from their host, causing intense itching and skin irritation; the adults are very small but visible with the naked eye. They can be killed with anti-lice treatments, but all clothes and bedding should be thoroughly washed in hot water to prevent reinfestation.

✅ **Quick Check** *Overall, which sex do you think is more likely to get STDs—women or men? Why?* ▪

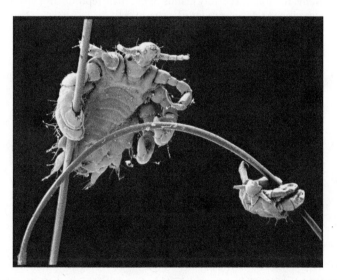

Figure 16.17 The pubic louse, *Phthirus pubis*. (Approximately × 30)

Protecting yourself against STDs

We've just reviewed a group of diseases with symptoms ranging from painful urination to brain damage and outcomes ranging from full recovery to death. The good news is that you can probably avoid contracting an STD, but you need to know what to do and, more importantly, be willing to do it.

Previously (Chapter 9) we presented a number of safer-sex recommendations that can lower your risk of STDs. Many of them are just commonsense precautions:

- Select your partner wisely. A monogamous relationship with someone you know and trust is your best defense.
- Communicate with your partner. If you have questions or concerns, share them, and be willing to do the same yourself.
- Use suitable barriers, depending on the sexual activity in which you engage. Be aware, though, that barrier methods of birth control are not a cure-all for risky behavior. For example, condoms are only marginally effective in preventing the transfer of HIV, HPV, and genital herpes, and they will not protect against pubic lice.

Finally, know your own health. If you or your partner think you are at risk for (or may have) a certain disease, get tested. It's confidential, it's not difficult, and it can save you a lot of embarrassment. It may even save your life.

🔄 **Recap** Major bacterial STDs include gonorrhea, syphilis, and chlamydia. The most dangerous viral STD is HIV. Hepatitis B can be prevented by a vaccine. Genital herpes is irritating but not particularly deadly. HPV can cause warts and is a risk factor for cervical cancer—it, too, can be prevented by a vaccine. Yeast, normally present in the vagina, can multiply and cause a yeast infection. Pubic lice are tiny arthropods that are transmitted during intimate contact or by contact with clothes or bedding. You can reduce your risk of contracting an STD with a little effort. Choose your partner wisely, use a barrier method of birth control, and, if you suspect you have a disease, get tested promptly. ▪

Chapter Summary

The male reproductive system delivers sperm *p. 378*

- Sperm are produced in the male reproductive organs, called the *testes*, and stored in the epididymis and ductus deferens.
- Semen contains sperm and the secretions of three glands: the seminal vesicles, the prostate gland, and the bulbourethral glands.
- Tens of millions of sperm are formed every day throughout the male's adult life. The production of sperm is under the control of three hormones: testosterone, LH, and FSH.

The female reproductive system produces eggs and supports pregnancy *p. 381*

- The female reproductive organs (the ovaries) produce mature oocytes and release them one at a time on a cyclic basis.
- Fertilization of the oocyte (if it occurs) takes place in the oviduct.
- The fertilized egg makes its way to the uterus, where it implants and begins to develop into a fetus.
- The vagina contains glands that produce lubricating fluid during sexual arousal.
- The hormone estrogen causes the mammary glands to enlarge at puberty.

Menstrual cycle consists of ovarian and uterine cycles *p. 384*

- The cyclic changes in the female reproductive system are called the *menstrual cycle*. The menstrual cycle consists of an ovarian cycle that produces mature oocytes, and a uterine cycle in which the uterus prepares for pregnancy.
- The menstrual cycle is controlled by the hormones estrogen, progesterone, LH, and FSH. A surge in LH secretion triggers ovulation.

Human sexual response, intercourse, and fertilization *p. 387*

- Both males and females are aroused by certain stimuli and respond in ways that facilitate intercourse and ejaculation. In males, the penis swells and hardens. In females, glandular secretions provide lubrication.
- Both males and females experience a pleasurable reflex event called an *orgasm*. Orgasm is accompanied by ejaculation, or the expulsion of semen, in the male.
- Sperm deposited in the vagina during intercourse make their way through the cervix and uterus and migrate up the oviducts to the egg. Only one fertilizes the egg.

Birth control methods: Controlling fertility *p. 389*

- The most effective methods of preventing pregnancy are abstinence and female or male surgical sterilization. Sterilization should be considered permanent, though it may be reversible.
- Other effective methods of birth control include intrauterine devices (IUDs) and manipulation of hormone levels with pills, patches, injections, or vaginal rings.
- Moderately effective methods of birth control include condoms, cervical caps and diaphragms, and various spermicides. The "natural" methods (withdrawal and periodic abstinence) are the least effective.
- Morning-after pills are now available to be used as emergency contraceptives up to 72 hours after intercourse.

Infertility: Inability to conceive *p. 392*

- Infertility is defined as the failure to achieve a pregnancy after a year of trying. Nearly 15% of all couples are infertile.
- For male infertility, the primary option is artificial insemination. When the male has a low sperm count but still some viable sperm, the sperm can be concentrated before insemination. In many cases, donor sperm are used.
- Female infertility may be overcome by several methods. In *in vitro* fertilization, egg and sperm are combined under laboratory conditions. The fertilized egg is allowed to develop for several days and then inserted into the uterus. In GIFT, the egg and sperm are inserted directly into an oviduct immediately after collection. In ZIFT, the egg and sperm are combined first, and then the fertilized egg is inserted into the oviduct.

Sexually transmitted diseases *p. 394*

- The common feature of sexually transmitted diseases (STDs) is that they are transmitted during sexual contact. Their disease effects are not necessarily on the reproductive system.
- Bacterial STDs include gonorrhea, syphilis, and chlamydia. Syphilis is the most dangerous; chlamydia, the most common. All are treatable with antibiotics.
- Viral STDs include HIV (the virus that causes AIDS), hepatitis B, genital herpes, and genital warts (HPV). HIV is particularly deadly, and there is as yet no cure. There are now vaccines for hepatitis B and HPV.
- Avoiding the diseases caused by STDs is a matter of reducing your risk of exposure and paying attention to (and taking responsibility for) your own health.

Terms You Should Know

cervix, *383*	ovarian cycle, *384*
clitoris, *383*	ovaries, *382*
corpus luteum, *385*	oviduct, *382*
ductus (vas) deferens, *378*	ovulation, *385*
egg, *378*	penis, *379*
endometrium, *382*	progesterone, *382*
epididymis, *378*	semen, *379*
erection, *379*	sperm, *378*
estrogen, *382*	testes, *378*
follicle, *384*	testosterone, *381*
gametes, *380*	uterine cycle, *385*
menstrual cycle, *384*	uterus, *382*
menstruation, *385*	vagina, *383*
orgasm, *388*	

Concept Review

Answers can be found in the Study Area in MasteringBiology.

1. Name the three accessory glands of the male reproductive system.
2. Describe the development of a sperm cell.
3. Explain where fertilization takes place in the female reproductive system.
4. Describe the phases of the uterine cycle.
5. Describe what is happening in the uterus that leads to menstruation, and explain why menstruation does not occur during pregnancy.
6. Compare and contrast the male and female sexual responses.
7. Describe how *in vitro* fertilization is done.
8. Name three viral STDs.
9. Describe birth control options, and list those that afford at least some protection against STDs.
10. Describe the various STDs of worldwide concern.

Test Yourself

Answers can be found in Appendix A.

1. Which of the following might interfere with a sperm's ability to swim?
   a. an acrosome with defective enzymes
   b. a defective flagella
   c. a defective midpiece lacking an appropriate number of mitochondria
   d. both choice (b) and (c)

2. Anabolic steroids are similar in structure and function to testosterone. Which of the following would be a likely outcome in a male taking anabolic steroids?
   a. Testosterone production by the interstitial cells would increase.
   b. Release of GnRH by the hypothalamus would increase.
   c. Testosterone production by the interstitial cells would decrease.
   d. Testosterone production would be unaffected.

3. Which of the following structures is correctly matched with its function?
   a. myometrium: contracts during labor and child birth
   b. cervix: transports oocyte from ovary to uterus
   c. oviduct: transports oocyte from uterus to vagina
   d. endometrium: birth canal

4. Which of the following statements about oocytes and ovulation is correct?
   a. The production of primary oocytes continues in women from the onset of puberty until the onset of menopause.
   b. Meiotic divisions are complete at the time of ovulation.
   c. At ovulation, the structure released from the follicle includes a secondary oocyte and polar body.
   d. All of these statements are correct.

5. Which of the following would provide the most accurate prediction of ovulation?
   a. a surge of progesterone
   b. a sudden drop in FSH
   c. a sudden drop in estrogen
   d. a surge of LH

6. What is the role of the corpus luteum during early pregnancy?
   a. It produces the hormones that will support the early pregnancy.
   b. The fertilized egg will implant in the corpus luteum.
   c. The corpus luteum nourishes the rapidly growing embryo.
   d. The corpus luteum protects the fertilized egg during its transport to the uterus.

7. Which of the following lists the female reproductive structures that sperm will pass through on their way to fertilize an oocyte, in the correct order?
   a. cervix...vagina...oviduct...ovary
   b. cervix...oviduct...vagina...uterus
   c. uterus...cervix...vagina...ovary
   d. vagina...cervix...uterus...oviduct

8. The prescription drugs used currently to treat erectile dysfunction primarily affect:
   a. testosterone levels
   b. blood flow to the penis
   c. contraction of skeletal muscles
   d. sympathetic nervous system

9. Which two means of birth control are most similar in the way they prevent pregnancy?
   a. tubal ligation and IUDs
   b. oral contraceptives and spermicides
   c. tubal ligation and condoms
   d. oral contraceptives and hormone patch

10. The most widely used hormonal methods of birth control:
    a. prevent fertilization by killing sperm
    b. prevent ovulation by inhibiting release of FSH and LH
    c. prevent implantation into the endometrium
    d. block transport of fertilized egg to uterus

11. If a woman is infertile as a result of oviducts blocked by the scarring of pelvic inflammatory disease, which of the following methods would enable her to become pregnant?
    a. artificial insemination
    b. hormonal treatments
    c. *in vitro* fertilization
    d. all of the above

12. Which of the following STDs is most likely to infect a fetus and cause birth defects?
    a. syphilis
    b. gonorrhea
    c. chlamydia
    d. trichomoniasis

13. Which of the following STDs can be prevented by vaccination?
    a. genital herpes
    b. syphilis
    c. gonorrhea
    d. hepatitis B

14. Which of the following STDs is associated with the development of cervical cancer?
    a. genital herpes
    b. human papillomavirus infection
    c. hepatitis B infection
    d. trichomoniasis

15. Pelvic inflammatory disease may be associated with:
    a. chlamydia
    b. syphilis
    c. gonorrhea
    d. both (a) and (c)

Apply What You Know

Answers can be found in the Study Area in MasteringBiology.

1. Male sexual responsiveness and secondary sex characteristics remain unchanged after a vasectomy. Explain why this is so.
2. What keeps the ovarian and uterine cycles always exactly in phase with each other, even though the length of the menstrual cycle can vary slightly?
3. Why is it important for a new mother to breastfeed her baby immediately after birth if she wishes to breastfeed the baby once she gets home?
4. What provides the force that pushes the baby out of the uterus during childbirth?
5. Both women and men can have an STD and not have any symptoms. What might be the long-term consequences of an untreated STD?
6. If a woman does not have an intact hymen does that mean she's not a virgin?

BlogInFocus

Answers can be found in the Study Area in MasteringBiology.

1. In some countries (China and India are examples) there are reportedly more boys than girls born each year. What are some possible explanations for this phenomenon? (Visit MJ's blog in the Study Area in MasteringBiology and look under "Gender Preference.")

2. In Table 16.3 it is reported that the failure rate of condoms is 11–16%. Why do you think the failure rate is so high? (Hint: The withdrawal method is not 100% effective, either. Visit MJ's blog in the Study Area in MasteringBiology and look under "Birth Control Method Failures.")

MasteringBiology®

Go to MasteringBiology for practice quizzes, activities, eText, videos, current events, and more.

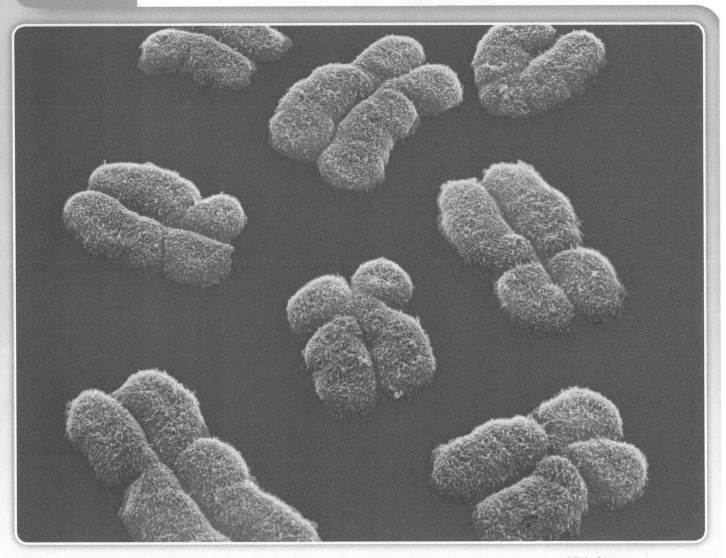

SEM of human chromosomes.

The Promises and Perils of Genetic Testing

Jeremy is having trouble in school, so his mother takes him to the doctor. After numerous tests and trips to several different doctors, genetic testing finally reveals that Jeremy has fragile X syndrome, an inherited form of mental retardation. His mother's insurance company promptly cancels Jeremy's health coverage on the basis that Jeremy has a "preexisting condition" that was not revealed to the company when his mother took out the insurance policy five years ago. After trying and failing to find an insurance company that will insure both of them, his mother is forced to quit her job so that she can become eligible for Medicaid.

Genetic testing (also called *DNA-based testing*) refers to the analysis of an individual's DNA to determine the risk for a particular health condition or to confirm the diagnosis of genetic disease. Genetic testing is increasingly available to anyone who wants it. For example, DNADirect.com sells a variety of genetic tests over the Internet. The company even offers consultations with genetic counselors (at $250/hr).

Genetic Testing Offers Many Benefits

Genetic testing can provide undeniable benefits. Genetic testing can confirm the diagnosis of a genetic disorder even before symptoms appear, enabling patients to start treatment early. A negative gene test can rule out the likelihood of ever having a particular inherited disorder, saving a person years of stress and worry.

Genetic testing can also help couples make informed reproductive choices. Couples can be tested to determine whether they are carriers of recessive

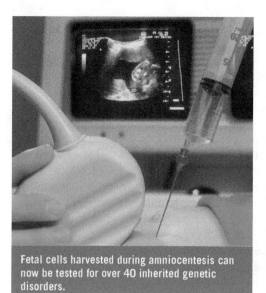
Fetal cells harvested during amniocentesis can now be tested for over 40 inherited genetic disorders.

disorders, enabling them to make an informed decision about whether or not to have a child at all. For couples who are already expecting a child, prenatal genetic testing can be used to test fetal cells for approximately 40 genetic defects. Early genetic testing of the fetus gives parents time to prepare emotionally or perhaps to terminate the pregnancy, depending on their beliefs and the severity of the disorder.

As mentioned earlier, some gene mutations do not necessarily cause a disease but are associated with a higher risk of it. Suppose you learn that you carry a gene that predisposes you to colon cancer. The American Cancer Society recommends that most people have their first colonoscopy at age 50. Given your genes, you might decide to have your first colonoscopy at age 35 instead. If you're at known high risk, earlier testing could save your life.

Social and Ethical Issues

Privacy Who should have access to your genetic data—you? your physician? the company that performed the test? the insurance company that paid for it? Parts of your existing medical records

are probably already available to your insurance company, as well as the physicians and staff of the various medical facilities you have visited over the years. Should your genetic data become part of this record?

Eligibility for health insurance As Jeremy's mother found out the hard way, many health insurance policies exclude preexisting conditions. If genetic testing revealed that you carried a gene that might increase your risk of a particular disease (such as cancer) later in life, it's conceivable that an insurer might try to exclude coverage for that disease from your policy. This could discourage you from having a genetic test.

But before we blame the insurers, consider that no private insurance company can lose money consistently and stay in business for long. The costs of health care are soaring. To an insurance company, information that helps them understand your likelihood of developing a disease, even if it's in the distant future, is like money in the bank.

Employment discrimination Some years ago, managers at the Burlington Northern Santa Fe Railroad became concerned about employees' high rate of insurance claims for carpal tunnel syndrome, and so they instructed company-paid physicians to secretly test employees for a rare genetic condition that can cause the syndrome. Employees were not informed that their DNA was being tested, and managers threatened to fire one staff member who refused the test.

In another case a social worker mentioned at work that her mother died of Huntington disease. One week later she was fired, despite a recent outstanding performance review.

These true stories demonstrate the potential for employment discrimination, even though it's now against the law.

Ethnic or racial discrimination Sickle-cell anemia is most common in people of African heritage. Tay-Sachs disease occurs most frequently in Ashkenazi Jews. People of Northern European descent are most likely to develop hemochromatosis, a genetic disorder that causes the body to absorb excess iron. Does this mean we should test all African Americans for sickle-cell anemia, all Jews for Tay-Sachs, or all Northern Europeans for hemochromatosis? Should we require members of high-risk groups to be tested if they are getting married or considering having children? Where do we want to draw the line between individual privacy and public health?

Psychological and emotional impact Discovering that you have a genetic predisposition for colon cancer might motivate you to take preventive steps. On the other hand, some health professionals are cautious about recommending widespread genetic testing of healthy people as a future health-predicting tool. They worry that the discovery that a person is likely to develop a genetic disease in the future might do more harm than good, especially if there is nothing that can be done about it.

Genetic testing and the law In 2008 the U.S. Congress passed the Genetic Information Nondiscrimination Act (GINA). GINA prevents insurers from setting higher insurance premiums or denying coverage to healthy people based on the results of genetic tests. GINA also makes it illegal for employers to use genetic information in making decisions about hiring or firing a person. However, GINA does not address other privacy issues, such as a genetic testing company selling genetic information to other companies or academic researchers.

The science of genetic testing is progressing far more rapidly than our solutions for the social and ethical challenges that it raises. Expect continued debate on these issues in the future.

THE FACTS...

- Genetic testing is a complex process for diagnosing genetic disorders by the direct examination of a person's DNA.

- Genetic testing is used to diagnose or rule out genetic disorders, help couples make informed reproductive choices, and prevent future health problems. Genetic testing raises difficult questions of privacy, eligibility for insurance, discrimination, and psychological or emotional harm.

QUESTIONS TO CONSIDER

1 If you might be a carrier of a gene for an unpreventable condition, would you want to know? Why or why not?

2 Should genetic counseling be required before a person is allowed to purchase a genetic test? What about counseling afterward, if anything negative is found?

>> **A *gene* is a segment of DNA that carries the code for making one or more proteins.** Humans have about 22,000 different genes on 23 pairs of chromosomes.

>> **Each person has two identical or nearly identical copies, called *alleles*, of most genes.** One allele was inherited from each parent. Differences between alleles are the result of rare mutations over millions of years of evolution.

>> **Your complete set of alleles, called your genotype, determines your particular physical and functional traits,** and even your susceptibility to certain diseases.

>> **When two alleles in an individual are different, one is usually *dominant* and the other is *recessive*.** A trait expressed by a recessive allele will only be present when there is no dominant allele, that is, when both alleles are recessive.

>> **The X and Y chromosomes, also called the *sex chromosomes*, carry the genes that determine the gender of the individual.** Females have two X chromosomes and males have an X and a Y chromosome.

As we have seen, the information necessary for the development of a new human being is contained in the DNA within the nucleus of the fertilized egg. This information is found in the form of **genes**, DNA sequences that code for one or more specific proteins. An organism's **genome** is the sum total of all of its DNA, even though not all of that DNA codes for proteins. **Genetics** is the study of genes and their transmission from one generation to the next.

The word **inheritance** often conjures up notions of money or possessions. The broader definition of inheritance, however, is something received from an ancestor or another person. In terms of genetics, each of us inherits one complete set of genes from our mother and one set from our father. Although everyone inherits two complete sets of genes, the sets vary slightly from individual to individual. Those variations help to account for the differences between us. In this chapter, we explore how genes are passed from generation to generation, and how genes affect our traits, or distinguishing features, such as our appearance, health, and possibly even our thoughts and actions.

19.1 Your genotype is the genetic basis of your phenotype

Chromosomes are partially composed of DNA. Genes are specific DNA sequences that represent the instructions for building proteins. Humans have 23 pairs of chromosomes—22 pairs of **autosomes**, plus a pair of sex chromosomes. The autosomes and the pair of X-chromosomes in a female are sometimes called *homologous chromosomes* because they look alike and they each have a copy of the same gene at the same location, or *locus*, on the chromosome (Figure 19.1). Humans inherit one of each pair of autosomes and one sex chromosome from each parent, giving us two copies of each gene.

Although autosomes may look alike, closer inspection reveals that they are not completely identical. Small differences in DNA sequence may exist between any pair of autosomes. These sequence differences may occur within genes, and when they do, they produce alternative versions of genes called **alleles**. Because they are different, alleles may code for different proteins with slightly different structures. As discussed in the chapter on the chemistry of living things, alterations in protein structure can affect how the protein functions. For example, the ability to roll your tongue is influenced by a single gene, but there are two alleles for that gene: One allele enables you to curl your tongue, the other allele does not.

If an individual possesses two identical alleles of a particular gene, the person is said to be **homozygous** for that gene (*homo*– means "same," and *zygous* means "yoked," or joined together). A person who has two different alleles of a gene is **heterozygous**. In many cases there are more than two alleles of a particular gene in the human population, although a given individual can inherit only two of them. For example, there are three alleles for ABO blood type: the A, B, and O alleles.

Pair of autosomes. Each autmsome carries the same genes at the locus

Gene locus (plural loci). The location of a specific pair of genes

A pair of genes. Normally both genes have the same structure and function

Alleles. Alternative versions of the same gene pair

Figure 19.1 **Autosomes.**

Where did these different alleles come from? Most likely, different alleles resulted from millions of years of **mutations**, or random changes to the DNA sequence, of cells destined to become sperm or eggs. Because those mutations were not corrected before cell division and meiosis, and because they did not cause the sperm or egg to be nonviable, they were passed on to the next generation as slight variations of the original gene, and they remain in the human population to this day. Collectively, all the various genes and their alleles in the human population are known as the *human gene pool*. There are enough different alleles among our approximately 22,000 genes to account for the uniqueness of each individual.

BlogInFocus (MB)

Genetic screening of newborn infants for certain known genetic disorders is required by law in all 50 states. For a current list of the tests required in your state and an explanation of the tests, visit MJ's blog in the Study Area in MasteringBiology and look under "Newborn Genetic Screening Tests."

Your complete set of alleles is called your **genotype**. Your genotype has a profound influence on your **phenotype**, or the observable physical and functional traits that characterize you. Among your phenotypic traits are your hair, eye, and skin color; your height and body shape; and your ability (or inability) to curl your tongue. Many phenotypic traits, such as blood type and susceptibility to disease, are less observable. Your phenotype is determined not only by the alleles you inherit from your parents (your genotype), but also by environmental factors and lifestyle choices such as how much you are exposed to the sun, whether you exercise, and how much and what you eat.

↩ **Recap** We inherit two alleles of every gene found on autosomes; these alleles may be identical or slightly different. The sum of our alleles is our genotype, and the physical and functional expression of those alleles is our phenotype. ▪

19.2 Genetic inheritance follows certain patterns

Punnett square analysis predicts patterns of inheritance

One easy way to designate two alleles of the same gene is to assign them uppercase (such as A) and lowercase (a) letters. Recall that people with the same two alleles of a gene (either aa or AA) are homozygous for that gene and people with different alleles (Aa) are heterozygous.

A **Punnett square** provides a simple way to represent patterns of inheritance of alleles and to predict the probability that a particular genotype will be inherited (Figure 19.2).

To create a Punnett square, place the possible alleles of the male gametes on one axis and the possible alleles of the

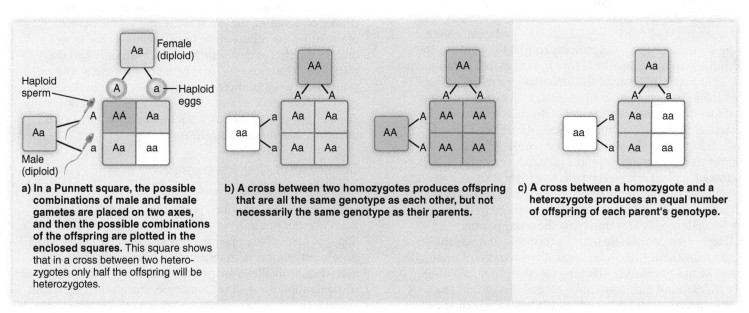

a) In a Punnett square, the possible combinations of male and female gametes are placed on two axes, and then the possible combinations of the offspring are plotted in the enclosed squares. This square shows that in a cross between two heterozygotes only half the offspring will be heterozygotes.

b) A cross between two homozygotes produces offspring that are all the same genotype as each other, but not necessarily the same genotype as their parents.

c) A cross between a homozygote and a heterozygote produces an equal number of offspring of each parent's genotype.

Figure 19.2 Punnett squares. Punnett squares are used to predict the outcomes of a particular combination of parental alleles.

✓ *Suppose the parents shown in the first Punnett square have a baby. How likely is it that this baby will have the genotype AA? How about Aa? More generally, how likely is each of the four "cells" in a Punnett square?*

female gametes on the other. Bear in mind that although the parents are diploid—they contain two copies of each chromosome—they will each donate *only one* of each chromosome to their offspring. By combining the letters for the sperm and egg in the appropriate squares, which represent the possible combinations that might occur during fertilization, we can see all of the possible genotypes of the offspring and the ratios of each possible genotype.

Mendel established the basic principles of genetics

In the 1850s, Gregor Mendel, a university-educated Austrian monk who specialized in natural history, described many of the fundamental principles of inheritance through a number of experiments involving controlled breeding of garden peas. He chose pea plants as a "model" organism because they were cheap and easy to grow, and matings between plants could be set up easily. Many biologists use model organisms to investigate the fundamental principles of biology because they can do experiments such as setting up matings that would be unethical to do with human subjects. Mendel followed the inheritance of traits such as flower color, pea color, pea texture, and plant height from one generation to the next. He collected an extensive set of data over a seven-year period, and proposed that there were discrete "factors" of heredity that united during fertilization and then separated again in the formation of sperm and eggs. He concluded that pea plants inherit two units of each factor, one unit from each parent. Today, we call these factors *genes* and we know that they are found on chromosomes. Even though Mendel knew nothing about chromosomes, DNA, or meiosis, his pioneering studies with pea plants provided great insight into the principles of genetics in many complex organisms, and his rules of inheritance hold for humans as well as pea plants.

To better understand the laws that govern the passage of traits from generation to generation, let's consider one of Mendel's experiments in detail. In this experiment, Mendel performed a one-trait cross, where he followed the inheritance of a single trait: pea color. Pea plants can produce either green or yellow peas; when Mendel mated, or crossed, a plant with green peas to a plant with yellow peas, he found that all of the offspring produced yellow peas. These peas were identical to those produced by the parent with yellow peas; it seemed that the green pea trait had disappeared completely in these offspring. But was the green trait really gone? To check, Mendel crossed two of these yellow pea–producing offspring together. To his surprise, Mendel found that only about 75% of this second group of offspring produced yellow peas, while the remaining 25% of these offspring produced green peas. Thus, the green pea trait hadn't disappeared; it was as if the green trait had simply "skipped" a generation. Mendel deduced that the information needed to produce green peas was still present in the first group of yellow pea–producing offspring but was somehow hidden. Based on this and other experiments,

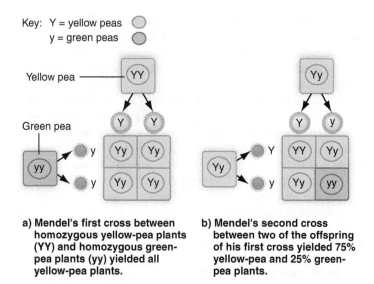

a) **Mendel's first cross between homozygous yellow-pea plants (YY) and homozygous green-pea plants (yy) yielded all yellow-pea plants.**

b) **Mendel's second cross between two of the offspring of his first cross yielded 75% yellow-pea and 25% green-pea plants.**

Figure 19.3 Mendel's one-trait crosses in pea plants.

Mendel reasoned that each pea plant must have two alleles of the gene for pea color, and that each parent contributes only one allele of the gene to the offspring (Figure 19.3).

This is now known as Mendel's first rule of inheritance, the **law of segregation**: When gametes are formed in the parents, the alleles separate from each other so that each gamete gets only one allele of each gene. Importantly, which allele a parent contributes to a gamete is determined in a completely random manner; a heterozygous parent harboring both the green and the yellow alleles has a 50% chance of donating the green allele and a 50% chance of donating the yellow allele to each gamete. Today we understand that gametes are haploid, with only half the number of chromosomes and genes of the parent. The primary reason that there is so much phenotypic variation among individuals of a species is that each parent randomly donates just one of their two alleles of each gene to each offspring, and there are 22,000 genes!

Dominant alleles are expressed over recessive alleles

In the experiment described previously, Mendel observed that the green pea trait "skipped" a generation. Why did this happen? Mendel reasoned that the yellow allele behaves in a **dominant** manner with respect to the green allele, meaning that when both alleles are present in the same plant, the plant will only show the yellow phenotype. The green allele is thus **recessive** to the yellow allele, and is only visible when no yellow alleles are present. Figure 19.3 shows the inheritance pattern of pea color that Mendel observed. It is customary to denote the dominant allele by an uppercase letter (in this case, Y) and the recessive allele by a lowercase letter (y).

Many human genes have dominant and recessive alleles as well. The gene that determines hairline pattern in humans has a dominant allele (W) that produces the widow's peak phenotype, and a recessive allele (w) that causes the straight hairline phenotype. If a person homozygous for the widow's peak allele (WW) were to have children with a person homozygous for the straight hairline allele (ww), all of their children would be heterozygous (Ww), and would show the dominant widow's peak phenotype. But, if one of these heterozygous children were to mate with another person who was also heterozygous for the hairline pattern gene, as shown in Figure 19.4, the recessive straight hairline phenotype could reappear in their offspring. It would appear that the straight hairline trait had skipped a generation, just like the green pea trait in Mendel's experiment.

Most recessive alleles—such as the allele for a straight hairline and also the allele for attached earlobes (Figure 19.5)—do not confer a distinct advantage or disadvantage to the homozygous recessive person. They just originated as mutations at some point in our evolutionary history, and they remain in the human gene pool because they do no harm.

However, some recessive alleles result in the absence of a functionally important protein. An example is cystic

Attached earlobes (Johnny Depp, left) and unattached earlobes (George Clooney, right).

Figure 19.5 Harmless dominant/recessive traits and alleles. The allele for unattached earlobes is dominant over that for attached earlobes. Johnny Depp (on the left) is homozygous for the recessive allele, whereas George Clooney (on the right) is either homozygous for the dominant allele or is heterozygous.

fibrosis (see Health & Wellness feature), which afflicts only homozygous recessive individuals. These alleles no longer code for a specific essential protein because their nucleotide sequence has been altered slightly from the dominant form. In principle, the frequency of truly harmful recessive alleles in a population is kept in check by the occasional premature death of homozygous recessives, but the allele can persist in the population in heterozygotes.

Finally, the term *dominant* refers only to how an allele behaves in combination with a recessive allele in a heterozygote. Dominance has nothing to do with the frequency with which an allele is found in a population; in fact, some dominant alleles are quite rare. Consider the number of human fingers and toes. Most people are homozygous recessive (pp) for the gene controlling the number of fingers and toes, and they have four fingers and a thumb on each hand and five toes on each foot. But some people possess a dominant allele (Pp or PP), and the presence of this allele causes them to have extra fingers and toes on each hand and foot (Figure 19.6a), a condition known as *polydactyly*. Even though this allele behaves in a dominant fashion with respect to the allele for the normal number of fingers and toes, it is extremely rare in the population. Interestingly, there is a dominant allele in cats that causes affected individuals to have extra toes, as well (Figure 19.6b).

Figure 19.4 Hairline patterns in humans. Hairline pattern is determined by a gene with a dominant allele (W) for widow's peak and a recessive allele (w) for straight hairline. The person on the left (widow's peak phenotype) must be either WW or Ww genotype. Only the homozygous recessive genotype (ww) will have the straight hairline phenotype, shown on the right.

☑ **Quick Check** *In humans and other mammals, red hair is recessive to dark hair. Suppose a husband and wife are both heterozygous for the red hair color gene. What are the husband's and wife's own hair colors? If they have a child, what is the probability that he/she will have red hair?* ●

Answers to ☑ questions can be found in Appendix A.

Cystic Fibrosis

Cystic fibrosis (CF), the most common fatal genetic disease in North America today, is caused by a recessive allele of a gene on chromosome 7. Because it is recessive, parents may have no idea that they are both carriers for cystic fibrosis until they have a child with the disease. Approximately 1 in 23 Caucasians carries the recessive allele and about 1 Caucasian child in 2,000 has the disease. Among African Americans, only 1 child in 17,000 is born with the disease.

The recessive allele produces a defective version of a protein that normally aids the transport of chloride across the cell membrane of epithelial cells. Impaired chloride transport affects the secretion of salt and water across cells that line the ducts in several organs. As a result, organs that normally produce a thin, watery mucus secrete a thick, sticky mucus instead.

In the lungs, the thick mucus clogs the bronchioles and leads to chronic inflammation and infections that can be fatal. In the pancreas, the mucus blocks ducts and prevents pancreatic enzymes from reaching the intestines. The sweat glands are also affected, but ordinarily this does not cause major problems.

Typical symptoms of cystic fibrosis include persistent coughing, wheezing, or pneumonia; excessive appetite but poor weight gain; and foul-smelling, bulky feces. The disease is usually diagnosed by age 3 by testing for high salt levels in perspiration.

Cystic fibrosis. This child with cystic fibrosis is receiving vigorous percussion therapy ("clap therapy") to loosen mucus in the lungs.

A DNA-based blood test can screen for variations on the gene responsible.

Management of cystic fibrosis focuses on reducing the damage caused by the symptoms, often a constant battle throughout life. Regular, vigorous chest physical therapy helps to dislodge mucus in the lungs, and antibiotics are often needed to treat lung infections. Researchers are working on gene therapy techniques in which copies of the normal gene are inserted into viruses such as those that cause colds, and then the modified viruses are delivered into the airways. Improved treatments and better understanding of the disease have increased the average life expectancy for patients with cystic fibrosis from just 5 years before we knew much about the disease, to over 37 years today. In addition, genetic testing can now identify couples who are at risk of having a child with the disease. Do not be surprised if cystic fibrosis is cured in our lifetime, or at least treated so effectively that patients live long and healthy lives. ■

a) A human infant with polydactyly.

b) A polydactyl cat.

Figure 19.6 Dominant alleles are not always common in a population. Polydactyly, or the presence of extra digits, is an uncommon phenotype in both humans and cats caused by a dominant allele.

Two-trait crosses: Independent assortment of genes for different traits

So far we have followed the inheritance patterns of single genes throughout multiple generations. But what happens when we follow *two* genes? Are they inherited as a set, or can they be inherited independently of each other? To answer this question, let's consider the human hairline pattern gene and a second gene that controls whether a person's earlobes hang freely or are attached (Figure 19.7). For the earlobe gene, the allele for free earlobes (E) is dominant over the allele for attached earlobes (e). If a person with a widow's peak and free earlobes who is homozygous dominant for both genes

Key:
E = free earlobes
e = attached earlobes
W = widow's peak
w = straight hairline

a) **A mating between a homozygous person with a widow's peak and free earlobes (EEWW) and a homozygous person with a straight hairline and attached earlobes (eeww).** All of the offpsring will have the dominant widow's peak and free earlobes phenotypes.

b) **A mating between two heterozygous people with widow's peaks and free earlobes (EeWw).** Because the alleles for the two traits assort independently, some of the offspring show one dominant and one recessive trait.

Figure 19.7 A two-trait cross showing independent assortment of alleles for different traits.

What is the ratio of the four possible phenotypes in the second mating (part b)? If you observed this same ratio in the offspring of an actual mating, what could you conclude about the parents?

(EEWW) mates with a person with a straight hairline and attached earlobes who is homozygous recessive for both genes (eeww), all of their children will be heterozygous for both genes (EeWw), and will have a widow's peak and free earlobes (Figure 19.7a).

But what happens if two people heterozygous for both genes mate? Would their children have either both dominant or both recessive phenotypes, or are other combinations possible? As shown in Figure 19.7b, a mating between two heterozygotes for both genes can indeed produce children with both dominant traits and children with both recessive traits, but other combinations are also possible. Some offspring may have the dominant widow's peak and the recessive attached earlobe phenotypes, and others may have the recessive straight hairline and the dominant free earlobe phenotypes.

When predicting the results of a two-trait cross, remember that each parent donates only one allele of each gene, and that the genes for different traits assort independently of each other during the formation of sperm and egg. That is, a parent can donate a dominant hairline pattern allele and a dominant earlobe allele, a recessive hair pattern allele and a recessive earlobe allele, or a mixture of the two. Each of these outcomes is equally probable because the hairline pattern and earlobe alleles are donated to egg and sperm independently of each other. The outcome of a two-trait cross can be predicted either by using a large Punnett square, as shown in Figure 19.7b, or simply by multiplying the ratios from small Punnett squares as shown in Figure 19.8. The latter works because the two events are independent of each other.

Mendel saw similar results in pea plants when performing two-trait crosses, and he formulated his **law of independent assortment**, which states that the alleles of different genes are distributed to egg and sperm cells independently of each other during meiosis. But, on this point Mendel was only partly right. Recall that he knew nothing about chromosomes or meiosis. We now know that the 22,000 or so genes in the human genome do not simply float around independently of each other in the cell's nucleus. Instead, genes are structurally part of the 23 pairs of chromosomes found in the cell's nucleus. Only genes that are located on different chromosomes always assort truly independently. Alleles located on the same chromosome, called *linked alleles*, may or may not be inherited together, as discussed later in this chapter.

Figure 19.8 Another method of calculating phenotypic ratios from two-trait crosses. Instead of drawing the large Punnett square in Figure 19.7b, each trait can be considered individually. The phenotypic ratios obtained can then be multiplied together to get the same results shown in Figure 19.7b.

↻ **Recap** A Punnett square is a useful method for predicting the ratios of possible offspring genotypes from a particular mating. Mendel's law of segregation holds that when sperm and eggs form, the two alleles of each gene separate from each other so that each sperm or egg receives only one allele of each gene. Where two alleles of each gene exist in the human gene pool, one is often dominant over the other and controls the phenotype of a heterozygote. According to Mendel's law of independent assortment, during the formation of sperm and egg, alleles for different traits are distributed independently of each other provided they are located on different chromosomes. ●

19.3 Other dominance patterns

Incomplete dominance: Heterozygotes have an intermediate phenotype

Some alleles do not follow the dominant/recessive pattern described previously. In **incomplete dominance**, the heterozygous genotype results in a phenotype that is intermediate between the two homozygous phenotypes. An example of incomplete dominance in Caucasian humans is the trait of having straight, wavy, or curly hair (**Figure 19.9**).

Another example is *familial hypercholesterolemia*. People homozygous for familial hypercholesterolemia may have blood cholesterol concentrations more than six times the normal level. The homozygous condition is quite rare (around one in a million people) because most homozygous individuals have heart attacks in childhood or adolescence and die by age 20. In contrast, the heterozygous condition is fairly common (about 1 in 500 people). People heterozygous for the disease may have blood cholesterol concentrations that are two to three times the normal level. With diagnosis and treatment, most can live fairly normal, healthy lives.

Codominance: Both gene products are equally expressed

In **codominance** the products of both alleles are expressed equally. One important example of codominance is the gene for blood type. There are three alleles for this gene: A, B, and O. The O allele is recessive; when combined in a heterozygous person with either the A allele or the B allele, the person will have A or B blood type. But the A and B alleles are codominant. If an individual is heterozygous with an A allele and a B allele, that person will have type AB blood with *both* A and B antigens on his or her red blood cells, rather than a mixed or intermediate antigen (see **Figure 19.10**). Blood phenotype has important implications for which types of blood can be given to which patients, as you learned in the chapter on blood.

Another example of codominance is **sickle-cell anemia**. Sickle-cell anemia is a disease caused by one of two alleles involved in the production of hemoglobin for red blood cells. One of the two alleles codes for a hemoglobin

molecule (designated Hb^S) that differs from the normal hemoglobin molecule (designated Hb^A) by just one amino acid. People homozygous for *sickle-cell anemia* (Hb^SHb^S) have only Hb^S hemoglobin in their red blood cells, whereas heterozygous individuals, who are said to have *sickle-cell trait* (Hb^AHb^S), have equal amounts of each type of hemoglobin. As shown in **Figure 19.11a**, a mating between two individuals with the sickle-cell trait can result in children who are phenotypically normal (Hb^AHb^A), children with sickle-cell trait (Hb^AHb^S), and children with sickle-cell anemia (Hb^SHb^S).

In people with sickle-cell anemia, breathing air with even slightly lower oxygen concentrations than normal can cause the Hb^S hemoglobin to crystallize within the red blood cells. When this happens their red blood cells take on a crescent, or sickle, shape (Figure 19.11b). Sickled cells rupture easily because they are more fragile than normal red blood cells. They are also less flexible, so they tend to clog small blood vessels and block blood flow, and they carry less oxygen. The resultant oxygen deprivation of tissues and organs produces symptoms of fatigue, chest pain, bone and joint pain, swollen hands and feet, jaundice, and visual problems due to retinal damage. If sickle-cell anemia is left untreated, long-term complications can include stroke, blindness, pneumonia, and other health problems. Many people with sickle-cell anemia do not live into their 30s. In contrast, people with the sickle-cell trait rarely suffer from any symptoms. The half of their hemoglobin that is normal is generally sufficient for them to lead normal lives. However, they may have mild episodes of red blood cell sickling when oxygen concentrations are lower than normal, such as at high altitudes or in airplanes in flight.

Sickle-cell anemia affects primarily Africans (and their descendants on other continents) and Caucasians of Mediterranean descent. In East Africa, sickle-cell anemia is fairly common and nearly 40% of the black population has the sickle-cell trait. In contrast, only about 1 in 500 African

Figure 19.9 Incomplete dominance. Wavy hair (Hh) is an intermediate phenotype between straight (HH) and curly (hh) hair because neither allele is dominant.

	Type A	Type B	Type AB	Type O
	Antigen A	Antigen B	Antigens A and B	Neither A nor B antigens
Red blood cells				
Possible genotypes	AA AO	BB BO	AB	OO

Figure 19.10 Blood type: An example of codominance. Characteristics of the four major blood types are shown, including their surface antigens and the genotypes that cause each blood type phenotype.

✔️ *A woman with blood type AB and a man with blood type O have a baby. What is the probability that the baby has blood type O, like his father? Explain your answer.*

Key:
Hb^A = normal hemoglobin
Hb^S = sickle-cell allele

a) A Punnett square showing a mating between two individuals with the sickle-cell trait.

b) A sickled red blood cell next to a normal red blood cell.

Figure 19.11 Sickle-cell anemia: an example of codominance. If two people with the sickle-cell trait have children, each child will have a 25% chance of being phenotypically normal, a 50% chance of having the sickle-cell trait, and a 25% chance of having sickle-cell anemia.

Americans is born with sickle-cell anemia and only 8% have the sickle-cell trait. Why the big difference?

It turns out that the sickle-cell allele protects against malaria, a deadly parasitic disease common in tropical climates. The malaria parasite spends part of its life cycle in humans (in the liver and in red blood cells) and the other part in mosquitoes. When the malaria parasite enters the red blood cell of a person with sickle-cell trait or sickle-cell disease, the cell sickles and eventually ruptures, killing the parasite before it can reproduce.

Malaria kills one million people every year worldwide. Where malaria exists, having sickle-cell trait (but not sickle-cell anemia) is a distinct advantage. Were it not for malaria, we could surmise that sickle-cell anemia and the sickle-cell trait would become rare in Africa, just as they are becoming rarer in the United States.

BlogInFocus MB

In addition to sickle-cell disease, there is now a second genetic disorder that has been found to be protective against a specific disease. To learn more about it, visit MJ's blog in the Study Area in MasteringBiology and look under "A Protective Genetic Disorder."

Because our phenotype includes all of our unique characteristics from our physical appearance to our biochemical makeup, the definition of an inheritance pattern as either incompletely dominant or codominant depends on the context. At the biochemical level, sickle-cell trait is an example of codominance because both the normal hemoglobin (Hb^A) and the sickle-cell hemoglobin (Hb^S) are produced in equal amounts. However, at the level of the whole person, the sickle-cell trait is an example of incomplete dominance, because the person with the sickle-cell trait exhibits a disease pattern that is intermediate between the two homozygous conditions. Understanding the concept is more important than an argument over whether the sickle-cell trait is one or the other.

Recap People heterozygous with incompletely dominant alleles have a phenotype that is intermediate between the phenotype of either homozygous genotype. People heterozygous with codominant alleles express the products of both alleles equally. Examples of codominance are AB blood type and sickle-cell anemia. ▪

19.4 Other factors influence inheritance patterns and phenotype

Polygenic inheritance: Phenotype is influenced by many genes

Many traits result from not just one pair of genes, but many genes acting simultaneously. Inheritance of phenotypic traits that depend on many genes is called **polygenic inheritance**.

Eye color, for example, is controlled by at least three genes, yielding a range of different eye color phenotypes from nearly black to light blue (Figure 19.12). Both skin and eye color are determined by the amount of a light-absorbing pigment called melanin in the skin and iris. The striking differences in eye color occur because in people with relatively low amounts of melanin we see different wavelengths of light (green, gray, or blue) reflected from the iris.

Physical characteristics such as height, body size, and shape are also examples of polygenic inheritance. Traits governed by polygenic inheritance generally are distributed in the population as a continuous range of values, with more people at the middle (or median) and fewer people at the extremes. As an example of a trait influenced by multiple genes, let's consider height. We will simplify matters and assume that height is influenced by only three genes, each of which has two alleles. Each gene has a tall allele (A, B, or C) that behaves in an incompletely dominant manner with respect to the short alleles (a, b, or c). In this example, an individual homozygous for tall alleles for all three genes (AABBCC) would be very tall, whereas an individual homozygous for short alleles for all three genes (aabbcc) would be very short. Heterozygotes for all three genes (AaBbCc) would have an intermediate phenotype and would be of medium height. Now, consider a cross between individuals of medium height. Most of their offspring would be similar in height to their parents, inheriting a mix of tall and short alleles, but by random chance, some offspring might inherit mostly tall or mostly short alleles, and a few might be very tall or very petite (Figure 19.13). This phenotypic distribution occurs throughout the human population, and a plot of the numbers of individuals at each value for the trait typically forms a normal (bell-shaped) curve.

We are just beginning to understand that many health conditions may be caused or at least influenced by polygenic inheritance. Examples include cancer, high blood pressure, heart disease, and stroke.

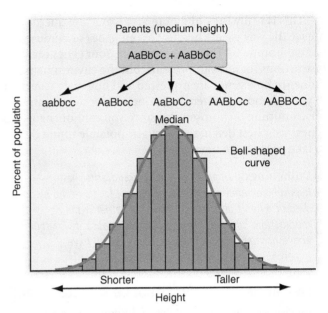

Figure 19.13 Continuous range of variation in traits governed by polygenic inheritance. Polygenic traits, such as height, appear in the population as a continuous range of phenotypes, with more people in the middle than at either extreme. In this hypothetical example, three genes influence height. Heterozygotes for all three genes have an intermediate (average) height, and can produce a wide range of heights among their offspring, depending on how many tall alleles and short alleles each child inherits.

Both genotype and the environment affect phenotype

Phenotype is determined in part by our genotype and in part by environmental influences. A prime example of an environmental influence is the effect of diet on height and body size. Analysis of human populations reveals a clear trend toward increased height and weight in certain populations, particularly in developed countries. The changes in height and weight have sometimes occurred within one generation—too short a time to be due to changes in the gene pool. The trend is primarily due to improvements in diet and nutrition, especially early in childhood.

Except for a few rare genetic diseases such as Huntington disease (more on this later in the chapter), our genotype is not the sole determinant of whether we will actually develop a heritable disease (that is, have the disease phenotype). Usually we inherit only a slightly increased *risk* of developing the disease, with those risks modifiable by environmental factors and our own actions. If you know that certain heritable conditions or diseases run in your family, it would be prudent to reduce any environmental risk factors associated with that disease. For example, if your family has a history of skin cancer, limit your exposure to the sun. If your family has a history of heart disease due to high cholesterol, have your cholesterol measured regularly and change your diet or begin other corrective measures if your cholesterol levels are above normal.

Figure 19.12 Polygenic inheritance. Eye color is determined by at least three genes, not just one. Different combinations of the alleles of the genes account for a range of eye colors.

This is really the old nature-versus-nurture question: Are we the way we are because of our genes or because of our environment? The answer is both. Your genes carry the instructions for all your proteins, but the environment can influence how genes are expressed and how they contribute to your phenotype. There is no one answer to the nature-versus-nurture dichotomy. But since you cannot change your genes, your best defense against any possible future disease is to take proper care of yourself.

✅ **Quick Check** *Imagine that your grandfather had hypercholesterolemia (high cholesterol levels in his blood) and died of a heart attack, and that your father is taking medications to lower his cholesterol because it was found to be above normal. Does this mean that you will have hypercholesterolemia later in life too?* ▪

Linked alleles may or may not be inherited together

As previously mentioned, alleles of different genes are distributed to egg and sperm cells independently of each other during meiosis. But, because humans have only 23 pairs of chromosomes, it doesn't always work this way. Many alleles for different traits are often inherited together because they are physically joined on the same chromosome. These alleles are called **linked alleles**, and the closer they are located to each other on the chromosome the more likely they are to be inherited together. However, they are not *always* inherited together because of crossing-over, which partially reshuffles alleles across each pair of autosomes during meiosis. How often two linked alleles are inherited together is directly proportional to how close together they are and inversely proportional to how often crossing-over occurs (the more crossing-over occurs, the less likely the linked alleles will be inherited together).

To get a feel for how often linked alleles might be inherited together, consider that the average pair of chromosomes may have 2,000 or more genes, and that crossing-over occurs approximately 30 times per pair of chromosomes. Alleles located close to each other, then, may be inherited together quite often. Scientists have learned that they can map the positions of genes by studying how often particular linked alleles are inherited together, a technique called *linkage mapping*.

Adding it all up, there are three major sources of genetic variability as a result of sexual reproduction:

- Independent assortment of alleles located on different chromosomes
- Partial shuffling of linked alleles as a result of crossing-over between autosomes
- Random fertilization of an egg by a sperm

↩ **Recap** In polygenic inheritance, many different genes influence a single phenotype, such as height or eye color. In addition, some phenotypes can be influenced by environmental factors such as diet. Alleles located close together on the same chromosome are inherited together, except when crossing-over occurs. ▪

19.5 Sex-linked inheritance: X and Y chromosomes carry different genes

Chromosomes are identifiable in cells only just before cell division. At this time each chromosome can be identified by its characteristic size, centromere location, and distinct banding pattern. A composite display of all the chromosomes of an organism is called a **karyotype**.

The karyotype in **Figure 19.14** shows the 23 pairs of human chromosomes. Of these, 22 are matched pairs (autosomes). The two chromosomes of the last pair, however, do not look alike and do not match up. These are the sex chromosomes, X and Y. The sex chromosomes are not a homologous pair. They look different from each other, and they function differently because they carry different genes. They represent a pair only in that you get one from each parent as a consequence of meiosis. As seen in **Figure 19.15**, the sperm from the father determines the gender of the offspring. Females have two X chromosomes and will donate one of them to the offspring, whereas

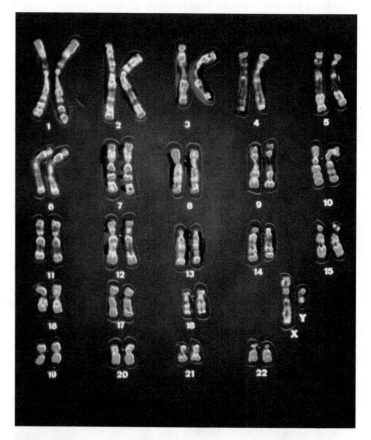

Figure 19.14 The human karyotype. Chromosomes are identified and paired according to their size, centromere location, and characteristic banding patterns. A numbered arrangement of all 23 pairs is called the *human karyotype*. This karyotype is from a male, as indicated by the dissimilar X and Y chromosomes of the unnumbered 23rd pair.

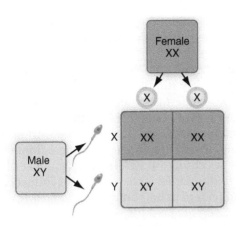

Figure 19.15 Sex determination in humans. The sex of the embryo is determined by the male's sperm, about 50% of which carry an X chromosome and 50% of which carry a Y chromosome. Maleness is determined by the inheritance of a Y chromosome.

males have an X and a Y chromosome, only one of which is donated to the offspring. If the male donates an X chromosome, the fertilized egg will have two X chromosomes and will develop into a female. If the male donates a Y chromosome, the fertilized egg has an X and a Y chromosome and will develop into a male.

Sex-linked inheritance depends on genes located on sex chromosomes

Gender determination by inheritance of sex chromosomes is not without cost, especially to males. The advantage of having pairs of autosomes is that you have two copies of each gene—a backup file, if you will. If something goes wrong with one copy, the other can still carry out its function.

In sexually reproducing animals in which the Y chromosome determines maleness, females have a homologous pair of X chromosomes but males do not. This means that males have a greater susceptibility for diseases associated with recessive alleles on the sex chromosomes. In fact, males are more likely to display any recessive trait found on the X chromosome, not just those that cause disease.

Sex-linked inheritance refers to inheritance patterns that depend on genes located on the sex chromosomes. Sex-linked inheritance is *X-linked* if the gene is located only on the X chromosome and *Y-linked* if the gene is located only on the Y chromosome. There are plenty of examples of X-linked inheritance because many of the genes on the X chromosome are not related to sex determination at all. However, there are relatively few well-documented examples of Y-linked inheritance. The reason is that the Y chromosome is relatively small and many of its genes relate to "maleness." Genes on the Y chromosome apparently influence differentiation of the male sex organs, production of sperm, and the development of secondary sex characteristics, but not much else.

In the female, X-linked inheritance behaves just like inheritance of autosomes with paired genes. Not so in the male, because he inherits only one X chromosome. In the male, X-linked genotype and phenotype are both determined solely by the single X chromosome he inherited from his mother.

The best known example of an X-linked disease is hemophilia, also known as *bleeder's disease*. Hemophiliacs lack a blood-clotting factor that is encoded by an X-linked gene with two alleles. The recessive allele (X^h) is a mutant that cannot produce the clotting factor, whereas the dominant allele (X^H) produces the clotting factor. Individuals have the disease only if they do *not* have at least one normal dominant allele (that is, if they are an X^hX^h female or an X^hY male).

The inheritance of hemophilia and other X-linked recessive diseases follows this pattern:

- Many more males have the disease than females. Females can be protected by inheriting at least one normal allele (X^H) out of two, whereas males inherit only one allele because they inherit only one X chromosome.
- The disease is passed to sons solely through their mothers even though the mothers may only be *carriers*. Carriers are heterozygous (X^HX^h); therefore, they can pass on the recessive hemophilia allele even though they do not suffer from the disease themselves. Statistically, half of the sons of carrier mothers will have the disease and half of the daughters will be carriers.
- A father cannot pass the disease to a son, but his daughters will all be carriers (unless the mother is also a carrier or has the disease, in which case the daughters may also have the disease).

The inheritance pattern of a genetic disorder can be followed through many generations by using a pedigree chart to map out a family's lineage. Figure 19.16 shows a pedigree following the hemophilia trait. Muscular dystrophy and red-green color blindness are also X-linked recessive conditions that follow this inheritance pattern. Nearly all X-linked diseases are caused by a recessive allele rather than a dominant one.

✅**Quick Check** *Can a father ever pass an X-linked trait to his son(s)? Why or why not?* ∎

Sex-influenced traits are affected by actions of sex genes

A few genes that you might suspect are located on the sex chromosomes are actually located on one of the 22 autosomal pairs of chromosomes. A good example is a gene that influences baldness. The normal allele (b^+) and the allele for baldness (b) can be present in both men and women. However, the baldness allele is recessive in women. Women must be (bb) and probably have other baldness genes or factors as well before their hair loss is significant.

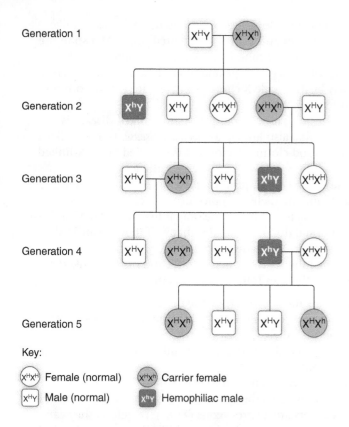

Key:

(X^HX^H) Female (normal)   (X^HX^h) Carrier female

[X^HY] Male (normal)   [X^hY] Hemophiliac male

a) A pedigree chart following the passage of hemophilia for five generations. Female carriers pass the hemophilia allele to half their daughters and the disease to half their sons. Males with the disease pass the hemophilia allele to all their daughters (if they survive long enough to have children), but never to their sons.

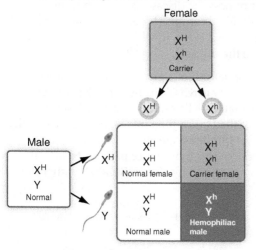

b) A Punnett square showing the possible outcomes of the mating in Generation 1.

Figure 19.16 A typical inheritance pattern for hemophilia, an X-linked recessive disease.

✅ *Suppose that one of the women in Generation 5 marries and has a daughter (not a son) who has full-fledged hemophilia. How could this happen?*

Men become very bald if they are (bb) and develop significant pattern baldness even if they are heterozygous (bb⁺).

Why the difference between men and women? Testosterone strongly stimulates the expression of the baldness allele, in effect converting it from a recessive to a dominant allele in males. This is an example of a *sex-influenced* phenotype, one not inherited with the sex chromosomes per se but influenced by the actions of the genes on the sex chromosomes. In fact, a number of genes in addition to this particular baldness gene influence the presence and pattern of hair on the head.

↩ **Recap** In humans, the sex chromosome carried by the male sperm determines the gender of the fertilized embryo. Males have only one X chromosome, and are more susceptible to sex-linked recessive diseases than females. Sex-linked inheritance depends on genes located on the sex chromosomes; sex-influenced traits depend on genes located on autosomes that are influenced by the actions of sex-linked genes. ▪

19.6 Chromosomes may be altered in number or structure

During mitosis of diploid cells and meiosis of the precursor cells of sperm and eggs, duplicated chromosomes must separate appropriately into two different cells. Just as duplication of DNA is not always perfect, neither is separation of the chromosomes.

Failure of homologous chromosomes or sister chromatids to separate properly is called **nondisjunction**. Sometimes both sister chromatids go to one of the two cells formed during mitosis. Occasionally homologous chromosomes or sister chromatids fail to separate during meiosis (**Figure 19.17**), resulting in an alteration in chromosome number of sperm or egg cells. Very rarely, a piece of a chromosome may break off and be lost, or it may reattach to another chromosome where it doesn't belong.

For the most part we never see these chromosomal alterations. If mitosis goes awry, the two daughter cells probably just die and their place is taken by other dividing cells. Alterations that arise during meiosis are more serious because they have at least the potential to alter the development of an entire organism. However, it appears that we never see most of these either because so many of the genes on the chromosomes are essential for embryonic development. Any sperm, egg, or developing embryo with errors as great as an extra or missing chromosome is unlikely to survive. Most die early in embryonic development before we are even aware of their presence.

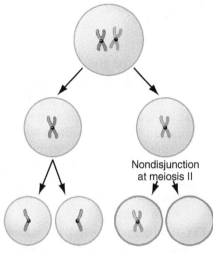

a) **Normal meiosis.** Duplicated homologous chromosomes separate during meiosis I, sister chromatids separate during meiosis II.

b) **Nondisjunction during meiosis I.** The duplicated homologous chromosomes fail to separate from each other.

c) **Nondisjunction during meiosis II.** Sister chromatids fail to separate from each other.

Figure 19.17 Nondisjunction during meiosis. Abnormal gametes have red outlines. This figure shows just one of the 23 pairs of human chromosomes.

Down syndrome: Three copies of chromosome 21

A few alterations of autosomal chromosome number do result in live births. The most common alteration of autosomal chromosome number is *Down syndrome*. There are actually three types of Down syndrome, but the overwhelming majority (95% of all cases) is caused by having three copies of chromosome 21 (trisomy 21) (Figure 19.18). Other disorders resulting from altered autosomal chromosomal number are Edwards syndrome (trisomy 18) and Patau syndrome (trisomy 13).

People with Down syndrome are typically short with round faces and other distinctive physical traits; most are friendly, cheerful, and affectionate. They generally are slow to develop mentally and are prone to respiratory complications or heart defects that can lead to death at a young age. However, with improved care many now live well into their adult years.

Down syndrome affects approximately 1 in every 1,000 live births in the United States. The risk of giving birth to a Down syndrome baby rises markedly with the mother's increasing age. The chance is around 1 in 1,300 for mothers under 30, 1 in 100 at age 40, and 1 in 25 for mothers over age 45. Recent evidence suggests that paternal age may also be a factor when both parents are 35 or older.

BlogInFocus (MB)

There's a new, highly sensitive and accurate test for Down syndrome in a fetus, but not everyone is happy about it. To learn why, visit MJ's blog in the Study Area in MasteringBiology and look under "Down Syndrome Test."

Some pregnant women elect to undergo fetal testing to detect Down syndrome and other disorders. In amniocentesis, a sample of amniotic fluid containing fetal cells is withdrawn and tested. Another option is chorionic villi sampling, in which a small sample of fetal tissue is suctioned from the placenta for examination. Fetal cells are examined for the presence of third copies of chromosome 21 (Down syndrome), third copies of chromosomes 18 and 13, and for alterations of sex chromosome number. Chromosomal damage can also sometimes be detected.

Figure 19.18 A person with Down syndrome. Down syndrome is caused by inheriting an extra copy of chromosome 21. Note that alterations in chromosome number can happen for any of the chromosomes, but most alterations are not seen in the population because they are lethal during fetal development.

☑**Quick Check** *Is Down syndrome caused by a gene mutation? Explain.* ▪

Alterations of the number of sex chromosomes

Nondisjunction of the sex chromosomes can produce a variety of combinations of sex chromosome number, several of which are fairly common in the human population. In general, an individual with at least one Y chromosome will be essentially a male phenotype. An individual lacking a Y chromosome will be a female phenotype, regardless of the number of X chromosomes. The four most common alterations of sex chromosome number are the following:

XYY—Jacob syndrome XYY individuals are males who tend to be tall but otherwise fairly normal, except that some show impaired mental function. At one time it was thought that XYY males had a tendency toward violent criminal behavior, but careful study has shown this is not true. Whether their rate of minor, nonviolent criminality tends to be higher than normal is still a disputed issue.

XXY—Klinefelter syndrome People with Klinefelter syndrome are also tall male phenotype. They are sterile, may show mild mental impairment, and may develop enlarged breasts because of the extra X chromosome (Figure 19.19a).

XXX—Trisomy-X syndrome Trisomy-X syndrome individuals are female phenotype. Typically they are nearly normal except for a tendency toward mild mental retardation.

XO—Turner syndrome Individuals with only one X chromosome (XO) are phenotypically female. However, they tend to be short with slightly altered body form and small breasts (Figure 19.19b). Most are not mentally retarded and can lead normal lives, though they are sterile and may have shortened life expectancies. Turner syndrome is relatively rare compared to the other three because the XO embryo is more likely to be spontaneously aborted.

Table 19.1 summarizes the most common alterations of chromosomal number and gives their frequencies of occurrence.

☑**Quick Check** *Given the information above, what exactly causes an XY individual to be male? That is, is it the presence of the Y that causes maleness, or the number of X chromosomes?* ▪

Deletions and translocations alter chromosome structure

A **deletion** occurs when a piece of chromosome breaks off and is lost. In general we cannot afford to lose genes, and therefore nearly all deletions are lethal to the sperm, egg, or embryo. There are a few rare conditions in which a

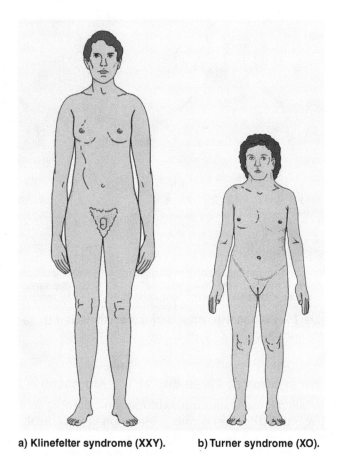

a) Klinefelter syndrome (XXY).   b) Turner syndrome (XO).

Figure 19.19 Alterations of sex chromosome number.

chromosome deletion results in a live birth. An example is *cri-du-chat* (French, meaning "cat-cry") syndrome, caused by a deletion from chromosome 5. Babies born with this syndrome are often mentally and physically retarded, with a characteristic kittenlike cry due to a small larynx.

Translocation occurs when a piece of a chromosome breaks off but reattaches at another site, either on the same chromosome or another chromosome. Conceptually you might think that translocations are not a problem because all of the genes are still present, just in different locations. However, translocations result in subtle changes in gene expression and therefore their ability to function. For instance, translocation appears to increase the risk of certain cancers, including one form of leukemia.

↺ **Recap** Nondisjunction leads to altered numbers of chromosomes in daughter cells. Down syndrome is usually caused by inheriting three copies of chromosome 21. When nondisjunction occurs in the sex chromosomes, usually people with at least one Y chromosome are male phenotype and people without a Y chromosome are female phenotype. A deletion occurs when part of a chromosome is lost; deletions rarely result in a live birth. ▪

Table 19.1 Some common alterations of chromosome number

Chromosome genotype	Sexual phenotype	Common name	Approximate frequency among live births
Trisomy 21	Male or female	Down syndrome	1/1,000
Trisomy 18	Male or female	Edwards syndrome	1/6,000
Trisomy 13	Male or female	Patau syndrome	1/5,000
XYY	Male	Double-Y syndrome	1/2,000
XXY	Male	Klinefelter syndrome	1/2,000
XXX	Female	Trisomy-X syndrome	1/2,000
XO	Female	Turner syndrome	1/10,000

19.7 Many inherited genetic disorders involve recessive alleles

People express inherited genetic disorders caused by recessive alleles only if they inherit two of the defective alleles. People who inherit only one defective allele can pass the gene to their children, but they do not get the disease themselves because their good allele is dominant. For this reason, recessive disease–causing alleles are likely to remain in a population more readily than dominant ones.

In some cases more than one gene pair may contribute to a disease. Hypertension and heart disease are examples of diseases that apparently have a heritable component but aren't associated with any single gene pair.

One of the better known recessive genetic disorders is cystic fibrosis, discussed in the Health & Wellness feature in this chapter. In this section we discuss two other genetic disorders caused by recessive alleles (phenylketonuria and Tay-Sachs disease), as well as one (Huntington disease) that is caused by a dominant allele.

Phenylketonuria is caused by a missing enzyme

Phenylketonuria (PKU) is a human inherited disease in which homozygous recessive individuals are unable to make an enzyme that is needed for the normal metabolism of phenylalanine, an amino acid. If phenylalanine accumulates, some of it is used in other metabolic pathways, including one in which excess phenylalanine is converted to phenylpyruvic acid instead. Phenylpyruvic acid is toxic at high concentrations and can lead to mental retardation, slow growth rate, and early death.

Phenylketonuria occurs in about 1 in 12,000 births in Caucasians, so it is considerably less prevalent than cystic fibrosis. The disease is caused by mutation of the gene on chromosome 1 that is responsible for producing the enzyme phenylalanine hydroxylase.

Fortunately, people homozygous for the recessive allele are not affected before birth because the mother's enzymes metabolize phenylalanine for the fetus. After birth, the blood level of phenylalanine is very much dependent on the amount of phenylalanine in the diet. Given the seriousness of mental retardation, all states now require that newborns be tested for PKU by a simple blood test called the *Guthrie test*, which detects excess phenylalanine in the blood.

Treatment of PKU requires limiting the dietary intake of phenylalanine. This is not easy because most proteins contain phenylalanine, but it can be done for about $5,000 per year by substituting a carefully controlled mixture of amino acids for most protein. In addition, individuals with phenylketonuria cannot use the artificial sweetener NutraSweet because it contains aspartame, a chemical consisting of just two amino acids, phenylalanine and aspartic acid, linked together. When aspartame is broken down, people with PKU may experience a dangerous increase in phenylalanine.

✅**Quick Check** *Suppose a mother and father have a child with PKU, though neither parent exhibits the disorder. What is the probability that their next child will also have PKU? Explain your answer.* ∎

Tay-Sachs disease leads to brain dysfunction

Tay-Sachs disease is another enzyme deficiency disease, this one caused by a recessive gene located on chromosome 15. Individuals homozygous for the recessive allele are unable to make an enzyme that is responsible for the metabolism of a particular type of lipid, called a *sphingolipid*, found primarily in the lysosomes of brain cells. Without this enzyme, the sphingolipid accumulates in brain cells, causing cerebral degeneration. Infants seem unaffected at birth, but by 4–8 months of age motor function and brain function begin to decline. The child gradually develops seizures, becomes blind and paralyzed, and usually dies by age 3 or 4. There is no known cure or treatment.

Tay-Sachs disease is rare in the general population. However, it is fairly common among Ashkenazi Jews of Central European descent, with about 1 in 3,500 children having the disease. Carriers of the disease remain unaffected because they have sufficient enzyme activity for normal function. Tests are available to determine whether either member of a couple is a carrier of the disease.

Huntington disease is caused by a dominant-lethal allele

Huntington disease is marked by progressive nerve degeneration leading to physical and mental disability and death. Afflicted individuals begin to show symptoms in their 30s, and most die in their 40s or 50s.

Huntington disease follows the simple rules of inheritance of a single pair of alleles, one or both of which may be the dominant (HD) or recessive (hd) form. However, in this case it is the *dominant* allele (HD) that causes Huntington disease. Anyone with even one HD allele will ultimately develop the disorder. The disease is fatal, and there is no known cure at the moment. For this reason HD is called a **dominant-lethal** allele.

Dominant-lethal alleles are by their nature uncommon because they tend to eliminate themselves from the population, especially if they cause disease before the affected individual's reproductive years. Huntington disease is unusual in this regard. The disease remains in the human population because in the past, individuals who carried the HD allele had no way of knowing they would develop Huntington disease, and so they would pass the allele on to half their children before they developed any symptoms. Folksinger/songwriter Woody Guthrie and his mother both died of Huntington disease, and Woody could have passed it to his son, Arlo (Figure 19.20). Today there is a test for the HD allele. Here is an example where genetic testing and counseling could have a dramatic effect on the prevalence of a disease in the future. (See the Current Issue box in this chapter for a discussion of the biological, social, and ethical issues raised by genetic testing.)

Genetic testing for Huntington disease and other inherited disorders is one of the great benefits of the *Human Genome Project.* Engaging scientists from around the world, this massive endeavor involved locating each of the approximately 22,000 genes in the human genome and identifying their functions. Researchers have already successfully identified the genes responsible for several disorders, including forms of breast cancer, skin cancer, and osteoporosis. This information holds promise for developing ways to prevent new cases of genetic diseases and treating existing cases with new technologies. One possibility might be to correct genetic defects with *gene therapy*. We discuss gene therapy in more detail in the chapter on DNA technology and genetic engineering.

Recap Recessive alleles such as those for phenylketonuria and Tay-Sachs disease cause disease only if the individual is homozygous recessive. Dominant disease-causing alleles are unusual because they tend to be eliminated from the population. Huntington disease is a rare example of a dominant-lethal disease. ∎

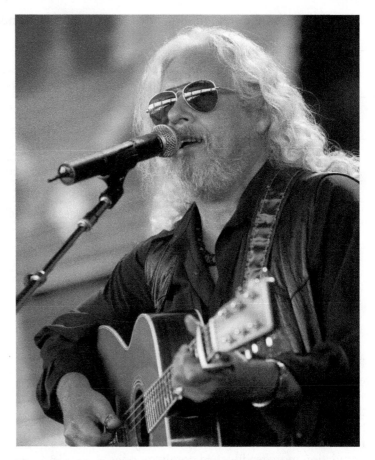

Figure 19.20 Genetic testing revealed that folksinger Arlo Guthrie would not suffer from Huntington disease as his father Woody Guthrie did.

19.8 Genes code for proteins, not for specific behaviors

Genes represent the set of instructions for a human being. The actions of genes can be very specific, such as determining hair patterns or earlobe shape. In terms of behavior, the logical conclusion might be that specific genes determine specific behaviors. Indeed, we read in the popular press of a heritable "schizophrenia gene." We hear of studies that show certain groups of criminals may share a common genetic defect; that some people may have a gene that predisposes them to depression; that there may even be a "happiness gene." Is any of this true?

The bottom line is that genes code for specific proteins. Specific genes code for proteins that give you curly hair or freckles. Other genes (and their protein products) may strongly *influence* whole patterns of behavior or moods, such as a tendency toward anxiety or aggression. However, genes do not necessarily cause *specific* behaviors. They do not lead to specific thoughts, and there is no one gene that causes you to turn to the left and another one that causes you to turn to the right. Nor are there any genes that cause people to commit specific crimes, as far as we know.

The key to understanding how genes influence behaviors lies in understanding the many roles of proteins. Proteins may act as hormones, neurotransmitters, enzymes, or intracellular messengers. They make up many of the structural components of cells, and they control cell functions. Some proteins influence a broad range of other genes and proteins; others have very specific effects within only certain target cells. Together, groups of genes and their protein products apparently do influence broad patterns of behavior, such as feeding, mating, or learning. They may also influence moods. Nevertheless, there is no evidence that specific genes or their protein products cause depression, lead to complete happiness, or produce specific physical behaviors.

 Recap Genes influence patterns of behavior. They do not cause specific behaviors. ▪

Chapter Summary

Your genotype is the genetic basis of your phenotype *p. 446*

- The DNA we inherit from both parents represents the complete set of instructions for creating a human being.
- The two copies of every gene (one from each parent) can differ very slightly because of mutations. Different versions of a gene are called alleles.
- Our genotype is the complete set of alleles that we inherit; our phenotype refers to the physical and functional expression of those alleles.

Genetic inheritance follows certain patterns *p. 447*

- A Punnett square can be used to show patterns of inheritance for one or two pairs of alleles.
- A common pattern of phenotypic inheritance is one in which one allele exerts complete dominance over the other.
- Genes for different traits assort independently of each other.

Other dominance patterns *p. 452*

- In incomplete dominance, heterozygotes exhibit an intermediate phenotype.
- In codominance, heterozygotes express both phenotypes equally.

Other factors influence inheritance patterns and phenotype *p. 454*

- In polygenic inheritance, multiple genes influence a single trait.
- Our phenotype is determined both by our genotype and by our environment.
- Alleles located on the same chromosome that may be inherited together are called linked alleles.

Sex-linked inheritance: X and Y chromosomes carry different genes *p. 456*

- Maleness is determined early during development by genes on the Y (male) sex chromosome. In the absence of this chromosome, the individual becomes a female.
- Sex-linked inheritance refers to inheritance of genes located on the sex chromosomes. Most of these genes have nothing to do with sex determination.
- Diseases associated with sex-linked inheritance include hemophilia, color blindness, and muscular dystrophy.

Chromosomes may be altered in number or structure *p. 458*

- Nondisjunction refers to the failure of homologous chromosomes or sister chromatids to separate properly during mitosis or meiosis; this causes altered chromosome number in the daughter cells.
- Down syndrome is a condition usually caused by the inheritance of three copies of chromosome 21. The primary risk factor is the age of the parents, especially the mother.
- Deletion of even part of a chromosome is usually fatal to a sperm, egg, or embryo. Translocation of a chromosome segment may alter a gene's ability to function properly.

Many inherited genetic disorders involve recessive alleles *p. 461*

- Most autosomal heritable genetic diseases are caused by recessive alleles.
- Phenylketonuria, Tay-Sachs disease, and cystic fibrosis are diseases caused by recessive alleles.
- Huntington disease is caused by a dominant-lethal allele. It has persisted in the human population because people who inherit it do not show symptoms until after reaching reproductive age.

Genes code for proteins, not for specific behaviors *p. 462*

- Genes influence only general patterns of behavior or mood. They do not determine specific behaviors.

Terms You Should Know

Concept Review

Answers can be found in the Study Area in MasteringBiology.

1. Where do we get the two copies we have of every gene?
2. What is the difference between a gene and an allele?
3. Distinguish between genotype and phenotype.
4. Describe the contributions of Mendel to the field of genetics.
5. Explain how alterations of chromosome number and structure can occur.
6. Distinguish between the concepts of dominance, incomplete dominance, and codominance.
7. Describe how genetic variability is accomplished via sexual reproduction.
8. Describe what is meant by sex-linked inheritance.
9. Explain why lethal diseases caused by dominant alleles are so rare.
10. Explain how genes affect mood or behavior.

Test Yourself

Answers can be found in Appendix A.

1. All of the following statements about homologous chromosomes are true except:
   a. One of each pair of homologous chromosomes comes from each parent.
   b. The alleles on homologous chromosomes are identical to each other.
   c. They have genes for the same traits at the same loci.
   d. Homologous chromosomes physically pair up and may exchange parts during meiosis.

2. How many different kinds of gametes (with respect to a particular gene locus) are formed by an individual who is homozygous at that locus?
   a. 1
   b. 2
   c. 4
   d. It can't be determined from this information.

3. Which of the following statements correctly expresses the relationship between dominant and recessive alleles?
   a. A dominant allele is always the preferred or most beneficial allele.
   b. A dominant allele is only expressed when it is homozygous.
   c. A dominant allele masks the expression of a recessive allele in a heterozygote.
   d. A dominant allele is always the most numerous allele in the population.

4. Which of the following would provide an exception to Mendel's law of independent assortment?
   a. adjacent genes on the same chromosome
   b. dominant genes
   c. recessive genes
   d. genes located on different chromosomes

5. Two parents are heterozygous for familial hypercholesterolemia, with blood cholesterol levels two to three times the normal level. What is the probability that their child will be unaffected by this disorder?
   a. 0%
   b. 25%
   c. 50%
   d. 100%

6. What is the likelihood that a parent with Type AB blood would have a child with Type O blood?
   a. 50%
   b. 25%
   c. 0%
   d. This can't be determined without knowing the blood type of the other parent.

7. All of the following human traits are determined by the interaction of multiple genes and alleles except:
   a. eye color
   b. hair color
   c. height
   d. sickle cell anemia

8. Which of the following results in the separation (or unlinking) of linked genes?
   a. crossing-over during meiosis I
   b. independent assortment during mitosis
   c. segregation during meiosis
   d. separation of sister chromatids during mitosis

9. What is the likelihood that a man with hemophilia mating with a woman who is homozygous for the normal form of the blood clotting factor gene will have a son with hemophilia?
   a. 100%
   b. 50%
   c. 25%
   d. 0%

10. Which of the following could be detected by preparing a karyotype?
    a. sickle-cell anemia
    b. cystic fibrosis
    c. Klinefelter syndrome
    d. hemophilia

11. What tool is used to determine the probabilities of different genetic outcomes from various crosses?
    a. preparation of a karyotype
    b. chorionic villus testing
    c. biochemical testing of the amniotic fluid
    d. Punnett square analysis

12. Which of the following statements is/are true?
    a. Genotype determines phenotype.
    b. Phenotype determines genotype.
    c. Environment can affect phenotype.
    d. Both (a) and (c) are true.

13. What is the basis for the tremendous genetic diversity resulting from sexual reproduction?
    a. independent assortment during gamete production
    b. crossing-over and shuffling of linked genes during meiosis
    c. random fertilization
    d. all of these choices

14. Examination of a karyotype reveals 23 pairs of chromosomes, with each homologous pair illustrating similar size and

centromere location. Which of the following can be concluded from this karyotype?
a. The individual has Down syndrome.
b. The individual is a female.
c. The individual does not have cystic fibrosis.
d. The individual does not have sickle-cell anemia.

15. Which of the following events or processes can result in Patau syndrome, Turner Syndrome, or Klinefelter syndrome?
a. nondisjunction
b. deletion of part of a chromosome
c. crossing-over
d. independent assortment

Apply What You Know

Answers can be found in the Study Area in MasteringBiology.

1. What fraction of the offspring of two wavy-haired Caucasians would have wavy hair? Explain using a Punnett square. *Hint:* The allele for curly hair exhibits incomplete dominance over the allele for straight hair.
2. Why is it that the range of resting blood pressures of humans is best represented by a bell-shaped curve covering a continuous range rather than by two populations, one with high blood pressure and one with normal blood pressure?
3. How is it that each parent is able to contribute only a single allele of each gene to his/her offspring, rather than both alleles?
4. Geneticists often study patterns of gene transfer in a variety of model organisms, including plants, fruit flies, and even worms. If they're really interested in patterns of inheritance in humans, why don't they use humans or at least larger animals more similar to humans, such as pigs or even primates?

5. Can a father who is blood type A and a mother who is blood type B have a child who is blood type O?
6. Hemophilia is a sex-linked trait that mothers pass on to male offspring. Is it possible for females to have hemophilia too? How would such a thing happen?
7. Nondisjunction during meiosis can lead to the formation of gametes (sperm or eggs) with extra copies of one or more chromosomes. Normally, fertilizations involving extra copies of chromosomes simply do not result in a live birth because too many developmental events are altered in some way. The most common extra-chromosomal condition that *does* lead to live births is Down syndrome (trisomy 21). Why do you suppose that trisomy 21 is more common than other trisomies?

BlogInFocus

Answers can be found in the Study Area in MasteringBiology.

1. Do identical twins have identical DNA? Explain the rationale behind your answer. (To view a research paper on this question, visit MJ's blog in the Study Area in MasteringBiology and look under "DNA in Identical Twins.")

MasteringBiology®

Go to MasteringBiology for practice quizzes, activities, eText, videos, current events, and more.

Glossary

A

ABO blood typing Technique for classifying blood according to the presence or absence of two protein markers, A and B.

accommodation The adjustment of lens curvature in the eye so we can focus on either near or far objects.

acetylcholine (ACh) (AS-uh-teel-KOL-een) Neurotransmitter released by some nerve endings in both the peripheral and central nervous systems.

acid A substance that releases hydrogen ions when in solution. A proton donor.

acid precipitation Rain that has become acidic as the result of the airborne environmental pollutants sulfur dioxide and nitrogen oxide.

acromegaly (AK-roh-MEG-uh-lee) A condition of enlargement of the bones and muscles of the head, hands, face, and feet caused by an excess of growth hormone in an adult.

acrosome (AK-roh-sohm) A cap containing enzymes that covers most of the head of a sperm. Helps sperm penetrate an egg.

actin (AK-tin) A contractile protein of muscle. Forms the thin filaments in the myofibrils.

action potential A brief change in membrane potential of a nerve or muscle cell due to the movement of ions across the plasma membrane. Also called a nerve impulse.

active immunization The process of activation of the immune system in advance of the presence of a disease. Generally, active immunization is accomplished by administration of a vaccine.

active transport Process that transfers a substance into or out of a cell, usually against its concentration gradient. Requires a carrier and the expenditure of energy.

adaptation General term for the act or process of adjusting. In environmental biology the process of changing to better suit a particular set of environmental conditions. In sensory neurons, a decline in the frequency of nerve impulses even when a receptor is stimulated continuously and without change in stimulus strength.

adaptive radiation A short burst of evolutionary activity in which many new life-forms develop in a brief span of time from a single ancestor.

Addison's disease A condition caused by a failure of the adrenal cortex to secrete sufficient Cortisol and aldosterone.

adipocyte (AH-di-po-syt) An adipose (fat) cell.

adipose tissue (AH-di-pohs) A connective tissue consisting chiefly of fat cells.

ADP (adenosine diphosphate) (uh-DEN-oh-seen dy-FOSS-fate) A nucleotide composed of adenosine with two phosphate groups. When ADP accepts another phosphate group it becomes the energy-storage molecule ATP.

adrenal cortex (ah-DREE-nul KOR-teks) External portion of the adrenal gland. Its primary hormones, aldosterone and Cortisol, influence inflammation, metabolism, interstitial fluid volume, and other functions.

adrenal glands (ah-DREE-nul) Hormone-producing glands located atop the kidneys. Each consists of medulla and cortex areas.

adrenal medulla (ah-DREE-nul meh-DUL-uh) Interior portion of the adrenal gland. Its hormones, epinephrine and norepinephrine, influence carbohydrate metabolism and blood circulation.

adrenocorticotropic hormone (ACTH) (uh-DREE-noh-kort-ih-koh-TRO-pic) Anterior pituitary hormone that influences the activity of the adrenal cortex.

aerobic metabolism (air-OH-bik) Metabolic reactions within a cell that utilize oxygen in the process of producing ATP.

afferent Directed to or toward a point of reference. In the kidney, an afferent arteriole carries blood to each glomerulus.

agglutination (uh-glue-tin-AY-shun) The clumping together of (foreign) cells induced by cross-linking of antigen-antibody complexes.

agranular leukocyte A white blood cell that does not contain distinctive granules. Includes lymphocytes and monocytes.

AIDS (acquired immune deficiency syndrome) Disease caused by human immunodeficiency virus (HIV). Symptoms include severe weight loss, night sweats, swollen lymph nodes, and opportunistic infections.

albumins (AL-byoo-mins) The most common group of proteins in blood plasma. Albumins have osmotic and transport functions.

aldosterone (al-DOS-ter-ohn or AL-do-STEER-ohn) Hormone produced by the adrenal cortex that regulates sodium reabsorption.

alleles (uh-LEELS) Genes coding for the same trait and found at the same locus on homologous chromosomes.

allergen (AL-ur-jen) Any substance that triggers an allergic response.

allergy (AL-ur-jee) Overzealous immune response to an otherwise harmless substance.

all-or-none principle The principle that muscle cells always contract completely each time they are stimulated by their motor neuron, and that they do not contract at all if they are not stimulated by their motor neuron.

alveolus (pl. alveoli) (al-VEE-oh-lus) One of the microscopic air sacs of the lungs.

Alzheimer's disease (AHLTZ-hy-merz) Degenerative brain disease resulting in progressive loss of motor control, memory, and intellectual functions.

amino acid (uh-MEE-no) Organic compound containing nitrogen, carbon, hydrogen, and oxygen. The 20 amino acids are the building blocks of protein.

amniocentesis A form of fetal testing in which a small sample of amniotic fluid is removed so that cells of the fetus can be examined for certain known diseases and genetic abnormalities.

amnionic fluid (am-nee-AHN-ik) A fluid similar to interstitial fluid that surrounds and protects the fetus during pregnancy. Amniotic fluid is in continuous exchange with maternal interstitial fluid.

ampulla (am-PULL-la) Base of a semicircular canal in the inner ear.

anabolic steroid Any one of over 100 synthetic and natural compounds, all of which are related to the male sex steroid hormone testosterone. Anabolic steroids increase muscle mass and contribute to the development and maintenance of masculine characteristics.

anabolism (ah-NAB-o-lizm) Energy-requiring building phase of metabolism, during which simpler substances are combined to form more complex substances.

analogous structures Structures that share a common function but not necessarily a common origin.

anaphase Third stage of mitosis, in which the two sets of daughter chromosomes move toward the poles of a cell.

androgen (AN-dro-jen) A hormone that controls male secondary sex characteristics, such as testosterone.

anemia (uh-NEE-mee-uh) A condition in which the blood's ability to carry oxygen is reduced because of a shortage of normal hemoglobin or too few red blood cells.

aneurysm (AN-yur-iz-um) A ballooning or bulging of the wall of an artery caused by dilation or weakening of the wall.

angina pectoris (AN-jin-uh PEK-tor-is) Sensation of severe pain and tightness in the chest caused by insufficient blood supply to the heart.

angiogram (AN-jee-oh-gram) An X-ray image of blood vessels.

angiotensin II (AN-jee-oh-TEN-sinTOO) A potent vasoconstrictor activated by renin. Also triggers the release of aldosterone from the adrenal gland.

anorexia nervosa (ah-nuh-REK-see-uh nur-VOH-suh) An eating disorder characterized by abnormally low body weight and unrealistic fear of becoming obese.

antibiotic (AN-tih-by-AH-tik) A substance that interferes with bacterial metabolism. Administered to cure bacterial diseases.

antibody A protein molecule released by a B cell or a plasma cell that binds to a specific antigen.

anticodon The three-base sequence in transfer RNA that pairs with a complementary sequence in messenger RNA.

antidiuretic hormone (ADH) (AN-tih-dy-yu-RET-ik) Hormone produced by the hypothalamus and released by the posterior pituitary. Stimulates the kidneys to reabsorb more water, reducing urine volume.

antigen (AN-tih-jen) A substance or part of a substance (living or nonliving) that the immune system recognizes as foreign. It activates the immune system and reacts with immune cells or their products, such as antibodies.

antigen-presenting cell (APC) A cell that displays antigen-MHC complexes on its surface. Triggers an immune response by lymphocytes.

antioxidant An agent that inhibits oxidation; specifically a substance that can neutralize the damaging effects of free radicals and other substances.

anus The outlet of the digestive tract.

aorta (ay-OR-tah) The main systemic artery. Arises from the left ventricle of the heart.

aortic bodies Receptors in the aorta that are sensitive primarily to the oxygen concentration of the blood. These receptors can also respond to H^+ and CO_2.

appendicular skeleton (ap-un-DIK-yuh-lur) The portion of the skeleton that forms the pectoral and pelvic girdles and the four extremities.

aquaporins Literally, water pores. Aquaporins are cell membrane proteins in certain specialized cells, especially the tubular cells in kidneys, that contain pores which permit the rapid diffusion of water.

appendix (uh-PEN-diks) A small finger-like pouch, with no known digestive function, that extends from the cecum of the large intestine.

aqueous humor (AY-kwee-us) Watery fluid between the cornea and the lens of the eye.

aquifer A deep underground reservoir of water.

Archaea (ar-KAY-uh) One of the three domains of life. The prokaryotes of Archaea have many of the features of eukaryotes, but they do not have true nuclei.

arrhythmia Irregular heart rhythm. Arrhythmias may be caused by defects in the cardiac conduction system or by drugs, stress, or cardiac disease.

arteriole (ar-TEER-ee-ohl) The smallest of the arterial blood vessels. Arterioles supply the capillaries, where nutrient and gas exchange takes place.

artery A blood vessel that conducts blood away from the heart and toward the capillaries.

arthritis Inflammation of the joints.

artificial insemination A technique to enhance fertility in which sperm are placed into the vagina or uterus with a syringe.

asthma (AZ-muh) A recurrent, chronic lung disorder characterized by spasmodic contraction of the bronchi, making breathing difficult.

astigmatism (uh-STIG-muh-tiz-um) An eye condition in which unequal curvatures in different parts of the lens (or cornea) lead to blurred vision.

atherosclerosis (ath-er-o-skler-OS-is) Buildup of fatty deposits on and within the inner walls of arteries. Atherosclerosis is a risk factor for cardiovascular disease.

atom Smallest particle of an element that exhibits the properties of that element. Atoms are composed of protons, neutrons, and electrons.

ATP (adenosine triphosphate) (uh-DEN-oh-seen try-FOSS-fate) A nucleotide composed of adenosine and three phosphate groups. ATP is an important carrier of energy for the cell because energy is released when one of the phosphate groups is removed.

atrial natriuretic hormone (ANH) (AY-tree-ul NAH-tree-u-RET-ik) A hormone secreted by the atria of the heart. Helps regulate blood pressure by causing the kidneys to excrete more salt.

atrium (pl. atria) (AY-tree-um) One of the two chambers of the heart that receive blood from veins and deliver it to the ventricles.

auditory canal Part of the outer ear. The auditory canal channels sounds to the eardrum.

auditory tube Hollow tube connecting the middle ear with the throat. The auditory tube is important for equalizing air pressure in the middle ear with atmospheric pressure.

autoimmune disorder A condition in which the immune system attacks the body's own tissues.

autonomic division Division of the peripheral nervous system composed of the sympathetic and parasympathetic divisions. The autonomic division carries signals from the central nervous system that control automatic functions of the body's internal organs. Sometimes referred to as the autonomic nervous system (ANS).

autosomes (AW-tow-sohms) Chromosomes 1 to 22. The term *autosome* applies to all chromosomes except the sex chromosomes.

autotroph An organism that uses carbon dioxide and energy from its physical environment to build its own large organic molecules.

AV (atrioventricular) bundle Bundle of specialized fibers that conduct impulses from the AV node to the right and left ventricles.

AV (atrioventricular) node Specialized mass of conducting cells located at the atrioventricular junction in the heart.

AV (atrioventricular) valve Valve located between the atria and their corresponding ventricles which prevent blood from flowing back into the atria when the ventricles contract.

axial skeleton (AK-see-ul) The portion of the skeleton that forms the main axis of the body, consisting of the skull, ribs, sternum, and backbone.

axon (AK-sahn) An extension of a neuron that carries nerve impulses away from the nerve cell body. The conducting portion of a nerve cell.

B

B cell (B lymphocyte) (LIM-fo-syt) A white blood cell that matures in bone marrow and gives rise to antibody-producing plasma cells.

bacteria One of the three domains of life. Bacteria are prokaryotic microorganisms responsible for many human diseases.

balloon angioplasty Treatment to open a partially blocked blood vessel. The technique involves threading a small balloon into the blood vessel and then inflating the balloon, pressing the blocking material against the sides of the vessel.

baroreceptor Sensory receptor that is stimulated by increases in blood pressure.

base A substance capable of binding with hydrogen ions. A proton acceptor.

basement membrane Layer of nonliving extracellular material that anchors epithelial tissue to the underlying connective tissue.

basophil (BAY-so-fll) White blood cell whose granules stain well with a basic dye. Basophils release histamine and other substances during inflammation.

bile Greenish-yellow or brownish fluid that is secreted by the liver, stored in the gallbladder, and released into the small intestine. Bile is important in emulsifying fat.

biodiversity The variety of living species on Earth.

biogeochemical cycle A cycle in which the chemicals that compose living organisms are recycled between organisms and Earth itself.

biogeography Study of the distribution of plants and animals around the world.

biological magnification Process by which non-excreted substances become more concentrated in organisms that are higher in the food chain.

biology The study of living things and life's processes.

biomass Total living component of an ecosystem.

biosphere (BY-oh-sfeer) The portion of the surface of Earth (land, water, and air) inhabited by living organisms.

biotechnology The technical application of biological knowledge for human purposes.

biotic potential (by-AHT-ic) Maximum growth rate of a population under ideal conditions.

birth control pill Oral contraceptive containing hormones that inhibit ovulation.

blastocyst (BLAS-toh-sist) Stage of early embryonic development. The product of cleavage.

blood A fluid connective tissue consisting of water, solutes, blood cells, and platelets that carries nutrients and waste products to and from all cells.

blood-brain barrier A functional barrier between the blood and the brain that inhibits passage of certain substances from the blood into brain tissues.

blood doping The practice of increasing a person's red blood cell production above normal by artificial means, for the purpose of increasing oxygen-carrying capacity.

blood pressure The force exerted by blood against blood vessel walls, generated by the pumping action of the heart.

blood type Classification of blood based on the presence of surface antigens on red blood cells, and the presence of antibodies to surface antigens other than one's own.

BMR (basal metabolic rate) Rate at which energy is expended (heat produced) by the body per unit of time under resting (basal) conditions.

bone A connective tissue that forms the bony skeleton. Bone consists of a few living cells encased in a hard extracellular matrix of mineral salts.

bottleneck effect Evolutionary effect that occurs when a major catastrophe wipes out most of a population without regard to any previous measure of fitness.

botulism A form of poisoning caused by a bacterium, *Clostridium botulinum*, occasionally found in inadequately cooked or preserved foods.

Bowman's capsule Double-walled cup at the beginning of a renal tubule. Bowman's capsule, also called the glomerular capsule, encloses the glomerulus.

brain The command center of the body.

bronchiole (BRAHNG-kee-ohl) Small airways within the lungs that carry air to the alveoli. The walls of bronchioles are devoid of cartilage.

bronchitis (brahng-KI-tis) Inflammation of the bronchi.

bronchus (pl. bronchi) (BRAHNG-kus) Any one of the larger branching airways of the lungs. The walls of bronchi are reinforced with cartilage.

buffer Any substance that tends to minimize the changes in pH that might otherwise occur when an acid or base is added to a solution.

bulimia (byoo-LEE-mee-uh) Eating disorder involving episodes of binging and purging.

C

calcitonin (kal-suh-TOW-nin) Hormone released by the thyroid glands that promotes a decrease in blood calcium levels.

Calorie Amount of energy needed to raise the temperature of 1 kilogram of water 1° Celsius.

cancer A malignant, invasive disease in which cells become abnormal and divide uncontrollably. May spread throughout the body.

capillary (KAP-uh-lair-ee) The smallest type of blood vessel. Capillaries are the site of exchange between the blood and tissue cells.

carbohydrate (kar-boh-HY-drayt) Organic compound composed primarily of CH_2O groups. Includes starches, sugars, and cellulose.

carbonic anhydrase (kar-BAHN-ik an-HY-drase) Enzyme that facilitates the combination of carbon dioxide with water to form carbonic acid.

carcinogen (kar-SIN-o-jen) Cancer-causing agent.

cardiac cycle (KAR-dee-ak) Sequence of events encompassing one complete contraction and relaxation cycle of the atria and ventricles of the heart.

cardiac muscle Specialized muscle tissue of the heart.

cardiac output The amount of blood the heart pumps into the aorta each minute.

cardiovascular system The organ system composed of the heart and blood vessels.

carnivore (KAR-nih-vor) Organism that feeds only on animals.

carrying capacity The maximum number of individuals in a population that a given environment can sustain indefinitely

cartilage (KAR-til-ij) White, semiopaque, flexible connective tissue.

catabolism (kah-TAB-o-lizm) The process whereby larger molecules are broken down to smaller ones and energy is released.

catalyst (KAT-uh-list) A substance that changes the rate of a chemical reaction without itself being altered or consumed by the reaction.

cataracts (KAT-uh-rakts) Clouding of the eye's lens. Cataracts are often congenital or age-related.

cecum (SEE-kum) The blind-ended pouch at the beginning of the large intestine.

cell The smallest structure that shows all the characteristics of life. The cell is the fundamental structural and functional unit of all living organisms.

cell body Region of a nerve cell that includes the nucleus and most of the cytoplasmic mass, and from which the dendrites and axons extend.

cell cycle A repeating series of events in which a eukaryotic cell grows, duplicates its DNA, and then undergoes nuclear and cytoplasmic division to become two cells. Includes interphase (growth and DNA synthesis) and mitosis (cell division).

cell doctrine Theory consisting of three basic principles: (1) All living things are composed of cells and cell products. (2) A single cell is the smallest unit that exhibits all the characteristics of life. (3) All cells come only from preexisting cells.

cell junctions Various proteins that connect epithelial cells to each other.

cellular respiration The collective term for all cellular metabolic processes that result in the production of ATP.

central canal In bone, the hollow central tube of an osteon that contains nerves and blood vessels.

central nervous system (CNS) The brain and spinal cord.

centriole (SEN-tree-ohl) Small organelle found near the nucleus of the cell, important in cell division.

centromere (SEN-troh-meer) Constricted region of a chromosome where sister chromatids are attached to each other and where they attach to the mitotic spindle during cell division.

cerebellum (ser-ah-BELL-um) Brain region most involved in producing smooth, coordinated skeletal muscle activity.

cerebral cortex (suh-REE-brul KOR-teks) The outer gray matter region of the cerebral hemispheres. Some regions of the cerebral cortex receive sensory information; others control motor responses.

cerebral hemispheres The large paired structures that together form most of the cerebrum of the brain.

cerebrospinal fluid (suh-REE-broh-SPY-nul) Plasmalike fluid that fills the cavities of the CNS and surrounds the CNS externally. Protects the brain and spinal cord.

cerebrum (suh-REE-brum) The cerebral hemispheres and nerve tracts that join them together. Involves higher mental functions.

cesarean delivery (C-section) Surgical delivery of a baby.

chemical bonds Attractive forces between atoms that cause atoms to be bound to each other.

chemoreceptor (KEE-moh-rih-sep-tur) Type of receptor sensitive to various chemicals.

chemotherapy The use of therapeutic drugs to selectively kill cancer cells.

chlamydia (kla-MID-ee-uh) Sexually transmitted disease involving infection by the bacterium *Chlamydia trachomatis*.

cholecystokinin (CCK) (kohl-uh-sis-tuh-KYN-in) An intestinal hormone that stimulates contraction of the gallbladder and the release of pancreatic juice.

cholesterol (ko-LES-ter-ahl) Steroid found in animal fats as well as in most body tissues. Made by the liver.

chondroblast A cartilage-forming cell. In the fetus, chondroblasts produce the hyaline cartilage that forms the rudimentary models of future bones.

chorion (KOR-ee-ahn) Outermost fetal membrane. Helps form the placenta.

chorionic villi (kor-ee-AHN-ik VIL-eye) Extensions of the fetal chorion that project into maternal tissues. Samples of chorionic villi are sometimes taken in early pregnancy to obtain fetal cells for diagnosis of fetal disease.

choroid (KOR-oyd) The vascular middle layer of the eye.

chromatin (KROH-muh-tin) Threadlike material in the nucleus composed of DNA and proteins.

chromosome (KROH-muh-som) Rodlike structure of tightly coiled chromatin. Visible in the nucleus during cell division.

chyme (kym) Semifluid mass consisting of partially digested food and gastric juice that is delivered from the stomach into the small intestine.

cilium (pl. cilia) (SIL-ee-um) A tiny hair-like projection on cell surfaces that moves in a wavelike manner.

circulatory system The system consisting of the heart, blood vessels, and the blood that circulates through them.

cirrhosis (sir-ROH-sis) Chronic disease of the liver, characterized by an overgrowth of connective tissue (fibrosis).

citric acid cycle The metabolic pathway within mitochondria in which acetyl groups are completely disassembled into CO_2 and high-energy compounds. Also called the Krebs cycle.

clavicle The collarbone.

cleavage An early phase of embryonic development consisting of rapid mitotic cell divisions without cell growth.

climax community The stable result of ecological succession in a given environment.

clitoris (KLIT-uh-ris) In the female, a sensitive erectile organ located in the vulva.

cloning Production of identical copies of a gene, a cell, or an organism.

cochlea (KOK-lee-uh) Snail-shaped chamber in the inner ear that houses the organ of Corti.

codominance Pattern of inheritance in which both alleles of a gene are equally expressed even though the phenotypes they specify are different.

codon (KOH-dahn) The three-base sequence on a messenger RNA molecule that provides the code for a specific amino acid in protein synthesis.

coenzyme A small molecule that assists an enzyme by transporting small molecular groups. Most vitamins are coenzymes.

collagen fiber Strong and slightly flexible type of connective tissue fiber, made of protein.

colon (KOH-lun) The region of the large intestine between the cecum and the rectum. The colon includes ascending, transverse, descending, and sigmoid portions.

colostrum (koh-LAHS-trum) Milky fluid secreted by the mammary glands shortly before and after delivery. Contains proteins and antibodies.

community Array of several different populations that coexist and interact within the same environment.

compact bone Type of dense bone tissue found on the outer surfaces and shafts of bones.

complement system A group of bloodborne proteins which, when activated, enhance the inflammatory and immune responses and may lead to lysis of pathogens.

complete dominance Pattern of genetic inheritance in which one allele completely masks or suppresses the expression of its complementary allele.

complete protein A protein containing all 20 of the amino acids in proportions that meet our nutritional needs.

concussion An injury to the brain resulting from a physical blow that may result in a brief loss of consciousness.

cone cell One of the two types of photoreceptor cells in the retina of the eye. Cone cells provide for color vision.

congestive heart failure Progressive condition in which the pumping efficiency of the heart becomes impaired. The result is often an inability to adequately pump the venous blood being returned to the heart, venous congestion, and body fluid imbalances.

connective tissue A primary tissue; form and function vary extensively. Functions include support, energy storage, and protection.

consumer In ecosystems, an organism that cannot produce its own food and must feed on other organisms. Also called a heterotroph.

continental drift The slow movement over time of the Earth's tectonic plates.

control center In control system theory, a structure that receives input from a sensor, compares it to a correct, internally set value of the controlled variable, and sends an output to an effector. The most important control center in a living organism is the brain.

control group In scientific experiments, a group of subjects that undergoes all the steps in the experiment except the one being tested. The control group is used to evaluate all possible factors that might influence the experiment other than the experimental treatment. Compare *experimental group*.

controlled variable Any physical or chemical property that might vary from time to time and that must be controlled in order to maintain homeostasis. Examples of controlled variables are blood pressure, body temperature, and the concentration of glucose in blood.

core temperature The body's internal temperature. In humans, normal core temperature is about 98.6°F (37°C).

cornea (KOR-nee-uh) The transparent anterior portion of the eyeball.

coronary artery (KOR-uh-nair-ee) One of the two arteries of the heart leading to capillaries that supply blood to cardiac muscle.

coronary artery bypass graft (CABG) Surgery to improve blood flow. A piece of blood vessel is removed from elsewhere in the body and grafted onto a blocked coronary artery to bypass the damaged region.

corpus luteum (KOR-pus LOOT-ee-um) Structure that develops from cells of a ruptured ovarian follicle. The corpus luteum secretes progesterone and estrogen.

cortex (KOR-teks) General term for the outer surface layer of an organ.

Cortisol (KOR-tih-sahl) Glucocorticoid produced by the adrenal cortex, also called hydrocortisone.

covalent bond (koh-VAY-lent) Chemical bond created by electron sharing between atoms.

coxal bones The two large bones that connect the femur bones to the sacrum of the vertebral column. The coxal bones form our hips.

cranial nerve (KRAY-nee-ul) One of the 12 pairs of peripheral nerves that originate in the brain.

creatinine (kree-AT-uhn-een) A nitrogenous waste molecule excreted by the kidneys.

crossing-over Exchange of DNA segments between homologous chromosomes during prophase I of meiosis.

cystic fibrosis (SIS-tikfy-BRO-sys) Genetic disorder in which oversecretion of mucus clogs the respiratory passages. Cystic fibrosis can lead to fatal respiratory infections.

cytokines Signaling molecules secreted by helper T cells. Cytokines have a variety of functions, including promoting immune cell development, stimulating their activity, and attracting them to an area of infection.

cytokinesis (sy-tow-kih-NEE-sis) The division of cytoplasm that occurs after a cell nucleus has divided.

cytoplasm (SY-tow-plaz-um) The cellular material surrounding a cell nucleus and enclosed by the plasma membrane.

cytoskeleton A cell's internal "skeleton." The cytoplasm is a system of microtubules and other components that support cellular structures and provide the machinery to generate various cell movements.

cytotoxic T cell (sy-toh-TAHK-sik) A "killer T cell" that directly lyses foreign cells, cancer cells, or virus-infected body cells.

D

data Numerical information that can be organized and interpreted.

decomposer An organism that obtains energy by chemically breaking down the products, wastes, or remains of other organisms.

dehydration synthesis Process by which a larger molecule is synthesized by covalently bonding two smaller molecules together, with the subsequent removal of a molecule of water.

demographic transition A progression of changes followed by many nations, in which the society gradually moves from poor living conditions and a high death rate to improved economic conditions and a declining death rate.

denaturation (dee-nay-chur-AY-shun) Loss of a protein's normal shape and function produced by disruption of hydrogen bonds and other weak bonds.

dendrite (DEN-dryt) Branching neuron extension that serves as a receptive or input region. Dendrites conduct graded potentials toward the cell body.

denitrification (dee-nyt-ruh-fih-KAY-shun) Process in which nitrate is converted to nitrogen gas (N_2). Denitrification is part of the nitrogen cycle.

deoxyhemoglobin Hemoglobin that has given up its oxygen.

depolarization Loss of a state of polarity. In nerve and muscle cells, the loss or reduction of the inside-negative membrane potential.

dermis Layer of skin underlying the epidermis. Consists mostly of dense connective tissue.

desertification (deh-ZERT-uh-fuh-KAY-shun) Process by which marginal lands are converted to desertlike conditions.

detritus (dih-TRY-tus) Nonliving organic matter.

diabetes mellitus (dy-uh-BEE-teez MEL-ih-tus) Disease characterized by a high blood sugar concentration and glucose in the urine, caused by either deficient insulin production (Type 1 diabetes) or insufficient glucose uptake by cells (Type 2 diabetes).

dialysis (dy-AL-ih-sis) General term for several techniques that attempt to take the place of kidney function in patients whose kidneys have failed by letting the patient's blood exchange waste materials with artificial fluids. Two dialysis techniques are *continuous ambulatory peritoneal dialysis (CAPD)* and *hemodialysis*.

diaphragm (DY-uh-fram) A dome-shaped sheet of muscle that separates the thoracic cavity from the abdominal cavity. Also, a contraceptive device inserted into the vagina to cover the cervical opening.

diastole (dy-AS-toh-lee) Period of the cardiac cycle when a heart chamber is relaxed.

diastolic pressure (DY-uh-STAHL-ik) Lowest point of arterial blood pressure during a cardiac cycle. Diastolic pressure is the second of two numbers recorded by the health care provider, the first being systolic pressure.

dietary supplement A product not normally part of a diet, but can be taken to improve overall health or well-being.

differentiation Process by which a cell changes in form or function.

diffusion (dih-FYOO-shun) The movement of molecules from one region to another as the result of random motion. Net diffusion proceeds from a region of higher concentration to a region of lower concentration.

digestion Chemical or mechanical process of breaking down foodstuffs to substances that can be absorbed.

digestive system The system of organs that share the common function of getting nutrients into the body.

diploid The number of chromosomes in a body cell (*2n*), twice the chromosomal number (*n*) of a gamete. In humans, *2n* = 46.

disaccharide (dy-SAK-uh-ryd) Literally, a double sugar. A disaccharide consists of two monosaccharides linked together. Sucrose and lactose are disaccharides.

diuretic (dy-yoo-RET-ik) Any substance that enhances urinary output.

DNA (deoxyribonucleic acid) (dee-OX-ee-RY-bo-new-CLAY-ik) A nucleic acid found in all living cells. Carries the organism's hereditary information.

DNA fingerprinting A technique for identifying the source of a fragment of DNA after it has been sufficiently copied by PCR.

DNA ligases A class of enzymes that join fragments of DNA together.

DNA polymerase (poh-LIM-ur-ays) Enzyme that links separate nucleotides together as a new strand of DNA is formed.

dominant allele An allele that masks or suppresses the expression of its complementary allele.

Down syndrome A condition caused by inheriting three copies of chromosome 21.

duodenum (doo-oh-DEE-num) First part of the small intestine.

dysplasia (dis-PLAY-zhee-uh) Abnormal changes in the shape and/or organization of cells. Dysplasia may precede the development of cancer.

E

ECG (electrocardiogram) Graphic record of the electrical activity of the heart.

ecological pyramid Graph representing the bio-mass, energy content, or number of organisms of each level in a food web. An ecological pyramid includes both producer and consumer populations.

ecology (ee-KAHL-uh-jee) Study of the relationships between organisms and their physical environment.

ecosystem (EEK-oh-sis-tem) All living organisms, all matter, and all energy in a given environment.

ectoderm Embryonic germ layer. Ectoderm forms the epidermis of the skin and its derivatives, and nerve tissues.

ectopic pregnancy (ek-TOP-ik) A pregnancy that results from implantation outside the uterus. The most common form of ectopic pregnancy is a tubal pregnancy.

efferent Directed from or away from a point of reference. In the kidney, an efferent arteriole carries blood away from each glomerulus.

effector An effector takes the necessary action to correct an imbalance, in accordance with the signals it receives from the control center.

egg An ovum; a mature female gamete.

ejaculatory duct In the male, a short duct that carries sperm from the ductus deferens and seminal fluid from the seminal vesicle to the ureter.

elastic fibers Thin, coiled, fibrous connective tissues made primarily of the protein elastin, which can stretch without breaking.

electrocardiogram (ECG) Graphic record of the electrical activity of the heart.

electron Negatively charged subatomic particle with almost no weight. Electrons orbit the atom's nucleus.

electron transport system A series of electron and energy-transfer molecules in the inner membrane of mitochondria that provide the energy for the active transport of hydrogen ions across the membrane. The electron transport system is essential to the ability of the mitochondria to produce ATP for the cell.

element One of a limited number of unique varieties of matter that composes substances of all kinds. Elements each consist of just one kind of atom.

embolus (EM-bo-lus) Material, such as a blood clot, that floats in the bloodstream and may block a blood vessel.

embryo (EM-bree-oh) An organism in an early stage of development. In humans, the embryonic period extends from the beginning of week 3 to the end of week 8.

embryonic disk A flattened disk of cells that develops in the blastocyst shortly after implantation. The embryonic disk will develop into the embryo.

emphysema (em-flh-SEE-muh) Chronic respiratory disorder involving damage to the bronchioles and alveoli. In emphysema, loss of elastic tissue in the bronchioles causes them to collapse during expiration, trapping air in the alveoli and eventually damaging them as well.

endocrine gland (EN-duh-krin) Ductless gland that secretes one or more hormones into the bloodstream.

endocrine system Body system that includes all of the hormone-secreting organs and glands. Along with the nervous system, the endocrine system is involved in coordination and control of body activities.

endocytosis (en-do-sy-TO-sis) Process by which fluids, extracellular particles, or even whole bacteria are taken into cells. In endocytosis, the materials become enclosed by a vesicle composed of cell membrane material and then internalized within the cell. Phagocytosis is an example of endocytosis.

endoderm (EN-do-derm) Embryonic germ layer. Endoderm forms the lining of the digestive tube and its associated structures.

endometrium (en-do-MEE-tree-um) Inner lining of the uterus. The endometrium becomes thickened and more vascular during the uterine cycle in preparation for pregnancy.

endoplasmic reticulum (ER) (en-do-PLAS-mik reh-TIK-yuh-lum) Membranous network of tubular or saclike channels in the cytoplasm of a cell. The endoplasmic reticulum is the site of most of the cell's production of proteins and other cell compounds.

energy The capacity to do work. Energy may be stored (potential energy) or in action (kinetic energy).

environmental resistance Factors in the environment that limit population growth in a particular geographic area.

enzyme (EN-zym) A protein that acts as a biological catalyst to speed up a chemical reaction.

eosinophil (ee-oh-SIN-oh-fil) Granular white blood cell whose granules stain readily with a red stain called eosin. Eosinophils attack parasites and function in allergic responses.

epidermis (ep-ih-DUR-mus) Outermost layer of the skin. The epidermis is composed of keratinized stratified squamous epithelium.

epididymis (ep-ih-DID-ih-mis) Portion of the male reproductive system in which sperm mature. The epididymis empties into the vas deferens.

epiglottis (ep-ih-GLAHT-is) Flaplike structure of elastic cartilage at the back of the throat that covers the opening of the larynx during swallowing.

epilepsy (EP-ih-lep-see) Condition involving abnormal electrical discharges of groups of brain neurons. Epilepsy may cause seizures.

epinephrine (ep-ih-NEF-rin) Primary hormone produced by the adrenal medulla, also called adrenaline.

epithelial tissue (ep-ih-THEE-lee-ul) A primary tissue that covers the body's surface, lines its internal cavities, and forms glands.

erection An increase in the length, diameter, and stiffness of the penis that facilitates its entry into the vagina.

erythrocyte (red blood cell) Blood cell that transports oxygen from the lungs to the tissues and carbon dioxide from the tissues to the lungs.

erythropoietin (ih-rith-roh-PO-ih-tin) Hormone that stimulates production of red blood cells.

esophagus (ih-SOF-uh-gus) Muscular tube extending from the throat to the stomach. The esophagus is collapsed when it does not contain food.

essential amino acids Group of eight amino acids that the body cannot synthesize. Essential amino acids must be obtained from the diet.

estrogen (ES-tro-jen) Female sex hormone that stimulates the development of female secondary sex characteristics, helps oocytes mature, and affects the uterine lining during the menstrual cycle and pregnancy.

Eukarya One of the three domains of life. Eukarya includes all life-forms whose cells have nuclei.

eukaryote (yoo-KAIR-ih-ot) An organism composed of cells with nuclei and internal membrane-bound organelles. Animals, plants, protists, and fungi are all eukaryotes.

eutrophication (yoo-troh-flh-KAY-shun) Process by which mineral and organic nutrients accumulate in a body of water, leading to plant overgrowth and loss of oxygen. Eutrophication maybe accelerated by pollution.

evolution An unpredictable and natural process of descent over time with genetic modification. Evolution is influenced by natural selection, chance, historical events, and changing environments.

exocrine gland Specialized epithelial tissue that secretes a product directly into a hollow organ or duct.

exocytosis (ex-oh-sy-TO-sis) Mechanism by which substances are moved from the cell interior to the extracellular space. In exocytosis, a membrane-bound secretory vesicle fuses with the plasma membrane and releases its contents to the exterior.

exon A nucleotide sequence of DNA that specifies a useful informational sequence. Compare *intron*.

experiment A procedure designed to test a working hypothesis. In a controlled experiment, all conditions of the environment are controlled except the specific factor dictated by the working hypothesis.

experimental group In a controlled experiment the group of subjects that receives the experimental treatment. Compare *control group*.

exponential growth Growth pattern of a population that follows a characteristic J-curve. A population undergoing exponential growth will double repeatedly over similar time periods.

external nose The visible portion of the nose.

extinction The loss of a particular life-form completely.

F

facilitated transport Passive transport of a substance into or out of a cell along a concentration gradient. Facilitated transport requires a carrier protein.

FAD A transport molecule within mitochondria that can accept hydrogen ions and electrons liberated by the citric acid cycle, forming high-energy $FADH_2$.

farsightedness Condition in which the eyeball is too short, causing nearby objects to be focused behind the retina; also called hyperopia.

fatigue A decline in muscle performance during exercise.

fatty acid Linear chain of carbon and hydrogen atoms (hydrocarbon chains) with an organic acid group at one end. Fatty acids are constituents of fats.

femur The large bone found in the upper leg. The femur is the longest and strongest bone in the body.

fertility rate Number of children that each female has during her lifetime.

fertilization Fusion of the nuclei of sperm and egg, thereby creating a zygote.

fever Body temperature that has risen above the normal set point (in humans, approximately 37°C, or 98.6°F). Afever often indicates illness.

fiber General term for a thin strand. A muscle fiber is a single muscle cell. A connective tissue fiber is a thin strand of extracellular material. In the digestive system, fiber refers to material that is indigestible but beneficial in the diet.

fibrin (FY-brin) Fibrous insoluble protein formed during blood clotting.

fibrinogen (fy-BRIN-oh-jen) A blood protein that is converted to fibrin during blood clotting.

fibroblast (FY-broh-blast) Young, actively mitotic cell that forms the fibers of connective tissue.

fibula The thinner of the two bones found in the lower leg.

fimbriae (FYM-bree-ay) Fingerlike projections at the open end of an oviduct that help move an oocyte into the oviduct.

flagellum (pl. flagella) (flah-JEL-um) Long, whiplike extension of the plasma membrane used by sperm and some bacteria for propulsion.

follicle (FAHL-ih-kul) Ovarian structure consisting of a developing egg surrounded by one or more layers of granulosa cells.

follicle-stimulating hormone (FSH) Hormone produced by the anterior pituitary that stimulates ovarian follicle production in females and sperm production in males.

food web Hierarchy consisting of numerous food chains. A food web depicts interactions between producers and consumers in an ecosystem.

forebrain Anterior portion of the brain that includes the cerebrum, the thalamus, and the hypothalamus.

fossil Preserved remnant of an organism. The fossil record is one of our richest sources of information about life-forms that lived in the past.

fossil fuel A carbon-containing compound (coal, oil, or gas) that was formed millions of years ago by living organisms, then covered by sediments.

fovea centralis (FOH-vee-uh-sen-TRA-lis) A small region at the center of the macula of the retina that is responsible for the highest visual acuity. The fovea centralis consists of densely packed cone cells.

fraternal twins Twins resulting from the ovulation and fertilization of more than one oocyte in a particular cycle. Fraternal twins are as different as any two children by the same parents.

free radicals Highly reactive chemicals with unpaired electrons that can disrupt the structure of proteins, lipids, and nucleic acids.

functional food A food or drink product that is said to have benefits beyond basic nutrition (also called a nutraceutical).

fungi (FUN-jy) One of the five kingdoms of life. The fungi include yeasts, molds, and mushrooms.

G

gallbladder Organ located beneath the right lobe of the liver. The gallbladder stores and concentrates bile.

gallstones Hard crystals containing cholesterol, calcium, and bile salts that can obstruct the flow of bile from the gallbladder.

gamete (GAM-eet) Haploid sex or germ cell. Sperm and eggs are gametes.

ganglion (pl. ganglia) (GANG-lee-on) Collection of nerve cell bodies outside the central nervous system.

gastric glands Glands located beneath the stomach lining. Gastric glands secrete gastric juice.

gastric juice Collective term for the hydrochloric acid, pepsinogen, and fluid secreted by gastric glands.

gastrin (GAS-trin) Hormone secreted into the blood by cells located in the gastric glands. Gastrin regulates the secretion of gastric juice by stimulating production of hydrochloric acid.

gastrointestinal (GI) tract A hollow tube that extends from the mouth to the anus. The GI tract includes mouth, pharynx, esophagus, stomach, small intestine, large intestine, rectum, and anus.

gel electrophoresis A technique for separating fragments of DNA or protein according to size.

gene (JEEN) The unit of heredity. Most genes encode for specific polypeptides, and each gene has a specific location on a particular chromosome.

gene flow The physical movement of alleles caused by movement of individuals into (immigration) or out of (emigration) a population. Gene flow tends to mix pools of genes that might not otherwise mingle.

gene therapy Technique in which defective genes are repaired or replaced with their normal counterparts.

genetic drift Random changes in allele frequency because of chance events.

genetic engineering The planned alteration of the genetic makeup of an organism by modifying, inserting, or deleting genes or groups of genes.

genital herpes (JEN-ih-tul HUR-peez) A sexually transmitted disease that results from infection by the herpes simplex type 2 virus.

genital warts A sexually transmitted disease caused by the human papillomavirus (HPV). Genital warts are a potential risk factor for cancers of the cervix or penis.

genome (JEE nohm) The complete set of DNA in the chromosomes of a particular organism.

genotype An individual's particular set of genes.

genus (JEE-nus) Level of taxonomic classification. Modern humans belong to the genus *Homo*.

geographic range The area of Earth over which a particular species is distributed.

GIFT (gamete intrafallopian transfer) Technique to enhance fertility in which unfertilized eggs and sperm are placed directly into an oviduct (Fallopian tube) through a small incision in a woman's abdomen.

gigantism Pituitary disorder caused by hypersecretion of growth hormone during childhood and adolescence.

gingivitis (jin-jih-VY-tis) Condition of inflamed gum tissue (gingiva), often caused by tooth decay and poor oral hygiene.

gland One or more epithelial cells that are specialized to secrete or excrete substances.

glaucoma (glaw-KO-muh) Eye condition caused by blockage of the ducts that drain the aqueous humor in the eye, resulting in high intraocular pressures and compression of the optic nerve. Glaucoma can result in blindness unless detected early.

glial cells (GLEE-ul) Cells in the nervous system that surround and protect neurons and supply them with nutrients. Glial cells do not generate action potentials.

global warming Increase in average global temperature.

globulins A group of proteins in blood plasma having transport and immune functions. Many antibodies are globulins.

glomerular filtration The process of filtering protein-free plasma fluid from the glomerular capillaries into Bowman's capsule.

glomerulus (glow-MAIR-yoo-lus) Cluster or tuft of capillaries inside the glomerular capsule in a kidney. The glomerulus is involved in the formation of the glomerular filtrate.

glottis (GLAHT-tis) Opening between the vocal cords in the larynx.

glucagon (GLOO-kah-gon) Hormone formed by alpha cells in the islets of Langerhans in the pancreas. Glucagon raises the glucose level of blood by stimulating the liver to break down glycogen.

glucocorticoids (gloo-kah-KOR-tih-koyds) Adrenal cortex hormones that increase blood glucose levels and help the body resist long-term stressors. The principal glucocorti-coid is Cortisol.

glycogen (GLY-ko-jen) Main carbohydrate stored in animal cells. A polysaccharide.

glycolysis (gly-KOL-ih-sis) Breakdown of glucose to pyruvic acid. Glycolysis is an anaerobic process.

goiter (GOY-tur) An enlarged thyroid, caused by iodine deficiency or other factors.

Golgi apparatus (GOHL-jee) Membranous system within a cell that packages proteins and lipids destined for export, packages enzymes into lysosomes for cellular use, and modifies proteins destined to become part of cellular membranes.

gonad (GOH-nad) An organ that produces sex cells. The gonads are the testes of the male and the ovaries of the female.

gonadotropins (goh-nad-o-TRO-pinz) Gonad-stimulating hormones produced by the anterior pituitary. The gonadotropins are FSH and LH.

gonorrhea (gahn-o-REE-uh) Sexually transmitted disease caused by the bacterium *Neisseria gonorrhoeae*.

graded potential A local change in membrane potential that varies directly with the strength of the stimulus. Graded potentials decline with distance from the stimulus.

granular leukocyte (GRAN-yoo-lur LOO-ko-syt) A type of white blood cell with granules that stain readily.

Graves' disease A disorder in which the thyroid gland produces too much thyroxine.

gray matter Area of the central nervous system that contains cell bodies and unmyelinated fibers of neurons. The gray matter is gray because of the absence of myelin.

greenhouse effect A natural phenomenon in which atmospheric gases allow sunlight to pass through but trap most of the heat that radiates outward from Earth's surface.

greenhouse gases Atmospheric gases, notably CO_2 and methane, responsible for the greenhouse effect.

growth hormone Hormone produced by the anterior pituitary that stimulates growth in general.

growth plate Cartilage plate located near the ends of bone. Bones become longer during childhood and adolescence because new cartilage is continually being added to the outer surface of the growth plates.

growth rate The percentage increase in a population per unit time. Growth rate is calculated as the number of births per year minus the number of deaths per year, divided by population number.

H

habitat The type of location where an organism chooses to live. An organism's habitat typically is determined by its tolerance for certain environmental conditions.

hair cells The mechanoreceptor cells of the ear.

haploid (HAP-loyd) Half the diploid number of chromosomes; the number of chromosomes in a gamete.

heart attack Condition characterized by the death of heart tissue caused by inadequate oxygen supply. The medical term for a heart attack is *myocardial infarction*.

heart failure A condition where the heart may become weaker and less efficient at pumping blood.

helper T cell Type of T lymphocyte that orchestrates cell-mediated immunity by direct contact with other immune cells and by releasing chemicals called lymphokines.

hematocrit (hee-MAHT-oh-krit) The percentage of blood that consists of red blood cells.

hemoglobin (HEE-moh-gloh-bin) Oxygen-transporting protein in red blood cells that gives the cells their characteristic red color.

hemophilia (hee-moh-FIL-ee-uh) Collective term for several different hereditary bleeding disorders with similar symptoms. Hemophilia is caused by a deficiency of one or more clotting factors.

hemostasis (HEE-mo-STAY-sis) Stoppage of bleeding or of the circulation of blood to a part.

hepatic portal system (heh-PAT-ik) The system of blood vessels connecting the organs of the digestive tract to the liver.

hepatitis (hep-uh-TY-tis) General term for inflammation of the liver. Hepatitis is sometimes caused by viral infections.

herbivore (HUR-buh-vor) An organism that feeds on plants, utilizing the energy stored in them. Also called a primary consumer.

heterotroph (HET-ur-oh-trof) An organism that cannot utilize the sun's energy to synthesize the molecules it needs. Instead, it must consume foods that contain stored forms of energy. Also called a consumer.

heterozygous (HET-ur-oh-ZY-gus) Having different alleles at the same location (on a pair of homologous chromosomes).

hindbrain Region of brain connected to the spinal cord. The hindbrain comprises the medulla oblongata, cerebellum, pons, and part of the reticular formation.

hippocampus (hip-po-KAM-pus) In the brain, a region of the limbic system that plays a role in converting new information to long-term memories.

histamine (HIS-ta-meen) Substance produced by basophils and mast cells that causes vasodilation and increases vascular permeability.

HIV (human immunodeficiency virus) Virus that destroys helper T cells, thus depressing cell-mediated immunity. Symptomatic AIDS gradually appears when lymph nodes can no longer contain the virus.

homeostasis (ho-mee-oh-STAY-sis) State of body equilibrium characterized by a relatively constant and stable internal environment.

hominids (HAHM-ih-nids) Common name for members of the family *Hominidae*. Hominids include present-day humans (*Homo sapiens*) and all of their extinct ancestors of the genus Australopithecus and the genus *Homo*.

hominoids (HAHM-ih-noyds) A sub-group of primates that diverged from a common ancestor of old-world monkeys to become the great apes (gibbons, orangutans, gorillas, chimpanzees) and modern humans.

Homo erectus (HOH-moh ih-REK-tus) A species of *Homo* that diverged from *Homo ergaster* and spread across Africa into Asia and Europe. *Homo erectus* died out only 50,000 years ago.

Homo ergaster (HOH-moh er-GAS-tur) A species of *Homo* that arose from *Homo habilis* ancestors about 1.9 million years ago and migrated out of Africa to establish colonies as far away as Java and China.

Homo habilis (HOH-moh HAB-ih-lus) First distinctly human ancestor. *Homo habilis* showed brain enlargement, changes in teeth and facial features, a decline in sexual dimorphism, and conversion to a diet that included meat. *Homo habilis* may also have used tools.

Homo heidelbergensis (HOH-moh HY-del-bur-GEN-sus) Sometimes called "archaic" *Homo sapiens*, this species descended from *Homo ergaster* and eventually gave rise to modern humans, *Homo sapiens*.

Homo sapiens (HOH-moh SAY-pee-enz) Genus and species of modern humans, thought to have evolved about 140,000 to 100,000 years ago.

homologous chromosomes (ho-MAHL-uh-gus) Chromosomes that look identical under the microscope. Homologous chromosomes have the same genes in the same locations.

homologous structures Body structures that share a common origin.

homozygous (hoh-moh-ZY-gus) Having identical alleles at the same location (on a pair of homologous chromosomes).

hormone (HOR-mohn) A chemical messenger molecule secreted by an endocrine gland or cell into the bloodstream that has effects on specific target cells throughout the body.

human papillomavirus (HPV) (pap-ih-LOH-ma-vy-rus) Virus that causes genital warts. HPV is a risk factor for cancers of the cervix or penis.

humerus The long bone of the upper arm.

hydrogen bond Weak bond that forms between a hydrogen atom with a partial positive charge and a nearby atom with a partial negative charge.

hydrolysis (hy-DRAHL-ih-sis) Process in which water is used to split a molecule into two smaller molecules.

hydrophilic A substance that is attracted to water. Most polar and charged compounds are hydrophilic, and therefore they dissolve easily in water.

hydrophobic A substance that is not attracted to water or is repelled by water. Nonpolar compounds such as oils are hydrophobic.

hyperopia (hy-per-OH-pee-uh) Condition in which the eyeball is too short, causing nearby objects to be focused behind the retina; also called farsightedness.

hyperplasia (hy-per-PLAY-zhee-uh) An increase in the number of cells in a tissue caused by an increase in the rate of cell division.

hyperpolarization Transient local change in the resting potential of a neuron that makes it even more negative than usual.

hypertension High blood pressure. Clinically hypertension is defined as a systolic blood pressure of 140 mm Hg or higher or a diastolic blood pressure of 90 mm Hg or higher.

hypertonic General term for above-normal tone or tension. In biology, a hypertonic solution is one with a higher solute concentration than plasma. Cells shrink when placed in a hypertonic solution.

hypertrophy (hy-PER-tro-fee) An enlargement or increase in size of an organ or tissue due to an increase in the size of its constituent cells, rather than an increase in cell number.

hypotension Low blood pressure.

hypothalamus Region of the brain forming the floor of the third ventricle. The hypothalamus helps regulate the body's internal environment by secreting releasing factors that affect the secretion of the hormones of the anterior pituitary.

hypothesis An explanation or description of a proposed truth. A hypothesis is expressed as a testable statement about the natural world.

hypotonic General term for below-normal tone or tension. In biology, a hypotonic solution is one with a lower solute concentration than plasma. Cells swell when placed in a hypotonic solution.

I

identical twins Twins that arise when a single fertilized ovum splits in two shortly after fertilization. Identical twins have identical genotypes.

immune response The activities of the immune system.

immune system A complex group of cells, proteins, and structures of the lymphatic system that work together to provide the immune response.

immunity Resistance to disease and pathogens.

immunization (im-yoo-nuh-ZAY-shun) A strategy for causing the body to develop immunity to a specific pathogen. Immunization may be active (the administraion of a vaccine) or passive (the administration of specific antibodies).

immunoglobulin (Ig) (im-yoo-noh-GLAHB-yoo-lin) Blood plasma proteins (gamma globulins) that play a crucial role in immunity. There are five classes.

immunosuppressive drugs Medications that block the immune response. Examples are corticosteroid drugs to suppress inflammation and cytotoxic medications to block activated lymphocytes.

immunotherapy Treatments that promote the general responsiveness of the immune system so that it can fight cancer more effectively.

incomplete dominance A pattern of genetic inheritance in which the heterozygous genotype results in a phenotype that is intermediate between the two homozygous phenotypes.

independent assortment Mendelian principle that genetic factors separate completely independently of each other during the formation of sperm and egg. Independent assortment applies fully only to genes located on different chromosomes.

inflammation (in-fluh-MAY-shun) A non-specific defensive response of the body to tissue injury characterized by dilation of blood vessels and an increase in vessel permeability. The presence of inflammation is indicated by redness, heat, swelling and pain.

inheritance Characteristics or traits that are transmitted from parents to offspring via genes.

inner ear Region of the ear consisting of the cochlea and the vestibular apparatus. The cochlea sorts sounds by tone and converts them into nerve impulses. The vestibular apparatus helps maintain balance.

insertion The end of a muscle that attaches to another bone across a joint.

insulin (IN-suh-lin) A hormone secreted by the pancreas that enhances the uptake of glucose by cells, thus lowering blood glucose levels.

integumentary system The proper name for the skin and its accessory structures such as hair, nails, and glands.

interferon (in-tur-FEER-ahn) Chemical that is able to provide some protection against virus invasion of the body. Interferon inhibits viral reproduction.

interleukin (in-tur-LOO-kin) A substance that promotes development of immune cells.

internal environment The environment that surrounds the cells of a multicellular organism.

interneuron A neuron within the central nervous system located between two other neurons. Interneurons receive input from one or more neurons and influence the functioning of other neurons.

interphase One of two major periods in the cell life cycle. Includes the period from cell formation to cell division.

interstitial fluid (in-tur-STISH-ul) Fluid between body cells.

intervertebral disk (in-tur-vur-TEE-brul) A disk of fibrocartilage between vertebrae.

intron A noncoding nucleotide sequence of DNA. Compare *exon*.

ion (EYE-ahn) An atom or molecule with a positive or negative electric charge.

ionic bond (eye-AHN-ik) Chemical bond formed by the attractive force between oppositely charged ions.

iris (EYE-ris) A colored disk-shaped muscle that determines how much light enters the eye.

isotonic General term for normal tone or tension. In biology an isotonic solution is one with the same solute concentration as plasma. Cells maintain their normal cell volume in isotonic solutions.

isotopes Different atomic forms of the same element, varying only in the number of neutrons they contain. The heavier forms tend to be radioactive.

IUD (intrauterine device) Contraceptive device that is inserted into the uterus by a health care provider.

IVF (in vitro fertilization) Fertilization outside the body. Eggs are harvested from a woman and fertilized, and the embryo is inserted into the woman's uterus through her cervix.

J

jaundice (JAWN-dis) Yellowish color of the skin, mucous membranes, and sometimes the whites of the eyes. Jaundice is often caused by liver malfunction and high circulating levels of bilirubin.

jejunum (jeh-JOO-num) The part of the small intestine between the duodenum and the ileum.

joint The junction or area of contact between two or more bones; also called an articulation.

juxtaglomerular apparatus In the kidney, a region near the glomerulus where the afferent arteriole and the efferent arteriole make contact with the distal tubule. The hormone renin is secreted by specialized cells of the afferent arteriole of the juxtaglomerular apparatus.

K

karyotype (KAIR-ee-oh-typ) The diploid chromosomal complement in any species. The human karyotype typically is shown as a composite display of the 22 pairs of autosomes arranged from longest to shortest, plus the sex chromosomes X and Y.

keratinocyte (kair-uh-TIN-oh-syt) Type of cell in the epidermis that produces a tough, waterproof protein called keratin.

killer T cell T lymphocyte that directly lyses foreign cells, cancer cells, or virus-infected body cells; also called a cytotoxic T cell.

kinetic energy Energy in motion; energy actually doing work.

Klinefelter syndrome A condition caused by an XXY genotype. People with Klinefelter syndrome show a tall male phenotype.

Krebs cycle See *citric acid cycle*.

L

lactation Production and secretion of milk.

lacteal (LAK-tee-ul) Small lymphatic vessel in a villus of the small intestine that takes up lipids.

lactose intolerance (LAK-tohs) A common disorder of digestion and absorption caused by insufficient quantities of the enzyme lactase, which digests the lactose in milk and dairy products.

large intestine Portion of the digestive tract extending from the small intestine to the anus. Consists of the cecum, appendix, colon, rectum, and anal canal.

larynx (LAIR-inks) Cartilaginous organ containing the vocal cords, located between the trachea and pharynx. The larynx is also called the voice box.

law of independent assortment All alleles of different genes are distributed to egg and sperm cells independently of each other during meiosis.

law of segregation When gametes are formed in the parents, the alleles separate from each other so that each gamete gets only one allele of each gene.

lens A transparent, flexible, curved structure that focuses incoming light on the retina at the back of the eye.

leukemia (loo-KEE-mee-uh) Cancer of the cells that form white blood cells, resulting in overproduction of abnormal white blood cells.

leukocyte (white blood cell) One of several types of blood cells that are part of the body's defense system. Leukocytes are diverse in structure and specific function. They compose only about 1% of the volume of blood.

Leydig cell (LAY-dig) Cells located between the seminiferous tubules of the testes. Leydig cells produce testosterone.

ligament Dense fibrous connective tissue that connects bone to bone.

limbic system Functional brain system involved in emotional responses.

linked alleles Alleles physically joined on the same chromosome.

lipase (LY-pace) Any lipid-digesting enzyme.

lipid (LIP-id) Organic compounds formed of carbon, hydrogen, and oxygen. Fats, oils, and cholesterol are lipids. Lipids are not very soluble in water.

lipoprotein (ly-poh-PRO-teen) A compound containing both lipid and protein. Two medically important lipoproteins are the low-density lipoproteins (LDLs) and high-density lipoproteins (HDLs) that transport cholesterol.

liver Large, lobed organ that overlies the stomach in the abdominal cavity. The liver produces bile to help digest fat, and serves other metabolic and regulatory functions.

lonevity How long a person lives.

loop of Henle (HEN-lee) Hairpin-shaped tubular structure that extends into the medulla of a nephron. The loop of Henle (also called the loop of the nephron) is important in the ability of the kidney to form either concentrated or dilute urine.

lumen (LOO-men) Cavity inside a tube, blood vessel, or hollow organ.

lupus erythematosis (LOO-pus air-uh-them-uh-TOW-sis) An autoimmune disorder in which the body attacks its own connective tissue.

luteinizing hormone (LH) (LOO-tee-in-eye-zing) Anterior pituitary hormone that aids maturation of cells in the ovary and triggers ovulation. In males, LH causes the interstitial cells of the testis to produce testosterone.

lymph (LIMF) Fluid derived from interstitial fluid transported by lymphatic vessels.

lymph nodes Small masses of tissue and lymphatic vessels that contain macrophages and lymphocytes, which remove microorganisms, cellular debris, and abnormal cells from the lymph before it is returned to the cardiovascular system.

lymphatic system System consisting of lymphatic vessels, lymph nodes, and other lymphoid organs and tissues. The lymphatic system returns excess interstitial fluid to the cardiovascular system and provides a site for immune surveillance.

lymphocyte (LIM-foh-syt) One of several types of white blood cells (T cells and B cells) that participate in nonspecific and specific (immune) defense responses.

lymphoma General term for cancers of the lymphoid tissues.

lysosome (LY-soh-sohm) Organelle originating from the Golgi apparatus that contains strong digestive enzymes.

lysozyme (LY-soh-zym) Enzyme in saliva and tears that kills certain kinds of bacteria.

M

macroevolution Large-scale evolutionary trends or changes that apply to whole groups of species, often as a result of changing environments or major historical events.

macrophage (MAK-roh-fayj) Large phagocytic white blood cell derived from a monocyte; it engulfs damaged tissue cells, bacteria, and other foreign debris. Macrophages are important as antigen presenters to T cells and B cells in the immune response.

macula (MAK-u-luh) The central region of the retina, where photoreceptor density is the highest.

malignant tumor A mass of cells that has metastasized to become invasive cancer.

mammal Vertebrates that have hair during all or part of their lives, and mammary glands in the female that produce milk.

mammary gland Milk-producing gland of the breast.

mast cell Immune cell that detects foreign substances in the tissue spaces and releases histamine to initiate a local inflammatory response against them. Mast cells typically are clustered deep in an epithelium or along blood vessels.

matter The material substance, composed of elements, that makes up the natural world. Matter takes up space and has weight.

mechanoreceptor (meh-KAN-oh-ree-sep-tur) Receptor sensitive to mechanical pressure or distortion, such as that produced by touch, sound, or muscle contractions.

medulla (meh-DUL-uh) General term for the inner zone of an organ. In the kidney, an inner pyramid-shaped zone of dense tissue that contains the loops of Henle. The term is also used for an area of the brain (medulla oblongata) and for the inner zone of the adrenal glands.

medulla oblongata (meh-DUL-uh ahb-long-GAH-tah) Portion of the brain stem. Contains reflex centers for vital functions such as respiration and blood circulation.

meiosis (my-OH-sis) Nuclear division process that reduces the chromosomal number by half. Meiosis results in the formation of four haploid (n) cells. It occurs only in certain reproductive organs.

melanocyte (meh-LAN-oh-syt) Type of cell located near the base of the epidermis. Melanocytes produce a dark brown pigment called melanin that is largely responsible for skin color.

melanoma (mel-ah-NO-mah) Least common but most dangerous form of skin cancer.

melatonin (mel-ah-TON-in) A hormone secreted by the pineal gland that seems to synchronize our body's daily rhythms and may induce sleep. It may also play a role in determining the onset of puberty.

memory The act of storing information and retrieving it later, as needed.

memory cell Members of T cell and B cell clones that provide for immunologic memory.

meninges (meh-NIN-jeez) Protective coverings of the central nervous system.

meningitis (meh-nin-JY-tis) Inflammation of the meninges.

menopause (MEN-oh-pawz) Period of a woman's life when, prompted by hormonal changes, ovulation and menstruation cease.

menstrual cycle (MEN-stroo-ul) Pattern of changes in the ovaries and uterus. The menstrual cycle lasts about 28 days and is controlled by hormones.

menstruation (men-stroo-AY-shun) Process in which the endometrial lining disintegrates, its small blood vessels rupture, and the tissue and blood are shed through the vagina.

mesoderm (MEEZ-oh-durm) Primary germ layer that forms the skeleton and muscles of the body.

messenger RNA (mRNA) Long nucleotide strand that complements the exact nucleotide sequence of genetically active DNA. Messenger RNA carries the genetic message to the cytoplasm.

metabolism Sum total of the chemical reactions occurring in body cells.

metaphase Second stage of mitosis, during which the chromosomes align themselves on one plane at the center of the cell.

metastasis (meh-TAS-tuh-sis) The spread of cancer from one organ or location to another not directly connected to it.

MHC (major histocompatibility complex) proteins A group of proteins on the cell surface that identify an individual's cells as "self" and normally signal the immune system to bypass the individual's cells.

microevolution Evolution as a result of genetic changes that give rise to new species.

microvilli (sing, microvillus) Tiny projections on the surface of some epithelial cells that function to increase a cell's surface area. Microvilli are often found on the luminal surface of cells involved in absorption of fluids, nutrients, and ions.

midbrain Region of the brain stem. The midbrain is a coordination center for reflex responses to visual and auditory stimuli.

middle ear Region of the ear consisting of an air-filled chamber within the temporal bone of the skull, bridged by the malleus, incus, and stapes. The middle ear amplifies sound.

mineral An inorganic chemical compound found in nature. Some minerals must be in the diet because they are necessary for normal metabolic functioning.

mineralocorticoid (MIN-er-al-oh-KOR-tih-koyd) Steroid hormone of the adrenal cortex that regulates salt and fluid balance.

mitochondrion (pl. mitochondria) (my-toh-KAHN-dree-ahn) A cytoplasmic organelle responsible for ATP generation for cellular activities.

mitosis (my-TOH-sis) Process of nuclear division during which duplicated chromosomes are distributed to two daughter nuclei, each with the same number of chromosomes as the parent cell. Mitosis consists of prophase, metaphase, anaphase, and telophase.

mitral valve (MY-trul) Left atrioventricular valve in the heart, also called the bicuspid valve.

molecule Particle consisting of two or more atoms joined together by chemical bonds.

Monera One of the five kingdoms of life, comprising the bacteria.

monoclonal antibodies Pure preparations of identical antibodies produced in the laboratory by a colony of genetically identical cells.

monocyte (MAHN-oh-syt) Large agranular leukocyte that can differentiate into a macrophage that functions as a phagocyte.

mononucleosis (mahn-oh-nu-klee-OH-sis) A contagious infection of lymphocytes in blood and lymph tissues, caused by the Epstein-Barr virus.

monosaccharide (mahn-oh-SAK-uh-ryd) Simplest type of carbohydrate with only one sugar unit. Glucose is a monosaccharide.

morphogenesis (mor-foh-JEN-ih-sis) Process involving dramatic changes in shape and form that an organism goes through during development.

motor neuron A neuron in the peripheral nervous system that conducts nerve impulses from the central nervous system to body tissues and organs.

motor unit A somatic motor neuron and all the muscle cells that it stimulates.

MRI (magnetic resonance imaging) Technique that uses short bursts of a powerful magnetic field to produce cross-sectional images of body structures.

mRNA (messenger RNA) Long nucleotide strand that complements the exact nucleotide sequence of genetically active DNA. Messenger RNA carries the genetic message to the cytoplasm.

mucosa (myoo-KO-suh) The innermost tissue layer in the wall of the gastrointestinal tract.

mucus (MYOO-kus) A sticky, thick fluid secreted by mucous glands and mucous membranes. Mucus keeps the surfaces of certain membranes moist.

multiple sclerosis (skler-OH-sis) Progressive disorder of the central nervous system in which the myelin sheath around neuron axons disappears and is replaced by fibrous connective tissue.

muscle spindle Encapsulated receptor in skeletal muscles that is sensitive to stretch.

muscle tension The force exerted by a contracting muscle.

muscle tissue Tissue consisting of cells that are specialized to shorten or contract, resulting in movement of some kind. There are three types of muscle tissue: skeletal, cardiac, and smooth.

muscular dystrophy (DIS-trof-ee) A group of inherited muscle-destroying diseases.

muscularis One of the four tissue layers of the gastrointestinal tract wall. The muscularis consists primarily of smooth muscle.

mutation A change in the DNA base pair sequence of a cell.

mutator gene A class of gene that normally is involved in DNA repair during DNA replication. Mutated mutator genes may contribute to cancer because errors in DNA replication may not be corrected.

myelin sheath (MY-ih-lin) Fatty insulating sheath that surrounds the neuron axons of some types of neurons.

myocardial infarction (my-oh-KAR-dee-ul in-FAHRK-shun) Condition characterized by death of heart tissue caused by inadequate oxygen supply; also called a heart attack.

myocardium (my-oh-KAR-dee-um) Middle and largest layer of the heart wall, composed of cardiac muscle.

myofibrils Long cylindrical structures arranged in parallel inside a muscle cell.

myometrium The outer later of the uterus.

myopia (my-OH-pee-uh) A condition in which the eyeball is too long, causing distant visual objects to be focused in front of the retina. Also called nearsightedness.

myosin (MY-oh-sin) One of the principal contractile proteins found in muscle. Myosin is composed of thick filaments with cross-bridges.

N

NAD⁺ A transport molecule within mitochondria that can accept hydrogen ions and electrons liberated by the citric acid cycle, forming high-energy NADH.

nasal cavity The internal portion of the nose.

natural killer (NK) cells A type of lymphocyte that can lyse and kill cancer cells and virus-infected body cells before the immune system is activated.

natural selection The process by which, according to Darwin, individuals with traits that make them more fit for their local environments tend to survive and reproduce. Most changes in allele frequency in a population are the result of mutations coupled with natural selection.

natural world Matter and energy.

negative feedback A homeostatic control mechanism in which a change in a controlled variable triggers a series of events that ultimately opposes (negates) the initial change, returning the controlled variable to its normal value, or set point.

neonate (NEE-oh-nayt) A newborn baby during its first 28 days after birth.

neoplasm (NEE-oh-plazm) Abnormal mass of proliferating cells; also called a tumor. Neoplasms may be benign or malignant.

nephron (NEF-rahn) Structural and functional unit of the kidney. A nephron consists of the renal tubule and the blood vessels that supply it.

nerve Cablelike bundle of many neuron axons, all wrapped together in a protective connective tissue sheath. Nerves carry nerve impulses to and from the central nervous system.

nerve impulse A self-propagating wave of depolarization, also called an action potential.

nervous tissue Tissue consisting of cells that are specialized for generating and transmitting nerve impulses throughout the body. Nervous tissue forms a rapid communication network for the body.

neuroendocrine cell A type of cell in the hypothalamus that essentially functions as both a nerve cell and an endocrine cell because it generates nerve impulses and releases a hormone into blood vessels.

neuroglial cells (noo-RAHG-lee-ul) Cells that provide physical support and protection to neurons and help maintain healthy concentrations of important chemicals in the fluid surrounding them.

neuromuscular junction Region where a motor neuron comes in close contact with a muscle cell. At the neuromuscular junction, neurotransmitter released by the motor neuron causes an electrical impulse to be generated in the muscle cell.

neuron (NYOOR-ahn, NOOR-ahn) Cell of the nervous system specialized to generate and transmit nerve impulses.

neurotransmitter A chemical released by a neuron that may stimulate or inhibit other neurons or effector cells.

neutron Uncharged subatomic particle found in the atomic nucleus.

neutrophil (NOO-truh-fil) Most abundant type of white blood cell. Neutrophils respond rapidly during an infection, surrounding and engulfing bacteria.

niche The role of an organism in its community.

nitrification The formation of nitrate (NO_3^-) by any of several means, including nitrifying bacteria, lightning, and nitrate-producing fertilizer factories.

nitrogen fixation The process whereby certain bacteria convert N_2 gas to ammonium (NH_4^+). Nitrogen fixation is an important part of the nitrogen cycle.

node of Ranvier (RAHN-vee-ay) A short unmyelinated gap between adjacent Schwann cells where the surface of a neuron axon is exposed.

nondisjunction Failure of sister chromatids to separate during mitosis or failure of homologous pairs to separate during meiosis. Nondisjunction causes abnormal numbers of chromosomes in the resulting daughter cells.

nonsteroid hormone A hormone that consists of, or at least is partly derived from, the amino acid building blocks of proteins. Nonsteroid hormones generally are lipid insoluble, so they tend to act by binding to a receptor on the cell surface rather than by entering the cell cytoplasm.

norepinephrine (NOR-ep-ih-NEF-rin) A neurotransmitter and adrenal medullary hormone, associated with sympathetic nervous system activation.

nucleolus (pl. nucleoli) (noo-KLEE-oh-lus) A dense spherical body in the cell nucleus involved with ribosomal subunit synthesis and storage.

nucleotide A structural unit consisting of a nitrogen base, a five-carbon sugar, and one or more phosphate groups. Nucleotides are the structural units of DNA and RNA. ATP and ADP are also nucleotides.

nucleus General term for a central or essential part. The nucleus of an atom consists of neutrons and protons and contains most of the atomic mass. The nucleus of a eukaryotic cell contains the cell's DNA.

nutrients Substances in food that are required for cell growth, reproduction, and the maintenance of health.

O

obesity The condition of weighing more than 20% above ideal body weight.

olfactory receptor cell A modified sensory neuron, located in the upper part of the nasal passages, that detects odors.

oligosaccharide A short string of monosaccharides (single sugars) linked together by dehydration synthesis.

omnivore (AHM-nih-vor) An organism that can derive energy from either plants or animals. Humans, pigs, and bears are omnivores.

oncogene (AHNG-koh-jeen) A mutated or damaged proto-oncogene that contributes to cancer.

oocyte An immature egg in the female ovary or newly released from the ovary.

optic disk The area of the retina where the axons of the optic nerve exit the eye. The optic disk has no photoreceptors, so its presence creates a "blind spot" in each eye.

optic nerve One of the two cranial nerves that transmit nerve impulses from the retina to the brain.

organ A part of the body formed of two or more tissues and adapted to carry out a specific function. The stomach and the heart are examples of organs.

organ of Corti Collective term for the hair cells and tectorial membrane of the inner ear. The organ of Corti converts pressure waves to nerve impulses.

organelle (or-guh-NEL) One of many small cellular structures that perform specific functions for the cell as a whole.

organic molecule A molecule that contains carbon and other elements, held together by covalent bonds.

organ system A group of organs that together serve a broad function important to the survival of an organism or species.

orgasm (OR-gazm) A brief, intensely pleasurable reflex event consisting of rhythmic, involuntary muscular contractions.

origin The end of a muscle that is attached to the bone that does not move during muscular contraction.

osmosis (ahz-MO-sis) The net diffusion of water across a selectively permeable membrane, such as a cell membrane.

osteoblast (AHS-tee-oh-blast) A boneforming cell.

osteoclast (AHS-tee-oh-klast) A cell that resorbs or breaks down bone.

osteocyte (AHS-tee-oh-syt) A mature bone cell.

osteodystrophy (AHS-tee-oh-DIS-troh-fee) Progressive disorder in which the bones become weak because of an abnormal mineral composition of bone.

osteon (AHS-tee-ahn) A cylindrical structure in bone composed of layers of living bone cells and hard extracellular material, arranged like the layers of an onion. In the center is a central canal through which nerves and blood vessels pass.

osteoporosis (AHS-tee-oh-poh-ROH-sis) Progressive disorder involving increased softening and thinning of the bone. Osteoporosis results from an imbalance in the rates of bone resorption and bone formation.

otoliths (OH-toh-lith) Hard crystals of bonelike material embedded in gel in the inner ear. Otoliths contribute to sensations of head position and movement.

outer ear Region of the ear consisting of the pinna (visible portion) and the auditory canal. The outer ear channels sound waves to the eardrum.

ovarian cycle (oh-VAIR-ee-un) Monthly cycle of follicle development, ovulation, and corpus luteum formation in an ovary.

ovaries (OH-vair-eez) The two female sex organs (gonads) in which ova (eggs) are produced.

oviduct (OH-vih-dukt) Tube that leads from an ovary to the uterus, also called the Fallopian tube or uterine tube.

ovulation (AHV-yoo-LAY-shun) Ejection of an immature egg (oocyte) from the ovary.

ovum (pl. ova) (OH-vum) Female gamete, also called an egg.

oxidative phosphorylation The process of producing ATP from ADP plus a phosphate group (P_i), using the energy derived from the electron transport system within mitochondria. The process is called *oxidative* because it requires oxygen, and *phosphorylation* because a phosphate group is added (to ADP).

oxygen debt The amount of oxygen required after exercise to oxidize the lactic acid formed by anaerobic metabolism during exercise.

oxyhemoglobin (ahk-see-HEE-moh-gloh-bin) Oxygen-bound form of hemoglobin.

oxytocin (ahk-sih-TOH-sin) Hormone secreted from the posterior pituitary by neuroendocrine cells of the hypothalamus. Oxytocin stimulates contraction of the uterus during childbirth and the ejection of milk during nursing.

ozone In the stratosphere, a thin layer of O_3 gas that shields Earth from ultraviolet rays. Also an environmental pollutant near Earth's surface.

P

Pacinian corpuscle (puh-SIN-ee-un) Type of encapsulated mechanoreceptor located in the dermis that responds to deep pressure or high-frequency vibration.

pain receptors Receptors that respond to tissue damage or excessive pressure or temperature.

pancreas (PANG-kree-us) Organ located behind the stomach. The pancreas secretes digestive enzymes and bicarbonate into the small intestine and the hormones insulin and glucagon into the bloodstream.

pancreatic amylase (pang-kree-AT-ik AM-ih-lays) Pancreatic enzyme that continues the digestion of carbohydrates begun by salivary amylase.

parasympathetic division (par-uh-sym-puh-THET-ik) The division of the autonomic nervous system that generally promotes activities associated with the resting state, such as digestion and elimination.

parathyroid glands (par-uh-THY-royd) Small endocrine glands located on the thyroid gland that produce parathyroid hormone.

parathyroid hormone (PTH) Hormone released by the parathyroid glands that regulates blood calcium levels.

Parkinson's disease Progressive disorder of the nervous system involving death and degeneration of dopamine-containing nerve cells in the midbrain. Symptoms of Parkinson's disease include persistent tremor and rigid movements.

partial pressure The pressure exerted by one particular gas in a mixture of gases.

passive immunization The process of fighting an existing or anticipated infection by the administration of specific antibodies against the infective agent. The antibodies usually are isolated from a human or animal with immunity to the infective agent.

passive transport Membrane transport processes that do not require cellular energy. Diffusion is a form of passive transport.

pathogen (PATH-uh-jen) Disease-causing microorganism, such as a bacterium or virus.

pectoral girdle (PEK-tur-ul) Portion of the skeleton that attaches the upper limbs to the axial skeleton, composed of the clavicle and scapula.

pelvic girdle Portion of the skeleton that supports the weight of the upper body and attaches the lower limbs to the axial skeleton, composed of the two coxal bones and the sacrum and coccyx of the vertebral column.

pelvic inflammatory disease (PID) Infection of the internal female reproductive organs. PID can result in scarring that blocks the oviducts.

penis The male organ of sexual intercourse.

pepsin (PEP-sin) Protein-digesting enzyme secreted by the gastric glands of the stomach.

peptic ulcer An open, sometimes bleeding sore that forms in the inner lining of the stomach, the esophagus, or the upper part of the small intestine.

perforin (PUR-for-in) A chemical released by secretory vesicles of a cytotoxic T cell that perforates the membrane of an abnormal or foreign cell and kills it.

pericardium (pair-ih-KAR-dee-um) Tough fibrous sac that encloses and protects the heart and prevents it from overfilling.

peripheral nervous system (PNS) Portion of the nervous system that lies outside of the brain and spinal cord.

peristalsis (pair-ih-STAHL-sis) Progressive wavelike contractions of muscle in a tubular structure. Peristalsis moves food through the digestive tract and urine through the ureters.

peritubular capillaries (pair-ih-TOO-byoo-lur) Capillaries that form a network surrounding the proximal and distal tubules in the cortex of a nephron.

peroxisome (per-OX-ih-sohm) Membrane-bound vesicle in the cell cytoplasm containing powerful enzymes that detoxify harmful or toxic substances.

PET (positron emission tomography) Technique that employs radioactive substances to create three-dimensional images showing the metabolic activity of body structures.

pH The measure of the relative acidity or alkalinity of a solution. Any pH below 7 is acidic and any pH above 7 is basic.

phagocyte (FAG-uh-syt) A white blood cell that destroys foreign cells through the process of phagocytosis.

phagocytosis (fag-uh-sy-TOH-sis) Process by which phagocytes surround, engulf, and destroy foreign cells.

pharynx (FAIR-inks) The region of the digestive and respiratory systems that extends from behind the nasal cavities to the esophagus, also called the throat. Both air and food pass through the pharynx.

phenotype (FEE-noh-typ) The observable physical and functional traits of an organism.

phospholipid A modified lipid that has a polar (water-soluble) region containing a phosphate group. Phospholipids are the main structural components of the cell membrane.

photodynamic therapy A therapy for cancer. First, the patient takes light-sensitive drugs that are drawn into the rapidly dividing cancer cells. Then laser light is focused on the tumor, triggering a series of chemical changes in the light-sensitive drugs that kill malignant cells.

photopigment Any one of several proteins located in the rods and cones of the eye that changes its shape when exposed to energy in the form of light. The change in shape causes the rod or cone to alter the amount of neurotransmitter it releases.

photoreceptor A specialized receptor cell that responds to light energy.

photosynthesis The process by which plants capture the energy in sunlight and convert it into chemical energy for their own use.

pineal gland (PY-nee-ul) Endocrine gland thought to be involved in setting the biological clock and influencing reproductive function. The pineal gland secretes melatonin.

pituitary gland (pih-TOO-ih-tair-ee) Neuroendocrine gland located just below the hypothalamus of the brain. Together, the anterior and posterior lobes of the pituitary gland secrete eight hormones.

pituitary portal system A system of small blood vessels between the hypothalamus and anterior lobe of the pituitary gland.

placebo (pluh-SEE-bow) A false treatment in a controlled experiment, given or performed to minimize the possibility of bias by suggestion.

placenta (plah-SEN-tuh) Temporary organ formed from both fetal and maternal tissues that provides nutrients and oxygen to the developing fetus, removes fetal metabolic wastes, and produces the hormones of pregnancy.

plasma (PLAZ-muh) The fluid component of blood in which the formed elements are suspended.

plasma cell A cell derived from a B cell lymphocyte specifically to mass-produce and release antibodies.

plasma membrane Membrane surrounding the cell, consisting of a phospholipid bilayer with embedded cholesterol and proteins. The plasma membrane regulates the passage of substances into and out of the cell.

plasma proteins The largest group of solutes in plasma which include albumins, globulins, and clotting proteins.

plasmid (PLAZ-mid) A small circular molecule of DNA found in the cytoplasm of some bacteria. Plas-mids are used in recombinant DNA technology.

platelets (PLAYT-lets) Small cell fragments that are derived from certain cells in the bone marrow. Platelets are important in blood clotting.

pleural membranes (PLUR-ul) Membranes that line the thoracic cavity and cover the external surface of the lungs.

pneumonia (noo-MOHN-yuh) Respiratory condition involving inflammation and infection of the lungs. Pneumonia is usually caused by viruses or bacteria.

polar body Small nonfunctional cell with almost no cytoplasm that is formed when the primary oocyte completes stage I of meiosis.

pollution Chemicals or particles that have adverse effects on living organisms.

polygenic inheritance (pahl-ee-JEN-ik) Pattern of inheritance in which a phenotypic trait depends on many genes. An example is eye color, controlled by three or more genes.

polymerase chain reaction (PCR) (poh-LIM-ur-ays) A technique for making multiple identical copies of DNA in a test tube.

polypeptide A chain of 3–100 amino acids (poly means "many"). Chains of more than 100 amino acids are generally referred to as proteins.

polysaccharide A chain of monosaccharides. Starch and glycogen are polysaccharides.

population A group of individuals of the same species that occupy the same geographic area and interact with each other.

positive feedback A control system in which a change in the controlled variable sets in motion a series of events that amplifies the original change. The process of childbirth once labor has started is an example of positive feedback.

potential energy Stored or inactive energy.

precapillary sphincter (SFINK-ter) Band of smooth muscle that controls blood flow into individual capillaries.

pre-embryo An organism during the first two weeks after fertilization. The term preembryo is used because many of the cells that result from cleavage and morphogenesis in the first two weeks will eventually not be part of the embryo at all, but will instead constitute extra-embryonic membranes and parts of the placenta.

premenstrual syndrome (PMS) Recurring episodes of discomfort during the menstrual cycle, generally beginning after ovulation and lasting until menstruation. PMS can include symptoms such as food cravings, mood swings, anxiety, back and joint pain, water retention, and headaches.

presbyopia (prez-bee-OH-pee-uh) Eye condition in which an increase in stiffness of the lens results in an inability to focus on near objects. Presbyopia typically begins after age 40.

primary motor area Region of the frontal lobe of the brain that initiates motor activity.

primary somatosensory area Region in the parietal lobe of the brain that receives sensory input from the skin.

primate (PRY-mayt) An order of mammals with five digits on their hands, fairly flat fingernails and toenails rather than hooves or claws, and forward-facing eyes adapted for stereoscopic vision. Primates include lemurs, monkeys, apes, and humans.

primer A short double-stranded piece of DNA used to initiate DNA synthesis during DNA sequencing.

prion (PREE-on) An infectious mis-folded protein that replicates by causing a normal protein in the infected animal to misfold, producing another prion. Prions technically are not alive since they cannot reproduce on their own.

producer In ecosystems, an organism that makes its own organic molecules from inorganic compounds found in water, air, and soil, utilizing energy provided by the sun. Also called an autotroph. Green plants (on land) and algae (in water) are producers.

product In chemistry and biology, the end result of a chemical reaction.

progesterone (proh-JES-tur-ohn) Hormone partly responsible for preparing the uterus for the fertilized ovum. Progesterone is secreted by the corpus luteum of the ovary and by the placenta.

prokaryote (proh-KAIR-ee-oht) A single-celled organism that lacks the nucleus and the membrane-bound organelles characteristic of eukaryotes. Bacteria are prokaryotes.

prolactin (proh-LAK-tin) Hormone secreted by the anterior pituitary gland that stimulates the mammary glands to produce milk.

promoter A unique base sequence that marks the beginning of a gene.

prophase The first stage of mitosis. During prophase the chromosomes condense and thicken, the pairs of centrioles migrate to opposite sides of the cell, and the mitotic spindle forms.

prostaglandins (prahs-tuh-GLAN-dins) A group of lipid-based chemicals synthesized by most tissue cells that act as local messengers. Some prostaglandins dilate blood vessels and others constrict them.

prostate gland (PRAHS-tayt) Accessory reproductive gland in males that produces approximately one-third of the semen volume, including fluids that activate sperm.

protein One or more polypeptide chains of more than 100 amino acids. The three-dimensional structure of a protein is determined by the sequence of amino acids and by hydrogen bonds between different regions of the protein.

proteinuria (proh-tee-NYUR-ee-uh) Appearance of protein in urine. Persistent proteinuria may indicate glomerular damage.

prothrombin (proh-THRAHM-bin) A plasma protein that is converted to thrombin as part of the process of blood clot formation.

prothrombin activator Substance released by blood vessels and nearby platelets when blood vessels are damaged. Prothrombin activator activates the conversion of prothrombin into thrombin, facilitating the process of blood clotting.

Protista One of the five kingdoms of life, comprising unicellular and relatively simple multicellular eukaryotes such as protozoa, algae, and slime molds.

proton Positively charged subatomic particle in the nucleus of an atom.

proto-oncogene (proh-toh-AHNG-koh-jeen) Regulatory gene that promotes cell growth, differentiation, division, or adhesion. A proto-oncogene may contribute to cancer if it becomes mutated or damaged in such a way that it is turned on all the time.

proximal tubule Segment of a nephron that starts at Bowman's capsule and extends to the renal medulla.

puberty (PYOO-bur-tee) Period of life when reproductive maturity is achieved.

pulmonary circuit That part of the vascular system that takes deoxygenated blood to the lungs and returns oxygenated blood to the heart.

pulmonary embolism (EM-buh-liz-um) Condition that occurs when an embolus (blood clot) blocks an artery supplying blood to the lungs. A pulmonary embolism can cause sudden chest pain, shortness of breath, and even sudden death.

pulse Rhythmic expansion and recoil of arteries resulting from heart contraction that can be felt from the surface of the body.

Punnett square (PUN-et) A grid used for predicting patterns of inheritance and the probability that a particular genotype will be inherited.

pupil (PYOO-pul) Opening in the center of the iris through which light enters the eye.

Purkinje fibers (pur-KIN-jee) Modified cardiac muscle fibers that are part of the electrical conduction system of the heart.

pyloric sphincter (py-LOHR-ik SFINK-tur) A thickening of the circular layer of muscle at the distal end of the stomach that controls the rate at which the stomach empties.

pyrogen (PY-roh-jen) A fever-inducing agent. Macrophages and certain bacteria and viruses release pyrogens.

R

radiation High-energy waves or particles emitted by radioactive isotopes.

radius The smaller of the two bones in the lower arm.

receptor In sensory physiology, a specialized cell or nerve ending that receives a sensory signal such as touch, smell, light, or a chemical, and ultimately generates nerve impulses in a sensory neuron.

receptor protein A protein molecule of the cell membrane whose function is to transmit information across the cell membrane. Typically, when a particular molecule in the interstitial fluid binds to the receptor protein, a specific series of events is triggered within the cell.

recessive allele An allele that does not manifest itself in the presence of a more dominant allele. Two recessive alleles must be present in order for the recessive phenotypic trait to be expressed.

recombinant DNA technology Field of applied science that explores applications of cutting, splicing, and creating DNA.

Recommended Dietary Allowance (RDA) The U.S. National Research Council's current best estimate of how much of each vitamin and mineral we need to maintain good health.

recruitment Increasing the tone (or force) of a muscle by activating more motor units.

red blood cell (RBC) Blood cell that transports oxygen from the lungs to the tissues, and carbon dioxide from the tissues to the lungs. Also called an erythrocyte.

reflex An involuntary, automatic response to a stimulus.

refractory period (rih-FRAK-tuh-ree) Period immediately following a nerve impulse during which a neuron is unable to conduct another nerve impulse.

regulatory gene A gene that codes for a repressor or activator regulatory protein.

REM (rapid eye movement) sleep Stage of sleep in which rapid eye movements occur. REM sleep is accompanied by an alert EEC pattern and dreaming.

renin (REE-nin) An enzyme secreted into the bloodstream by the kidneys that leads to an increase in blood pressure and the secretion of aldosterone.

replacement fertility rate The fertility rate required to achieve long-term zero population growth. Replacement fertility rate is estimated to be an average of 2.1 children per woman.

replication The process of copying DNA prior to cell division.

repolarization In a nerve or muscle cell, return of the membrane potential to the initial resting (polarized) state after depolarization.

reproductive system Organ system that functions to produce offspring.

residual volume The amount of air remaining in the lungs even after a forceful, maximal expiration. Normal residual volume is approximately 1200 ml.

respiratory center Groups of nerve cells in the medulla oblongata near the base of the brain that are responsible for the cyclic nature of respiration.

respiratory system Organ system responsible for gas exchange. The respiratory system includes the nose, pharynx, larynx, trachea, bronchi, and lungs.

resting potential The slight difference in voltage (electrical potential) between the inside and outside of a cell.

restriction enzyme An enzyme found in bacteria that can be used to cut DNA at specific nucleotide sequences called restriction sites.

reticular activating system (RAS) (reh-TIK-yoo-lur) A group of neurons in the reticular formation that controls levels of sleep and wakefulness.

reticular fibers Thin, interconnecting fibers of collagen found in fibrous connective tissue. Reticular fibers provide an internal structural framework for soft organs such as the liver, spleen, and lymph nodes.

reticular formation Collective term for neurons in the pons that work with the cerebellum to coordinate the skeletal muscle activity required to maintain posture, balance, and muscle tone. The reticular formation is also responsible for maintaining the level of wakefulness.

retina (RET-ih-nuh) Layers of tissue at the back and sides of the eye. The retina is composed primarily of photoreceptor cells, neurons, and a few blood vessels.

retrovirus (REHT-roh-vy-rus) A class of viruses that replicate by using their RNA to produce double-stranded DNA, which is inserted into the host cell's DNA. The host cell then produces RNA for new viruses. HIV is a retrovirus.

Rh factor A red blood cell surface antigen, first discovered in rhesus monkeys, that is a crucial consideration in blood transfusions.

rheumatoid arthritis (ROO-muh-toyd) A type of chronic arthritis involving inflammation of the synovial membrane that lines certain joints.

rhodopsin (rho-DOP-sin) The photopigment found in the rods of the eye.

ribosomal RNA (rRNA) The RNA component of a ribosome. Ribosomal RNA assists in protein synthesis.

ribosome (RY-boh-sohm) A cellular structure consisting of rRNA and protein at which amino acids are assembled into proteins. Some ribosomes float freely within the cytoplasm; others are attached to the endoplasmic reticulum.

RNA (ribonucleic acid) Nucleic acid that contains ribose and the bases A, G, C, and U. RNA carries out DNA's instructions for protein synthesis. Types of RNA include mRNA, rRNA, and tRNA.

RNA polymerase (poh-LIM-ur-ays) One of several enzymes that recognizes a promoter (the starting point of transcription). RNA polymerase attaches to the promoter, starts the DNA unwinding process, and assists in attaching the appropriate RNA segments to the growing chain.

rod cell One of the two types of photo-sensitive cells in the retina.

S

salivary amylase (SAL-ih-vair-ee AM-uh-layz) Enzyme in saliva that begins the process of digesting starch.

salivary glands Three pairs of glands that produce saliva to begin the process of digestion. The three pairs of salivary glands are the parotid, submandibular, and sublingual glands.

saltatory conduction Form of rapid transmission of a nerve impulse along a myelinated fiber, in which the nerve impulse leaps from node to node.

sarcomere (SAR-koh-mir) The smallest contractile unit of a muscle myofibril. A sarcomere extends from one Z-line to the next.

sarcoplasmic reticulum (sar-koh-PLAZ-mik reh-TIK-yuh-lum) Specialized endoplasmic reticulum of muscle cells that surrounds the myofibrils and stores the calcium needed for the initiation of muscle contraction.

saturated fat Type of fat with two hydrogen atoms for every carbon atom in the fatty acid tails. Saturated fats are found in meat and dairy products and in a few plant sources such as coconut and palm kernel oil.

scapulas The shoulder blades.

Schwann cell A type of supporting cell in the peripheral nervous system. Schwann cells form the myelin sheaths around myelinated neurons and are vital to peripheral nerve fiber regeneration.

science The study of the natural world.

scientific method The process of science; the way scientific knowledge is acquired.

sclera (SKLEAR-uh) White, opaque outer layer of the eyeball.

scrotum (SKROH-tum) External sac of skin enclosing the testes.

second messenger Any intracellular messenger molecule generated by the binding of a chemical messenger (hormone or neurotransmitter) to a plasma membrane receptor on a cell's outer surface. A second messenger mediates intracellular responses to an extra-cellular (first) messenger.

secondary oocyte The haploid female reproductive cell that is released from an ovary and begins traveling down the oviduct during the ovarian cycle. A secondary oocyte has completed stage I of meiosis but not stage II.

secretion General term for the movement of a substance out of a cell of an endocrine or exocrine gland. Also, the substance secreted. The term is also used to denote the movement of any substance into the lumen of a tubule in the kidney.

segmentation Type of gastrointestinal motility in which short sections of smooth muscle contract and relax in seemingly random fashion, mixing the contents of the intestinal lumen.

segregation Mendelian principle that diploid organisms inherit two genes for each trait (on a pair of homologous chromosomes), and that during meiosis the two genes are distributed to different gametes.

selective gene expression The principle that, in any cell at any time, only a few of the genes are actually being expressed. Selective gene expression is responsible for differences in structure and function among different cells and for changes in cell function at different times.

selectively permeable The quality of allowing certain substances to pass while restricting the movement of others. The plasma membrane of a cell is selectively permeable.

SEM (scanning electron microscope) Microscope that bombards an object with beams of electrons to reveal what appears to be a three dimensional view of the object's surface.

semen (SEE-men) Thick, whitish fluid mixture containing sperm and the secretions of the male accessory reproductive glands.

semicircular canals Three fluid-filled canals in the vestibular apparatus of the inner ear that are important in sensing rotational movements of the head.

semilunar valves (sem-ee-LOO-nur) Heart valves located between the ventricles and the two major arteries of the body (pulmonary and aortic) that prevent blood from returning to the ventricles after contraction.

seminal vesicles (SEM-ih-nul) Male accessory reproductive structures that add fructose and prostaglandins to semen. Fructose serves as an energy source for sperm, and prostaglandins may induce muscle contractions in the female reproductive tract to help sperm travel more effectively.

seminiferous tubules (sem-ih-NIF-ur-us) Highly convoluted tubes within the testes in which sperm are formed.

senescence (seh-NES-ens) The progressive deterioration of multiple organs and organ systems over time; old age.

sensor In control system theory, any structure that monitors the current value of the controlled variable and sends the information to a control center. In biology, also called a receptor. Most receptors send information in the form of either action potentials in nerves or hormones in the bloodstream.

sensory neuron A neuron of the peripheral nervous system that is specialized to respond to a certain type of sensory stimulus, such as pressure or light. Sensory neurons conduct information about a stimulus to the central nervous system in the form of nerve impulses.

septicemia (sep-tih-SEE-mee-uh) Systemic disease caused by the spread of microorganisms or their toxins in blood. Also called blood poisoning or toxemia.

septum (SEP-tum) The muscular partition that separates the right and left sides of the heart.

serosa The outermost tissue layer of the gastrointestinal tract wall. It consists of a thin layer of connective tissue that surrounds the other three layers and attaches the gastrointestinal tract to the walls of the body cavities.

Sertoli cells Large cells that represent most of the bulk of seminiferous tubules in males. Also called *sustentacula cells,* they surround and nourish the developing sperm.

set point The internally set (expected, normal) value of a controlled variable.

sex chromosomes The chromosomes, X and Y, that determine gender (XX-female, XY-male). The 23rd pair of chromosomes.

sex-influenced trait A trait not inherited with a sex gene but influenced by the actions of the sex genes. An example is the phenotypic trait of male baldness.

sex-linked inheritance Pattern of inheritance that depends on genes located on the sex chromosomes. Sex-linked inheritance is X-linked if the gene is located only on the X chromosome, and Y-linked if it is located only on the Y chromosome.

sickle-cell anemia An inherited disorder in which the red blood cells assume a sickle shape when the oxygen concentration is low.

sinoatrial (SA) node (sy-noh-AY-tree-ul) Group of specialized myocardial cells in the wall of the right atrium that initiates the heartbeat. The SA node is called the pacemaker of the heart.

sinus Mucous-membrane-lined, air-filled cavity in certain cranial bones.

sister chromatids The two identical chromosomes that remain attached at the centromere after replication. The centromere holds the sister chromatids together until they are physically pulled apart during the mitotic phase.

skeletal muscle Muscle composed of cylindrical multinucleate cells with obvious striations. Skeletal muscles attach to the body's skeleton.

skeleton The body's physical support system. The skeleton consists of bones and the various connective tissues that hold them together.

skepticism A questioning attitude.

skull Over two dozen bones that protect the brain and form the structure of the face.

sliding filament mechanism The mechanism of muscle contraction. Muscles contract when the thick and thin filaments slide past each other and sarcomeres shorten.

smog Hazy brown or gray layer of atmospheric pollution that tends to hover over the region where it is produced. The burning of fossil fuels (coal and oil) and automobile exhaust are the primary culprits.

smooth muscle Spindle-shaped muscle cells with one centrally located nucleus and no externally visible striations. Smooth muscle is found mainly in the walls of hollow organs.

sodium-potassium pump An active transport protein of the plasma membrane that simultaneously transports three sodium ions (Na^+) out of the cell and two potassium ions (K^+) in. The sodiumpotassium pump is important for maintaining cell volume and for generating the resting membrane potential.

solute Any substance dissolved in a liquid.

solvent A liquid in which other substances dissolve.

somatic sensations Sensations that arise from receptors located at many points throughout the body. The somatic sensations include temperature, touch, vibration, pressure, pain, and awareness of body movements and position.

somatostatin (soh-mah-toh-STAHT-in) Hormone secreted from several locations in the body. In the pancreas, somatostatin inhibits the secretion of glucagon and insulin.

species The smallest classification category of life. A species is a group of organisms that under natural conditions tend to breed within that group.

sperm Male reproductive cell (gamete).

sphincter (SFINK-tur) General term for a ring of muscle around a hollow tube or duct that functions to restrict the passage of materials.

sphygmomanometer (SFIG-moh-mah-NOM-uh-tur) Device used to measure blood pressure.

spinal cord The portion of the central nervous system that lies outside the brain, extending from the base of the brain to about the second lumbar vertebra. The spinal cord provides a conduction pathway to and from the brain.

spinal nerve Any one of the 31 paired nerves that arise from the spinal cord.

spinal reflex An involuntary muscle response that is mediated at the level of the spinal cord, with little or no involvement of the brain.

spleen Largest lymphoid organ. The spleen removes old and damaged red blood cells and helps fight infections.

spongy bone Type of bone tissue characterized by thin, hard interconnecting bony elements enclosing hollow spaces. Red blood cells are produced in the spaces between the bony elements.

starch The storage polysaccharide utilized by plants.

stem cells General term for any cells that have not yet differentiated. Stem cells in bone marrow are the source of all blood cells and platelets.

steroids (STEER-oydz) Group of lipids having four interconnected rings that includes cholesterol and several hormones. Steroids are fat-soluble molecules.

sternum A flat blade-shaped bone composed ot three separate bones that fuse during development and is found at the top of the chest cavity. Also called the breastbone.

stimulus (plural: stimuli) Sensory input that causes some change within or outside the body.

stomach Organ of the gastrointestinal tract where food is initially stored and where chemical breakdown of proteins begins.

stretch reflex Type of spinal reflex, important in maintaining upright posture and coordinating movement. Stretch receptors in a skeletal muscle stimulate sensory nerves when stretched, causing the sensory nerves to transmit nerve impulses to the spinal cord.

stroke Condition in which brain tissue is deprived of a blood supply, most often caused by blockage of a cerebral blood vessel. Also called a cerebrovascular accident.

stroke volume Volume of blood pumped out of a ventricle during one ventricular contraction.

structural gene A gene that codes for an enzyme or a structural protein.

submucosa The middle layer of the gastrointestinal tract wall. The submucosa is a layer of connective tissue that contains blood vessels, lymph vessels, and nerves.

substrate In chemistry and biology, the starting material of a chemical reaction.

succession A natural sequence of change in terms of which organisms dominate in a community.

summation Accumulation of effects, especially those of muscular or neural activity.

suppressor T cell Regulatory T lymphocyte that suppresses the immune response.

surfactant (sur-FAK-tant) Secretion produced by certain cells of the alveoli that reduces the surface tension of water molecules, preventing the collapse of the alveoli after each expiration.

sustainable development Development that meets the needs of the present without compromising the ability of future generations to meet their economic needs.

sympathetic division The division of the autonomic nervous system that helps the body cope with stressors (danger, excitement, etc.) and with situations requiring high mental or physical activity.

synapse (SIN-aps) Functional junction or point of close contact between two neurons or between a neuron and an effector cell.

synaptic cleft (sih-NAP-tik) Fluid-filled space at a synapse.

synaptic transmission The process of transmitting information from a neuron to its target across a synapse.

synovial joint (sih-NO-vee-ul) A movable joint having a thin fluid-filled cavity between the bones.

syphilis (SIF-uh-lis) Sexually transmitted disease caused by infection with the bacterium *Treponema pallidum*.

systemic circuit The system of blood vessels that transport blood to all cells of the body except those served by the pulmonary circuit.

systole (SIS-toh-lee) Period when either the ventricles or the atria of the heart are contracting.

systolic pressure (sis-TOL-ik) The highest pressure reached in the arterial blood vessels during the cardiac cycle, and the first of two blood pressure numbers recorded by the health care provider. Systolic pressure is achieved during ventricular systole.

T

T cells (T lymphocytes) Lymphocytes responsible for cell-mediated immunity, which depends on the actions of several types of T cells.

taste bud A cluster of taste receptor cells and supporting cells that respond to dissolved food chemicals in the mouth. The human tongue has about 10,000 taste buds.

taxonomy (tak-SAHN-uh-mee) The science of classifying and naming life-forms.

technology The application of science.

tectorial membrane (tek-TOR-ee-ul) The gelatinous noncellular material in which the mechanoreceptor hair cells of the inner ear are embedded. With the hair cells, the tectorial membrane forms the organ of Corti, which converts pressure waves to nerve impulses.

telomerase (tel-OH-mer-ays) An enzyme produced primarily by cancer cells and reproductive cells that builds new telomeres to replace telomeres lost during cell division.

telomeres (TEEL-oh-meer) Short segments of DNA at the end of each DNA molecule that do not encode for a protein. In most cells, telomeres are removed every time a cell divides until there are no telomeres left.

telophase In cell division, the last phase of mitosis in which the two new sets of chromosomes arrive at opposite poles of the cell, new nuclear membranes form around the chromosomes, and the chromosomes uncoil and are no longer visible under a microscope.

TEM (transmission electron microscope) Microscope that bombards a very thin sample with a beam of electrons, some of which pass through the sample. A TEM provides images that are two-dimensional but highly magnified.

tendon A cord of dense fibrous connective tissue attaching muscle to bone.

teratogenic (TAIR-uh-toh-JEN-ik) Capable of producing abnormal development of a fetus. Teratogenic substances are one cause of birth defects.

testis (pl. testes) The male primary sex organ (gonad); produces sperm.

testosterone (tes-TAHS-teh-rohn) Male sex hormone produced primarily by the testes. (The adrenal cortex produces a small amount of testosterone in both sexes.) Testosterone promotes the development of secondary sexual characteristics and is necessary for normal sperm production.

tetanus (TET-uh-nus) In a muscle, a sustained maximal muscle contraction resulting from high-frequency stimulation. In medicine, an infectious disease also called lockjaw that is caused by an anaerobic bacterium.

thalamus (THAL-uh-mus) A region of the fore-brain that receives and processes sensory information and relays it to the cerebrum.

theory A main hypothesis that has been extensively tested over time and that explains a broad range of scientific facts with a high degree of reliability. An example is the theory of evolution.

thermal inversion A situation in which a warm stagnant upper layer of air traps a cooler air mass beneath it. Thermal inversions can cause air pollutants to accumulate close to the ground by preventing them from dissipating.

thermoreceptor Receptor sensitive to temperature changes.

threshold In an excitable cell such as a nerve or muscle, the membrane voltage that must be reached to trigger an action potential, or nerve impulse.

thrombin Enzyme that facilitates the conversion of fibrinogen into long threads of fibrin. Thrombin promotes blood clotting.

thymus gland Endocrine gland that contributes to immune responsiveness. T cells mature in the thymus.

thyroid gland An endocrine gland, located in the neck, that produces the hormones thyroxine, triiodothyronine, and calcitonin.

thyroid-stimulating hormone (TSH) Hormone produced by the anterior pituitary. TSH regulates secretion of thyroxine and triiodothyronine.

thyroxine (thy-RAHK-sin) A hormone containing four iodine molecules that is secreted by the thyroid gland. Thyroxine and a closely related three-iodine hormone (triiodothyronine) accelerate cellular metabolism in most body tissues.

tibia The thicker of the two bones found in the lower leg.

tidal volume Volume of air inhaled and exhaled in a single breath. Normal tidal volume is approximately 500 milliliters, or about a pint.

tissue A group of similar cells (and their intercellular substance) specialized to perform a specific function. Primary tissue types of the body are epithelial, connective, muscle, and nervous tissue.

tissue membrane A layer of connective tissue and (with one exception) a layer of epithelial cells that line each body cavity and form our skin.

tonsils Masses of lymphatic tissue near the entrance to the throat. Lymphocytes in the tonsils remove microorganisms that enter in food or in the air.

trachea (TRAY-kee-uh) Tube extending from the larynx to the bronchi that is the passageway for air to the lungs. Also called the windpipe.

transcription The production of a single strand of RNA from a segment (representing a gene) of one of the two strands of DNA. The base sequence of the RNA is complementary to that of the single strand of DNA.

trans fats Vegetable oils that have been turned into solids by partial hydrogenation of their fatty acid tails. *Trans* fats increase the shelf life and stability of foods, but they also increase the risk of heart disease.

transfer RNA (tRNA) Short-chain RNA molecule that transfers amino acids to the ribosome.

transfusion reaction The adverse reaction that occurs in a recipient when a donor's red blood cells are attacked by the recipient's antibodies. During a transfusion reaction the donated cells may clump together (agglutinate), blocking blood flow in blood vessels.

transgenic organism A living organism that has had foreign genes inserted into it. Transgenic organisms are sometimes created to produce substances useful to humans, including human proteins.

translation The process by which the genetic code of mRNA is used to string together the appropriate amino acids to produce a specific protein.

translocation A change in chromosome location that occurs when a piece of a chromosome breaks off but reattaches at another site, either on the same chromosome or another chromosome. Translocations can result in subtle changes in gene expression and ability to function.

transport protein A protein molecule of the cell membrane whose function is to transport one or more molecules across the cell membrane.

tricuspid valve (try-KUS-pid) The right atrioventricular valve of the heart.

triglyceride A neutral fat molecule consisting of a molecule of glycerol and three fatty acid tails. Triglycerides are the body's most concentrated source of energy fuel.

triiodothyronine (try-i-oh-doh-THY-roh-neen) Hormone secreted by the thyroid gland, similar to thyroxine except that it contains three atoms of iodine instead of four. Like thyroxine, triiodothyronine accelerates cellular metabolism in most body tissues.

triplet code The genetic code of mRNA and tRNA in which three successive bases encode for one of the 20 amino acids.

trisomy-X syndrome (TRY-soh-mee) A condition caused by having three X chromosomes. Trisomy-X syndrome individuals are female phenotype, sometimes showing a tendency toward mild mental retardation.

trophoblast Outer sphere of cells of the blastocyst.

tubal ligation Procedure for female sterilization in which each oviduct is cut and tied.

tuberculosis Infectious disease of the lungs caused by the bacterium *Mycobacterium tuberculosis.*

tubular reabsorption The movement of fluid and solutes (primarily nutrients) from the renal tubules into the blood.

tubular secretion The movement of solutes (primarily undesirable substances such as drugs, metabolic wastes, and excess ions) from the blood into the renal tubules.

tumor A mass of cells derived from a single cell that began to divide at an abnormally high rate. The cells of a benign tumor remain at the site of origin, whereas those of a malignant tumor travel to distant sites (metastasize).

twitch A complete cycle of contraction and relaxation in a muscle cell.

tympanic membrane (tim-PAN-ik) Membrane between the outer ear and inner ear that receives sound waves and transmits the vibrations to the bones of the middle ear. The eardrum.

U

ulna The larger of the two bones in lower arm.

ultrasound Fetal imaging technique in which high-frequency (ultrasound) sound waves are aimed at the mother's uterus. The sound waves rebound when they hit hard tissues in the fetus. These reflecting waves are analyzed and converted to an image by a computer.

umbilical cord (um-BIL-uh-kul) Cablelike structure connecting the fetus to the mother, through which arteries and veins pass.

unsaturated fat Type of fat with fewer than two hydrogen atoms for every carbon atom in their fatty acid tails. Examples include plant oils—such as olive, safflower, canola, and corn oil—and fish oil.

urea (yoo-REE-uh) Main nitrogen-containing waste excreted in urine.

ureter (YUR-uh-tur) One of two tubes that transport urine from the kidneys to the urinary bladder.

urethra (yoo-REE-thruh) Tube through which urine passes from the bladder to the outside of the body.

uterine cycle (YOO-tur-in) A series of changes that occur in the uterus in preparation for the arrival of a fertilized egg. A complete cycle generally takes about 28 days.

uterus (YOO-tur-us) Hollow, thick-walled organ that receives, retains, and nourishes the fertilized egg. The uterus is the site of embryonic/fetal development.

urinary system Organ system that transports and stores urine until it is eliminated from the body.

V

vaccine Antigens prepared in such a way that when injected or taken orally they induce active immunity without causing disease.

vagina (vah-JY-nuh) Hollow muscular female organ extending from the cervix to the body exterior. The vagina functions as an organ of sexual intercourse and as the birth canal.

variable A factor that might vary during the course of an experiment.

varicose veins (VAIR-ih-kohs) Permanently dilated veins, often caused by improperly functioning venous valves. Varicose veins can appear anywhere but are most common in the legs and feet.

vasa recta Long, straight capillaries that perfuse the inner (medullary) portion of the kidney, supplying the loops of Henle and collecting ducts.

vasectomy (vuh-SEK-tuh-mee) Procedure for male surgical sterilization in which the vas deferens (ductus deferens) is cut and tied in two places.

vasoconstriction A narrowing of blood vessel diameter caused by contraction of the smooth muscle in the vessel wall.

vasodilation A widening of blood vessel diameter caused by relaxation of the smooth muscle in the vessel wall.

vein A thin-walled blood vessel that returns blood toward the heart from the venules.

ventricle (VEN-trih-kul) A general term for a cavity. In the heart, one of the two chambers that receives blood from an atrium and pumps it into an artery. In the central nervous system, one of four hollow cavities in the brain.

ventricular fibrillation (ven-TRIK-yoo-lur fib-rih-LAY-shun) A type of abnormal heart rhythm involving rapid irregular ventricular contractions.

venule (VEEN-yool, VEN-yool) A small blood vessel that transports blood from capillaries to a vein.

vertebral column (VUR-tuh-brul) Structure of the axial skeleton formed of a number of individual bones (vertebrae) and two composite bones (sacrum and coccyx). Also called the spine or backbone.

vertebrate (VUR-tuh-brayt) Any animal with a backbone composed of vertebrae.

vesicle (VES-ih-kul) A small membrane-bound, fluid-filled sac that encloses and contains certain substances within a cell.

vestibular apparatus (ves-TIB-yoo-lur) A system of fluid-filled canals and chambers in the inner ear. The vestibular apparatus consists of three semicircular canals for sensing rotational movement of the head, and the vestibule for sensing static (non-moving) position and linear acceleration and deceleration.

vestigial structure (ves-TIJ-ee-ul) A structure that may have had a function in some ancestor but which no longer serves any function. The human coccyx (tailbone) is a vestigial structure.

villus (pl. villi) (VIL-us) Fingerlike projection of the small intestinal mucosa that functions to increase the surface area for absorption.

virus A noncellular infectious agent that can replicate only within a host cell. Viruses consist only of one or more pieces of genetic material (DNA or RNA) surrounded by a protein coat.

vital capacity The maximum volume of air that can be expelled from the lungs by forcible expiration after the deepest inspiration.

vitamin Any one of more than a dozen organic compounds that the body requires in minute amounts but generally does not synthesize.

vitreous humor (VIT-ree-us) The clear fluid within the main chamber of the eye, between the lens and the retina.

vocal cords Two folds of connective tissue that extend across the airway. Audible sounds are heard when the vocal cords vibrate as air passes by.

vulva Female external genitalia that surround the opening of the vagina.

W

white blood cell (WBC) One of several types of blood cells that are part of the body's defense system. WBCs are diverse in structure and specific function. They compose only about 1% of the volume of blood. Also called a leukocyte.

X

X chromosome One of the two human sex chromosomes. An embryo that inherits two X chromosomes will develop into a female.

Y

Y chromosome One of the two human sex chromosomes. An embryo that inherits a Y chromosome will develop into a male.

yolk sac Extraembryonic membrane that serves as the first source for red blood cells for the fetus and as the source for primordial germ cells.

Z

zero population growth The condition that exists in a population when the birth rate equals the death rate.

ZIFT (zygote intrafallopian transfer) (ZY-goht IN-trah-fuh-LO-pee-un) A technique for enhancing fertility in which an egg is fertilized outside the body, then inserted into an oviduct through a small incision in the abdomen.

zona pellucida (ZO-nuh peh-LOOS-ih-duh) A noncellular coating around an oocyte.

zygote (ZY-goht) The diploid cell formed by the union of the ovum and a sperm. The zygote is the product of fertilization.

Answers to Figure Check, Quick Check, and Test Yourself Questions

Chapter 1 **Check Figure 1.8, p. 12:** Inductive reasoning takes a specific example and develops a generalization from it; deductive reasoning does the reverse, using a general statement to develop specific predictions. The scientific method uses both because science involves reasoning back and forth between a general hypothesis and specific experimental predictions to test the hypothesis. **Check Figure 1.9, p. 13:** Worse. The two groups of subjects would have different blood pressure even *before* receiving the drug, and this will make it very difficult to interpret the results. For example, the experimental group might respond to the drug, but their blood pressure, even after being lowered, may still be higher than the other group; this would make it appear as if the drug did not work at all. Alternatively, people with high blood pressure might simply respond *differently* to the drug than do people with normal blood pressure, making their results impossible to compare. Random assignment is a much better experimental design because it ensures that the only difference between the two groups is whether or not they receive the drug. **Check Figure 1.10, p. 17:** Standard error bars give us an indication of how confident we should be about our estimate of the average value of the whole population. That's because standard error bars are determined by a mathematical formula that takes into account both the variability of the data and the size of the sample. The large standard error bar of the last data column, compared to the first one, means that we have much lower confidence in our estimate of average freshman enrollment in large universities as compared to small universities. (Note that there are fewer larger universities and their sizes are more variable.)

Quick Check, p. 7: Animals require energy for movement, of course, but *all* living things require energy to synthesize the molecules of life (proteins, carbohydrates, lipids, and nucleic acids). These molecules are not found naturally in the environment; they have to be synthesized from simpler atoms and molecules. Synthesizing these complex molecules requires energy. Animals get their energy from the food they eat (i.e., other animals and/or plants). Plants get their energy from the sun. Ultimately, all the energy used by living systems is derived from the sun. **Quick Check, p. 8:** The cell without a nucleus is in either the domain Bacteria or the domain Archaea; you can't tell which from what you were given, and neither is further subdivided into kingdoms. The cell with a nucleus is in the domain Eukarya (cells with nuclei), kingdom Protista (single and the simpler multicellular eukaryotes). Eukaryotes are more closely related to human cells because both have a nucleus. **Quick Check, p. 9:** Promising areas to study would be the skull (to estimate the size of the brain); the hands (to look for opposable thumbs); and the hips, knees, and feet (to look for signs of bipedalism). The fourth trait of humans, complex language, cannot be determined by examining skeletal material. **Quick Check, first question on p. 13:** No. A scientific hypothesis is any statement about the natural world that can lead to testable deductions. This statement is about the natural world, but it can't lead to a testable deduction because if Sasquatches leave no evidence of their existence, there is no way to test whether they exist! **Quick Check, second question on p. 13:** Hypothesis: "If regular exercise helps people sleep better…" Your prediction based on the hypothesis should specify the type and extent of exercise, and the exact nature of

"sleeping better," in as much detail as possible. For example, one prediction could be: "…then people who jog for at least 40 minutes per day for at least two weeks will fall asleep more rapidly at night than people who do not do any exercise." Many other predictions are possible, but the main point is that the prediction must be testable and quantifiable and address the "if" statement that was your hypothesis **Quick Check, p. 14:** Several obvious problems are that the subjects were not randomly assigned to the jogging or nonjogging groups, and how "well" a person sleeps is too subjective to be quantifiable. He could have been more specific and asked, or better yet measured in a laboratory setting, the actual hours of sleep each subject got each night over a period of time. In addition, if he intended to study only joggers, perhaps the researcher should have reworded his hypothesis to "jogging helps people sleep better," because jogging is just one form of exercise. **Quick Check, p. 17:** Both cold medications are relying what is called anecdotal evidence. This type of evidence is notoriously unreliable because it is highly selected, so it will invariably give a very positive spin. It doesn't matter how many people give anecdotal evidence, or who that person is. It gives us no imperical information about the likelihood that the medications will work for other people, nor about whether either supplement might be superior to the other (or, in fact, whether they're any better than a placebo).

Test Yourself, p. 22: 1. b; **2.** d; **3.** a; **4.** b; **5.** c; **6.** d; **7.** d; **8.** a; **9.** d; **10.** b; **11.** d; **12.** d; **13.** b; **14.** d; **15.** c.

Chapter 2 **Check Figure 2.5, p. 29:** Your diagram should show one carbon atom in the center, surrounded by four hydrogen atoms. Each hydrogen atom should be sharing a pair of electrons (i.e., forming a single covalent bond) with the carbon atom. **Check Figure 2.15, p. 38:** Starch and cellulose. They are both made from glucose subunits. We can digest starch, but not cellulose, because of the way the glucose subunits are attached together. **Check Figure 2.17, p. 40:** The phospholipid head is polar—meaning it is partially charged—and that means the head is electrically attracted toward the polar water molecules outside the membrane. The phospholipid tails, in contrast, are nonpolar and are not attracted toward water molecules; they're attracted only to the tails of other phospholipid molecules in the middle of the membrane. Any molecule of phospholipid that was oriented in the wrong direction would, on the basis of its polar head and neutral tail, simply flip around to the proper orientation.

Quick Check, p. 27: An atomic number of 7 means a nitrogen atom always has 7 protons. Because in most atoms the number of protons equals the number of neutrons, it is a safe bet that a typical nitrogen atom also has 7 neutrons. If it's electrically neutral, it must also have 7 electrons—2 in the first shell and 5 in the second shell. **Quick Check, p. 30:** Carbon dioxide's structure is $O{=}C{=}O$; a carbon atom in the center connected by double covalent bonds to each of the two oxygen atoms. We can deduce this from our knowledge of the number of electrons in each atom's outer shell. Carbon has four electrons in its outermost shell and each oxygen has six. With double covalent bonds between each oxygen and the carbon, all three atoms have eight electrons in their outermost shell. And that is a very stable configuration.

Quick Check, p. 33: Water is a polar liquid; it attracts polar and charged molecules and repels neutral ones. Oil is neutral; it attracts neutral molecules and repels polar and charged ones. So we can say that the dye is either polar or charged, but we cannot tell which. (It would also be called hydrophilic, or water-loving.) **Quick Check, p. 35:** Before the chemist added the solution, the concentration of hydrogen ions was 10^{-3} moles /liter (0.001 moles/liter); after, it was 10^{-5} moles/liter (0.00001 moles/liter). She must have added a base, which lowered the hydrogen concentration; that is, increased the pH. **Quick Check, p. 38:** Water. Each time a monosaccharide is added to a growing oligosaccharide chain, an H^+ is removed from one molecule and an OH^- is removed from the other. These will combine to produce a new water molecule. **Quick Check, p. 39:** Canola oil has more double bonds and fewer than two hydrogen atoms per carbon. When there are fewer than two hydrogens per carbon, double bonds form between adjacent carbons, and that puts a kink in the tail. The kink prevents the molecules from packing closely together as a solid. **Quick Check, p. 42:** It's probably a lipid. Lipids are generally insoluble in water and contain very few oxygen molecules. Some proteins are insoluble in water too, but proteins always contain nitrogen. Carbohydrates would contain a substantial amount of oxygen as well as carbon and hydrogen, and most are soluble in water.

Test Yourself, p. 47: 1. a; **2.** c; **3.** b; **4.** a; **5.** b; **6.** d; **7.** c; **8.** a; **9.** d; **10.** a; **11.** e; **12.** a; **13.** d; **14.** c; **15.** d

Chapter 3   **Check Figure 3.7, p. 58:** There will be a net movement of water from left to right, both because of diffusion (because initially the *concentration* of glucose will be higher on the right side) and also because of osmotic pressure, which will also be driving water to the right. Water will continue to move to the right until the height of the water columns is the same. **Check Figure 3.13, p. 63:** Sweat is hypotonic. Therefore her extracellular fluid will probably become hypertonic— that is, it will have more solutes (and less water) than her cells. If it is extremely hypertonic, her red blood cells will start to shrivel. **Check Figure 3.28, p. 74:** The ATP synthase is "powered" entirely by the "downhill" flow of H^+ ions from one side of the inner mitochondrial membrane to the other. NADH and $FADH_2$ never interact with ATP synthase directly; they just cause more H^+ ions to be pumped across the membrane, making the concentration gradient stronger.

Quick Check, p. 58: Na^+, Cl^-, and water molecules cannot cross a lipid bilayer on their own. Although they might be small enough, they also are either charged (the ions) or polar (water). Charged or polar molecules are not soluble in lipids, and thus, they cannot diffuse through lipid bilayers. **Quick Check, p. 60:** The fructose is moving "downhill," from high to low concentration, which is the natural direction that it would diffuse on its own. Therefore, the membrane protein is most likely allowing facilitated diffusion (a form of passive transport) and should not require any ATP. **Quick Check, p. 61:** The cell will tend to swell. A living cell always tends to accumulate a greater concentration of solutes inside than are present outside, which would (if uncorrected) result in a continual influx of water into the cell. Sodium-potassium pumps reduce this problem by removing sodium from the cell, thus reducing the concentration of solutes inside the cell. **Quick Check, p. 65:** Ribosomes are responsible for making proteins, so cells whose primary function is to secrete proteins typically have abundant ribosomes and rough ER, but don't have much smooth ER. **Quick Check, p. 67:** It's probably a vesicle. The nucleus and mitochondrion would have a double membrane,

whereas ribosomes have no membranes at all; they're composed just of proteins and RNA. It might contain products recently produced by the Golgi apparatus, or it might be a peroxisome or a lysosome. **Quick Check, p. 74:** Yes, but not very much. Without ATP synthase, oxidative phosphorylation does not occur—that is, the electron transport chain cannot generate any ATPs—but four ATP molecules can still be produced from each glucose molecule by substrate-level phosphorylation (2 from glycolysis, and 2 more from the 2 acetyl CoA molecules that enter the citric acid cycle). **Quick Check, p. 76:** Aside from the obvious problem of becoming very hungry, a most important reason is that when you reduce caloric intake a little bit at each meal, the primary "extra" source of energy for the body (above daily caloric intake) is fat. But during prolonged fasting, the body also turns to utilization of protein. Protein is not primarily a storage depot for energy; it's there for a reason, meaning that it is of structural and functional significance. Prolonged periods without food result in muscle wasting, including the muscle of the heart.

Test Yourself, p. 78: 1. c; **2.** b; **3.** e; **4.** a; **5.** c; **6.** b; **7.** d; **8.** e; **9.** c; **10.** b; **11.** a; **12.** e; **13.** b; **14.** a; **15.** c

Chapter 4   **Check Figure 4.2, p. 84:** Gap junctions. The tiny pores in gap junctions allow exchange of ions, molecules, and other raw materials between cells; the other two types of junctions do not allow exchange between cells. **Check Figure 4.9, p. 93:** He has a blister on the bottom of his right foot, on his heel. **Check Figure 4.13, p. 98:** Your diagram should look like the diagrams in Figures 4.12 and 4.13. The "sensors" are probably in the brain, along with the control center. If fat stores increase above the set point, hunger decreases and less food is eaten, causing fat stores to return to the set point. If fat stores decrease, hunger increases and more food is eaten, again causing fat stores to return to the set point. The effector is most likely a "hunger center" in the brain that stimulates you to eat (or not). What isn't known precisely is what the "sensors" are actually sensing.

Quick Check, p. 84: Columnar epithelium. Columnar epithelium contains the goblet cells that can secrete mucus. A single cell layer, such as simple epithelium, would also absorb the food molecules more efficiently than a stratified layer. **Quick Check, p. 87:** Ehler-Danlos syndrome (EDS) is a disorder of dense connective tissue caused by defective collagen. The connective tissue still has some normal elastin, but it has very little collagen, resulting in weak, stretchy ligaments that allow bones to dislocate easily and weak, stretchy skin. **Quick Check, p. 89:** No. Every skeletal muscle cell is individually controlled by a nerve fiber, allowing for fine control and a wide range of muscle power. If there were gap junctions, then whenever one skeletal muscle cell started to contract, all of the other cells in the muscle would contract too, causing a forceful, simultaneous contraction of all the entire muscle. There would be no way to do a less forceful or a slow contraction. **Quick Check, p. 93:** A serous membrane. Each pleural cavity contains a lung. The lubrication provided by a serous membrane reduces friction, allowing the lung to smoothly expand and contract without sticking to the inside of the pleural cavity. **Quick Check, p. 94:** If your keratinocytes began dividing more rapidly, your epidermis would simply become thicker (and might start flaking, as occurs in dandruff and psoriasis). Your skin should still be able to perform all of its major functions. In fact, it might improve the speed of skin healing after a minor injury. **Quick Check, p. 98:** It's a negative feedback system, because an elevation in the refrigerator's temperature will cause a response that brings the temperature back down; that is, negating the original change. The *controlled variable* is internal temperature; the *sensor* is a thermometer; the *control center* is a thermostat (wired to the thermometer); the *set point* is the temperature the thermostat is set at; and the *effector* is the refrigerator's compressor and refrigeration coils. **Quick Check, p. 99:** During a fever, the negative feedback system continues to work, but for some reason the set point is shifted to a higher-than-normal temperature. The "chills" and shivering represent the body's attempt to warm up to the new set point. When a fever "breaks" the set point returns to normal; this causes sweating to lower the temperature.

Test Yourself, p. 100: 1. a; **2.** a; **3.** d; **4.** b; **5.** b; **6.** d; **7.** d; **8.** e; **9.** a; **10.** c; **11.** d; **12.** e; **13.** c; **14.** d; **15.** c

Chapter 7   Check Figure 7.6, p. 149: If too few red blood cells were produced the oxygen-carrying capacity of the blood would decline. The decreased oxygen availability would cause the kidneys to increase their production and secretion of erythropoietin, which would (under normal circumstances) cause the bones to increase their production of RBC and bring oxygen-carrying capacity back to normal. But with bone disease, getting RBC production back even to normal might not be possible. The patient would be left with a decreased number of RBC (a low hematocrit) and an elevated blood concentration of erythropoietin. **Check Figure 7.12, p. 155:** Native Americans are most able to accept blood transfusions from each other without reactions, because 91% of the people in this population share the same blood type (type O) which has neither A or B antibodies. However, it would still be risky to try this. **Check Figure 7.14, p. 157:** Your sketches should show that the Rh-positive blood will agglutinate when mixed with Rh antibodies; the Rh-negative blood will not.

Quick Check, p. 146: Since humans have 4–6 liters of blood, the immediate effect would be roughly a 20% expansion of blood volume and a 20% decrease in the concentration of all formed elements (RBC, WBC, and platelets). There would be a modest decline in oxygen carrying capacity per liter of blood because of the 20% reduction in hematocrit (the percentage of the blood that is RBC), but a decline of that magnitude is not life threatening. Twenty percent reductions in the concentrations of WBC and platelets would also be well within survivable limits. However, if *all* of the blood was replaced with plasma the patient would die almost immediately. In the absence of RBCs, blood plasma alone cannot carry enough oxygen for survival. **Quick Check, first question on p. 147:** Both of these features will make hemoglobin less likely to release oxygen to body tissues. Hemoglobin releases oxygen most readily under conditions of high body temperature and low (acidic) pH. **Quick Check, second question on p. 147:** This sample is probably from a man—the hematocrit is 44%, which is in the normal range for men but is slightly high for women. **Quick Check, p. 151:** These are symptoms of inflammation, and they are most likely caused by basophils, a type of granular leukocyte that is activated by injured body tissues. Basophils secrete histamine, which initiates the inflammatory process that brings in the nutrients, cells, and chemicals needed for tissue repair. **Quick Check, p. 155:** He can donate blood to people of any blood type—A, B, AB, or O. The fact that he does not have A or B antigens means that his red blood cells will not be attacked by the recipient's antibodies, no matter what their blood type. **Quick Check, p. 156:** No. First, the Rh-positive woman does not have any Rh antibodies (because the Rh antigen is a normal "self" protein for her); and second, the Rh-negative fetus doesn't have any Rh antigens anyway. **Quick Check, p. 158:** Anemia due to renal failure

is caused by low erythropoietin levels, so adding exogenous erythropoietin corrects the problem nicely. In the other four types, the low oxygen-carrying capacity has already caused erythropoietin secretion to increase in an attempt to increase RBC production and bring oxygen-carrying capacity back to normal. With endogenous erythropoietin levels already high, adding even more erythropoietin does little good.

Test Yourself, p. 160: 1. d; **2.** a; **3.** c; **4.** d; **5.** a; **6.** b; **7.** b; **8.** c; **9.** d; **10.** b; **11.** a; **12.** b; **13.** c; **14.** d; **15.** a

Chapter 8   Check Figure 8.4, p. 167: Water is drawn back into the capillary at the distal end because there is a slightly higher concentration of dissolved molecules (especially proteins) in the capillary compared to the interstitial fluid, and also because the blood pressure is lower at the distal end. Both of these forces favor movement of fluid back into the capillary. **Check Figure 8.11, p. 175:** The AV and semilunar valves open and close passively due to changes in blood pressure. If blood pressure is higher "downstream" of the valve than "upstream," the valve automatically shuts. **Check Figure 8.16, p. 178:** The noise is heard only when the cuff pressure is between systolic and diastolic pressure because only then does the artery keep opening and shutting with every cardiac cycle. This repeated opening and shutting of the artery causes turbulence, which is what creates the audible tapping noise. When cuff pressure is above systolic pressure, the artery stays closed and so there are no sounds; when cuff pressure is below diastolic pressure the artery stays open, flow is smooth and steady, and again there are no sounds.

Quick Check, p. 167: The walls of arteries and arterioles are too thick for gases and nutrients to be able to diffuse across them. Arteries must have thick muscular walls to withstand the high pressure of blood pumping out of the heart. Even the walls of arterioles, because they have a layer of muscle, are still too thick for effective diffusion. **Quick Check, p. 168:** If the lymphatic system in a limb is completely blocked, the excess fluid that leaves the capillaries every day cannot be drained from the limb. In that situation the limb will become very swollen—sometimes to several times its normal size. **Quick Check, p. 172:** The pulmonary arteries are the only arteries in the body that carry deoxygenated blood. They are considered arteries because, by definition, arteries are thick-walled blood vessels that carry blood at high pressure away from the heart. **Quick Check, p. 173:** The problem is that the systemic circuit is almost completely isolated from the pulmonary circuit. Most of the blood in the systemic circuit would go to the body over and over again, without ever going to the lungs—and without picking up oxygen! Babies born with this condition can survive about a week without corrective surgery, because in the newborn there are open passages between the two atria and also between the pulmonary artery and aorta, allowing for some crossover of blood. But these passages close within 10 days. That's why this defect must be corrected surgically within a week or so of birth. **Quick Check, p. 176:** The atria contract silently—no valves close when they contract, and the blood flows smoothly, so there is no noise. Contraction of the ventricles, however, makes the AV valves snap shut, which produce the first heart sound (the "lub" of the "lub-dub"). **Quick Check, p. 180:** Systolic blood pressure is 141 mm Hg, and diastolic blood pressure is 95 mm Hg. This indicates this patient may have Stage 1 Hypertension, but because one measurement is not considered sufficient to diagnose hypertension accurately (blood pressure does vary from moment to moment), the patient should be tested again on several different days before a final diagnosis is made. **Quick Check, p. 181:** Initially, the blood pressure will drop, causing the baroreceptors to send neural signals to the brain, which in turn will increase sympathetic nervous activity and decrease parasympathetic nervous activity. The increased sympathetic nervous activity will cause the heart to beat faster (both by direct nerve input and also via epinephrine), and the sympathetic nerves activation will cause blood vessels to constrict. Blood pressure will be restored to normal or close to it within minutes.

Test Yourself, p. 186: 1. d; 2. c; 3. a; 4. a; 5. c; 6. b; 7. c; 8. b; 9. b; 10. a; 11. d; 12. b; 13. d; 14. c; 15. b

Chapter 9   Check Figure 9.13, p. 204:

Clonal expansion has to occur because typically only a very few T cells (sometimes just one) have a receptor that can bind to that antigen. With so few T cells able to recognize the antigen, very few cytokines will be produced unless clonal expansion occurs to produce many more identical T cells that all can recognize the same antigen. **Check Figure 9.16, p. 207:** A person lacking memory cells will not be able to mount a normal secondary immune response. Their first response will be normal (exactly like the green line), but their second response will be just like a first response (exactly like the green line again)—much smaller and slower than a normal secondary response.

Quick Check, p. 192: It is most likely a virus. A bacterium would have a cell membrane (and usually a cell wall); a prion would consist only of protein without any nucleic acid. **Quick Check, p. 199:** Nasal congestion is due to histamine's vasodilation effect, which makes capillary walls "leaky" and causes swelling in the nasal tissues as part of the inflammation response to the common cold. When antihistamines prevent histamine from working, the capillaries in the nose return to their normal "non-leaky" state and the swelling diminishes. **Quick Check, first question on p. 201:** During pregnancy, the mother's immune system must somehow tolerate the presence of a fetus and a placenta that are genetically different from the mother, and that therefore have different (non-self) MHC proteins. (It is still not understood why the mother's immune system does not attack the placenta during pregnancy.) **Quick Check, second question on p. 201:** The child should still be able to produce at least some antibodies, which are made by B cells. B cells arise from the bone marrow, not the thymus. **Quick Check, p. 203:** A memory cell can make only a single type of antibody that has unique amino acid sequences in the variable regions of the light and heavy chains. Because of the unique variable regions, these antibodies will (most likely) only bind to a certain antigen on the surface of the hepatitis virus, and will not be able to bind to the different antigens that occur on other pathogens. **Quick Check, p. 206:** Memory cells undergo clonal expansion when they come in contact with a specific antigen-presenting cell (usually a macrophage, but it can be an activated B cell as well). When a macrophage captures a foreign cell, it digests the cell and then displays a fragment of the cell (the antigen) on its surface as a sort of "red flag" that signals that a foreign cell has been found and captured. When the macrophage makes contact with a memory cell that can recognize that particular antigen, the memory cell undergoes clonal expansion. **Quick Check, p. 208:** This was passive immunization that provided only temporary protection. It was essentially a gamma-globulin shot from another species. **Quick Check, p. 210:** After each exposure, B cells produce more IgE antibodies, which bind to mast cells and basophils that were not previously involved in the allergy. On the next exposure, these mast cells and basophils will also react, causing a greater release of histamine, which causes worse symptoms.

Test Yourself, p. 217: 1. c; 2. a; 3. b; 4. c; 5. d; 6. c; 7. c; 8. b; 9. c; 10. c; 11. c; 12. a; 13. d; 14. c; 15. c

Chapter 11   Check Figure 11.4, p. 247:

The new action potential will look exactly the same as the first one (same height, same duration), because action potentials are "all or none." Graded potentials summate, but action potentials do not. And because an action potential was triggered by three successive stimuli in the graph, that's what would happen if you tried it again with four stimuli: the action potential would be triggered after the first three stimuli and the fourth stimulus would not have any additional effect. **Check Figure 11.5, p. 248:** The green line represents *permeability* to K^+. When the green line goes up, that means K^+ channels have opened so that the membrane is now very permeable to K^+. K^+ ions then rush out of the cell, causing the interior of the cell to become *less positive* relative to the outside—which means the cell's membrane potential (blue line) falls. **Check Figure 11.16, p. 262:** This can happen if the occipital lobe is damaged. The occipital lobe is at the back of the head, and its major function is processing visual information from the eyes. **Quick Check, p. 247:** The unusual pumps are producing a net movement of two (rather than the usual one) positive ions outward for every pumping cycle. This should make the resting potential more negative than the resting potential of a normal neuron. **Quick Check, p. 249:** No. Once the threshold voltage is reached the neuron's voltage-gated Na^+ channels would open, but there would be no Na^+ ions to enter the cell. Without Na^+ ions entering the cell, the neuron would not depolarize and thus no action potential would be produced. **Quick Check, p. 252:** The presynaptic neuron would still be able to produce and propagate action potentials in the usual fashion, because an action potential only requires the presence of the usual concentrations of Na^+ and K^+ However, it would not be able to release neurotransmitters because a requirement for neurotransmitter release is that Ca^{++} enter the neuron from the synaptic cleft. **Quick Check, p. 255:** Both reflexes are produced at the level of the spinal cord, without requiring the brain. Both trigger muscle contractions. Differences include: 1) different types of receptors; the patellar reflex is triggered by stretch receptors and reflex responses to pain are triggered by pain receptors. 2) Site and effect of response; the patellar reflex only causes contraction in the muscle being stretched, whereas the pain reflex to a foot causes contraction of flexor muscles in the leg with the painful stimulus (to withdraw the leg), and also contraction of extensor muscles in the opposite leg (to keep you from falling down.) **Quick Check, p. 257:** This would reduce the activity of the sympathetic division, but would not affect the parasympathetic or somatic divisions. Likely symptoms would include reduced heart rate and blood pressure, pupillary contraction, increased blood flow to the digestive tract, etc.—all the symptoms of *reduction* of sympathetic nervous activity. **Quick Check, p. 259:** The walls of the capillaries that produce cerebrospinal fluid (CSF) are fused tightly together with no slits between them, so it is more difficult for large and charged particles to gain access to the CSF than to the interstitial fluid. Compared to interstitial fluid, then, the CSF will have almost the same concentrations of electrolytes, gases, and small sugars, but it will have very few large protein molecules (including antibodies, which as you know are proteins). The CSF is also largely free of the bacteria and viruses that can so easily invade most of the rest of the body. Although bacterial or viral infections of the CNS are rare, when they do occur they are particularly difficult to fight because most antibiotics are also too large and too polar to gain access to the CNS. **Quick Check, p. 261:** Cessation of activity of the medulla oblongata function would cause death within minutes, because the medulla oblongata is required for the most basic of human functions, including respiration. Cessation of activity of the cerebellum would severely disrupt the ability to move normally, but if the person simply lies still, he would probably survive.

Test Yourself, p. 272: 1. a; **2.** d; **3.** c; **4.** c; **5.** a; **6.** d; **7.** c; **8.** b; **9.** a; **10.** d; **11.** b; **12.** c; **13.** a; **14.** b; **15.** c

Chapter 12   Check Figure 12.8, p. 284: The new graph should have more waves per unit time (high frequency, i.e., high pitch) than the "high" sounds illustrated in the original figure. The height of each wave (the "loudness") should be intermediate compared to the "loud" and "soft" sounds in the original figure. **Check Figure 12.10, p. 286:** A person with this condition would probably hear a very high pitched sound, such as a high-pitched hum or buzz. This is because activity of hair cells at the beginning of the cochlea normally generates impulses in sensory neurons that are interpreted by the brain as high-pitched sounds. **Check Figure 12.23, p. 296:** Yes. Though she lacks blue cones, she has normal green cones and red cones, which will allow her to distinguish between the colors green and red. The greens and reds will not look quite like the greens and reds a normal person sees, however.

Quick Check, p. 277: The person will most likely perceive action potentials from this neuron as some sort of light—even though the neuron was actually detecting sound waves. This is because the brain interprets sensory information according to the specific brain area being stimulated, and in this case the visual area of the brain would be stimulated. **Quick Check, p. 280:** Though your friend might briefly touch his toes during the "downward" part of the bounce, the muscle spindles will immediately trigger a stretch reflex that will cause the hamstrings to contract. After the bounce, the hamstrings will probably be tighter than before—so this is not a good method for stretching muscles. **Quick Check, p. 282:** The tastants in foods must dissolve in saliva (or water) before they can bind to the chemoreceptor cells in the taste buds. The chemoreceptors must be stimulated for the brain to perceive any sensations of taste. **Quick Check, p. 285:** Our sense of hearing would be much less sensitive—that is, all sounds would seem much softer, and we would probably be unable to detect very faint sounds. This is because the functions of the outer and middle ears are to channel and amplify sounds. The range of frequencies that we could hear would probably be unaffected, however. **Quick Check, p. 288:** When you suddenly stop spinning, the fluid in the semicircular canals keeps moving under its own inertia for a few moments, flowing around the canals on its own. This will bend at least one of the cupulas, and the hair cells within it. The brain interprets this as if the head is moving in the other direction. **Quick Check, p. 291:** The absence of a lens in the eye is called *aphakia*. A person with aphakia would be able to see blurry images because most of the focusing of the light is done by the cornea. The lens is necessary only for fine-tuning, bringing the blurry images produced by the cornea into sharp focus. **Quick Check, p. 294:** Animals that are active only at night have poor or no color vision—they see the world in shades of grey. This is because their retinas contain mostly rods, which provide sharp vision in very dim light, and very few (if any) cones, which are required for color vision.

Test Yourself, p. 298: 1. d; **2.** c; **3.** d; **4.** a; **5.** c; **6.** d; **7.** a; **8.** b; **9.** c; **10.** d; **11.** c; **12.** c; **13.** b; **14.** b; **15.** d

Chapter 13   Check Figure 13.3, p. 305: In this example, 100,000 molecules of final product will be produced by a single hormone molecule. This example illustrates how hormones can be present at very low concentrations in the blood but still have a significant impact on the body. **Check Figure 13.15, p. 316:** The top (and starting point) of your diagram should be blood glucose concentration. Your diagram should show alpha and beta cells of the pancreas on the right side of the diagram, responding to an increase in blood glucose by reducing glucagon (alpha cells) and increasing insulin (beta cells). On the left side should be three major effectors: the liver, muscle, and fat tissue. The "increased insulin" arrow should go to all three effectors, whereas the "decreased glucagon" arrow should go to the liver alone. The liver and muscle both respond by converting the excess glucose into glycogen; fat cells respond by converting some of the excess glucose to fat. Arrows from these three effectors back to the starting point (increased glucose) should show that the changes caused by the three effectors will bring glucose back to normal.

Quick Check, p. 305: No. Steroid hormones generally don't use second messengers, because a second messenger is only needed for hormones that can't enter the cell. A second messenger is a molecule that relays the hormone's message into the interior of the cell. Steroid hormones simply enter the cell themselves. **Quick Check, p. 307:** The hypothalamus would detect that the blood has too much water, that is, low solute concentration, and would secrete less ADH, causing a decline in the ADH concentration in the blood. The reduction in ADH would cause the kidney to reabsorb less water from the urine, so that more water would be excreted in the urine. **Quick Check, p. 309:** If you answered that she would have trouble giving birth and difficulty nursing you would have been on the right track, at least in theory. Interestingly, women who are oxytocin-deficient do undergo normal labor and delivery, indicating that there are other powerful forces driving childbirth besides oxytocin. She will still produce milk, because milk production is mainly under the influence of prolactin. However, a mother who is oxytocin-deficient will have trouble nursing normally because oxytocin is responsible for milk ejection. **Quick Check, p. 312:** Responding to a stressful situation usually requires energy (ATP). For example, healing a physical injury requires ATP (to rebuild the damaged tissues), and stressful emotions such as fear often indicate that we might need to run or fight, which also requires ATP. Cortisol helps raise blood glucose levels so that body tissues can use the glucose to produce more ATP. Put simply, cortisol gives you energy to do whatever needs doing. It also helps reduce inflammation after injury. **Quick Check, p. 315:** Thyroxine levels usually drop sharply during starvation. They also plummet during crash diets. This represents the body's attempt to save energy by reducing its metabolic rate, and its one of the reasons that the harder you try to diet, the harder it is to lose weight. **Quick Check, p. 318:** People who are exposed only to dim office lights during the day often have elevated melatonin levels during the day as well as during the night, so they must not have a normal 24-hour sleep-wakefulness cycle. They might be lethargic during the day and have trouble falling asleep at night. High daytime levels of melatonin are thought to be one of the underlying causes of Seasonal Affective Disorder, a syndrome of low energy and poor mood that is associated with wintertime. **Quick Check, p. 320:** It is almost always easier to treat failure to produce a hormone, because you can simply give the patient an injection of the missing hormone if it's available. Failure to respond to a hormone is a much more difficult condition to treat because neither giving the hormone nor blocking its action does very much of anything.

Test Yourself, p. 322: 1. c; **2.** b; **3.** a; **4.** d; **5.** a; **6.** d; **7.** a; **8.** d; **9.** c; **10.** c; **11.** b; **12.** a; **13.** d; **14.** a; **15.** d

Chapter 14   Check Figure 14.14, p. 338: Chylomicrons are too big to enter a blood capillary. The gaps between adjacent cells in a lacteal are wide enough to accommodate chylomicrons, however. **Check Figure 14.21, p. 349:** Obesity is most prevalent in southeastern states and the Appalachian mountains, especially West Virginia, Kentucky, and Tennessee. These areas are notable for a preponderance of fried, high-fat foods in people's diets. (Many other cultural factors may also contribute, including a lack of exercise.)

Quick Check, p. 333: The stomach would still produce pepsinogen, the precursor molecule to pepsin, but in the absence of an acidic environment it would not be converted to pepsin. The stomach could still perform its food storage and regulation-of-delivery functions, and could still mechanically break up large pieces of food, but it would not be able to digest proteins effectively because of the lack of pepsin. Nor would bacteria ingested with the food be killed as readily. **Quick Check, p. 336:** Liver is generally a very nutritious food because it contains not only glucose stores and fat stores, but also iron and many vitamins. Liver is especially high in vitamin A, so pregnant women are advised to eat it in moderation and it should not be fed regularly to young children in order to avoid vitamin A toxicity. It could also be dangerous if the animal has been exposed to environmental toxins that tend to accumulate in the liver, but that should be rare. Eaten in moderation, liver is definitely good for you. **Quick Check, p. 339:** No—the duodenum releases the hormone cholecystokinin (CCK) in response to the arrival of proteins and fats, but does not release any hormones in response to the arrival of carbohydrates. Carbohydrates are partially broken down in the mouth by the enzyme salivary amylase, and then are further broken down by enzymes from the pancreas and the small intestine. No hormones are involved. **Quick Check, first question on p. 342:** Cold-water fish must use unsaturated fats so that their fat tissue will stay soft and pliable. If cold-water fish stored lipids as saturated fats, the saturated fats would be in solid form, making the fish too stiff to swim. Warm-water fish, in contrast, are free to use saturated fats—and they do. **Quick Check, second question on p. 342:** Yes, eggs and milk both contain complete proteins. Unhatched bird embryos and baby mammals must assemble every protein in their bodies solely from the amino acids contained in the egg (for birds) and in milk (for mammals). **Quick Check, p. 343:** Vitamin B12. B12 is the only vitamin that is obtained only from animal products, and vegans do not eat any animal products. For this reason, many vegans take vitamin supplements and/or eat tofu that has been fortified with vitamin B12. **Quick Check, p. 346:** The woman who is lifting weights will probably lose more body fat. In addition to the 200 calories burned during the exercise itself, the extra muscle that she develops will also increase her BMR throughout the rest of the day. **Quick Check, p. 347:** Peptic ulcers tend to occur only in the stomach and first portion of the duodenum because of the high acidity in those regions. The acid is neutralized by mid-duodenum by bicarbonate delivered from the pancreas.

Test Yourself, p. 352: 1. b; **2.** c; **3.** c; **4.** a; **5.** d; **6.** b; **7.** d; **8.** d; **9.** b; **10.** c; **11.** a; **12.** d; **13.** c; **14.** c; **15.** b

Chapter 16   Check Figure 16.2, p. 381: A spermatogonium. A spermatogonium ultimately gives rise to millions of sperm, because it continually buds off new primary spermatocytes. Each primary spermatocyte gives rise to just four sperm. **Check Figure 16.7, p. 387:** The corpus luteum is the source of this progesterone. Progesterone levels rise when the corpus luteum forms from the remnants of the follicle just after ovulation. Progesterone levels fall when the corpus luteum degenerates approximately 12 days later—unless pregnancy occurs. **Check Figure 16.8, p. 388:** In both sexes, GnRH from the hypothalamus triggers release of LH and FSH from the anterior pituitary. FSH then stimulates development of the egg (and its follicle) or the sperm, while LH stimulates production of the sex steroids: estrogen and progesterone in women, testosterone in men. The steroids support development of the egg or sperm, and also exert negative feedback on the anterior pituitary and hypothalamus—until ovulation in women, that is. **Check Figure 16.14, p. 398:** The symptoms of a chlamydia infection are very mild at first and so the infection may go undiagnosed, especially in men. Undiagnosed infections are easily spread. Both gonorrhea and syphilis have symptoms that are severe enough to send a person to the doctor, and easily diagnosed by the doctor. **Quick Check, p. 382:** Oocytes must pass from the ovary into the oviduct, where fertilization normally occurs. Embryos can sometimes escape into the abdominal cavity because the oviduct has an open end. **Quick Check, p. 386:** She will still have all of her primary oocytes, because those are all produced before birth. She won't be able to ovulate, though, because LH is the hormone that triggers ovulation. **Quick Check, p. 391:** The woman will be sterile immediately unless she ovulated right before the operation, in which case it might be 3–4 days before she cannot conceive. The man will not be sterile for several weeks. Maturing sperm are stored in the ductus deferens, so some viable sperm are usually present in the duct past the site of the vasectomy. It can take several weeks to get rid of these sperm. **Quick Check, p. 392:** Pregnancy. In fact, most hormonal birth control methods are specifically designed to mimic the hormonal conditions of pregnancy. This makes sense because pregnancy is the one physiological state during which ovulation is completely prevented for a period of several months. **Quick Check, p. 395:** Progesterone enables the uterus to thicken and maintain its inner lining, the endometrium—along with the embryo that is inside the endometrium. If progesterone is not high enough, the uterus will automatically lose its lining, just as it does during menstruation. A series of several miscarriages may indicate that the woman's progesterone is too low to maintain the uterine lining. If that's the case, then administering progesterone may help. **Quick Check, p. 400:** Assuming equal levels of exposure, women would most likely be more susceptible to STDs than men. The vagina is lined by a warm, moist mucus membrane. The outer surface of the penis is covered with dry skin, which is a much less hospitable environment for microbes.

Test Yourself, p. 402: 1. d; **2.** c; **3.** a; **4.** c; **5.** d; **6.** a; **7.** d; **8.** b; **9.** d; **10.** b; **11.** c; **12.** a; **13.** d; **14.** b; **15.** d

Chapter 19   Check Figure 19.2, p. 449: Each cell in a Punnett square has an equal probability of occurring. In this case, because there are four cells, each cell has a 25% probability of occurring. Therefore, the baby has a 25% chance of having the AA genotype and a 50%

chance of having Aa (50% = 25 + 25, because there are two different cells with this genotype). **Check Figure 19.7, p. 453:** The ratio is 9:3:3:1, which is to say, 9 out of 16 offspring have both dominant phenotypes (widow's peaks and free earlobes), 3 out of 16 offspring have widow's peaks and attached earlobes, another 3 out of 16 offspring have no widow's peaks and free earlobes, and 1 out 16 offspring has both recessive phenotypes (no widow's peak, attached earlobes). If you observed a similar 9:3:3:1 ratio in a natural mating that involved two traits, you could conclude that the parents were heterozygous for both traits. **Check Figure 19.10, p. 455:** Zero. The baby must inherit either the B or the A allele from his mother, and thus cannot be blood type O. **Check Figure 19.16, p. 460:** The daughter must have inherited the hemophilia allele from *both* parents. This can only occur if the woman was a carrier and she married a hemophiliac man.

Quick Check, p. 452: The man and the woman both have dark hair. Each of their children will have a 25% probability of having red hair. That does NOT mean that if they have four children, one will have red hair, however. The 25% chance of each child having red hair is independent of all other children that the couple may have. **Quick Check, p. 458:** Possibly, but not necessarily. Although it's possible that your father and your grandfather have a genetic makeup that predisposes them to hypercholesterolemia and that you inherited that predisposition, it's equally possible that your father's and your grandfather's high cholesterol levels were due primarily to their diets. Knowing their history helps you, because you can change your diet if you wish. That alone may keep you from developing hypercholesterolemia. In addition, you could choose to be tested for high cholesterol regularly, just in case it's primarily genetic. Then if your cholesterol ever rose above normal you could begin treatment early enough to reduce your chances of cholesterol-related medical issues. **Quick Check, p. 460:** No. Sons always inherit their father's Y chromosome, but never receive their father's X chromosome. (If they received their father's X chromosome, they would be daughters.) **Quick Check, first question on p. 462:** No. Down syndrome does not involve any gene mutations. There are extra copies of some genes (the ones on chromosome 21), but each copy is a normal copy. **Quick Check, second question on p. 462:** It is the presence or absence of the Y chromosome that primarily determines gender. The number of X's has only a minor effect, if any. That is, females are females not because they have two X's, but because they lack a Y. **Quick Check, p. 463:** The baby must be a homozygous recessive (because only homozygous recessives have PKU), and therefore must have inherited a PKU allele from each parent. Since neither parent has the disorder, they can't be homozygous recessives themselves, so they must be heterozygotes. The probability that a child of two heterozygous parents will be homozygous recessive is 25%.

Test Yourself, p. 466: 1. b; **2.** a; **3.** c; **4.** a; **5.** b; **6.** c; **7.** d; **8.** a; **9.** d; **10.** c; **11.** d; **12.** d; **13.** d; **14.** b; **15.** a

Index

Citations followed by *b* refer to material in boxes; citations followed by *f* refer to material in figures or illustrations; and citations followed by *t* refer to material in tables.

A

AB blood type, 142*b*, 152–153
  characteristics of, 153*f*
  testing for, 155*f*
ABCD rule for melanoma, 439
Abdominal aorta of newborn, 496–497, 497*f*
Abdominal cavity, 90*f*
Abduction and synovial joints, 115*f*
AbioCor heart, 184, 184*f*
A blood type, 142*b*, 152–153
  characteristics of, 153*f*
  testing for, 155*f*
ABO blood typing. *See* Blood types
Abortion
  elective abortion, 392
  Mifeprex and, 392
Abortion pill, 392
Abscesses, 197
Abscissa of graphs, 16
Absolute refractory period, 250–251, 251*f*
Absorption in digestive system, 328
Accessory glands, 379*t*
Accommodation by lens, 292, 292*f*
ACE inhibitors, 369
Acetylcholine (ACh). *See* ACh (acetylcholine)
Acetyl CoA, 68–69, 69*f*
  in citric acid cycle, 71, 71*f*
Acetyl group, 70
ACh (acetylcholine), 127, 127*f*
  actions of, 254*t*
  in Alzheimer's disease, 271
Achilles tendon, 123*f*
  tendinitis and, 115
Acid-base balance
  kidneys and, 369–370, 370*f*
  tubular secretion and, 364
Acidic solutions, 33
Acid precipitation, 546
Acid reflux, 331
Acids. *See also* Nucleic acids; pH scale
  defined, 33
  digestive acids, 196
  in gastric juice, 332
  in vagina, 196
Acquired immune deficiency syndrome (AIDS). *See* HIV/AIDS
Acromegaly, 310, 310*f*
Acrosome of sperm, 380*f*, 484–485, 485*f*
ACTH (adrenocorticotropic hormone), 303*f*, 306*t*, 307–308, 309*f*
  labor, effect on, 495
Actin, 125, 129*f*
  in sarcomeres, 125–126
  sliding filament mechanism and, 128, 128*f*
Actinic keratosis, 427–428, 427*f*
Action potentials, 132, 246*b*
  as all-or-none, 251
  of hair cells, 288*f*
  light converted to, 293
  neurons activating, 248–251
  as self-propagating, 251
  sensory mechanisms and, 278*b*
  synapses and, 253, 253*f*
Active immunization, 207
Active transport, 57–58, 57*f*
  carbohydrate absorption by, 336–337, 336*f*
  protein absorption by, 336–337, 336*f*
Acu-Gen Biolab, Inc., 376–377
Acute leukemia, 157

Acute pain, 282
Acute renal failure, 371
ADA (adenosine deaminase), 478
Adam's apple, 222, 225
Adaptation, receptor, 279–280
Adaptive radiation, 514
Addiction and psychoactive drugs, 268
Addison's disease, 320
Adduction and synovial joints, 115*f*
Adductor longus, 123*f*
Adenine (A), 43
  RNA (ribonucleic acid) and, 409*f*
Adenoids, 193, 194*f*
  functions of, 195
Adenosine, 45
Adenosine deaminase (ADA), 478
Adenosine diphosphate (ADP). *See* ADP (adenosine diphosphate)
Adenosine triphosphate (ATP). *See* ATP (adenosine triphosphate)
ADH (antidiuretic hormone), 303*f*, 306–307, 306*t*, 307, 307*f*
  blood volume excess and, 369, 370*f*
  concentrated urine, production of, 365, 365*f*
  hyposecretion of, 309–310
  negative feedback loops, 367–368, 368*f*
  water balance and, 367–368, 368*f*
Adhesion junctions, 82–83, 82*f*
Adipocytes, 78, 78*f*, 83*t*, 84*f*, 86
Adipose tissue, 83*t*, 85*f*, 86
  triglycerides in, 38
Adolescents. *See also* Puberty
  growth and development in, 499
  key concepts, 484*b*
ADP (adenosine diphosphate), 45
  in active transport, 57–58, 57*f*
  in citric acid cycle, 71, 71*f*
  phosphate groups and, 67–68
Adrenal cortex, 312
  Addison's disease, 320
  hormones produced by, 317*t*
  mesoderm and, 490*t*
Adrenal glands, 312–313
  Cushing's syndrome, 321, 321*f*
  hormones produced by, 303*f*
Adrenaline. *See* Epinephrine
Adrenal medulla, 312
  ectoderm and, 490*t*
  hormones produced by, 312–313, 317*t*
Adrenocorticotropic hormone (ACTH). *See* ACTH (adrenocorticotropic hormone)
Adulthood, transition to, 499
Advertising and smoking, 432, 433*f*
Aerobic exercise, 135
  cardiac muscle and, 172
Aerobic metabolism, 516
  as energy source for muscles, 130, 130*t*
Afferent arteriole, 360–361, 360*f*
Aflatoxin, 431
Africa
  Ebola virus, 193
  HIV/AIDS in, 188–189, 215
  Homo sapiens and, 520
  modern humans and, 517–521
  sickle-cell anemia and, 453–454
African Americans
  genetic testing and, 445
  sickle-cell anemia and, 453–454
Afterbirth, 495*f*, 496
Age-related macular degeneration (AMD), 296–297, 296*f*

Aging, 482–505, 499–502
  acid reflux and, 331
  antioxidant supplements and, 68*b*
  atherosclerosis and, 171*b*
  body systems and, 501–502
  calorie needs and, 345
  cause of, 500–501
  cell damage and, 500–501
  Down syndrome and, 459
  healthy aging, 502
  heart failure and, 183
  hypertension and, 178*t*
  infertility and, 393
  key concepts, 484*b*
  kidney cancer and, 438
  skin cancer and, 429
  telomeres and, 500, 500*f*
  as whole body process, 501
Agranular leukocytes, 146*f*, 148–149. *See also* Lymphocytes; Monocytes
Agriculture
  desertification and, 550, 550*f*
  genetically engineered (GE) plants and, 466–467
  habitats and, 552, 553*f*
  science and, 18*f*
  sustainable development and, 554
  transgenic plants, 474–475, 474*f*
Agriculture and air pollution, 544*f*
AIDS. *See* HIV/AIDS
Airline travel and disease, 525
Air pollution, 544–547
  acid precipitation and, 546–547
  CFCs (chlorofluorocarbons) and, 545–546, 545*f*, 546*f*
  major sources of, 544*f*
  New York City and, 542*f*
  smog, 546–547, 546*f*
Alanine (Ala), 40*f*
  synthesis of proteins and, 41*f*
Alaska, Nunivak Island, 527*f*
Albanese, Jaclyn, 140–141, 140*f*
Albumins, 143, 143*t*
Alcohol
  blood-brain barrier and, 261
  breast milk, transfer in, 208*b*
  cancer prevention and, 440–441
  cell differentiation and, 418
  cerebellum, effect on, 263
  as diuretic, 368
  healthy diet recommendations, 340
  hypertension and, 178*t*
  placenta, passage through, 491
Aldosterone, 303*f*, 312
  Addison's disease, 320
  angiotensin II and, 368–369
  blood volume excess and, 369, 370*f*
  salt balance and, 368
Alendronate for osteoporosis, 117
Algae
  eutrophication and, 548, 548*f*
  phosphates and, 539
  as producer organisms, 526*b*, 532
Ali, Muhammad, 48, 49*f*
Allantois, 490
Alleles, 446. *See also* Dominant alleles; Recessive alleles
  codominance, 452–453, 453*f*
  dominant alleles, 448–449
  key concepts, 446*b*
  linked alleles, 451, 456
  mutations and, 512–513
  Punnett squares and, 447–448, 447*f*

  recessive alleles, 448–449
  two-trait crosses, 450–452, 451*f*, 452*f*
Allergens, 211
Allergies, 211–212
  auditory tube and, 287
  development of reaction, 211*f*
All-or-none principle, 132
Alpha cells, 311
Alpha (α) helix, 41
ALS (amyotrophic lateral sclerosis)
  breathing, effect on, 235
  creatine phosphate and, 130
  sclerotic areas in, 253
Altruistic kidney donors, 355
Alveoli, 223*f*, 224*f*
  emphysema and, 237
  endoderm and, 490*t*
  gas exchange in, 227–228, 228*f*
Alzheimer's disease, 48, 271–272, 475
  PET scan of patient with, 271*f*
American Academy of Pediatrics on Gardasil, 398*b*
American Association of Poison Control Centers on dietary supplements, 23
American Cancer Society
  as cancer prevention source, 441
  colonoscopy recommendations, 445
  mammogram recommendations, 437*b*
  web site, 15
American Heart Association
  cholesterol level requirements, 171*b*
  on hypertension, 177
  web site, 15
American Medical Association on kidney donations, 355
American Red Cross and blood donation, 151*b*
American Society of Aesthetic Plastic Surgery on Lipodissolve, 79
American Society of Dermatologic Surgery on Lipodissolve, 79
American Society of Plastic Surgeons on Lipodissolve, 79
American Society of Reproductive Medicine on preimplantation genetic diagnosis (PGD), 377
Amine group (-NH$_2$), 75
Amino acids, 39, 40*f*, 75
  codons and, 409, 409*f*
  in complete proteins, 341–342, 342*f*
  with negatively charged R groups, 40*f*
  with nonpolar R groups, 40*f*
  with positively nonpolar R groups, 40*f*
  proximal tubule, steps in reabsorption in, 363–364, 364*f*
  synthesis of proteins and, 41*f*
  with uncharged nonpolar R groups, 40*f*
Amino group (NH$_3$), 39
Ammonia (NH$_3$)
  in Earth's atmosphere, 514
  kidneys and, 357
Ammonium
  kidneys excreting, 370
  tubular secretion and, 364
Amniocentesis, 487*b*
  Down syndrome, detection of, 459
  genetic testing and, 445
Amnion, 489, 490*f*
  in dilation phase of labor, 495–496, 495*f*
Amniotic fluid, 489, 490*f*
  in dilation phase of labor, 495–496, 495*f*